THE ORIGIN OF
COSMIC RAYS

THE ORIGIN OF COSMIC RAYS

V. L. Ginzburg and S. I. Syrovatskii

ERRATA

Page 79.

In equation (4.56) replace B_{12} by: $B_{12}\left(\dfrac{E}{E - h\nu}\right)^2$

After equation (4.56) insert:

where the factor $E^2/(E - h\nu)^2$ takes into account the energy-dependence of the phase volume, $4\pi p^2\,dp = (4\pi/c^3)E^2\,dE$, in momentum space (for transitions in momentum space, $B_{12} = B_{21}$).

In equation (4.57) replace $\dfrac{\partial N_e}{\partial E}$ by $\dfrac{E^2\partial(N_e/E^2)}{\partial E}$

In equation (4.59) omit the factor $\dfrac{\gamma}{\gamma + 2}$

Two lines after equation (4.59) replace $0 \cdot 96$ and $1 \cdot 77$ by: $2 \cdot 88$ and $2 \cdot 48$

THE ORIGIN OF
COSMIC RAYS

BY

V. L. GINZBURG AND S. I. SYROVATSKII

P. N. Lebedev Institute of Physics
Academy of Sciences of the USSR, Moscow

Translated by H. S. H. MASSEY and edited by D. TER HAAR

Authorised translation incorporating
additional chapter and revisions supplied
by the authors in 1964

A Pergamon Press Book

THE MACMILLAN COMPANY
NEW YORK
1964

THE MACMILLAN COMPANY
60 Fifth Avenue
New York 11, N.Y.

This book is distributed by
THE MACMILLAN COMPANY
pursuant to a special arrangement with
PERGAMON PRESS LIMITED
Oxford, England

Library of Congress Catalog Card Number 64-21218

This is the authorised translation of the book
Происхождение космических лучей
published by Izd. Akad. Nauk SSSR, Moscow 1963
incorporating new and revised text supplied by the
authors in 1964

Set in Monotype Times 10 on 12pt.
by Santype Ltd. of Salisbury
and printed in Great Britain by
A. Wheaton & Co. Ltd., Exeter

CONTENTS

PREFACE TO THE ENGLISH EDITION

THE most recent additions to the Russian edition of this book were made at the beginning of 1963. Less than a year has passed since then but quite a few new results have already appeared which should be reflected in this book. This circumstance is obviously a consequence of the rapid development of cosmic ray physics. At the same time, we think that the hope expressed in the foreword to the Russian edition, that the book as a whole is devoted to well enough established material, has been confirmed.

The major additions made to the English edition deal with the question of the nature of radio-emitting electrons, the problem of the explosion of galactic cores and gamma astronomy. In addition quite a few minor changes have been made in which we have made use of both published papers and certain material we have received from the recent International Conference on Cosmic Rays (India, December 1963).

In order to speed up publication of the English edition it has been more convenient to put the majority of the new material at the end of the book in the form of separate sections (these are Sections 17, 18, and 19 and are articles written by us in 1963 which have since been altered slightly; they can be read separately from the rest of the text).

It is our earnest hope that the appearance of the English translation of this book will prove useful and will enable a better exchange of scientific information and understanding between Soviet physicists and astrophysicists and their colleagues in other countries.

In conclusion we should like to take the opportunity of expressing our great gratitude to Dr. D. ter Haar who so kindly undertook the considerable work of editing the English translation.

Moscow   V. L. GINZBURG
January 1964   S. I. SYROVATSKII

FOREWORD

UNTIL the forties of this century almost all the information on the cosmos was obtained via optical "channels". In observations from the Earth's surface this channel is limited to wavelengths between 0·3 micron in the ultraviolet region and tens of microns in the infrared region due to the absorption of light in the atmosphere. In the majority of cases observations are made in the even narrower range of visible radiation (0·4–0·8 μ). Despite the successes of astronomy, particularly in the last hundred years, the relative narrowness of the optical channel has undoubtedly considerably limited the possibilities and tempo of astrophysical research.

The most important recent feature in the development of astronomy is, in our opinion, the appearance and increasing use of two new channels of astrophysical information. We have in mind the reception of cosmic radio emissions (the "radio channel" used in radio astronomy) and the study of cosmic rays (the "cosmic ray channel").

This book discusses these very questions, but basically only the field of research which can be called the astrophysics of cosmic rays. Problems of radio astronomy are touched upon only insofar as they are connected with cosmic rays. A look at the list of contents and the introduction will give a fuller idea of the nature and volume of the material.

The book has been rewritten but it should be borne in mind that it is the result of reworking and expanding general articles which we had written earlier on (1953–61). At the same time the authors have not tried to survey the rather extensive literature on the subject, compile a detailed bibliography, give the history of the question, and so on. Our aim was merely to describe the present state of the problem. Moreover, most attention is paid only to those concepts in whose development the authors have participated. At the same time we have tried to discuss work with which we do not agree and indicate the present difficulties and obscurities.

A monograph dealing with a fast developing scientific subject is soon out of date. We feel, however, that a considerable part of the material discussed has "settled" sufficiently and at the same time a knowledge of it is necessary to quite a wide circle of people. It is to be hoped, therefore, that the basic part of the book will fulfil its purpose for quite a long time. Lastly we should like to say that the title of the book reflects its content only if the phrase "the origin of cosmic rays" is used in the broadest possible sense. In the narrow sense, of course, the origin of cosmic rays is taken to mean only the question of the sources of cosmic rays and the mechanism of their acceleration. It would perhaps have been more correct to avoid this ambiguity and call the book "The Astrophysics of Cosmic Rays". We decided against this since any changes in terminology can easily lead to confusion and need to be made familiar by the passage of time.

Finally we should like to thank A. A. Korchak and S. B. Pikel'ner for their comments and advice. Our thanks are also due to M. N. Bogoyavlenskaya for her great care in preparing the manuscript for the printers.

September 1962   V. L. GINZBURG
                                                            S. I. SYVORATSKII

SYMBOLS†

A — atomic weight

$A(\gamma, v)$ — coefficient in expression (6.16) for energy of relativistic electrons in a source (see (6.17))

$a(\gamma), y_1(\gamma), y_2(\gamma)$ — coefficients given in Table 6

a_{ik}, a_{ikl} — coefficients in the solutions of the fragmentation equations (see (14.16)–(14.20))

$b_i(E) = \dfrac{dE_i}{dt}$ — systematic change in particle energy due to losses or acceleration

D — diffusion coefficient

$d_i(E) = \dfrac{d}{dt}\overline{(\Delta E_i)^2}$ — mean square of energy increase due to losses or acceleration

E — total energy of a particle

$E_k = E - Mc^2$ — kinetic energy of a particle

E_{cr} — energy above which the diffusion coefficient varies with the energy

$\mathcal{E}$ — total energy per nucleon

$\mathcal{E}_k = \mathcal{E} - M_p c^2$ — kinetic energy per nucleon

$\mathcal{E}_{max}$ — maximum energy of cosmic rays in sources

$\mathscr{E}$ — electrical field strength

F_v — density of energy flux of radio emission at a frequency v

$F_{\Omega,i} = \displaystyle\int_\Omega I_i \cos\theta\, d\Omega$ — flux density of particles of a kind i (θ — angle between the normal to the plane and direction of motion of a particle, $d\Omega$ — element of a solid angle)

$F = \pi I$ — flux density (from a hemisphere of directions) for isotropic emission

---

† Rare or generally accepted symbols (e.g., e, $\hbar = h/2\pi$, c—elementary charge, the quantum constant and the speed of light) are not given here. Different quantities denoted by the same letter are found, as a rule, in different sections.

$F_i(x)$—model functions in the solutions of the fragmentation equations (x: thickness of the matter)

$f_\pi(\gamma_\pi)$—π-meson generation spectrum for the absorption path of cosmic rays in matter ($\gamma_\pi = E_\pi/m_\pi c^2$, E_π and m_π—total energy and rest mass of a π-meson)

H and $H_\perp$—strength of the magnetic field and its component at right angles to the velocity of a particle

$H_{eq} = \sqrt{4\pi\rho u^2}$—magnetic field strength when kinetic and magnetic energies are equal

$h = 1/T_{Mg}$—Hubble's constant

I_i—intensity of particles of a kind i (the number of particles incident along the normal per unit area, unit time and unit solid angle)

$I_i(E)\,dE$—intensity of particles in the range E, $E + dE$

$I_i(> E)$—intensity of particles with energies $\geqslant E$

I, Q, U, V—Stokes parameters

i—an index (I_i, F_i, K_i and N_i) denoting the kind of particle; for nuclei the index A is sometimes used as are also the following indices: e—electrons, γ—gamma rays, p—protons, α—alpha particles, L, M, H and VH—groups of nuclei (see Table 2), ν—neutrinos. The index ν also relates to radio emission (I_ν, F_ν)

J—specific energy flux of cosmic rays (see (1.7))

K—coefficient in the exponential energy spectrum of particles $KE^{-\gamma}$

$K_e(k)$—coefficient in the expression $K_e(k)E^{-\gamma}\,dE$ for the differential energy spectrum of electrons along a line of sight in the direction k

$K_e = \dfrac{4\pi}{L}K_e(k)$—coefficient in the expression $K_e E^{-\gamma}\,dE$ for the differential energy spectrum of isotropically distributed electrons per unit volume

$K_V = VK_e$—coefficient in the differential electron energy spectrum for the whole volume of the source

k—wave vector

L—extent, path, characteristic dimension

L—luminosity

l—effective length of free flight, characteristic scale

M — mass; the mass of a nucleus is taken to be $M = AM_p$

M_p — mass of a proton

$M_\odot$ — mass of the Sun

M_r — absolute radio-star magnitude

m — mass of an electron

N_i — concentration of particles of kind i (for isotropic emission $N_i = (4\pi/v)I_i$)

$N_e(k)$ — number of electrons on a line of sight in the direction k, whose velocities are towards the observer, per unit solid angle

N_e — total number of relativistic electrons in a source

N_G — concentration of galaxies

n — gas concentration

n_e — concentration of electrons in the interstellar gas

$\tilde{n}$ — refractive index

P — emitted power

P_{ik} — probability of fragmentation (destruction of a nucleus of a kind i with the formation of a nucleus of a kind k during an interaction in the interstellar gas)

$p_{ik} \dfrac{P_{ik}}{1-P_{ii}}$ — probability of fragmentation per absorption path

p and $p_\perp$ — momentum of a particle and its component at right angles to the magnetic field

$p_\nu^{(1)}$ and $p_\nu^{(2)}$ — flux density of emission with two basic directions of polarisation for an individual electron

p_ν — spectral distribution of emission power of an individual electron

p — pressure

$p_i = 1/T_i$ — probability of absorption of a nucleus per unit time

$Q_i(E)$ — energy spectrum of sources

q_i — power of sources with respect to nuclei of kind i

R — distance, radius of system

R_{ph} — photometric radius of the Metagalaxy

$R_H = \dfrac{cp}{eZ} = \dfrac{p\,(\mathrm{GeV}/c)}{Z}$ — (magnetic) rigidity (when the last expression is used R_H is measured in GV — thousand millions of V)

r — radius vector of a point

$$r_H = \frac{v \sin \theta}{\omega_H} = \frac{cp_\perp}{eH}$$ — radius of curvature of a particle (radius of the projection of an electron's trajectory onto a plane at right angles to the field H); for ultra-relativistic particles

$$r_H = \frac{E \sin \theta}{eH} = \frac{E(\text{eV}) \sin \theta}{300 H(\text{oersted})}, r_H \text{ being in cm}$$

S_d — number of particles leaving a system per unit time due to drift

S_{nucl} — number of particles disappearing per unit time due to nuclear collisions

T — life time, characteristic time

T_i, $T_{\text{nucl},i}$ — nuclear life time

T_d — life time connected with leakage of particles from a system

$T_{\text{sn}} = 1/\nu_{\text{sn}}$ — mean time between supernova flares

T and T_{eff} — temperature and effective temperature

U — energy losses per unit time for cosmic rays in the volume of the Galaxy

U_{nucl} — nuclear collision energy losses

U_s — power of cosmic ray sources

U_{sn} — power of supernovae as cosmic ray sources

U_{new} — power of new stars as cosmic ray sources

U_e — power of relativistic electron sources

$\boldsymbol{u}$ — velocity of gas

V — volume

$\boldsymbol{v}$ and $v_\parallel$ — velocity of a particle and its projection along the magnetic field

W and W_{cr} — cosmic ray energy in a system

$$W_H = \int \frac{H^2}{8\pi} \, dV$$ — magnetic field energy

W_{turb} — kinetic energy of turbulent motion

W_k — kinetic energy of a gas

W_e — energy of electrons in a source

W_{sn} — cosmic ray energy in supernova shells

w — energy density

w, w_{cr} — cosmic ray energy density

w_G — cosmic ray energy density in the Galaxy

w_r — energy density of remnant cosmic rays

w_{Mg} — cosmic ray energy density in the Metagalaxy

w_e — energy density of the electron component of cosmic rays

w_{ph} — thermal emission energy density

$x = \rho L = \rho ct$ — path (thickness of matter passed through) in g/cm^2

$x = v/v_c$

Z — atomic number of an element, eZ — charge of nucleus

α — spectral emission index [$I_\nu \sim \nu^{-\alpha}$; for the exponential spectrum of emitting electrons $\alpha = (\gamma - 1)/2$]

$\alpha = u^2/cl$ — acceleration parameter

$\beta = R^2/3DT_d$ — coefficient defining the condition for leakage of particles from a system

γ — index in the differential energy spectrum of particles $I(E)dE \sim E^{-\gamma}dE$

$\gamma_e = E/mc^2$ — energy of an electron in units of rest mass energy mc^2

$\gamma_\mu = E_\mu/m_\mu c^2$ — energy of a μ-meson in units of rest mass energy $m_\mu c^2$

$\gamma_\pi = E_\pi/m_\pi c^2$ — energy of a π-meson in units of rest mass energy $m_\pi c^2$

∇^2 — Laplace operator

δ — degree of anisotropy of cosmic rays

$\delta = \dfrac{W_{cr}}{W_{tot} - W_{cr}}$ — fraction of energy contained in cosmic rays

ε — dielectric constant

$\zeta = x \sin \theta = (v/v_c) \sin \theta$

$\eta = 4D/a^2\beta$ (see (17.29))

θ — angle between the direction of the magnetic field H and the velocity of the particle v

ϑ — angle between the direction of the magnetic field H and the direction of emission k

ϑ, ϕ — polar angles

κ — gravitational constant

Λ_i — length of mean free path (in g/cm^2) for the interaction of a nucleus of kind i with nuclei of the interstellar medium

$\lambda = 2\pi/k$ — wavelength

λ_i — mean free path (in g/cm^2) with respect to absorption

μ — coefficient of absorption of electromagnetic radiation (gamma rays, radio waves)

$v = \omega/2\pi$ — frequency

$$v_c = \frac{3eH}{4\pi mc}\left(\frac{E}{mc^2}\right)^2 = v_0\left(\frac{E}{mc^2}\right)^2$$

$$v_0 = \frac{3eH}{4\pi mc}$$

$\xi = mc^2/E$

$\xi = r_H/R$

Π — degree of polarisation

ρ — density of a substance

σ, σ_i — effective cross section

τ — unit vector in the direction of a particle's velocity

$\tau = \int \mu \, dr$ — optical thickness

ϕ — gravitational potential

ϕ — angle of rotation of plane of polarisation

$\phi = L/R$ — angular size of source

$\chi(\mathscr{E}, \mathbf{r}, t)$ — distribution function of sources

ψ — angle between the velocity of particle v and the direction of emission k

Ω — gravitational energy

$$\omega_H = \frac{eH}{mc} \cdot \frac{mc^2}{E}$$ — angular frequency of rotation of an electron in a magnetic field

INTRODUCTION

Cosmic rays were discovered about fifty years ago but even now their study is one of the important problems in physics and astrophysics.

The existence of cosmic rays was discovered as the result of studying the "dark" current in ionisation chambers. The fact that we can observe a current flowing in ionisation chambers without any artificial sources of ionisation (this is called a dark current) was established as early as the beginning of the century. Its appearance in ionisation chambers placed near the Earth's surface could be ascribed to the effect of radiation emitted by radioactive impurities in the objects surrounding the chamber, so the cosmic (extra-terrestrial) origin of the dark current was proved only after experiments with balloons. The current in the ionisation chamber due to radioactivity of the Earth and various objects should decrease as the ionisation chamber is taken further from the Earth's surface. The ionisation current proved to drop only at low altitudes as the chamber went upwards and then started to rise. For example, in experiments made in 1914, when an altitude of 9 km was reached, the ionisation proved to be much greater than at sea level. It is true that even after these experiments a terrestrial origin was proposed for cosmic rays; their appearance was connected, for example, with thunderstorms or radioactivity of the upper atmosphere. All these hypotheses, however, have long been abandoned.

Because of their great power of penetration cosmic rays were first taken to be a form of γ-rays. It was later shown that there are charged particles in the primary cosmic rays, this being discovered by studying the motion of cosmic rays in the Earth's magnetic field. Charged particles moving in this field are deflected. As a result the flux of the primary cosmic rays, i.e., the rays reaching the Earth's atmosphere, depends on the geomagnetic latitude. In the atmosphere the primary cosmic rays form secondary particles and it is only these that are observed on the Earth. The observed dependence of their flux on the geomagnetic latitude also allows us to conclude the presence of charged particles in primary cosmic rays. In actual fact the primary

1

rays have not been studied for long because of the difficulty of lifting apparatus to a great height. The absence of reliable data on primary cosmic rays made it impossible to explain their origin, so for many years the question of the origin of cosmic rays remained open.

Moreover the position did not change very significantly even after it had been shown that the primary cosmic rays consist of protons and the nuclei of a number of elements (the presence of nuclei was established in 1948). The point is that cosmic rays are distributed isotropically, i.e., reach the Earth evenly from all directions. A study of them therefore provides no direct information on the position of the sources of cosmic rays. For a better understanding of how difficult the isotropy of cosmic rays makes the solution of the question let us imagine that the optical emission of all the heavenly bodies is mixed up and has then to be analysed. In this case, instead of studying the spectrum and intensity of the light emission of the individual stars and nebulae, it would be necessary to study the same emission characteristics but from all these objects taken together. It is quite clear that under these conditions practically nothing would have been left of modern astrophysics. However, information on primary cosmic rays relates to all sources at once. Any attempt to analyse these data is thus similar to attempting a spectral analysis of the total light emission of all stars and nebulae.

Is it possible, however, to obtain information about cosmic rays in different parts of the Universe far from the Earth?

A negative answer would have been given to this question even comparatively recently. But, as has already been the case more than once in the history of physics and astrophysics, the position has changed rapidly and radically as the result of discoveries made in quite a different field. We have in mind radio astronomy which started to develop rapidly in 1945. It turned out (as was shown in 1950–53) that the basic part of the radio emission reaching us from space is generated by cosmic rays. By considering cosmic radio emission it is possible to establish certain properties of cosmic rays not only in our own stellar system (the Galaxy) but even far beyond it. The development of radio astronomy and the establishment of a connexion between cosmic radio emission and cosmic rays has led to the problem of the origin of cosmic rays and the discovery of their properties in different parts of the Universe now occupying an important place in astrophysics. This has thus made it possible, as in the solution of other astrophysical problems, to start with observational data and carry out an analysis using a combination of all the information obtained by different methods. Cosmic rays have proved to be interesting not only as an independent subject but also, as has become clear later, they play an important part from the point of view of the dynamics of the interstellar medium and the shells of supernovae and are one of the basic facts determining the evolution of galaxies. We should point out that the study of cosmic rays is connected not only with radio astronomy but also with the new subjects of gamma and neutrino astronomy.

Two main lines of approach have almost always been apparent in cosmic ray physics. The first is the study of elementary particles in cosmic rays and the interactions of these particles at high energies. Here we are dealing simply with the possibilities of observing high-energy particles offered by Nature herself. These possibilities have been used with great success; positrons, $\mu^{\pm}$, $\pi^{\pm}$ and K-mesons and also certain hyperons were discovered in cosmic rays. The study of these particles is of such great importance that for a long time, in particular from 1929 to about 1955–56, a study of elementary particles was the basic part of cosmic ray physics. The position has changed considerably with the appearance of powerful accelerators. In the range of energies reached with accelerators (an energy E up to 3×10^{10} eV) cosmic rays, generally speaking, cannot compete with the accelerators as a means of studying elementary particles. The centre of gravity of this first aspect of cosmic ray physics has therefore moved into the high-energy range ($E > 3 \times 10^{10}$ eV). In this range the measurements are chiefly made with photo-emulsions, Wilson cloud chambers in combination with ionisation calorimeters, and systems of counters for recording the extensive atmospheric showers. Since the maximum energy recorded in cosmic rays is about 3×10^{19} eV it is quite clear that the use of cosmic rays for purely physical research will probably continue for a very long time yet.† Even so the relative "weight" of such elementary particle research has undoubtedly dropped considerably and of latter

† As we have indicated, the energy reached at present with accelerators is 3×10^{10} eV, i.e., nine orders of magnitude less than the maximum energy of particles observed in cosmic rays. It is unlikely that the near future will bring accelerators producing particles with an energy greater than 3×10^{11} eV. We should mention, however, that the use of the so-called "colliding beams" method will allow us, although it involves great difficulties, to study collisions of particles with an energy corresponding in the laboratory system to a value of $E' = 2(E/Mc^2)^2 Mc^2$, where E is the energy of the particles in each of the beams consisting of particles with a rest mass M. However even for electrons with

years cosmic ray physics have begun to be dominated by the second line of approach, i.e., the study of the geophysical and astrophysical aspects of cosmic rays. At present considerably more than half of all cosmic ray research is on these lines. Here the subjects studied are:

1. Primary cosmic rays on the Earth (composition, energy spectrum, spatial distribution).

2. Cosmic rays beyond the solar system (in the Galaxy and Metagalaxy) and the effect of the interstellar medium and interstellar magnetic fields on them.

3. The origin of cosmic rays (in the narrow sense of this term: see foreword).

4. Solar cosmic rays, their generation, motion towards the Earth and effect on processes taking place in the space around the Earth.

5. The effect on cosmic rays (of both galactic and solar origin) of the interplanetary medium and interplanetary magnetic fields; the high-latitude cut-off and different variations of cosmic rays on the Earth and within the solar system.

6. The radiation belts round the Earth and other planets.

Artificial satellites and space probes together with the general progress in solar geophysics and physics, on the one hand, and the rapid development of radio astronomy and astrophysics, on the other hand, have led to the appearance of a large number of investigations in all these questions. Moreover they are all not only interconnected but are also linked with other scientific disciplines (solar physics, physics of the interstellar and interplanetary medium, particle acceleration theory, radio astronomy, and so on).

The purpose of the present book is to discuss basically only the first three fields of research: the properties of primary cosmic radiation on the Earth, data on cosmic rays in the Universe (beyond the solar system), and the origin of cosmic rays. Since, however, there are no sharp dividing lines between the various fields we shall also touch on other questions to a greater or lesser degree (in particular we shall discuss the problem of high-latitude cut-off).†

$E = 5 \times 10^9$ eV the energy is $E' = 10^{14}$ eV, and for protons with $E = 3 \times 10^{10}$ eV the energy is $E' = 2 \times 10^{12}$ eV.

† A general review of cosmic ray physics is given by Dobrotin and Feinberg,[1] the question of solar cosmic rays and cosmic ray variations is discussed by Dorman[2] and data on the radiation belts are given in refs. 2 and 3. Here we should also mention earlier surveys written by the authors[4-7] and certain other recent surveys[8, 9] devoted to the origin of cosmic rays.

CHAPTER I

PRIMARY COSMIC RAYS ON THE EARTH

COSMIC radiation reaching the Earth's atmosphere from outside undergoes considerable changes due to interactions with the atoms of the air. The consequences of this are that the properties of the observed radiation depend strongly on the thickness of the matter in the atmosphere it has passed through. The study of this dependence and of general questions relating to the interaction of cosmic rays with matter are important branches of cosmic ray physics. Much has been devoted to them[1,10,11] but these questions fall outside the scope of the present book.

For the theory of the origin of cosmic rays experimental data on the properties of what are called "primary" cosmic rays, i.e., cosmic rays far from the Earth's surface beyond its atmosphere, are of prime importance. For this purpose the "boundary" of the atmosphere can be taken as the altitude above which the thickness of the matter retained by terrestrial attraction is negligibly small when compared with the interaction path of all the particles making up the cosmic radiation. In practice the interaction of cosmic rays with atmospheric atoms can be completely ignored at altitudes over 50 km above sea level.

Even at these altitudes, however, the radiation cannot, generally speaking, be called primary because of the presence of secondary particles which have appeared as the result of the interaction of cosmic rays in the underlying layers of the atmosphere (cosmic ray albedo). Some of the secondary particles are scattered in the surrounding space, whilst some may be kept near the Earth by its magnetic field for a long time. The contribution of these particles is particularly significant in measurements of the intensity of comparatively low-energy protons and electrons. Primary cosmic radiation can thus be observed at distances from the Earth where not only the thickness of the remaining atmosphere but also the contribution made by albedo particles (and also, strictly speaking, the particles making up the radiation belts) are negligibly small.†

The rapid development of cosmic ray physics in the last decade and in particular the use of high-altitude sounding balloons, rockets and artificial satellites have made it possible to elucidate the influence of the "above-Earth" effects on the primary cosmic radiation. At the same time as providing a large accumulation of fresh data this has led to considerable progress in determining the most important characteristics of primary cosmic radiation which are discussed in this chapter.

In future we shall be interested largely in galactic cosmic rays coming into the solar system from outside.

If we are thinking of galactic cosmic rays, setting aside cosmic rays of solar origin, then we should give the title of "primary" to cosmic rays outside the solar system where the effect of solar corpuscular fluxes and the solar system's magnetic fields is insignificant. Processes taking place in the solar system cause noticeable changes in the cosmic radiation as is shown by phenomena such as the cosmic ray intensity variations connected with solar activity and "high-latitude cut-off".[2,13,14]

It is not the task of the present book to discuss the problem of cosmic ray variations or the nature of the high-latitude cut-off.[2,13] It should be pointed out that it is considerably more difficult to take into account the influence of extraterrestrial effects on primary cosmic radiation than in the case of the "terrestrial" effects discussed above. This is largely because the nature of certain important phenomena caused by solar activity (and the nature of the high-latitude cut-off in particular) is still not clear enough. The position is simplified, however, by the influence of these "solar" effects being mainly felt only in the comparatively low energy range and playing hardly any part in most of the observed cosmic rays.

When discussing the properties of primary cosmic rays below we shall therefore use results relating to cosmic rays on the Earth and take into account only the effects of the atmosphere and the albedo. In those cases when, according to modern ideas, processes occurring

† The primary cosmic ray flux near the Earth, e.g., at an altitude of 100 km, in the range of energies lower than tens of GeV differs from the cosmic ray flux far from the Earth also by virtue of the action of the Earth's magnetic field. This can, however, be comparatively simply allowed for in the first approximation by using the theory of geomagnetic effects.[10-12]

in the solar system may be expected to lead to a change in the properties of galactic cosmic rays coming from outside, the appropriate reservations will be made.

The basic characteristics of primary cosmic radiation, known in the majority of cases from experiment with a greater or lesser degree of accuracy, are: the chemical composition of the nuclear component, the number of electrons, positrons, γ-rays and neutrinos, the energy spectrum of all these particles including its lower boundary (high-latitude cut-off) and maximum energy region, and also the directional distribution of cosmic rays in space (degree of anisotropy). Reliable information on the corresponding values is a necessary premise for solving the problem of the origin of cosmic rays.

1. COMPOSITION OF THE NUCLEAR COMPONENT OF COSMIC RAYS

Protons and nuclei of the heavier elements are the basic component of cosmic rays on the Earth. The percentage content of nuclei of various elements in cosmic rays or, as we say, their composition is one of the most important characteristics of primary cosmic radiation and allows definite conclusions to be drawn about the sources, acceleration mechanisms and the nature of the motion of cosmic rays in interstellar space. It can be said with certainty that any theory of the origin of cosmic rays cannot expect serious success unless it rests on a detailed analysis of the observed composition of primary cosmic radiation.

The fullest of the data available on the composition relate to the range of cosmic ray energies of several GeV per nucleon and have been obtained chiefly with photo-emulsions exposed at great altitudes in sounding balloons. In this range of energies the fluxes of the various nuclei, which quickly decrease as the particles' energy increases, are still not too small, thus permitting satisfactory statistical measurement accuracy to be achieved during the exposure time. On the other hand the irregular contribution of solar cosmic rays and the influence of "solar" modulation effects are not felt as noticeably in this range of energies as at low energies. In addition, from the experimental point of view it is considerably simpler to identify the charges of relativistic particles† as opposed to non-relativistic or

---

† We call particles relativistic if their velocity when determining the ionisation losses with a sufficient degree of accuracy can be considered equal to the velocity of light c. This occurs at an energy of several GeV per nucleon and above. From the terminological point of view it might be more correct to call these particles

weakly relativistic ones, for the determination of whose charge it is no longer sufficient to measure the ionisation produced by the particles (the ionisation is determined by the charge and velocity of a particle).

In future discussions of the question of the composition of cosmic rays we shall use data relating to the above range of energies which has been most studied. At the same time in many cases the values of the total intensity (with all energies) and energy density for individual components of the primary cosmic rays are of importance. Let us first pause at these integrated values, bearing in mind, however, that they are not yet accurate enough.

Proton and Nucleus Intensity

The basic quantity characterising the number of cosmic rays is the intensity I. By definition the intensity is the number of particles incident per unit time on a unit area at right angles to the direction of observation with respect to a unit solid angle. The unit of measurement in this case is

$$\frac{\text{no. of particles}}{\text{m}^2 \cdot \text{sterad} \cdot \text{sec}} \quad \text{or} \quad \frac{\text{no. of particles}}{\text{cm}^2 \cdot \text{sterad} \cdot \text{sec}}.$$

Apart from the intensity I_i for particles of a kind i we sometimes also use the particle flux $F_{\Omega,i} = \int_\Omega I_i \cos \theta \, d\Omega$, where θ is the angle between the normal to the area and the particles' direction of motion and $d\Omega$ is an element of the solid angle. In the case of isotropic radiation the particle flux (from a hemisphere of directions) F_i and the particle concentration N_i are:

$$F_i = 2\pi \int_0^{\pi/2} I_i \cos \theta \sin \theta \, d\theta = \pi I_i, \qquad N_i = \frac{4\pi}{v_i} I_i, \qquad (1.1)$$

where v_i is the velocity of the particles in question.

If there are particles of different energies present in the flux in question their energy distribution (energy spectrum) is characterised by a spectral (differential) intensity $I_i(E)$, so $I_i(E) \, dE$ is the intensity of particles with energies in the range E, $E + dE$. In this case the

ultra-relativistic, but this is not very convenient when applied to cosmic rays when we are dealing with particles with the comparatively low energy of $E \sim 3$ to 10×10^9 eV/nucleon.

intensity of particles with an energy greater than a given one is

$$I_i(>E) = \int_E^\infty I_i(E)\,dE. \tag{1.2}$$

The quantities $I_i(E)$ and $I_i(>E)$ are often called the differential and integral spectra of particles respectively.

In the case of isotropic radiation the concentration of particles of a kind i with energies greater than a certain value is

$$N_i(>E) = 4\pi \int_E^\infty \frac{1}{v} I_i(E)\,dE, \tag{1.3}$$

where $v = c\sqrt{1 - (M_i c^2/E)^2}$ is the velocity of the particle and M_i and E are its mass and total energy.

The total intensity (with all energies) of cosmic rays on the Earth depends considerably on the level of solar activity. For example in the period near a solar activity minimum (1955–56) the total intensity of protons on the Earth was $I_p \simeq 0\cdot20$ proton/cm² · sterad · sec, whilst in a period of maximum activity (1958), it was $I_p \simeq 0\cdot1$ proton/cm² · sterad · sec. In both cases the α-particle intensity was 6·8 times less. According to data of Vernov et al.[264] the total cosmic ray intensity at great distances from the Earth (beyond the Earth's magnetic field) was $I_{cr} = 0\cdot18 \pm 0\cdot08$ particle/cm² · sterad · sec during the flight of the first space vehicle (2 January 1959).

Of the nuclei with the same energy per nucleon and an atomic number of $Z \geqslant 2$ about 90 per cent were α-particles and about 10 per cent heavier nuclei. Approximately 69 per cent of all the nucleons making up cosmic ray nuclei with $Z \geqslant 2$ belong to α-particles and about 31 per cent to heavy nuclei (see Table 1 below). These values relate to energies in the $\gtrsim 2\cdot5$ GeV/nucleon range. However, taking into consideration the similarity of the (magnetic) rigidity of the spectra of different nuclei[113] (for nuclei with $Z \geqslant 2$ this is also equivalent to a similarity of the spectra with respect to the energy per nucleon) it may be taken that a similar ratio exists between α-particles and the heavier nuclei right down to the minimum observable energies.

Then, if we ignore the possible presence of high-latitude cut-off (see below) during the period of measurements[113] carried out near the solar activity minimum, for the total intensities of the various components of primary cosmic rays within the solar system we find:

$$I_p \simeq 0.20 \text{ proton/cm}^2 \cdot \text{sterad} \cdot \text{sec,}$$

$$I_\alpha \simeq 0.03 \text{ } \alpha\text{-particle/cm}^2 \cdot \text{sterad} \cdot \text{sec,}$$

$$I_{Z>2} \simeq 0.003 \text{ (nuclei with Z} > 2)/\text{cm}^2 \cdot \text{sterad} \cdot \text{sec,} \qquad (1.4)$$

$$I_{cr} \simeq 0.23 \text{ particle/cm}^2 \cdot \text{sterad} \cdot \text{sec,}$$

$$I_{nucl} \simeq 0.38 \text{ nucleon/cm}^2 \cdot \text{sterad} \cdot \text{sec.}$$

Here I_{cr} is the total intensity of the particles making up the cosmic rays and I_{nucl} is the total intensity of nucleons in all the primary cosmic ray nuclei (including protons).

In the low-energy range the spectra of all cosmic ray components have a maximum near the rigidity $R_H \simeq 2$ GV which corresponds to a kinetic energy of $E_k \simeq 1.2$ GeV for protons and $\mathscr{E}_k \simeq 0.5$ GeV/nucleon† for nuclei with $Z \geqslant 2$. As the rigidity decreases the particle intensity drops rather rapidly at least to the observed minimum rigidity of $R_H \simeq 0.8$ GV (the kinetic energy of protons is $E_k \simeq 200$ MeV).

If we use the proton and α-particle spectra obtained by McDonald and Webber[113] and take into account the ratio given above for the intensities of α-particles and heavier nuclei we can determine the values of the total concentrations of the various particles making up the primary cosmic rays. These are:

$$N_p \simeq 1.0 \times 10^{-10} \text{ protons/cm}^3,$$

$$N_\alpha \simeq 0.18 \times 10^{-10} \text{ } \alpha\text{-particles/cm}^3,$$

$$N_{Z>2} \simeq 0.02 \times 10^{-10} \text{ (nuclei with Z} > 2)/\text{cm}^3, \qquad (1.5)$$

$$N_{cr} \simeq 1.2 \times 10^{-10} \text{ particles/cm}^3,$$

$$N_{nucl} \simeq 2.0 \times 10^{-10} \text{ nucleons/cm}^3.$$

In a similar way for the energy density

$$w = \int E_k N(E) \, dE = \int \frac{4\pi}{v} E_k I(E) \, dE$$

† The total energy per nucleon is $\mathscr{E} = M_n c^2 + \mathscr{E}_k$, where the rest mass energy of a nucleon $M_n c^2$ can be taken with sufficient accuracy to be equal to the rest mass energy of a proton $M_p c^2 = 0.939$ GeV.

of the primary cosmic rays in the vicinity of the solar system the following values are obtained:

$$w_p = 0.65 \text{ eV/cm}^3, \qquad w_\alpha = 0.18 \text{ eV/cm}^3, \qquad w_{Z>2} = 0.08 \text{ eV/cm}^3,$$

$$w_{cr} = 0.9 \text{ eV/cm}^3. \tag{1.6}$$

The specific energy flux transferred by the cosmic rays is

$$J = \int E_k I(E) \, dE = \int \frac{v}{4\pi} E_k N(E) \, dE. \tag{1.7}$$

For ultra-relativistic particles we clearly have

$$J = \frac{c}{4\pi} \int E_k N(E) \, dE = \frac{cw}{4\pi}. \tag{1.8}$$

Therefore, bearing (1.6) in mind, we find

$$J_{cr} \lesssim \frac{cw}{4\pi} \simeq 2 \times 10^3 \text{ MeV/cm}^2 \cdot \text{sterad} \cdot \text{sec}. \tag{1.9}$$

According to an estimate of Komori[16]

$$J_{cr} = 1300 \pm 30 \text{ MeV/cm}^2 \cdot \text{sterad} \cdot \text{sec}. \tag{1.10}$$

We must stress once again that all these values have been obtained on the assumption that during the measurement period[113] (1955–56) there was no cut-off at all of the primary spectrum in the solar system, i.e., an undistorted galactic cosmic ray spectrum was observed. Otherwise the values of (1.4)–(1.6) only give a lower estimate of the intensity, concentration and energy density of the cosmic rays in the Galaxy in the vicinity of the solar system. In this connexion we would mention that according to data by Neher[15] large numbers of low-energy particles (basically protons with energies $\gtrsim 100$ MeV) were present in the primary cosmic rays during the very low solar activity minimum (1954). At this time the total particle intensity was 4–5 times greater and the energy flux 40 per cent greater than their values at the activity maximum (1958). We shall return again to the question of the energy spectrum of particles in the low-energy region in section 3. For the moment we shall say that the present indefiniteness in the intensity of the low-energy particles for the period of minimum activity may not lead to a great error in the values of the energy densities (1.6) since the contribution of these particles to the total energy is not large.

Let us now turn to a discussion in greater detail of the data on the chemical composition.

The data given below on the cosmic ray composition at the top of the atmosphere (see Table 1) are based on the results published for measurements of the intensity or relative share of the various primary radiation nuclear components at the geomagnetic latitude $\lambda_m = 41°$, basically in Texas and northern Italy. The vertical rigidity threshold corresponding to this geomagnetic latitude is

$$R_H = \frac{pc}{eZ} = \frac{p(\text{GeV}/c)}{Z} = 4.5\,\text{GV}$$

(p is the particle's momentum and eZ its charge), therefore the total energy of nuclei with an atomic weight $A = 2Z$ reaching this latitude along the vertical with respect to one nucleon is equal to or greater than 2·5 GeV/nucleon. We note that at the same rigidity threshold (at the same geomagnetic latitude) the protons have a total energy of $E \geqslant 4.6$ GeV. Therefore if we compare, as is done in Table 1, the relative distribution of nuclei (including protons) with the same energies per nucleon, then to determine the proton intensity we should use the results of measurements at another geomagnetic latitude, in this case at $\lambda_m \simeq 51°$, for which the vertical rigidity threshold is 2·3 GV and the protons arriving along the vertical have an energy of $E \geqslant 2.5$ GeV.

Without stopping to analyse the experimental methods or make a detailed comparison of the available data we shall give here only the basic results relating to the observed composition of the primary cosmic radiation.

In the rigidity range in question ($R_H \geqslant 4.5$ GV) the cosmic ray intensity is still fairly sensitive to the level of solar activity,[17, 18] dropping noticeably (up to 30 per cent) at its maximum (1957–58) when compared with the minimum (1954–55). The values given for the intensities relate to the solar activity minimum when the cosmic rays arriving in the solar system from outside are least disturbed and the measured values, it may be assumed, are close to their true values in the adjacent region of the Galaxy.

Protons

Since protons (p) are the basic component of cosmic radiation the statistical accuracy of measurements is relatively high. However the complexity of taking the albedo into account and the inconstancy of the cosmic ray flux even in years of low solar activity lead to a large amount of variation in the results of different authors. Table 1 gives the values obtained by Charakhch'yan and Charakhch'yan[19] for latitude 51° in 1952 and 1954. For the geomagnetic latitude $\lambda_m = 41°$, i.e., in the same rigidity range as for the nuclei with $Z > 2$ given in Table 1, we note that the proton intensity is about half and amounts[25] to $I_p = 610 \pm 30$ protons/m^2·sterad·sec.

TABLE 1

Group of nuclei	Z	$\bar{A}$	Intensity m^{-2}·sterad^{-1}· sec^{-1}	No. of nucleons in flux	I/I_H $=N/N_H$	In universe (average)	
						After Suess and Urey[49]	After Cameron[50]
p	1	1	1300	1300	680	3360	6830
α	2	4	88	352	46	258	1040
L	3 to 5	10	1·9	19	1·0	10^{-5}	10^{-5}
M	6 to 9	14	5·7	80	3·0	2·64	10·1
H	$\geqslant 10$	31	1·9	59	1·0	1	1
VH†	$\geqslant 20$	51	0·53	28	0·28	0·06	0·05

Total number of nucleons   1810

† Included in the number of H-nuclei

The presence of deuterium nuclei in cosmic rays has still not been established. If their total corresponds to the natural distribution (0·014 per cent with respect to hydrogen) it would be very complicated to observe deuterium in cosmic rays. However, if cosmic ray sources generate only heavy nuclei (basically Fe) and the observed composition occurs as the result of their being broken up in the interstellar gas, then the deuteron flux at the edge of the atmosphere is about 5 per cent of the proton flux.[20] Measurements made recently[440] give only an upper limit for the flux of primary deuterium nuclei; the corresponding value is about 10 per cent of the flux of protons with the same magnetic rigidity $R_H \simeq 16$ GV (see also the recent results for non-relativistic energies[441, 442]).

In view of their comparatively short life (12 years) tritium atoms in cosmic rays could be only of solar origin. According to recent data[441] the flux of primary tritium nuclei in the low-energy range

($\mathscr{E}_k \sim 100$ MeV/nucleon) is less than 9 per cent of the flux of α-particles with the same energy.

Helium nuclei

More reliable are the measurements of the flux of helium nuclei (denoted by the letter α in Table 1) which, according to the data of various authors,[21-23] is about 90 ± 9 particles/m²·sterad·sec. The table takes the value of $I_\alpha = 88$ particles/m²·sterad·sec which also agrees with the more probable value of $I_\alpha = 88 \pm 2$ particles/m²·sterad·sec taken by Waddington.[24, 25]

The first results of measuring the isotopic composition of the helium in primary cosmic rays have been published recently.[26] According to these data the isotopes He^4 and He^3 are present in the primary component in comparable amounts: in the kinetic energy range $\mathscr{E}_k \sim 200$–400 MeV/nucleon the ratio $He^3/(He^3 + He^4) = 0\cdot31 \pm 0\cdot08$ was obtained. (We would point out that the natural distribution of these isotopes corresponds to a ratio of $He^3/(He^3 + He^4) = 3 \times 10^{-4}$.) A later paper,[443] however, gives the lower value of $0\cdot20 \pm 0\cdot05$ for this ratio. On the other hand, considerably lower values were obtained in recent work[444, 445]: $0\cdot10$ (for the energy range $\mathscr{E}_k = 155$ to 320 MeV/nucleon[444]) and even $0\cdot06 \pm 0\cdot03$ (for the range $\mathscr{E}_k = 260$ to 360 MeV/nucleon[445]). Bearing these results in mind we can clearly consider that in the primary cosmic rays $He^3/(He^3 + He^4) < 0\cdot20$.

A high content of the He^3 isotope may be connected either with the transformation of the cosmic ray composition as they move through the interstellar medium, or with a high He^3 content in the actual sources of cosmic rays. An analysis of the latter possibility shows that, although the presence of a large amount of He^3 may be accepted in the atmospheres of certain stars, there is no foundation for this assumption in the generation of the basic part of cosmic rays in the shells of supernovae.[27] At the same time a He^3 content of 10–20 per cent of all the helium can be explained by fragmentation of the cosmic ray nuclei as they pass through 3–7 g/cm² of interstellar hydrogen. The high He^3 content observed may therefore be looked upon as an indication of the essential rôle of fragmentation in the formation of the observed cosmic ray composition (in this case a considerable part of the helium composing the cosmic rays is formed as the result of heavier nuclei being broken up). We note that the share of the He^3 isotope in the helium formed when iron is irradiated by a flux of protons with an energy of several GeV is 20–30 per cent, as follows from an analysis of the isotope composition of iron meteorites and data obtained from accelerators.[28]

The M-group of nuclei

For the heavier nuclei one makes experimental measurements of the flux or relative share of the different nuclei at different altitudes of the atmosphere, chiefly at the altitudes reached by balloon flights. In order to increase the statistical reliability of the experimental data one generally combines nuclei with neighbouring atomic numbers into the following groups: L—the group of "light" nuclei (Li, Be, B), M—"medium" nuclei (C, N, O, F), H—"heavy" nuclei ($Z \geqslant 10$) and VH "very heavy" nuclei ($Z \geqslant 20$). In this definition the VH group of nuclei is part of the H-group of nuclei (we should point out that divisions of the nuclei into groups other than that used by us may also be met). The results of measurements made in recent years agree satisfactorily as a whole. However further extrapolation to the top of the atmosphere, which is necessary for determining the primary radiation composition when undistorted by spallation of heavy nuclei, is a source of considerable error. In addition, even when the cosmic ray composition is known in detail at a given depth in the atmosphere, this extrapolation inevitably blurs the finer properties such as the relative composition within the groups of nuclei, the presence of elements which are rare in nature, the isotope composition, and so on. Direct measurement of the composition beyond the atmosphere would therefore be very important for the theory of cosmic rays. The first steps have already been taken in this direction using Cherenkov counters and photo-emulsions fitted in artificial satellites and space probes.[29–31, 43] Although the accuracy of these experiments and the possibility of resolution between charges close in value is not yet high their results as a whole confirm the data obtained by sounding balloons near the top of the atmosphere.

Among the nuclei with $Z > 2$ the flux of the M-group nuclei (C, N, O, F) has been determined relatively reliably. According to the data of different authors it is within the limits $I_M = 5 \cdot 1$ to $6 \cdot 1$ particles/$m^2 \cdot sterad \cdot sec$. The average value taken in Table 1 is based on the data of several authors[21, 32–34] and agrees with the most probable value of $I_M = 5 \cdot 70 \pm 0 \cdot 28$ particles/$m^2 \cdot sterad \cdot sec$ given by Waddington.[25]

For the ratio I_H/I_M of the intensities of the heavy and medium nuclei at the top of the atmosphere the published values chiefly vary between 0·4[21, 35-37] and 0·5.[32-34] These values have been obtained by extrapolation of the composition observed at a certain depth in the atmosphere with certain assumptions about the effective absorption path and the fragmentation parameters of the group of heavy nuclei. A critical analysis of these assumptions and the experimental results of Daniel and Durgaprasad[38] indicate that the average value of $I_H/I_M = 0·45$ which was accepted earlier[6, 24] is too high.† According to Daniel and Durgaprasad[38] $I_H/I_M = 0·30 \pm 0·02$. In the determination of the H-nucleus intensity in Table 1 we have used the value $I_H/I_M = 0·34 \pm 0·04$ which is taken as the most probable one in Ref. 25.

The L-group of nuclei

The important question of the presence of the L-group of nuclei (Li, Be, B) has been cleared up considerably of late. Most papers devoted to this question[21, 33, 34, 36, 39] give the value $I_L/I_M \simeq 1/3$ used in Table 1.

It should be pointed out that an even greater value $I_L/I_M \geqslant 0·4$ has been obtained in many papers[32, 35, 37, 40]; in this case there are more L-nuclei than all the nuclei in the H-group. The discrepancy between these results and those[41] according to which $I_L/I_M < 0·1$, has now been eliminated[38] as the result of careful repeated processing of the latter data.[41] The value of $I_L/(I_M + I_H) = 0·24 \pm 0·09$ obtained is in close agreement with the results of other authors. The work by Aizu and other authors[37, 39, 42] is of great interest since here photo-emulsions were exposed at a very great altitude (the residual thickness of the atmosphere was 1·5 to 2·7 g/cm²) so the possible

---

† It should, however, be pointed out that this question is not yet fully cleared up. For example in a recent work[45] a value of $H/M = 0·55 \pm 0·06$ was obtained for the ratio H/M at the top of the atmosphere. This also allowed for the possible dependence indicated by Daniel and Durgaprasad[38] of the fragmentation parameters on the thickness of the matter passed through. According to recent data[455] for the rigidity $R_H > 16·8$ GV we have the ratio $H/M = 0·48 \pm 0·08$.

It is absolutely necessary to make a more precise experimental determination of the ratio H/M since the value of this ratio is of considerable importance for the problem of the chemical composition of cosmic rays: it determines to a considerable extent the thickness of matter passed through by the cosmic rays (before they hit the Earth) and the chemical composition of the cosmic rays in their sources (see section 15).

extrapolation errors are not very great. A ratio of $I_L/(I_M + I_H) =$ 0·18 $\pm$ 0·04 was obtained[42] thus producing $I_L/I_M = 0·26$ for $I_H/I_M = \frac{1}{3}$. A value of $I_L/I_M = 0·32 \pm 0·05$ was obtained[39] for the ratio of the intensities at the top of the atmosphere.

According to Koshiba et al.[37] this ratio is $0·32 \pm 0·03$ for the energy range $\mathscr{E}_k > 700$ MeV/nucleon and rises to $0·51 \pm 0·06$ in the lower energy range $\mathscr{E}_k = 200–700$ MeV/nucleon. Lastly, according to preliminary data obtained by Cherenkov counters in a satellite,[43] the L-nucleus flux reaches $0·31 \pm 0·1$ of the total flux of group M and H nuclei beyond the atmosphere ($\mathscr{E}_k > 600$ MeV/nucleon).

There is thus no doubt at present of the presence of a noticeable primary flux of Li, Be and B nuclei in the primary cosmic radiation. At the same time it remains an important experimental task to determine more accurately the data on the intensity of these and other primary nuclei.

In the region of non-relativistic energies,[37, 44] there is a tendency for the share of L-nuclei to rise in relation to the heavier ones. This tendency was clearly also discovered by Alekseeva et al.[31] However, before trying to interpret this result quantitatively from the standpoint of the theory of the origin of cosmic rays and their transformation in interstellar space, new measurements are necessary to confirm the reality of the effect. This is even more necessary since the very presence of L-nuclei in primary cosmic rays was doubted for a long time and finally established only recently. As for the actual possibility of the existence of a relationship between the percentage content of the various nuclei and the energy, this interesting question will be touched on in sections 15 and 16.

The H and VH-groups of nuclei

The heavy nuclei group (H-group) covers a very wide range of charges (from $Z = 10$ to at least $Z = 26$ to 28 observable in primary cosmic rays) which makes it difficult to determine the effective values of the atomic weight, the interaction path and the fragmentation probabilities for the group as a whole. As a result of the accumulation of experimental data it has recently become possible to separate out a sub-group VH of "very heavy" nuclei ($Z \geqslant 20$) from the H-group. Cr and Fe nuclei evidently compose most of this sub-group.[24, 45] The intensity ratio I_{VH}/I_H at the top of the atmosphere[24, 38, 44, 46, 103] is 0·26 to 0·31; for higher energies (at the equator[47]) $I_{VH}/I_H = 0.30 \pm 0.07$. We should point out that Wadding-ton[24] gives directly the value of $I_{VH}/(I_H - I_{VH})$ which, according to various data, is 0.35 ± 0.10 and 0.38 ± 0.08, respectively. According to Hasegawa[46] $I_{VH}/(I_H - I_{VH}) = 0.41 \pm 0.11$. Sometimes nuclei with $Z \geqslant 17$ are included in the VH-group. For example Kristiansson et al.[45] have determined the ratio as $I(Z \geqslant 17)/I(10 \leqslant Z \leqslant 16) = 0.36 \pm 0.07$ from which $I(Z \geqslant 17)/I(Z \geqslant 10) = 0.27$. Since the relative number of nuclei in the range $17 \leqslant Z \leqslant 19$ is not great and lies at the limit of measurement errors this difference in the determi-nation of the VH-group can be ignored in practice. For example according to Daniel and Durgaprasad[38] $I(16 \leqslant Z \leqslant 19)/I(Z \geqslant 10) \lesssim 0.05$. Kristiansson et al.[45] give the ratio $I(17 \leqslant Z \leqslant 21)/I(Z \geqslant 22) = 0.09 \pm 0.11$, i.e., there are considerably less nuclei with $Z = 17$ to 21 than heavier ones. On the other hand, later measurements[455] near the geomagnetic equator ($R_H \geqslant 16.8$ GV) lead for nuclei with $Z = 10$ to 15, $Z = 16$ to 19 and $Z = 20$ to the following flux values respectively: 0.22 ± 0.04, 0.04 ± 0.01 and 0.08 ± 0.02. The gap in the $Z = 16$ to 19 range is therefore not so large $[I(16 \leqslant Z \leqslant 19)/I(10 \leqslant Z \leqslant 15) = 0.20 \pm 0.05]$. In accordance with the available data Table 1 gives $I_{VH}/I_H = 0.28$ corresponding to an intensity of $I_{VH} = 0.53$ m$^{-2} \cdot$sterad$^{-1} \cdot$sec^{-1}. We should point out that a direct determination[30] of the intensity of nuclei with $Z \geqslant 14$ to 15 with $\mathscr{E} \geqslant 2$ GeV/nucleon with Cherenkov counters fitted in the second and third space probes led to the value $I(Z \geqslant 14$ to 15$) = 0.4$ to 0.5 m$^{-2} \cdot$sterad$^{-1} \cdot$sec^{-1}.

This value does not contradict that given in Table 1 if we take into consideration that the measurements were made at a period of comparatively high solar activity (September–October 1959).

Column five of Table 1 shows the number of nucleons contained in each of the charge components of cosmic rays. It can be seen that more than 1/4 (to be more precise 28 per cent) of the nucleons with the given energy belong to nuclei with $Z \geqslant 2$. It is interesting to note that at a given geomagnetic latitude (i.e., for a given magnetic rigidity) the nucleons making up the nuclei with $Z \geqslant 2$ carry about one third of all the cosmic ray energy and their flux is approximately equal to the primary proton flux.

Column six of Table 1 shows the ratio of the intensity of the nuclei of a given group to the intensity of the heavy nuclei, which is clearly equal to the ratio of the concentrations N_i of these nuclei in the cosmic rays (see (1.1); we are talking about particles with

$\mathscr{E} \geqslant 2 \cdot 5$ GeV/nucleon whose velocity is very close to the velocity of light c).

Distribution of elements in cosmic rays and in the Universe

Columns 7 and 8 of Table 1 give the abundance of the elements of the corresponding groups in the Universe relative to the abundance of group H nuclei according to the data of Suess and Urey[49] and Cameron.[50] A very important feature leaps to the eye: cosmic rays are considerably poorer in the light elements than the composition of matter on the average in the Universe. New data on the distribution of elements in the Universe[50] only strengthen this difference.† It becomes particularly sharp if we compare the number of nuclei of a given kind in cosmic rays and in the Universe belonging to a very heavy VH-nucleus. In cosmic rays there prove to be almost two orders less protons and α-particles in relation to the very heavy nuclei than the average in the Universe. The consequences of this will be discussed in detail in Chapter V.

There is evidently no further rise in the excess of heavy nuclei in the range $Z > 26$.[48, 52] Measurements of the ratio $I(Z \gtrsim 35)/I(Z \gtrsim 17)$ made by a satellite[52] have shown that this ratio does not exceed the value 1 to 3×10^{-4}. The natural distribution of these elements in the Universe is about the same.

The content of the individual nuclei in groups L, M and H

It is still early to judge with certainty the finer features of the cosmic ray composition but certain conclusions can nevertheless be drawn.[24, 25, 38, 44, 45, 53] Table 2 gives data on the percentage content of different elements in primary cosmic rays within each of the charge groups.[24, 25] In view of the low statistical reliability of these data (for example in the $Z > 10$ region the total number of observed nuclei whose data were used in compiling the table was only 390) the values given in the table are only very approximate.

The table shows that cosmic rays, just like the Universe on the

† The Fe abundance given by Cameron[50] is 7 times less than that given by Suess and Urey[49] in accordance with the abundance for the Sun and the Earth, whilst the Fe abundance was estimated by Suess and Urey from meteorite data. In addition, the hydrogen content is according to Cameron reduced by a factor of about 1·5 in accordance with fresh data for the Sun. We should point out that an examination of the table of the element distribution in the Universe given by Cameron[50] aroused discussion.[51] The disagreements, however, are basically about the heavier elements which have not yet been found in cosmic rays.

average, contain more nuclei with even Z than with odd; this is not, however, such a clear-cut feature of cosmic rays.† It is interesting to note that there is more B than Li in cosmic rays whilst the reverse position is observed in the Universe on the average. Fluorine, of which there is extremely little in the Universe, is clearly present to a noticeable degree in cosmic rays.

TABLE 2

Group of nuclei	L-nuclei			M-nuclei			
Element	Li	Be	B	C	N	O	F
%	23	10	67	44	21	31	4

Group of nuclei	H-nuclei									
Element	Ne	Na	Mg	Al	Si	P	S	Cl	A	K
%	21·4	13·4	23·2	4·5	8	0·9	0	0·7	2·4	0

Group of nuclei	H-nuclei (VH-nuclei sub-group)								
Element	Ca	Sc	Ti	V	Cr	Mn	Fe	Co	Ni
%	4·7	0·8	3	0·8	5	0	9·9	0	1·3

A number of even nuclei larger than that of odd[45, 46] and the small number of nuclei with $Z = 15$ to 19 (the "gap" in the charge spectrum) is sometimes[24, 25] looked upon as a considerable argument against the preferred acceleration of heavy particles in cosmic ray sources (see Chapter V). The point is that if only heavy nuclei are accelerated, then the stable nuclei formed as the result of spallation should, it seems, have a more or less smooth Z and A distribution and there should be no large "gaps" in the charge spectrum. It is

† According to data on the natural distribution of the elements the average ratio over the $Z = 10$ to 16 range of the numbers of odd and even nuclei is 0·02 to 0·06.[49, 50] For cosmic rays,[45] the corresponding ratio is 0·12 ± 0·04.

still not clear, however, how smooth the charge distribution should be for nuclei formed as the result of the spallation of heavier ones. For example Kristiansson et al.[45] assume the generation of a threefold excess of even nuclei in the fragmentation process in accordance with the share of them among the stable isotopes. This side of the question may be elucidated under laboratory conditions by studying the products from the spallation of heavy nuclei by a beam of protons and high-energy α-particles. The data on the amount of the individual elements in cosmic rays, on the other hand, can still not be considered reliable enough to judge with certainty the actual presence of sufficiently large gaps in the charge spectrum.[455]

The question of "gaps" in the charge spectrum and the objections against the hypothesis of preferred acceleration of heavy elements in cosmic ray sources can therefore be seriously discussed only on the basis of more reliable quantitative data. It should also be remarked that even without considering the question of preferred acceleration of heavy particles the presence of gaps in the charge spectrum would necessitate a radical re-examination of modern ideas if these gaps were large enough and could not be explained by fragmentation features. In actual fact, it is generally considered at present that group L nuclei appear in the primary cosmic rays on the Earth as the result of the spallation of heavier nuclei in collisions with nuclei of the interstellar medium. In other words the "gap" in the L-nucleus region is filled up as the result of fragmentation of nuclei in groups M and H. It follows from this that the thickness of the matter passed through by the cosmic rays is at least about 2·5 to 3·5 g/cm^2, i.e., not less than one absorption path for group VH nuclei. Therefore proceeding from the above ideas on the more or less smooth charge distribution of the spallation products it would be necessary to conclude that there can be no significant "gap" even in the $Z = 15$ to 19 charge range.

Antiprotons and antinuclei

To conclude this section we shall give some experimental data relating to the determination of the upper limit of the possible flux of antiparticles (antinuclei and antiprotons) in primary cosmic radiation. As the result of an analysis[44, 47] of the tracks of primary particles in photo-emulsions exposed near the top of the atmosphere it has been established that the antiparticle flux is not more than 0·1 to 1 per cent of the primary cosmic ray flux. Searches have been made[54] for antinuclei with $Z > 2$ in photo-emulsions exposed in the second space vehicle. According to the results of this work the number of these nuclei in cosmic rays is not more than 0·23 per cent of the ordinary primary nuclei with the same charge. In all the above measurements[44, 47, 54] we are dealing only with particles which stopped in the emulsion (in this case an antiparticle would give a star containing the annihilation products; no such stars were observed). We note that even if there are no regions in the Universe with any considerable quantity of anti-matter (the absence of such regions seems most likely particularly with respect to the Galaxy) a small number of antiprotons should be observed in the primary cosmic ray flux. According to an estimate[43, 55] the number of these antiprotons with an energy of $E > 1·8$ GeV formed by cosmic rays in nuclear collisions should be less than 0·05 to 0·1 per cent of the total cosmic ray flux in the same energy range.

2. ELECTRONS, GAMMA RAYS AND NEUTRINOS

Apart from the proton and nucleus component we should, generally speaking, also observe other stable particles in cosmic rays: electrons (and positrons), γ-quanta and neutrinos (antineutrinos). Experimental data on the fluxes of such particles are very scanty at present and most of the work in this direction is devoted to theoretical estimates. We shall give the present ideas on the origin of the electron and positron component of cosmic rays and the corresponding estimates of its intensity in subsequent chapters, particularly in connexion with the theory of cosmic radio emission (Chapter II). In the present section we shall limit ourselves merely to discussing the available experimental data on the electron (and positron) intensity at the top of the atmosphere. As for the γ-rays and neutrinos it is as well to give the corresponding theoretical estimates as well as the extremely limited data available so as not to have to return to this question again (compare footnote on p. 25).

Intensity of the electron-positron component on Earth

An attempt to find relativistic electrons† in primary cosmic radiation was made by Critchfield *et al.*[56] In this work the upper

---

† Below, unless reservations are made, the term electrons means both electrons and positrons (for example the intensity values given relate to the sum of the electrons and positrons).

intensity limit of primary electrons with an energy greater than 1 GeV obtained was $I_e(E > 1 \text{ GeV}) \leqslant 13$ electrons/m$^2 \cdot$sterad$\cdot$sec; this was about 0·6 per cent of the total cosmic ray intensity at the top of the atmosphere.

Recently fresh measurements have been made of the electron intensity above the atmosphere.[57, 58] A value of $I_e(E > 0.5 \text{ GeV}) = 32 \pm 10$ electrons/cm$^2 \cdot$sterad$\cdot$sec was obtained by Earl.[57] In the spectrum of the observed electrons a maximum was found corresponding to the local rigidity threshold (about 0·7 GV) and indicating that the electron spectrum beyond the Earth spreads into the low-energy range as well. An upper intensity limit of $I_e(E > 1.3 \text{ GeV}) < 80$ electrons/m$^2 \cdot$sterad$\cdot$sec was established by Meyer and Vogt.[58] At the same time the intensity in the low-energy region proved to be appreciable (in the 100 to 1300 MeV range a value of $I_e > 35$ electrons/cm$^2 \cdot$sterad$\cdot$sec was obtained) and rose as the energy decreased to energies of $E \simeq 25$ to 100 MeV.

It still cannot be said to what degree the results obtained provide information on the true electron flux in the primary (galactic) cosmic rays and not on the electrons occurring as the result of solar and geophysical processes.

In actual fact in the cosmic ray energy spectrum there is what is called high-latitude cut-off or an "elbow" which has been most fully studied in the α-particle spectrum (see section 3). The differential α-particle spectrum has a maximum near the kinetic energy $\mathscr{E}_k = 300$ MeV/nucleon (a rigidity of $R_H = 1.6$ GV) and decreases comparatively rapidly as the energy decreases. If, as is often considered, the maximum for all particles in the differential spectrum is located at one and the same rigidity, i.e., the high-latitude cut-off is determined only by the rigidity of the particles, then the intensity of the primary electrons with an energy less than 1·6 GeV will be reduced considerably.

Therefore, returning to Earl[57] and Meyer and Vogt's[58] data, the conclusion may be drawn that either the observed electrons are not galactic and are accelerated somewhere in the solar system, on the Sun[59] or in the neighbourhood of the Earth, or the cut-off is more complex in nature and, for example, is determined not only by the rigidity (in particular it occurs outside the solar system and is practically absent for secondary particles arising in collisions in the interstellar gas). An experimental elucidation of this question would provide important information on the nature of high-latitude cut-off.

It is specially important to carry out the corresponding measurements in the present period of a solar activity minimum (1964–65) when the contribution of the electrons of solar origin will, it may be assumed, be minimal.

In order to determine the number of electrons in the primary cosmic rays it would also be best to make measurements in the range of energies where high-latitude cut-off is no longer significant, i.e., at a rigidity $R_H > 2 \cdot 5$ to $3 \cdot 0$ GV which corresponds to a kinetic energy of $\mathscr{E}_k > 1$ GeV/nucleon for nuclei with $Z \geqslant 2$.

Using the data of Earl[57] we can at present only estimate the number of electrons with an energy greater than $1 \cdot 5$ GeV. The intensity of these particles is approximately 12 electrons/m$^2 \cdot$ sterad $\cdot$ sec which is about 1 per cent of the proton intensity ($I_p = 1100 \pm 100$ protons/m$^2 \cdot$ sterad $\cdot$ sec) observed by Earl.[57] Despite the remarks above the latter result allows us to conclude that in Earl's work[57] electrons were discovered which were part of the primary (galactic) cosmic rays. This conclusion does not contradict Critchfield's data[56] and agrees with radio-astronomical data (see Chapter II).

Some indications that the chromospheric flares on the Sun are not the direct source of generation of the electrons of energies 100 to 1000 MeV observed at the top of the atmosphere were obtained by Meyer and Vogt.[60] It was established in this work that the increase in the intensity of low-energy protons ($E_k > 350$ MeV) following on the flare of 3 September 1960 was not accompanied by an increase in the intensity of the electron component.† On the contrary, just as for the primary (galactic) cosmic rays, a considerable ($\sim 40\%$) Forbush decrease was found in the electron intensity at the top of the atmosphere. These results indicate that the electrons observed in the $E \lesssim 1$ GeV energy range are either galactic or, if they are of solar origin, accumulate in the solar system. In this last case it could be a question of, as it were, a "solar system radiation belt" in which the particles are supplied by the Sun. The origin of the large number of soft protons observed by Vogt[109] could be the same. The whole of this problem remains in a confused state.

The question of which part of the observed light particles are electrons and which part positrons is very important. In principle it would be best to make the appropriate measurements with satellites.[43]

---

† The appearance of relativistic electrons of solar origin has been established[61] recently after some other flares (this result agrees with the conclusion drawn by Ginzburg and Zheleznyakov[59]).

The first experimental results in this field were, however, obtained with balloons by De Shong *et al.*[446] According to these data the number of positrons in the $0.3 < E < 1$ GeV energy range is 16 ± 4 per cent of all the light particles (electrons and positrons). In the lower energy range the relative number of positrons rises. The value given is the upper limit for the ratio $N^+/(N^- + N^+)$ in the primary cosmic ray flux, since the secondary light particles of atmospheric origin were not separated from the primary ones by De Shong *et al.*[446] As has been pointed out, the possible part played by light particles of solar origin is not clear either. Despite these reservations it is most probable at present that the particles observed, at least for $E > 0.3$ GeV, are largely galactic electrons. The number of positrons among these light particles is not more than about 10 to 20 per cent.

Gamma rays in the primary radiation†

The possible sources of cosmic γ-radiation and the corresponding estimates of the intensity have been discussed by various authors[62–67] (see also sections 18 and 19 and the references listed in these sections). From the standpoint of the theory of the origin of cosmic rays and cosmic radio emission there is particular interest in the possibility of recording γ-quanta appearing in the interaction of cosmic rays with the interstellar and intergalactic medium as the result of the formation and decay of π°-mesons (for the other processes see Section 19). In order to estimate the expected intensity of γ-quanta with energies of $E \gtrsim 1$ GeV we may use the data on the generation of π-mesons in the atmosphere as is done by Greisen.[66] The differential energy spectrum of all the charged π-mesons generated by cosmic rays in the atmosphere takes the form,[66]

$$I_{\pi\pm}(E)\, dE = 0.156 E^{-2.64}\, dE \text{ cm}^{-2} \cdot \text{sterad}^{-1} \cdot \text{sec}^{-1}, \quad (2.1)$$

where the π-meson energy is measured in GeV. For neutral π°-mesons the coefficient 0.156 in the spectrum (2.1) must be halved (we are not dealing with the low-energy range where fewer π^--mesons are generated than π^+-mesons). It is natural to consider that in collisions in the interstellar medium π-mesons are generated

† The question of γ-rays is discussed in detail in sections 18 and 19. The present section has been only slightly changed from that in the original Russian edition.

with about the same intensity if the cosmic ray intensity is constant in space and the thickness of the matter they pass through corresponds to the path λ_E with respect to the energy loss due to nuclear collisions. If we take the length of the path for an inelastic interaction to be 72 g/cm² (see Table 10) and the amount of energy lost in one interaction (the coefficient of inelasticity) is 1/3, then the energy decreases $e = 2 \cdot 72$ times on a path $\lambda_E = 180$ g/cm². For an arbitrary thickness of matter expression (2.1) must be multiplied by

$$x = \frac{1}{\lambda_E} \int \rho \, dL,$$

where ρ is the density of the interstellar gas, $\lambda_E = 180$ g/cm² and integration is carried out in the direction of observation as far as the edge of the region occupied by the cosmic rays.

From an analysis of the kinematics of $\pi^\circ \to 2\gamma$ and $\pi^\pm \to \mu^\pm \to e^\pm$ decays it follows that the spectrum of the γ-rays, electrons and neutrinos formed differs from spectrum (2.1) only in the replacement of the coefficient 0·156 by 0·059, 0·020 and 0·055 respectively. With these assumptions the intensity of γ-quanta with an energy greater than 1 GeV incident on the top of the atmosphere in a certain direction is

$$I_\gamma(E > 1 \text{ GeV}) = 0 \cdot 036 \cdot x \text{ photons/cm}^2 \cdot \text{sterad} \cdot \text{sec}. \qquad (2.2)$$

This leads to the following estimates for the expected intensity of γ-quanta of the said energy.

At a mean hydrogen concentration in the galactic disk of 1 atom/cm³ in the direction of the galactic centre (the extent of the region occupied by the cosmic rays is about 20 kparsec) $x \simeq 5 \times 10^{-4}$ and the expected intensity is $I_\gamma \simeq 2 \times 10^{-5}$ photons/cm² · sterad · sec which is about 10^{-4} of the total primary proton flux with energies $\gtrsim 1$ GeV at the top of the atmosphere ($I_p \simeq 0 \cdot 2$ protons/cm² · sterad · sec). In the direction at right angles to the galactic disk (extent about 0·2 kparsec) the γ-ray intensity caused by the disk will be approximately two orders less. However here a noticeable contribution may be made by cosmic ray interactions in the halo with a density of about 0·01 atom/cm³ and an extent of about 10 kparsec. At these values $x \simeq 3 \times 10^{-6}$ and together with the disk's emission (at right angles) this gives $I_\gamma \lesssim 3 \times 10^{-7}$ photons/cm² · sterad · sec. We notice that according to (2.2) the flux of secondary photons with the same energy in the atmosphere is $3 \cdot 6 \times 10^{-2}$ photons/cm² · sterad · sec. However this will not create any special difficulties in measurements of the primary γ-radiation beyond the atmosphere (by satellites) if the Earth is outside the solid angle of the detector.

The possibility of finding γ-rays from intergalactic space is of particular interest. If the cosmic ray density in the Metagalaxy is the same as that observed on Earth, then it is easy to estimate the expected intensity of the γ-quanta if it is taken, as is generally done (see section 13), that the concentration of the intergalactic gas (largely hydrogen) is 10^{-5} cm^{-3} and the effective extent of the emitting region corresponds to the cosmological length $\sim 5 \times 10^{27}$ cm (emission from more remote regions of the Metagalaxy is insignificant due to the red shift caused by the expansion of the Metagalaxy). In this case $x \simeq 5 \times 10^{-4}$ and the expected intensity is $I_\gamma \simeq 2 \times 10^{-5}$ photons/cm$^2 \cdot$sterad$\cdot$sec. This value is only 10^4 times less than the primary proton flux at the top of the atmosphere. We note that, according to the estimates by Maze and Zawadzki[65] (see also section 18), metagalactic photons with an energy of $\gtrsim 10^{14}$ to 10^{15} eV must be about 3×10^{-6} of the primary cosmic rays with the same energy. It is assumed here that protons with an energy $\gtrsim 10^{15}$ eV fill the Universe with the density observed on Earth and the concentration of gas in the Metagalaxy is $n \simeq 10^{-5}$ cm^{-3} (we note that a greater value was actually obtained by Maze and Zawadzki[65] for I_γ due to selecting a concentration $n \sim 10^{-3}$ cm^{-3}; using such a large value of n is, however, not permissible; see section 13).

There are no reliable experimental data on the flux of γ-rays with an energy of $E \gtrsim 10^{14}$ eV. The preliminary results of measurements of the flux of hard gamma-rays (estimated from the number of extensive atmospheric showers with an anomalously low content of μ-mesons) are discussed in section 18.

Recently preliminary data have been published on the measurements of the intensity of primary γ-quanta with energies of $E > 50$ MeV made beyond the atmosphere by the American satellite Explorer XI.[68] The intensity averaged over all directions proved to be $I_\gamma(E > 50$ MeV$) = 3 \cdot 7$ to 11×10^{-4} photons/cm$^2 \cdot$sterad$\cdot$sec (Kraushaar and Clark[68] take the mean value as $I_\gamma = 5 \cdot 5 \times 10^{-4}$). According to recent data[447] obtained by these means $I_\gamma(E_\gamma > 40$ MeV$) \leqslant (3 \cdot 3 \pm 1 \cdot 3) \times 10^{-4}$ photons/cm$^2 \cdot$sterad$\cdot$sec; no noticeable anisotropy was found in the γ-ray flux. According to the estimates given by Kraushaar and Clark[68] the expected intensity of γ-radiation at the said energies of $E > 50$ MeV appearing in the Galaxy in interactions of cosmic rays with the interstellar gas is 7×10^{-5}

photons/cm^2·sterad·sec after averaging in all directions and should be greatest in the direction of the centre of the Galaxy. At the same time the intensity of the metagalactic γ-rays from π-meson decay at a density of matter in the Metagalaxy corresponding to a concentration of 10^{-5} protons/cm^3 and for a cosmic radiation intensity constant in space of 0·3 particle/cm^2·sterad·sec should be $I_\gamma = 1·6 \times 10^{-3}$ photons/cm·sterad·sec.† As is shown in section 19, relativistic electrons scattered on thermal photons are a more effective source of γ-rays. Therefore even if the value given for $I_\gamma \sim 3 \times 10^{-4}$ photons/cm· sterad ·sec is true and these γ-rays are generated in the Metagalaxy this still cannot be used to conclude that there is a cosmic ray flux in metagalactic space comparable to that in the Galaxy. It must be borne in mind that metagalactic γ-rays may also come from galaxies (for more detail see section 13). Because of this and for other independent reasons searches for γ-quanta from galaxies, radio-galaxies and other discrete sources of cosmic radio emission are of great interest. Searches of this kind, which were made by various authors[67—69] to date, allow only the upper limit of the γ-radiation for certain sources to be established. For example for the radio galaxy Cygnus A the flux of γ-quanta with an energy $E > 50$ MeV, according to the data of Kraushaar and Clark,[68] does not exceed $3·4 \times 10^{-4}$ cm^{-2} sec^{-1}; the flux of quanta with an energy $E > 5 \times 10^{12}$ eV, according to Chudakov et al.,[69] does not exceed a value of 5×10^{-11} cm^{-2} sec^{-1}. The upper flux limit of γ-quanta with energies $E > 50$ MeV, according to Kraushaar and Clark[68] is $3·7 \times 10^{-2}$ cm^{-2}· sec^{-1} for the Crab Nebula and $1·2 \times 10^{-2}$ cm^{-2}·sec^{-1} for radio source Cassiopeia A (further processing of these same measurements[447] leads to even lower values).

† For estimating the total number of γ-quanta (with energies >50 MeV) arising out of interactions of cosmic rays in the interstellar and intergalactic medium it is assumed by Kraushaar and Clark[68] that an average of two γ-quanta in the said energy range will result from each interaction of a primary proton with the interstellar hydrogen. The cross section σ of an inelastic p-p interaction is taken as 40 mb and the cosmic ray intensity I beyond the solar system to be 0·3 cm^{-2}·sterad^{-1}·sec^{-1}. Here $I_\gamma = 2\sigma I n R = 2·4 \times 10^{-26} n R$, where n is the concentration of the gas (protons) and R is the distance along the line of sight. Hence in the direction towards the centre of the Galaxy $I_\gamma = 1·4 \times 10^{-3}$ (for $n = 1$ cm^{-3} and $R = 20$ kpc) and for the Metagalaxy $I_\gamma = 1·2 \times 10^{-3}$ (for $n = 10^{-5}$ cm^{-3} and $R = 5 \times 10^{27}$ cm); Kraushaar and Clark[68] use the value $I_\gamma = 1·6 \times 10^{-3}$ given in the text. According to more detailed calculations made by V. M. Maksimenko using the cosmic ray spectrum[113] (see also section 3) and allowing for the dependence of the cross section and the multiplicity of π°-meson formation on the energy the intensity is $I_\gamma = 8 \times 10^{-27} n R$.

Absorption of gamma rays

In the range of energies $E \gtrsim 1$ GeV of interest to us the basic process leading to γ-ray absorption is the formation of electron-positron pairs. At lower energies Compton scattering on electrons of the medium is also responsible but at $E \gtrsim 10^7$ eV allowing for this effect does not yet alter the order of magnitude of the absorption.[70–73] Pairs are formed on both nuclei and electrons, the way being slightly different depending upon whether the gas is neutral or ionised. For $E \gtrsim 1$ GeV the formation of pairs on neutral atoms can in the first approximation be considered to occur under conditions of total screening. With total screening the coefficient of γ-ray absorption connected with the formation of pairs does not depend on the energy and for atomic hydrogen is†

$$\mu = 1 \cdot 25 \times 10^{-2} \text{ cm}^2/\text{g} = 2 \cdot 25 \times 10^{-26} n \text{ cm}^{-1}. \quad (2.3)$$

This means that the γ-ray intensity varies according to the law $I(L) = I_0 e^{-\mu L}$, where the path L is measured in g/cm^2 when using the first value of (2.3); when the second value is used the path L is measured in cm and n is the hydrogen atom concentration.

In an ionised gas (under the conditions of the interstellar medium) screening can always be ignored.[74] In this case[70]

$$\mu \simeq \frac{4e^2 Z(Z+1)}{\hbar c} \left(\frac{e^2}{mc^2}\right)^2 n \left(\frac{7}{9} \ln \frac{2E}{mc^2} - \frac{109}{54}\right)$$

$$= 3 \cdot 6 \times 10^{-27} n \left(\ln \frac{E}{mc^2} - 1 \cdot 9\right) \text{ cm}^{-1}$$

$$= 2 \cdot 1 \times 10^{-3} \left(\ln \frac{E}{mc^2} - 1 \cdot 9\right) \text{ cm}^2/\text{g}, \quad (2.4)$$

where E is the energy of a γ-quantum and $mc^2 = 5 \cdot 11 \times 10^5$ eV is the rest mass energy of an electron.

When changing to numerical values in (2.4) we put $Z = 1$ (in the formula for the probability of pair formation on a nucleus with a charge Z we have the factor Z^2; replacing this factor by $Z(Z+1)$

---

† The so-called "shower" or t-unit of length in atomic hydrogen[70] is 62 g/cm^2. At the same time at a distance equal to one t-unit the value of μL under conditions of total screening[70] is 7/9. Hence $\mu = (7/9) \cdot (1/62) = 0 \cdot 0125$ cm^2/g. A path of 1 g/cm^2 of hydrogen corresponds to a distance of $6 \times 10^{23}/n$ cm. A value of 66 g/cm^2 is used in section 19 as the best value for the t-unit in the interstellar medium.

attempts to allow for the generation of pairs on electrons). According to Cameron[50] 13 per cent of the interstellar medium is He atoms (according to Suess and Urey[49] the He content is 7 per cent). The coefficient of γ-ray absorption in He in the case (2.4) and also when there is total screening is $Z(Z + 1)/2 = 3$ times greater than in hydrogen (for the same concentration n, of course). Thus in a mixture of 90 per cent H and 10 per cent He the absorption co-efficient is 1·2 times greater than in pure hydrogen (for the same total concentration). The contribution of all the atoms heavier than He to the absorption is of the order of 2 per cent. We notice that expressions (2.3) and (2.4) are equal at a γ-quanta energy of $E \simeq 10^9$ eV. The equivalent thickness of gas in the Metagalaxy is of the order of 0·1 g/cm^2 and towards the pole in the Galaxy is about 10^{-3} g/cm^2, towards the anticentre about 10^{-2} g/cm^2 and towards the centre about 0·1 g/cm^2 (for more detail see section 18). At the same time, it is clear from (2.3) and (2.4) that γ-rays pass with hardly any attenuation even through a 1 g/cm^2 layer (to be more precise their flux is reduced by about 1 per cent).

For γ-rays with an energy of $E \gtrsim 10^{11}$ eV absorption due to the process $\gamma + \gamma' \to e^+ + e^-$, i.e., the production of $e^+ + e^-$ pairs on thermal photons (γ') in interstellar and intergalactic space[75] becomes significant. The energy density of thermal photons with a mean energy $E \sim 1$ eV in the Galaxy is of the order $w_{ph} \sim 0.3$ to 1 eV/cm^3 and in metagalactic space it is $w_{ph} \sim 10^{-3}$ eV/cm^3 (see section 8). For the sake of definition let us take it that the emission spectrum in intergalactic space is thermal and $kT = 0.5$ eV ($T = 5800$ °K). Then for the coefficient of γ-ray absorption due to pair formation on thermal photons with an energy density of $w_{ph} = 10^{-3}$ eV/cm^3 we obtain the values given in Table 3 (Nikishev[75] used a density of $w_{ph} = 0.1$ eV/cm^3 but in section 8 it is shown that $w_{ph} \sim 10^{-3}$ eV/cm^3).

The coefficient μ is proportional to the photon energy density w_{ph} so $\mu(w_{ph}) = \mu \cdot 10^3 w_{ph}$ (here μ is the value from Table 3 and w_{ph} is measured in eV/cm^3). The maximum value of the coefficient μ is at $E \simeq 10^{12}$ eV and is $\mu_{max} = 7 \times 10^{-26} w_{ph}$.

In the Galaxy for $w_{ph} \simeq 1$ eV/cm^3 and a distance $L \simeq 10^{23}$ cm the value is $\mu_{max}L \lesssim 10^{-2}$, i.e., there is little absorption. In the Meta-galaxy, however, (for $w_{ph} \sim 10^{-3}$ eV/cm^3) $\mu_{max}R \sim 0.35$ for $R \sim 5 \times 10^{27}$ cm. Since the mean density w_{ph} in the Metagalaxy may be several times greater than the accepted value the absorption of γ-rays with an energy of $\sim 10^{12}$ eV in metagalactic space may be considerable.

Hayakawa[76, 461] discusses the possible rôle of ultra-high energy γ-rays formed in the decay of π°-mesons generated as the result of the collision of cosmic rays and thermal photons. The latter process occurs at an energy of $\mathscr{E} \gtrsim 10^{17}$ eV/nucleon. However, if we use the

TABLE 3

γ-quanta energy, eV	$10^{29}\mu$, cm^{-1}	γ-quanta energy, eV	$10^{29}\mu$, cm^{-1}
10^{11}	0·05	5×10^{12}	4
5×10^{11}	5	10^{13}	2
10^{12}	7	5×10^{13}	0·7

value $w_{\mathrm{ph}} \sim 10^{-3}$ eV/cm^3 (instead of $w_{\mathrm{ph}} \sim 0.3$ eV/cm^3 used by Hayakawa[76]) it can be shown (see section 18) that the part played by the process in question when compared with the generation of π°-mesons in nuclear collisions is not large even in the Metagalaxy (with $n \gtrsim 10^{-5}$ cm^{-3}).

The formation and absorption of neutrinos

Neutrinos and antineutrinos are formed largely as the result of the following processes:

$$\pi^+ \to \mu^+ + \nu_\mu, \qquad \pi^- \to \mu^- + \bar{\nu}_\mu, \qquad \mu^+ \to e^+ + \bar{\nu}_\mu + \nu_e,$$
$$\mu^- \to e^- + \nu_\mu + \bar{\nu}_e, \qquad (2.5)$$
$$n \to p + e^- + \bar{\nu}_e, \qquad p \to n + e^+ + \nu_e \qquad (2.6)$$

Here ν_μ is a muon neutrino, ν_e is an electron neutrino, $\bar{\nu}_{\mu,e}$ are the corresponding antineutrinos,† n is a neutron, p is a proton and $\pi^\pm$ and $\mu^\pm$ are π and μ-mesons of the corresponding sign. There is now no doubt that the muon and electron neutrinos are different although this was first shown with a small amount of material in 1962.

The second of reactions (2.6) can occur, of course, only with a proton in a positron-active nucleus. The neutrinos obtained in π and μ-decays and from $\beta^\pm$ decay obviously lead to different reactions.

† Below, unless the opposite is said to be the case, the term neutrino will be taken to cover both neutrinos and antineutrinos (in the same way as we are generally calling electrons and positrons electrons).

For example

$$\nu_\mu + n \to p + \mu^-, \qquad \nu_e + n \to p + e^-, \qquad (2.7)$$

$$\bar{\nu}_\mu + p \to n + \mu^+, \qquad \bar{\nu}_e + p \to n + e^+. \qquad (2.8)$$

At neutrino energies of $E_\nu > 1$ GeV the cross section for each of the reactions (2.7) is approximately[77]

$$\sigma_\nu \simeq 1\cdot5 \times 10^{-38} E_\nu, \qquad (2.9)$$

where E_ν is measured in GeV and σ_ν in cm^2.

The cross section for reactions (2.8) is approximately a third of the value of (2.9). However, apart from reactions (2.8) there are also reactions

$$\bar{\nu}_\mu + n \to \Sigma^- + \mu^+, \qquad \bar{\nu}_\mu + p \to \Sigma^0 + \mu^+,$$

$$\bar{\nu}_\mu + p \to \Lambda^0 + \mu^+. \qquad (2.10)$$

Here Λ° and $\Sigma^{\circ,-}$ are hyperons and during the irradiation of matter by antineutrinos $\bar{\nu}_e$ (instead of antineutrettos $\bar{\nu}_\mu$) e^+ positrons are formed instead of μ^+-mesons. The cross sections for reactions (2.10) are of the same order as those for reactions (2.8). Therefore the total cross section for both $\bar{\nu}_\mu$ and $\bar{\nu}_e$ antineutrino absorption as the result of all reactions (2.8) and (2.10) is approximately equal to cross section (2.9).

The cosmic neutrino flux

The cross section (2.9) is so small† that the recording of neutrinos is very difficult although it is clearly possible using large equipments placed deep underground.[77, 78] The recording of slow neutrinos is also very difficult.[79, 80] As a result there are not yet any experimental data relating to the flux of neutrinos of any energy coming from the cosmos.

Nevertheless it is possible from various indirect considerations and estimates to indicate the upper limit of the neutrino flux from the cosmos.[80-82] This upper limit is still very high. According to recent data[81] the energy density even of only neutrinos with an energy of $E_\nu > 1$ GeV may be as much as 10 eV/cm^3; this estimate can be considerably reduced on the basis of more recent measurements of the intensity of penetrating particles at a depth of as much

† If a hypothetical heavy short-lived meson exists $B^\pm$ ($B^+ \to \mu^+ + \nu$, $B^- \to \mu^- + \bar{\nu}$) then neutrino absorption occurs with a cross section that is greater than cross section (2.9). Even in this case, however, the cross section is very small.[77]

as 8,400 m water equivalent and also by allowing for the isotropy of the flux of π-mesons generated by neutrinos a long way underground. According to recent data[448, 449] the energy density of muon neutrinos with $E_\nu > 1$ GeV does not exceed 0·1 eV/cm^3. This density is five orders less than the mean energy density of matter in the Universe† and an order less than the cosmic ray energy density in the Galaxy ($w \sim 1$ eV/cm^3).

The maximum possible energy density of all the neutrinos (with any energy) is still several orders higher than the above value and amounts to[81] 10^4 to 10^5 eV/cm^3. The accumulation of such a tremendous number of neutrinos in the Universe does not contradict certain cosmological models. On the other hand there are cosmological models (these include in particular models in which the mean density of matter in the Universe at certain stages in its evolution is sufficiently high) which are fully compatible with the assumption of an extremely small cosmic neutrino flux.

Therefore the question of the neutrino component of primary cosmic rays (i.e., of neutrinos with $E_\nu > 1$ GeV coming from outer space) remains to a considerable degree open. As the lower limit of the neutron component flux we can point to the values obtained as the result of neutrino formation in a $\pi \to \mu \to e$ decay in the interstellar and intergalactic medium. In a rough approximation it may be taken that this flux is three times greater (in number of particles) than the γ-ray flux from a π°-decay (see (2.2)). This estimate follows from the fact that on the average for one π°-meson giving two γ-quanta two charged π-mesons are formed which each produce three neutrinos in a $\pi \to \mu \to e$ decay (see 2.5)). Not to mention the fact that such a neutrino flux (intensity $I_\nu \lesssim 10^{-4}$ neutrinos/cm^2·sterad·sec; energy density about 5×10^{-5} eV/cm^3) is extremely hard to observe it is impossible by virtue of the formation of a considerably (two or three orders!) greater neutrino flux in the Earth's atmosphere. This is quite understandable since the total thickness of the layer of gas at the characteristic cosmological distance of about 10^{28} cm $= 10^{10}$ light years is 0·1 g/cm^3, whilst in the Earth's atmosphere the primary cosmic rays are totally absorbed. The intensity of neutrinos with $E_\nu > 1$ GeV generated by

---

† The mean concentration n of atoms of matter (basically hydrogen) in the Universe is assumed to be about 10^{-5} cm^{-3} (allowing for the matter included in the stars). This value corresponds to an energy density $nM_pc^2 \sim 10^{-5} \times 10^9 \sim 10^4$ eV/cm^3.

cosmic rays in the atmosphere is[78] $I_{v0} = 2 \times 10^{-2}$ neutrinos/cm$^2 \cdot$ sterad$\cdot$sec at sea level.

Therefore if the neutrino component of cosmic rays is formed only as the result of nuclear collisions of cosmic rays in interstellar space then it is not possible to record these neutrinos on the Earth (under the Earth). The creation of equipments for recording neutrinos beyond the Earth's atmosphere (on the Moon for example) is clearly impracticable at present. At the same time the making of underground measurements of the neutrino flux[77, 78] is important and desirable not only from the standpoint of studying weak elementary particle interactions[77] but also for astrophysical reasons. In actual fact, as we have seen, it is still not possible to affirm with certainty that the intensity of muon cosmic neutrinos with $E_v > 1$ GeV is less than approximately 0·3 neutrinos/cm$^2 \cdot$sterad$\cdot$sec (this value of the intensity I_v corresponds to an energy density

$$w_v \sim E_v N_v \sim \frac{4\pi}{c} E_v I_v \sim 0\cdot1 \text{ eV/cm}^3).$$

This flux is one order greater than the flux of neutrinos formed in the atmosphere from cosmic rays $I_{v0} \sim 2 \times 10^{-2}$ neutrinos/cm$^2 \cdot$sterad$\cdot$sec. Since the last flux can be measured in underground experiments[77, 78] we may hope that the upper limit of the flux of cosmic neutrinos with $E_v > 1$ GeV will be reduced by one or two orders.

We shall not stop here to discuss the question of low-energy neutrinos arriving from outer space.[80, 83, 84, 85, 450] We shall mention only one point which is indirectly connected with the theory of the origin of cosmic rays. The point is that supernovae are apparently the basic source of cosmic rays in the Galaxy (see section 11). At the same time it follows from theoretical considerations[83, 84] that during their explosion supernovae are a powerful source of neutrinos (with energies of tens of keV or less). These neutrinos arise basically from the process $\gamma + e \rightarrow e + v + \bar{v}$, i.e., as the result of the production of neutrino-antineutrino pairs on electrons, the γ-rays producing the neutrinos being of thermal origin inside the star.

In addition, if supernova explosion are caused by the formation in the star of a neutron core as the result of the reaction $p + e^- \rightarrow n + v$ these flares should be linked with the emission of a large number of neutrinos. It is significant that in this case only neutrinos (without antineutrinos) are formed and this in principle makes possible an experimental check of the hypothesis of the formation of a neutron core in flaring stars (V. I. Ritus has drawn attention to this).

Therefore, if the detection of neutrinos occurring in supernova flares proves to be possible in the future we shall be able to record the flares of supernovae which are not visible in the optical range because of the interstellar absorption of light and, what is most important, will provide additional data on the nature of the flares.

3. THE ENERGY SPECTRUM AND DEGREE OF ANISOTROPY OF COSMIC RAYS

In this section we shall discuss the experimental data available on the distribution of cosmic ray particles by energies and directions of arrival on the Earth from the surrounding space.

The spectrum in the $2 \times 10^9 \lesssim \mathscr{E} \lesssim 10^{15}$ eV/*nucleon energy range*

For the basic mass of cosmic rays with energies in the range from approximately 2×10^9 to 10^{15} eV/nucleon there is a smooth decrease in the intensity as the energy of the particles increases; this is described well by a power-law relationship

$$I_A(>\mathscr{E}) = \int_{\mathscr{E}}^{\infty} I_A(\mathscr{E}) \, d\mathscr{E} = K_A \mathscr{E}^{-(\gamma-1)},$$

$$I_A(\mathscr{E}) = (\gamma - 1)K_A \mathscr{E}^{-\gamma}. \tag{3.1}$$

Here $I_A (> \mathscr{E})$ is the intensity (number of particles/m² · sterad · sec) of group A nuclei with a total energy per nucleon greater than $\mathscr{E}$ (in GeV). The values of the coefficient K_A and the index $(\gamma - 1)$ in the integral spectrum (3.1) according to different research data are given in Table 4. Table 4a gives the corresponding values for the intensity of all the cosmic rays $I(>E) = KE^{-(\gamma-1)}$ with a total energy E greater than the set one.

It is very important that the spectrum index γ within the limits of measurement accuracy is identical for the different charge groups of cosmic rays and in the range of energies in question is $\gamma = 2 \cdot 5 \pm 0 \cdot 2$. The assumption[12] that nuclei with different Z have different spectra is not confirmed by later data.[24, 43] Even when the VH sub-group of very heavy nuclei is separated out its spectrum remains similar to the spectra of the other groups.[24, 47, 103] It should be pointed out, however, that there are reliable data on the spectra of nuclei with $Z \geqslant 2$ only for energies of $\lesssim 10^2$ GeV/nucleon. According to the latest data[451, 452] the spectral index in the energy range $10^{10} < E < 10^{15}$ GeV is $\gamma = 2\cdot6 \pm 0\cdot1$; Ref. 452 gives the best spectrum for this

TABLE 4

Group of nuclei	$\gamma - 1$	K_A	Energy range, GeV/nucleon	Refs.
	1·5	6600	4·0 to 16·0	22, 86
	1·40 ± 0·10	4800	4·7 to 16·0	87
p	1·40 ± 0·22	—	65 to 300	88
	1·45 ± 0·25	—	16 to 5000	89
	1·49 ± 0·22	360	2·5 to 800	90
	1·45 ± 0·11	300	2·5 to 8·0	87
α	1·5	415	1·3 to 8·0	22, 86
	1·58 ± 0·20	—	8 to 1500	47
	1·48 ± 0·12	360	1·4 to 4·0	90
	1·44	—	—	91
	1·54 ± 0·16	—	2·6 to 5·0	33
$M + H$	1·6 ± 0·15	—	8 to 100	47
	1·51 ± 0·18	—	2·5 to 8·0	87
	1·70 ± 0·25	—	1·23 to 10·0	92
	1·35 ± 0·15	—	1·4 to 50	93
	1·65 ± 0·30	—	1·23 to 10	92
M	1·57 ± 0·20	—	8 to 100	47
	1·57 ± 0·12	25·4 ± 4·2	2·5 to 8	35
	1·51 ± 0·1	—	2·5 to 8	24
	1·6 ± 0·15	26·0 ± 2·2	2·5 to 8	47
	1·35 ± 0·15	—	1·6 to 50	93
	1·78 ± 0·35	—	1·23 to 10	92
	1·62 ± 0·20	—	8 to 100	47
	1·82 ± 0·19	—	5 to 17	94
H	1·5 ± 0·3	—	2·6 to 50	33
	1·66 ± 0·21	11·3 ± 4·7	2·5 to 8	35
	1·60 ± 0·15	11·9 ± 2·0	2·5 to 8	47
	1·59 ± 0·15	—	2·5 to 8	24
	1·44	—	—	91

energy range as $I(>E) = (5\cdot3 \pm 1\cdot1) \times 10^{-6}(E/6 \times 10^{14})^{-1\cdot62\pm0\cdot05}$ particles/m$^2 \cdot$ sterad $\cdot$ sec, where E is measured in eV.

We notice that the mean cosmic ray intensity over long periods of time proves to be constant in order of magnitude. For example the study of the spallation products produced by cosmic rays in meteorites leads us to the conclusion that the cosmic ray intensity has hardly changed at all over the last millions or even hundreds of millions of years.[128-130, 453, 456]

TABLE 4A
Total intensity of cosmic rays: $I(>E) = KE^{-\gamma-1}$.

γ 1	K	Energy range, GeV	Refs.
$1\cdot7 - 1\cdot8$	—	10 to 50	19
$1\cdot7 \pm 0\cdot15$	$2\cdot1 \times 10^4$	2×10^2 to 2×10^4	95
$1\cdot53 \pm 0\cdot20$	—	15 to 2×10^6	96
$1\cdot6 \pm 0\cdot03$	$0\cdot93 \times 10^4$	10 to 6×10^5	97
$2\cdot2 \pm 0\cdot1$	—	10^7 to 2×10^8	98
$2\cdot17 \pm 0\cdot10$	$8\cdot7 \times 10^6$	5×10^6 to 10^9	99
$1\cdot5 \pm 0\cdot1$	—	8×10^5 to 8×10^6 ⎫	
$2\cdot2 \pm 0\cdot3$	—	8×10^6 to 3×10^7 ⎬	100
$1\cdot5 \pm 0\cdot2$	—	10^8 to 10^9 ⎭	
$2\cdot26$	$6\cdot0 \times 10^7$	10^8 to 10^{10}	101

The spectrum in the low-energy range. High-latitude spectrum "cut-off"

In the low-energy range (kinetic energy $\mathscr{E}_k \lesssim 1$ GeV/nucleon) the question of the primary cosmic ray spectrum is considerably more complex. The point is that the "primary" cosmic ray intensity observed on the Earth is determined by three factors (we shall not deal at present with the question of the albedo and geomagnetic effects). These factors are:

1. the primary cosmic ray intensity in the Galaxy in the region of the solar system;

2. the modulation effects caused by electromagnetic processes in the solar system and depending on the level of solar activity;

3. the intensity of solar cosmic rays formed within the solar system (near the active areas on the Sun or in the upper layers of the solar atmosphere).

In the energy range $\mathscr{E}_k \lesssim 1$ GeV in question the effect of the last two factors is particularly great. Only after explaining the part they play can we draw definite conclusions on the spectrum of the primary (galactic) cosmic rays in the low-energy region. At present much work is being done along these lines and a number of important results has already been obtained. We shall pause for a moment to discuss these. However, we shall be able to obtain a fuller idea on the variations in the primary spectrum occurring in the solar system only after regular observations at all stages of the present cycle of solar activity and in particular at its minimum expected in 1964–65.

The intensity observed on the Earth of cosmic rays in the low-energy region is subjected to strong variations in time. Apart from the purely modulation effects linked to the eleven-year solar activity cycle and Forbush-type irregular reductions in intensity[2] an important part is played here by sporadic fluxes of cosmic rays released by the Sun.

The solar cosmic ray fluxes can be nominally divided into the following three groups. The first of them includes powerful flares such as the flare of 23 February 1956 in which particles are generated with energies up to several tens of GeV. In flares like these a rise in the cosmic ray intensity can be observed even at sea level and at practically every geomagnetic latitude. Flares of this kind happen fairly rarely—once in several years; the time-averaged power of the Sun as a source of such cosmic rays is of the order of magnitude of 10^{23} erg/sec.†

The second group covers flares leading to the generation of cosmic rays with energies of several hundred MeV.[2, 104, 105] Flares of this kind (in the optical range they are largely chromospheric flares with an index of 3 or 3^+) occur considerably more often (practically every month at a period of high solar activity). They can be observed, however, only at high latitudes and, due to the strong absorption of cosmic rays of the corresponding energies in the atmosphere, practically only at high altitudes in the stratosphere (for example with counters fitted in balloons). The mean power transmitted to cosmic rays of these energies is clearly one or two orders greater than the power indicated above for large flares. In the cosmic rays generated by such flares there have been found nuclei of C, N, O and heavier elements whose relative distribution (at a fixed rigidity) is close to the distribution of the corresponding elements on the Sun.[106, 107, 462] Slightly earlier[108, 43] a short-lived flare was observed in the cosmic ray intensity during which the greatest rise in intensity was for the heavy nuclei ($Z > 15$). This can be looked upon as an indication that

† The energy given off in the flare of 23 February in the form of cosmic rays with energies of more than several hundred MeV was about 10^{32} erg.[13] The power of this flare was greater than that of all others observed in the last 20 years. Averaging for this period of time we obtain a mean power of $1·6 \times 10^{23}$ erg/sec.

in certain solar flares the conditions are satisfied for the preferred generation (or departure beyond the solar corona) of heavy nuclei. Lastly, the third group covers cosmic rays with energies of several tens and up to hundreds of MeV.[109] The intensity of these particles is more or less constant in time and comparatively small; in essence this is the "tail" of the observed cosmic ray spectrum in the low-energy range (kinetic energy $E_k < 200$ MeV for protons). The sources of such particles, as shown by Vogt,[109] may be weak, but at the same time more frequent, chromospheric flares with indices of 1 and 2. In this case the mean power of particle generation is about 10^{20} erg/sec. It is highly improbable that these particles are of galactic origin. This follows in particular from the presence of the so-called high-latitude "cut-off" or "elbow" which we shall now discuss.

It is well known that the rise expected from geomagnetic theory in the intensity of cosmic rays as the latitude increases (the latitude effect in intensity) is in fact observed only as far as latitudes $\lambda_m = 51$ to 55° for at least the greater part of the solar cycle. At higher latitudes the intensity remains practically constant, thus pointing to the absence in the cosmic rays of particles with a rigidity of $R_H \lesssim 1.5$ to 2.0 GV, i.e., with energies of $E_k \lesssim 0.8$ to 1.2 GeV for protons and $\mathscr{E}_k \lesssim 0.2$ to 0.4 GeV/nucleon for nuclei with $A = 2Z$. The corresponding break in the integral cosmic ray energy spectrum is called the high-latitude "elbow" and the effect itself is called the high-latitude spectrum "cut-off".[2, 15, 110]

Measurements of the proton energy spectrum in the $E_k > 350$ MeV range have been made for a considerable part of the solar cycle.[111–113] It was established that the differential energy spectrum has a maximum corresponding to the high-latitude elbow in the integral spectrum and decreases smoothly as the energy decreases further (Fig. 1).

The presence of a maximum in the differential proton spectrum does not contradict the fact that low-energy protons have been found[109] with a spectrum that rises as the energy decreases (see Fig. 1). The point is that the low-energy proton energy spectrum measured by Vogt[109] relates to a different range of energies ($E_k < 300$ MeV) and is not a smooth continuation of the spectrum established by McDonald and Webber[113] (the existence of a maximum or at least a plateau corresponding to high-latitude cut-off was also found by Vogt[109]). It is natural to assume, therefore, that a spectrum of primary (galactic) cosmic rays altered by modulation effects in the solar system was observed by McDonald and Webber,[111–113] whilst low-energy protons† of solar origin were found by Vogt.[109]

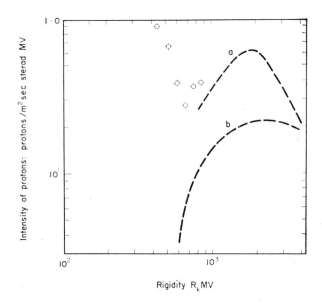

Fig. 1. Rigidity spectrum for protons in the low-energy range.

The dotted lines correspond to the results of McDonald and Webber[113]: *a*—geomagnetic latitude 59° N, measured 1955; *b*—geomagnetic latitude 59° N, measured 1959. Individual experimental points—results of Vogt,[109] measured in September 1960.

There is particular interest in measuring the energy spectrum in the low-energy region at the period of a solar activity minimum when

---

† Since these protons do not come directly from the Sun they must clearly be accumulated in the solar system. It would be very interesting to find out whether there is a similar accumulation of electrons, α-particles and heavier nuclei of low energy (in this connexion see section 2 and an earlier paper[43]).

In addition, Vogt's data[109] still need confirmation. According to measurements[454] made in 1962, i.e., at a time of low solar activity, there was no rise in proton intensity as the energy decreased. In the 100 to 350 MeV energy range the proton intensity remained constant although it was fairly high (about 1 protonm/^{2}·sec·sterad·MeV). These protons are considered to be galactic by Meyer and Vogt.[454]

modulation effects are least sharply defined in the primary spectrum or are perhaps completely absent. Unfortunately the results of measurements during the last solar activity minimum (1954–55) are contradictory. For example according to McDonald and Webber[113] the maximum in the differential spectrum (the high-latitude elbow) was also there in the period of low activity (1955) although the total cosmic ray intensity was about twice its value in the period of the next maximum (1958). In both cases the maximum in the differential energy spectrum is at about the same rigidity $R_H \simeq 1.5$ to 2.0 GV. On the other hand the measurements[115, 116] made during the deep solar activity minimum (August 1954) showed a rise in the proton intensity right down to the lowest energies observed ($E_k = 100$ to 150 MeV). This, it would appear, indicates that there was no break in the spectrum at this time. Such a discrepancy in results (without considering possible errors in interpretation of the data) can be explained either by higher solar activity during measurements of McDonald and Webber[111–113] when compared with the measurements of Neher[115] and Winkler and Anderson[116] during the deep activity minimum, or by a significant contribution made by low-energy solar protons to the intensity of the particles observed by these authors.[115, 116]

The question of the existence of high-latitude cut-off of galactic cosmic rays during deep solar activity minima is therefore still open. If there is no cut-off of solar origin during minima, measurements during such periods would make it possible to obtain some idea of the spectrum of low-energy primary cosmic rays beyond the solar system. In this connexion there are great hopes of the coming activity minimum of the Sun (1964–65). It is to be hoped that the coming International Year of the "Quiet Sun" will make possible a considerable elucidation both of the nature of the galactic cosmic ray spectrum in the low-energy range and of the nature of the high-latitude cut-off.

There is much interest in measuring the energy spectrum of nuclei with $Z \geqslant 2$ in the energy range in question. Measurements of the intensity of α-particles and heavier nuclei in this range of energies have been made by many authors.[17, 18, 23, 44, 117–120] As a result of these measurements it was established that the α-particle intensity rises as the energy decreases to $\mathscr{E}_k \sim 300$ to 500 MeV/nucleon and then passes through a maximum and decreases smoothly as the energy further drops. According to various data[23, 117–119] the maximum in the differential α-particle spectrum is located near $\mathscr{E}_k \simeq 300$ MeV/nucleon (a rigidity of $R_H \simeq 1.6$ GV), whilst Aizu et al.[44] observed a broad maximum in the range 500 to 600 MeV/nucleon (a rigidity of $R_H \simeq 2.2$ GV). As was pointed out by several authors,[44, 119] the discrepancy may be caused by the fact that the measurements by Aizu et al.[44] were made after a strong Forbush decay when the process of restoring a normal intensity level was not yet complete. It is important to point out that with the exception of Aizu's data[44] all the available data lead us to the conclusion that the position of the maximum hardly depends at all on the level of solar activity, whilst its magnitude is more than halved during an activity maximum when compared with a minimum.

The differential spectra of the heavier nuclei have a similar form (the presence of a maximum and a more or less smooth drop in the low-energy region). However, whilst the spectra found by Aizu et al.[44] for all nuclei with $Z \geqslant 2$ had a maximum at the same rigidity $R_H \simeq 2.2$ GV (a kinetic energy of 500 to 600 MeV/nucleon), it was found by Tamai[119] that as the charge of the nucleus increases the maximum in the differential spectrum shifts towards the higher energies: from $\mathscr{E}_k \simeq 300$ MeV/nucleon for α-particles to $\mathscr{E}_k \simeq 500$ to 600 MeV/nucleon for group M nuclei. This discrepancy in the results can be explained, as has already been indicated, by a strong Forbush decay accompanying the measurements.[44] Fresh measurements must be made, however, before any final conclusions can be drawn.

From the point of view of the nature of the high-latitude cut-off it is very important to compare the spectra of nuclei with $Z \geqslant 2$ and the proton spectrum in the low-energy range. In view of the difference between the ratios A/Z for protons and for nuclei with $Z \geqslant 2$ their rigidity at a given energy per nucleon is different. At present it can be taken as established that the "cut-off" of the cosmic ray spectrum on the low-energy side is according to the rigidity.[113, 114] In the region of non-relativistic energies, therefore, it is convenient to relate the cosmic ray spectrum to the magnetic rigidity R_H of the particle in question instead of the energy per nucleon of the nucleus. According to McDonald and Webber,[113] for example, the differential spectra of the rigidity of protons and α-particles are completely alike in shape [the proton intensity $I_p(R_H)$ differs from the α-particle intensity $I_\alpha(R_H)$ only by the factor of 6.8], this similarity being preserved both during the cycle of solar activity and during strong Forbush intensity decreases.

We should point out that measurements of proton, electron and nucleus fluxes by space vehicles travelling towards the Sun, away from the Sun and away from the plane of the ecliptic are very important and promising.[43]

Without stopping to interpret the high-latitude cut-off in detail[12, 13, 121-126] we shall merely make the following remarks. As we have seen, the "cut-off" energy does not depend, or at least depends only slightly, on the charge of the nucleus. This fact excludes the possibility of explaining high-latitude cut-off by ionisation losses in interstellar space or near the Sun. In addition, the similarity of the rigidity spectra $I_A(R_H)$ of protons and nuclei indicates the magnetic nature of high-latitude cut-off. This magnetic effect could in principle occur outside the solar system (in the cosmic ray sources mainly) and within the solar system. Since high-latitude cut-off has a strong dependence on the level of solar activity it is clear that it is in the solar system that it takes place to a considerable degree. As for the possible cut-off, i.e., the presence of a maximum, in the differential spectrum of galactic cosmic rays outside the solar system, if such an effect does exist we shall be able to discover it only as the result of measurements during a complete solar activity cycle and particularly during deep minima of solar activity.†

From the point of view of the theory of the origin of cosmic rays an elucidation of the nature of a cut-off outside the solar system could be significant, for example, in the following connexion. If it is in the cosmic ray sources that this cut-off occurs and the protons (or at least a considerable part of them) appear in cosmic rays as the result of the fragmentation of heavier nuclei (see Chapter V), then the maximum in the galactic proton spectrum should be located at the same energy per nucleon as for the heavy nuclei (i.e., at about half the rigidity). At the same time a considerable blurring of the proton maximum is possible due to the transfer (during fragmentation) of part of the energy to the meson component.

---

† As some indication of the presence of a maximum (i.e., the absence of low-energy particles) we can point to the constant position of the maximum found in the spectrum during the solar cycle. In actual fact, with the steady nature of the cosmic ray spectrum beyond the solar system the position of the observed maximum should, it would appear, depend strongly on the cut-off conditions in the solar system, i.e., on the level of the solar activity. The whole of this question, however, still needs detailed study.

High-latitude "cut-off", as follows from the shape of the spectrum, is by no means sharp in nature.† This circumstance clearly excludes the possibility of explaining the effect by a simple Störmer "cut-off" of low-energy particles in the ordered magnetic field of the solar system whose existence could be assumed.[74, 123] It is more probable that the spectrum "cut-off" is basically the result of the scattering of particles on moving random magnetic fields in the solar system and on the fields which carry the corpuscular fluxes.[124–126] The high-latitude cut-off effect is of great interest but primarily within the framework of a study of the magnetic fields in the solar system. As for the problem of the origin of cosmic rays, the high-latitude cut-off is a special question relating only to the upper limit of their energy spectrum. The absence of sufficient clarity in this field is therefore of no great importance for what is to be said in the following.

The spectrum in the very high energy range

In the very high energy range $E \gtrsim 10^5$ GeV $= 10^{14}$ eV it is hard to make direct observations of individual primary particles in view of the small flux of particles with these energies. For example, according to the data of Zatsepin et al.[452] (Fig. 2), the flux of particles with an energy greater than 10^{15} eV is $I(E > 10^{15}$ eV$) \simeq 2 \times 10^{-6}$ particles/ $m^2 \cdot$ sterad $\cdot$ sec $= 7 \times 10^{-3}$ particles/$m^2 \cdot$ sterad $\cdot$ hr. Even if the effective area of the detector were 1 m^2 hundreds of hours of flight at great altitudes would be necessary to "catch" even one such particle not to mention the complexity of identifying it. In the $E > 10^{14}$ to 10^{15} eV energy region, therefore, our information on the primary cosmic radiation is entirely based on the results of studying extensive atmospheric showers.

It is important to bear in mind that in the energy range of the extensive atmospheric showers the observed energy spectrum of the primary particles no longer relates to the energy per nucleon but to the total energy of the particles causing the showers. If protons are the largest component in a flux of cosmic rays with an energy per nucleon greater than a given one it is by no means the case for a flux of particles with a given total energy. In actual fact it is easy to

† As indicated by Appa Rao and Kaplon,[127] some smoothing out of the observed spectrum may occur even with a sharp cut-off on the low-energy side if the isotopic composition of the hydrogen and helium in the cosmic rays is allowed for. Since, however, even the heavier nuclei for which the effect[127] is insignificant have a broad maximum in the spectrum, the smooth nature of the spectrum cut-off on the low-energy side must be considered as genuine.

obtain from spectrum (3.1), which is with respect to the energy per nucleon, the spectrum in relation to the total energy per particle $E = A\mathscr{E}$:

$$I_A(>E) = K_A\left(\frac{E}{A}\right)^{-\gamma+1} = \frac{K_A A^{\gamma-1}}{E^{\gamma-1}}. \tag{3.2}$$

Table 5 gives the relative content (in percentages) of the various charge groups in the flux of cosmic rays with a set energy. The corresponding values are determined by expression (3.2) using the data on the composition of cosmic rays with a fixed energy per nucleon from Table 1. The spectrum index γ is considered to be the same for all the groups; the table uses the values $\gamma = 2\cdot5$ and $\gamma = 2\cdot7$.

TABLE 5

Group of nuclei	A	Relative content of nuclei, %		
		with a given energy per nucleon (see Table 1)	with a given total nucleus energy	
			$\gamma = 2\cdot5$	$\gamma = 2\cdot7$
p	1	93	49	37
α	4	6·3	26	27
L	10	0·14	2	3
M	14	0·42	11	14
H	31	0·14	12	19
VH	51	0·04	7	12

Note: The VH group is part of the H group. The percentage content of nuclei with a given energy and the percentage content of nuclei with energies greater than that energy are clearly the same.

It can be seen from Table 5 that nuclei with $Z \geqslant 2$ make up more than half of all the cosmic ray particles with an energy greater than the given one. These results, of course, can be extended into the energy region corresponding to extensive atmospheric showers only if the spectra of all the charge components remain alike. According to some data[47, 90] this is true at least up to an energy of 10^{12} eV. There are also some data obtained with photo-emulsions which point to a constant composition at high energies also.[89] The unvarying nature of the composition right up to energies of $E \sim 10^{15}$

eV also follows from an analysis of the intensity fluctuations of the Cherenkov glow of the extensive atmospheric showers.[452] In addition there are no peculiar features in the spectrum of the cosmic ray flux in the $\lesssim 10^{15}$ eV range. It is therefore natural to assume that the cosmic ray composition, and thus also the spectra of the various components, remain unchanged even in the transition to the range of the extensive atmospheric showers. In this case more than half the showers with a given energy E (in the range $E \gtrsim 10^{15}$ eV) are not caused by protons but by heavier nuclei with an energy per nucleon which is A times less.[131]

In the $E \gtrsim 10^{15}$ eV energy range the question of the primary cosmic ray spectrum is still insufficiently clarified. According to some authors[99, 132] the spectrum remains smooth and has no features right up to the highest energies $E \simeq 10^{19}$ eV. At the same time the value of γ rises at high energies and is $\gamma = 3 \cdot 17$ at $5 \times 10^{15} < E < 10^{18}$ eV or even $\gamma = 3 \cdot 26$ at $10^{17} < E < 10^{19}$ eV. Later data,[452, 457, 458] however, confirm the conclusion drawn by Kulikov and Khristiansen[100] about the fairly sharp change in the slope of the spectrum at an energy $E \sim 10^{15}$ eV from the value $\gamma = 2 \cdot 6 \pm 0 \cdot 1$ at lower energies to a value of $\gamma = 3 \cdot 1 \pm 0 \cdot 1$ at energies of $E \sim 10^{15}$ to 10^{18} eV. Zatsepin et al.[452] give for this range of energies the spectrum $I(> E) = (2 \cdot 0 \pm 0 \cdot 8) \times 10^{-6}(E/10^{15})^{-2 \cdot 2 \pm 0 \cdot 2}$ particles/m$^2 \cdot$sterad$\cdot$sec. The best value of the power exponent in this region is clearly the value of $\gamma = 3 \cdot 1 \pm 0 \cdot 1$ given recently.[457, 458]

No further increase is observed in γ in the transition to higher energies $(E > 10^{18}$ eV). On the other hand there are indications[458] that for energies $E > 10^{18}$ eV the spectrum flattens out again (the index γ returns to the value $\gamma \simeq 2 \cdot 6$).

The integral cosmic ray spectrum in the 10^{10} to 10^{20} eV energy range according to recent data[452, 457, 458] is shown in Fig. 2.

As well as the change found in the spectrum in the $E \sim 10^{15}$ to 10^{16} eV energy range (see Table 4a) a fairly sharp change is found[100, 133–138, 155, 463] in certain other properties of the extensive atmospheric showers (the share of nuclear-active particles and μ-mesons, the average number of cores in the showers, the nature of the absorption and the fluctuation of the atmospheric showers[97, 452]). The possible causes of these features are as follows.

1. *A change in the nature of the elementary act of nuclear interaction of ultra-high energy particles with nuclei in the atmosphere in the $E \gtrsim 10^{14}$ to 10^{15} eV energy range.*[134, 135, 452] Although this

assumption can in principle explain the change in some of the characteristics of the atmospheric showers in the $E \gtrsim 10^{15}$ eV region it is nevertheless clearly inadequate to explain the variation found in the primary cosmic ray energy spectrum over a large energy range.

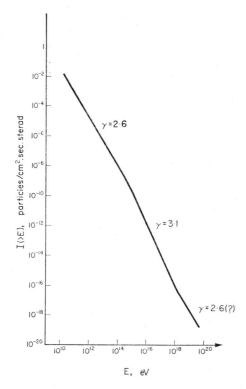

Fig. 2. Integral cosmic ray energy spectrum. The form of the spectrum in the $E > 10^{18}$ eV energy range is based on the results of Linsley[458] and cannot yet be considered to be finally established.

2. *A genuine change in the primary spectrum due to a change in the conditions for the disappearance of particles from the Galaxy at particle energies of* 10^{15} *to* 10^{16} *eV (see section 16).* The change in the spectrum is linked by some authors[100, 136] with the "transparency" of the Galaxy to particles with energies of $E \gtrsim 10^{16}$ eV. At the same time it has been suggested[100] that the particles with the highest energies have a metagalactic origin. There is a peculiar feature in the spectrum of the extensive atmospheric showers,

according to Kulikov and Khristiansen,[100] in the region of transition from the galactic to the metagalactic cosmic ray spectrum.

In later papers[136, 155] an attempt was made to explain the break in the observed spectrum without bringing in metagalactic cosmic rays. It was suggested[136] that there is a quadratic relationship between the diffusion coefficient and the energy (see section 10) in the $E > 5 \times 10^{15}$ eV energy range. This suggestion, however, leads to too steep a descent in the spectrum of the primary cosmic rays in this range of energies. Therefore the possibility has been discussed[155, 459, 460] of a weaker relationship between the diffusion coefficient and the energy caused by some specific distribution of the scattering clouds according to their sizes and the magnetic field strength in the clouds.

3. *The existence of a break in the spectrum of cosmic rays sources in the Galaxy.* There is a discussion by Peters[131] of the suggestion that there are several types of sources which have different powers and supply particles in different rigidity ranges. If the generation of cosmic rays in the Galaxy occurs in different types of sources, then a singularity will appear in the spectrum when there is a combination of the spectrum of the source producing most of the cosmic rays of comparatively low energies with the spectrum of the source producing cosmic rays of the highest energies. In this case, as is pointed out by Peters,[131] allowing for the chemical composition of the primary cosmic rays is of great significance when interpreting the observed spectrum of the atmospheric showers. For example if there is an upper limit for the rigidity of the cosmic rays generated by the first of the above sources there will be no sharp dividing line in the atmospheric shower spectrum due to the difference in the energies of nuclei with different atomic numbers Z with a fixed rigidity. By way of example the maximum energy of the iron nuclei from this source will be $Z = 26$ times greater than the maximum energy of the protons. In this case it is possible to have a smooth combination of the spectrum of the first source with the spectrum of considerable less intense (by a factor of up to 10^3) sources producing particles with greater rigidity.

The picture will be exactly the same (when there is cut-off at a certain maximum rigidity connected with the sources or in connexion with the apparent dependence of the diffusion coefficient on the energy) in the case of the secondary nature of protons (see Chapter V). The sole difference is that the energy spectrum will be blurred over twice as large an energy range since in this case the upper limit of the proton energy is not determined by the maximum rigidity but by the maximum energy per nucleon in the primary nuclei (for the nuclei in question $A \approx 2Z$).

The question of the interpretation of the break in the primary spectrum in the ultra-high energy range will be discussed in greater detail in section 16. Here all we shall say is that in all the cases discussed allowance must be made for the "chemical" blurring of the dividing line (break)[460] unless the composition in the $E > 10^{13}$ eV energy range differs from that known at lesser energies in the direction of a considerable decrease in the share of heavy nuclei. At the same time it must be stressed that the suggestion of the change in the nature of the elementary act of interaction is still quite unfounded unless it is proved that the showers in question are formed by protons.

Recently the question of the composition of cosmic rays in the ultra-high energy region has attracted great attention. This is natural since its solution is important not only for the theory of the origin of cosmic rays but also for the interpretation of the observed properties of the extensive atmospheric showers from the point of view of the theory of the elementary interactions of ultra-high-energy particles. There have been discussions[139, 140] of the possible changes in the characteristics of the atmospheric showers caused by an increase in the share of the heavy particles in the composition of the ultra-high-energy cosmic rays. As a result of an analysis of the available experimental data the conclusion was drawn[140] that the extensive atmospheric showers in the $E \gtrsim 10^{15}$ to 10^{16} eV range are largely caused by heavy primary nuclei.

On the basis of an analysis of the share of μ-mesons in showers with a given number of particles [144] it is also concluded that there is a noticeable number of heavy nuclei in cosmic rays with energies of $\sim 10^{16}$ to 10^{18} eV. On the other hand Linsley et al.[101, 102] come to the conclusion that particles with energies of $\gtrsim 10^{17}$ eV are homogeneous in their chemical composition and are most probably protons. However, as Nikolskii[145] shows, this conclusion cannot yet be taken as convincing.

The question of the maximum particle energy encountered is also of great importance to the theory of the origin of cosmic rays. The observed spectrum of the atmospheric showers extends into the $E > 10^{18}$ eV region and, according to some data[67, 99, 132, 141, 143, 458] as far as an energy of $\sim 10^{20}$ eV. Particles with this energy clearly cannot be retained within the Galaxy long enough even if they are heavy nuclei. It is therefore most probable that particles with $\mathscr{E} > 10^{18}$ eV/nucleon can leave the Galaxy comparatively easily and arrive in it from other galaxies. We shall call the particles in the Galaxy from outside metagalactic (see sections 11 and 13).

Directional distribution of cosmic rays (degree of anisotropy)

The degree of anisotropy of cosmic radiation is generally character-ised by the quantity

$$\delta = \frac{I_{max} - I_{min}}{I_{max} + I_{min}}, \qquad (3.3)$$

where I_{max} is the maximum and I_{min} is the minimum value of the observed intensity; the values of δ are given below as percentages.

Until recently, within the limits of the accuracy achieved, no anisotropy connected with the Galaxy or Metagalaxy was found in the primary cosmic radiation. For example a careful analysis was made by Rossi[99] of some "suspect" directions: the axis of the spiral arm and the directions lying in the galactic plane. Within the limits of statistical measurement errors (about 1 per cent for energies of $E \simeq 10^{15}$ eV) no deviations were found from an isotropic in-tensity distribution (thus, according to Rossi,[99] $\delta < 1$ per cent). According to the data of Greisen *et al.*[67, 141] the anisotropy, if it exists, does not exceed the measurement errors with $\delta \leqslant 0{\cdot}1$ per cent for $E \simeq 10^{14}$ eV, $\delta \leqslant 1$ per cent for $E \simeq 10^{16}$ eV and $\delta \leqslant 3$ per cent for $E \simeq 10^{17}$ eV.

As well as the data given on the high degree of isotropy of the basic mass of cosmic rays there are now indications of the presence of a genuine, although small, anisotropy of cosmic rays with energies of $E \gtrsim 50$ GeV. For example as the result of analysing data[142] for a solar activity minimum (1954–55) a slight anisotropy (a few tenths of one per cent) was clearly established for cosmic rays with energies of several tens of GeV corresponding to a preferred particle flux from the centre of the Galaxy.

Some indications of a slight anisotropy with a maximum in the galactic plane were also obtained[146] for particles with energies of $E \lesssim 10^{11}$ eV and for small showers caused by particles with an energy of $E \simeq 10^{14}$ eV.[143]

Experimental elucidation of the question of the degree of aniso-tropy of particles with the greatest observed energies of about

10^{18} to 10^{19} eV is of great interest. As will be seen later (see section 16 in particular), this question is closely linked with the problem of the chemical composition and energy spectrum of the cosmic rays in the region of the greatest energies observed. It will be as a result of studying particles of the highest energy that it will finally be possible to say whether cosmic rays with energies of $E \simeq 10^{18}$ to 10^{19} eV are of galactic origin or whether they reach the Galaxy from intergalactic space.

Unfortunately only the first steps have been taken in this direction and the data available do not allow of any definite conclusion on the presence of a genuine anisotropy, not to mention its qualitative characteristics (magnitude and direction). For example in papers[101, 143, 144] read at the International Conference on Cosmic Rays at Kyoto (1961) proofs were adduced in favour of the existence of a considerable anisotropy for cosmic rays with the greatest energies (a value δ up to 70 ± 30 per cent for particles with energies of $E \simeq 4 \times 10^{18}$ eV). In a later paper[458] based on the study of a considerably greater number of showers it is concluded that the anisotropy, if it really exists, does not exceed 10 per cent for particles with energies of $E \simeq 10^{18}$ eV and 30 per cent for the higher energies of $E \simeq 10^{19}$ eV. The total number of showers studied in the two energy ranges was about 1000 and 97 respectively.

Apart from the question of the degree of anisotropy of the total flux of cosmic rays with a given energy there is also definite interest in the question of the possible difference in the degrees of anisotropy of the various components making up the cosmic rays with a given energy. For certain models of the propagation of cosmic rays in the Galaxy (see sections 15 and 16) it is to be expected that the chemical composition of cosmic rays arriving from different directions will be different and the degree of anisotropy for protons and for very heavy nuclei will be different in particular. The measurement of this anisotropy in the chemical composition of cosmic rays is, of course, an even more complicated problem than measuring the anisotropy of the total flux.

Some indications of the existence of the effect in question were obtained by Hasegawa et al.[144, 147] These authors[144] made an analysis of the distribution in direction of arrival of showers with a high content of penetrating particles (μ-mesons) at a given total shower energy. As a result it was concluded that there is anisotropy of these showers which are rich in μ-mesons in the $E \simeq 10^{15}$ to 10^{16} eV energy range. If the showers with a large number of μ-mesons are caused, as they assumed, by heavy nuclei, then the anisotropy which has been found corresponds to the anisotropy in the composition of the cosmic rays since as a whole showers with an energy of $E \simeq 10^{15}$ to 10^{16} eV are isotropic to a very considerable degree. However, because of the subtlety of the effect and the as yet insufficient statistical accuracy of the measurements the conclusion obtained must be treated with great circumspection.

CHAPTER II

COSMIC MAGNETIC BREMSSTRAHLUNG (SYNCHROTRON) RADIO EMISSION AND COSMIC RAYS IN THE UNIVERSE

THE information available on cosmic rays beyond the solar system is chiefly based on radio astronomy data and above all on the results of measurements of the intensity, spatial distribution and spectrum of non-thermal cosmic radio emission.

In 1950–53 ideas were expressed and developed on the magnetic bremsstrahlung nature of the non-thermal cosmic radio emission.[4, 74, 149–154] This point of view was later confirmed by a number of fresh facts. Important milestones on the way were firstly the elucidation of the question of the sources of the non-thermal component which proved to be not hypothetical "radio stars" [156, 157] but extensive nebulae and galaxies, and secondly the discovery in certain cases of the polarised emission predicted by theory.† The magnetic bremsstrahlung theory has now been generally accepted and is the basis of the interpretation of all the data relating to the non-thermal cosmic radio emission.[4–9, 161–164]

In accordance with this theory the observed non-thermal emission is the emission of relativistic electrons in comparatively weak cosmic magnetic fields. Such emission is well known in physics. It can be observed in elementary particle accelerators (the synchrotron in particular) and is similar to bremsstrahlung. In the present case the "braking" agent is a magnetic field which distorts the trajectory of

† As far as we know Gordon in 1952 was the first to draw attention to the possible part played by magnetic bremsstrahlung optical emission in astronomy.[158] He indicated also the necessity of optical polarisation measurements particularly with respect to the optical emission of the Crab Nebula (the part of this emission with a continuous spectrum is originated by magnetic bremsstrahlung, as was shown by Shklovskii[159]). The possibility and desirability of polarisation measurements in the radio band were stressed by Ginzburg.[4, 154, 160]

the charged particle. Because of this we call the emission in question magnetic bremsstrahlung emission.†

In the first section of this chapter (section 4) we shall give the basic results of the theory of magnetic bremsstrahlung of relativistic electrons which we shall need for the following. We shall then dwell awhile on certain data from radio astronomy which are important for the theory of the origin of cosmic rays (section 5) and on the conclusions which can be drawn on the basis of these data on the spectrum, energy and spatial distribution of relativistic particles in the Universe (section 6).

4. MAGNETIC BREMSSTRAHLUNG (SYNCHROTRON EMISSION)

The strength of the cosmic magnetic fields is, as a rule, such that only ultra-relativistic electrons can be responsible for the emission in the radio band and even more so in the optical band. We shall therefore be interested only in ultra-relativistic magnetic bremsstrahlung (synchrotron emission). The only exceptions can be the regions with strong magnetic fields near stars and planets where we must use the results of the general theory of the emission of charged particles of arbitrary energy moving in a magnetic field. In the non-relativistic case magnetic bremsstrahlung is often called cyclotron radiation; we shall not have to deal with it here, however.

Emission of an individual electron

The characteristic feature of the emission of ultra-relativistic particles in a vacuum (the effect of a medium will be discussed at the end of this section) is that the emission is concentrated almost exclusively in the direction of the particle's instantaneous velocity. This is explained by the relativistic transformation of the field of emission of a fast-moving particle and follows formally from the presence of high powers of the factor

$$1 - \left(\frac{v}{c}\right) \cos \psi, \tag{4.1}$$

† Magnetic bremsstrahlung is more often called, particularly in non-Russian papers, synchrotron emission. The latter term was, however, coined by chance, and appears to us to be not a felicitous one. We should point out that as applied to the nonthermal radio emission of galactic halos, supernova shells and radio galaxies the magnetic bremsstrahlung mechanism is not only the most natural or probable but also the only one considered at present.

where ψ is the angle between the velocity of the particle v and the direction of emission k (Fig. 3) and c is the velocity of light in a vacuum, in the denominators of the expressions for the field strengths

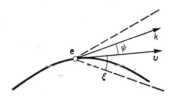

Fig. 3. Definition of the angle ψ.

Point e—position of electron on its trajectory at a given point in time; v— electron's velocity vector; k—direction of emission (wave vector); ψ—angle between vectors k and v. The ratio $\xi = mc^2/E$ defines the characteristic angle in which the largest part of the emission is concentrated.

and emission intensity.[165] In the ultra-relativistic case $v \simeq c$ and the corresponding expressions have a sharply defined maximum in a small range of angles

$$\psi \lesssim \xi = \frac{mc^2}{E}, \qquad (4.2)$$

where $E = mc^2/\sqrt{1 - v^2/c^2}$ is the total energy and m is the mass at rest of an electron.

We know that in a magnetic field H an electron moves along a helix with the angular frequency

$$\omega_H = \frac{eH}{mc} \cdot \frac{mc^2}{E}, \qquad (4.3)$$

where e is the absolute value of the charge of an electron. In this case the electron's velocity vector makes a certain constant angle θ with the direction of the magnetic field and describes a cone around this direction (Fig. 4). If $\theta \gg \xi$, an observer located on the surface of this cone at a great distance from the emitting particle would record successive pulses of radiation spaced at intervals of $\tau = 2\pi/\omega_H$ with a duration of

$$\Delta t \sim \frac{r_H^* \xi}{c} \left(\frac{mc^2}{E}\right)^2 = \frac{mc}{eH_\perp} \left(\frac{mc^2}{E}\right)^2, \qquad (4.4)$$

where $r_H^* = E/eH_\perp$ is the radius of curvature of the spatial trajectory of an ultra-relativistic electron, $H_\perp = H \sin \theta$ is the component of the magnetic field at right angles to the direction of motion (velocity) of the electron, and the factor $(mc^2/E)^2$ is a consequence of the Doppler

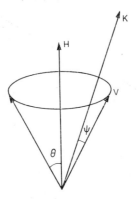

Fig. 4. Velocity cone for motion of an electron on a helical trajectory in a magnetic field H: θ—constant angle between electron's velocity v and direction of magnetic field H; k—emission wave vector; ψ—angle between wave vector and nearest generatrix of velocity cone. Emission is non-zero only in directions k for which $\psi \lesssim \xi = mc^2/E$.

effect.† As a result the emission spectrum consists of overtones of the frequency ω_H and in practice is continuous in the region of the most intense high harmonics, the maximum in the spectrum corresponding to a frequency

$$\omega \sim \frac{1}{\Delta t} \sim \frac{eH_\perp}{mc}\left(\frac{E}{mc^2}\right)^2. \tag{4.5}$$

† In the present case the Doppler effect consists simply of a compression of the pulse when compared with the case when the emitter is resting by an amount $v\Delta t'$, where $\Delta t' \simeq r_H*\xi/c = mc/eH_\perp$ is the interval of time in which the electron moves with a velocity $v \simeq c$ in the direction of the observer (within the angle ξ). Therefore the observed duration of the emission pulse is

$$\Delta t = \Delta t'\left(1 - \frac{v}{c}\right) \simeq 2\Delta t'\left(\frac{mc^2}{E}\right)^2.$$

We must also stress, in order to avoid misunderstandings, the difference between the radius of curvature of the spatial trajectory $r_H* = E/eH_\perp$ and the radius of the circle $r_H = v \sin \theta/\omega_H \simeq c \sin \theta/\omega_H = E \sin^2 \theta/eH_\perp$ described by the projection of the electron's velocity onto a plane at right angles to the direction of the field H (below we shall call the radius r_H the radius of curvature; this will not lead to misunderstandings since the radius of the spatial curvature r_H* will not be used in future).

Here it must be remembered that the pulses of radiation are not one-dimensional plane waves (the spectrum of one-dimensional pulses of duration (4.4) following each other at intervals $\tau = 2\pi/\omega_H$ has no maximum and only starts to drop at frequency (4.5)).

One of the most characteristic properties of magnetic bremsstrahlung is its polarisation. The emission of an individual electron is, generally speaking, elliptically polarised, the value of the electrical vector of the emission being at its maximum in the direction of the acceleration. The preferred direction of the oscillations is therefore at right angles to the projection of the magnetic field onto the plane of projection (as usual we are calling the plane at right angles to the line of sight the plane of projection).

Detailed calculations show[166] that at a distance r from an ultra-relativistic particle the amplitude of the n-th harmonic of the electrical field of emission in a direction k making an angle ψ with the velocity cone is defined with an accuracy up to terms of the order of ξ^3 by the expression†

$$\mathscr{E}_n = \frac{e^*\omega_H}{\sqrt{3}\pi cr} \exp\left(in\omega_H \frac{r}{c}\right) \frac{n}{\sin\theta} \times$$
$$\times \{(\xi^2 + \psi^2)K_{\frac{2}{3}}(g_n)l_1 - i\psi(\xi^2 + \psi^2)^{\frac{1}{2}}K_{\frac{1}{3}}(g_n)l_2\}. \quad (4.6)$$

Here e^* is the charge of the emitting particle (for an electron $e^* = -e$), l_1 and l_2 are two unit vectors at right angles to each other in the pictorial plane, l_2 being parallel to the projection of H onto this plane, whilst $l_1 = [k \wedge l_2]/|k|$; $K_{\frac{1}{3}}(g_n)$ and $K_{\frac{2}{3}}(g_n)$ are modified Bessel functions of the second kind of an imaginary argument (Macdonald functions) and

$$g_n = \frac{n}{3\sin\theta}(\xi^2 + \psi^2)^{\frac{3}{2}}. \quad (4.7)$$

The presence of i in front of the second term in the braces in equation (4.6) corresponds to elliptical polarisation of the radiation. One of the axes of the ellipse of the vibrations of the electrical vector is parallel to the component of H in the plane of projection, the second-major-axis is perpendicular to that component and their ratio which we denote by $\tan \beta$ is by virtue of (4.6) equal to

$$\tan \beta = \frac{\psi K_{\frac{1}{3}}(g_n)}{(\xi^2 + \psi^2)^{\frac{1}{2}}K_{\frac{2}{3}}(g_n)}. \quad (4.8)$$

† The absolute (Gaussian) system of units is used here as in the rest of the present book.

If $\psi > 0$, the direction of rotation is right-handed (clockwise for an observer) and left-handed if $\psi < 0$. The angle ψ is considered to be positive if the wave vector k and the magnetic field strength vector lie on one side of the velocity cone (Fig. 5).

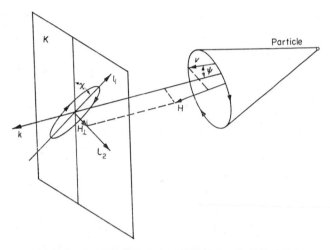

Fig. 5. Ellipse of oscillations of electrical vector of magnetic brems-strahlung of a charged particle. The particle's charge is taken to be positive. K—plane of projection (plane at right angles to the direction of emission or, what is the same thing, to the direction of observation); l_1 and l_2—two mutually orthogonal unit vectors in the plane of projection, l_2 being directed along the projection of the magnetic field H onto the plane of projection.

The polarisation degenerates into linear polarisation only if $\psi = 0$, i.e., if the wave vector lies strictly on the surface of the velocity cone. For large ψ the polarisation approaches circular polarisation since for large values of the argument $K_{2/3}(x) \simeq K_{1/3}(x) \simeq (\pi/2x)^{1/2}e^{-x}$, in this case, however, the radiation intensity becomes negligibly small (Fig. 6).

The average flux density of the emission energy contained in the n-th harmonic in a period is

$$p_n = \frac{c}{2\pi} |\mathscr{E}_n|^2. \tag{4.9}$$

Since for $\xi = mc^2/E \ll 1$ the emitted energy is almost entirely concentrated in the region of the very high harmonics where the spectrum is practically continuous it is convenient to change from the number of the harmonic $n = 2\pi v/\omega_H$ to the frequency ratio v/v_c where

$$v_c = 3eH \sin \theta/4\pi mc\xi^2 = \frac{3eH_\perp}{4\pi mc} \left(\frac{E}{mc^2}\right)^2. \tag{4.10}$$

Then, by virtue of (4.6), (4.9) and (4.10) the emission flux densities

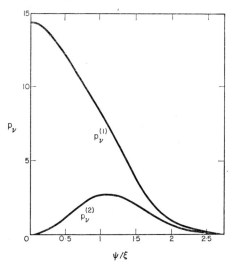

Fig. 6. Angular distribution of emission with polarisation at right angles to the projection of the magnetic field onto the plane of the figure $(p_v^{(1)})$ and along this projection $(p_v^{(2)})$ for $v/v_c = 0.29$. The scale unit on the vertical scale is the value of the coefficient $\dfrac{3}{4\pi^2 r^2} \dfrac{e^3 H}{mc^2 \xi} \left(\dfrac{v}{v_c}\right)^2$

in expressions (4.11) and (4.12).

with two basic directions of polarization l_1 and l_2 per unit frequency interval v are:

$$p_v^{(1)} = \frac{3}{4\pi^2 r^2} \frac{e^3 H}{mc^2 \xi} \left(\frac{v}{v_c}\right)^2 \left(1 + \frac{\psi^2}{\xi^2}\right)^2 K_{\frac{2}{3}}^2(g_v), \tag{4.11}$$

$$p_v^{(2)} = \frac{3}{4\pi^2 r^2} \frac{e^3 H}{mc^2 \xi} \left(\frac{v}{v_c}\right)^2 \frac{\psi^2}{\xi^2} \left(1 + \frac{\psi^2}{\xi^2}\right) K_{\frac{1}{3}}^2(g_v), \tag{4.12}$$

where

$$g_v = \frac{v}{2v_c} \left(1 + \frac{\psi^2}{\xi^2}\right)^{\frac{3}{2}}, \qquad p_v = p_n \frac{dn}{dv} = \frac{2\pi}{\omega_H} p_n. \tag{4.13}$$

The angular distribution of the radiation fluxes $p_v^{(1)}$ and $p_v^{(2)}$ is shown in Fig. 6. The scale unit selected on the vertical axis is the coefficient $(3e^3 H/4\pi^2 r^2 mc^2 \xi)(v/v_c)^2$ in expressions (4.11) and (4.12). The curves are plotted for $v/v_c = 0.29$ which corresponds, as we shall see below, to the maximum in the frequency spectrum of the global (in all directions) emission of an electron. Figure 6 shows that in the region of small ψ the basic contribution to the emission is provided by oscillations with the direction of the electric field across the projection of H onto the plane of projection, i.e., $p_v^{(1)}$.

Stokes parameters

An arbitrary emission flux apart from frequency dependence is, generally speaking, characterised by four independent parameters, for example, the position of the main polarisation axis, the intensities in the two main directions of polarisation and the direction of rotation of the electrical vector. It is more convenient, however, to use Stokes parameters as these parameters.[167, 168] For the emission of an individual particle these parameters I_e, Q_e, U_e and V_e can be expressed by emission flux densities with two basic directions of polarisation $p_v^{(1)}$ and $p_v^{(2)}$ and by $\tan \beta$ (the ratio of the minor and major axes of the ellipse of the electrical vector oscillations; see (4.8)) and the angle χ between a certain arbitrary fixed direction in the plane of projection and the major axis of this ellipse (i.e., a direction at right angles to the projection of H onto the plane of projection);† the corresponding expressions are

$$I_e = p_v^{(1)} + p_v^{(2)},$$
$$Q_e = (p_v^{(1)} - p_v^{(2)})\cos 2\chi,$$
$$U_e = (p_v^{(1)} - p_v^{(2)})\sin 2\chi,$$
$$V_e = (p_v^{(1)} - p_v^{(2)})\tan 2\beta.$$

$$(4.14)$$

The Stokes parameters (4.14), just like $p_v^{(1)}$ and $p_v^{(2)}$, have the dimensionality of the energy flux density per unit frequency interval; the index e denotes that these parameters relate to the emission of a single electron.

The Stokes parameters have two important advantages: they are quantities that can be measured directly and are additive for

† The angle χ is read clockwise and is obviously defined in the range $0 \leqslant \chi < \pi$.

independent (non-coherent) emission fluxes, i.e., emission fluxes with random phases which are averaged. The Stokes parameters can be determined experimentally by the usual methods of studying polarised emission, i.e., by introducing a certain phase difference ε for one of the projections of the electrical oscillation vector in the wave (e.g., in the direction s_1 in Fig. 7) when compared with the projection onto the direction at right angles (direction s_2 in Fig. 7). The subsequent analysis is reduced to establishing the dependence of the intensity of the resultant emission on the position of the analyser picking out the projection of the oscillations onto a certain arbitrary direction s (see Fig. 7). If the angle in the plane of projection between the directions s_1 and s is denoted by δ the intensity of the emission at the output of the analyser will be the following function of ε and δ (see, for example, Ref. 167):

$$I(\varepsilon, \delta) = \tfrac{1}{2}[I + Q \cos 2\delta + (U \cos \varepsilon - V \sin \varepsilon) \sin 2\delta]. \quad (4.15)$$

By an appropriate selection of the phase lag ε and the analyser position δ the values of all the Stokes parameters can be measured.

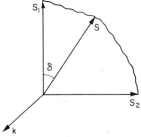

Fig. 7. Determination of angle δ (see formula (4.15)). A constant phase lag ε relative to the oscillations in the direction s_1 is introduced for oscillations in the direction s_2. The angle δ defines the position of the oscillation plane of the analyser s. The measured flux points towards the reader.

We notice that the first Stokes parameter I defines the total density of the emission flux (or the intensity in the case of spatially distributed sources; see below), whilst the degree of polarisation of the emission and the angle χ are expressed as

$$\Pi = \frac{\sqrt{Q^2 + U^2 + V^2}}{I} \quad (4.16)$$

and

$$\tan 2\chi = \frac{U}{Q}. \quad (4.16a)$$

Of the two values of the angle χ ($0 \leqslant \chi < \pi$) defined by equation (4.16a) the one is selected which lies in the first quarter if $U > 0$ and in the second if $U < 0$. The angle χ by definition characterises the direction in the plane of projection in which the intensity of the polarised component is at its maximum and is read clockwise from the selected direction of reading (from the direction s_1 in the present case). When there is no elliptical (or circular polarisation $V = 0$ and

$$\Pi = \frac{I_{\max} - I_{\min}}{I_{\max} + I_{\min}}.$$

Emission of a system of particles

Let us now examine the emission of a system of particles. Let $N(E, \boldsymbol{r}, \boldsymbol{\tau})dE \, dV \, d\Omega_\tau$ be the number of particles in a unit volume $dV = r^2 \, dr \, d\Omega$ whose energy lies in the range $E, E + dE$ and whose velocities inside the solid angle $d\Omega_\tau$ are near the direction $\boldsymbol{\tau}$. Since the emission of individual electrons is not coherent and the Stokes parameters in this case are additive the intensity of the emission of such a system in the direction of observation† $\boldsymbol{k}$ is

$$I_\nu = I(\nu, \boldsymbol{k}) = \int I_e(\nu, E, \boldsymbol{r}, \theta, \psi)N(E, \boldsymbol{r}, \boldsymbol{\tau}) \, dE \, d\Omega_\tau r^2 \, dr. \quad (4.17)$$

Here $I_e(\nu, E, \boldsymbol{r}, \theta, \psi)$ is defined by the first of expressions (4.14) and integration with respect to dr is carried out along the line of sight in the direction $-\boldsymbol{k}$. The other Stokes parameters can be similarly expressed.

We should stress that, unlike the Stokes parameters for the emission of a single electron (4.14) which have the dimensionality of the spectral density of the emission energy flux, expression (4.17) defines the emission intensity, i.e., the energy flux per unit area at right angles to the direction of observation per unit solid angle and unit frequency band. The usual unit of measurement of emission intensity in radio astronomy is 1 W/m$^2 \cdot$c/s$\cdot$sterad = 10^3 erg/cm$^2 \cdot$sec$\cdot$ (c/s)$\cdot$sterad.

If the source (electron-emitting system) is of small angular size

† In future the direction of observation (direction of the line of sight) will be taken to be the direction of the wave vector $\boldsymbol{k}$, i.e., the direction of arrival of the observed emission.

the quantity which is measured experimentally is (just as in the case of an individual particle) the spectral density of the emission flux

$$F_\nu = \int I_\nu \, d\Omega = \int I_e(\nu, E, r, \theta, \psi) N(E, r, \tau) \, dE \, d\Omega_\tau \, dV, \quad (4.18)$$

where $dV = r^2 \, dr \, d\Omega$ and integration is carried out over the whole volume of the source.

In expressions (4.17) and (4.18) and similar expressions for the other Stokes parameters integration can be carried out with respect to $d\Omega_\tau$ in the general form for an arbitrary electron distribution $N(E, r, \tau)$. In actual fact the integrand differs from zero in practice only over the small range of angles $\Delta\psi \sim mc^2/E$ so in integrating over $d\Omega_\tau$ the only contribution that is significant is that of the narrow annular sector $\Delta\Omega_\tau = 2\pi \sin \vartheta \Delta\psi$, where $\vartheta = \theta - \psi \simeq \theta$ is the angle between the direction of observation k and the magnetic field H.† Within the limits of the small solid angle $\Delta\Omega_\tau$ the directional distribution of the electrons hardly changes at all and we can put $N(E, r, \tau) \simeq N(E, r, k)$ where k is the direction of emission (the direction along the line of sight from the source to the observer) and integration with respect to ψ can be extended to the whole region from $-\infty$ to ∞. Then, bearing in mind the relations [166, 169]

$$\int_{-\infty}^{+\infty} p_\nu^{(1)} \, d\psi = \frac{\sqrt{3}\,e^3 H}{4\pi mc^2 r^2} \frac{\nu}{\nu_c} \left[\int_{\nu/\nu_c}^{\infty} K_{5/3}(\eta) \, d\eta + K_{2/3}\left(\frac{\nu}{\nu_c}\right) \right],$$

$$\int_{-\infty}^{+\infty} p_\nu^{(2)} \, d\psi = \frac{\sqrt{3}\,e^3 H}{4\pi mc^2 r^2} \frac{\nu}{\nu_c} \left[\int_{\nu/\nu_c}^{\infty} K_{5/3}(\eta) \, d\eta - K_{2/3}\left(\frac{\nu}{\nu_c}\right) \right], \quad (4.19)$$

we obtain from (4.17) and (4.14)

$$I_\nu = I(\nu, k)$$

$$= \frac{\sqrt{3}\,e^3}{mc^2} \int dE \, dr N(E, r, k) H \sin \theta \, \frac{\nu}{\nu_c} \int_{\nu/\nu_c}^{\infty} K_{5/3}(\eta) \, d\eta. \quad (4.20)$$

In the general case the field strength H, the angle $\vartheta \simeq \theta$ between H and k and the particle density $N(E, r, k)$ depend on r.

† In future no distinction is made between the angles ϑ and θ; this is obviously permissible since in practice an ultra-relativistic particle emits only in the direction of motion.

The other Stokes parameters can be similarly expressed, e.g.,

$$Q(v, k) = \frac{\sqrt{3}\,e^3}{mc^2} \int dE\ drN(E, r, k)H \sin \theta \cos 2\chi \frac{v}{v_c} K_{2/3}\!\left(\frac{v}{v_c}\right). \quad (4.21)$$

The parameter $U(v, k)$ differs from $Q(v, k)$ only in the replacement of cos 2χ in integrand of (4.21) by sin 2χ. As for the parameter $V(v, k)$ which characterises the presence of elliptically polarised emission it is equal to zero in the ultra-relativistic approximation under discussion. In fact, as can easily be confirmed from (4.8) and (4.14),

$$V_e \sim 2 \frac{\psi}{\xi}\left(1 + \frac{\psi^2}{\xi^2}\right)^{3/2} K_{1/3}(g_v)K_{2/3}(g_v).$$

Since this function is an odd one the integral of it over all ψ becomes zero so $V(v, k) = 0$. The emission of an electron system, therefore, is linearly polarised.[170] This result is valid with an accuracy up to terms of the order of mc^2/E and it can be easily understood if we remember that the sign of ψ determines the direction of rotation of the electrical vector in the wave emitted by an individual electron. Since the power of the emission (see (4.11) and 4.12)) does not depend on the sign of ψ and the distribution of particles over directions of motion within the limits of very small angles $\psi \lesssim mc^2/E$ is practically constant, the contribution to the emission in a given direction from particles with positive and negative ψ is the same and the polarisation will be linear.

Noticeable elliptical polarisation in the ultra-relativistic case could occur only when there is a sharply anisotropic distribution of the electron velocities. For this it is necessary that the distribution should change considerably over the limits of a very small angle $\psi \sim mc^2/E$, i.e., in essence there has to be a break in the angular distribution of the electrons and in the direction of observation at that. If, in addition, we take into consideraton the possible fluctuations in the direction of the magnetic field the realisation of such a possibility is highly improbable.

Intensity and polarisation of emission in the case of a mono-energetic and a power-law electron spectrum

We shall now give expressions for the intensity and emission polarisation in certain concrete cases.

If all the electrons have one and the same energy (mono-energetic spectrum) and the magnetic field is homogeneous, then the emission intensity in accordance with (4.20) is

$$I_1(k) = \frac{\sqrt{3}\,e^3}{mc^2}\,N_e(k)H\sin\theta\,\frac{v}{v_c}\int_{v/v_c}^{\infty} K_{5/3}(\eta)\,d\eta = N_e(k)p(v), \qquad (4.22)$$

where $N_e(k) = \int N_e(r, k)\,dr$ is the number of electrons per unit solid angle along the line of vision whose velocities are towards the observer. The degree of polarisation in this case can be seen from (4.16) and (4.21) to be:[169]

$$\Pi = \frac{K_{2/3}\left(\dfrac{v}{v_c}\right)}{\displaystyle\int_{v/v_c}^{\infty} K_{5/3}(\eta)\,d\eta} = \begin{cases} \frac{1}{2} & \text{if } v \ll v_c, \\ 1 - \dfrac{2v_c}{3v} & \text{if } v \gg v_c. \end{cases} \qquad (4.23)$$

Since in the case under discussion integration with respect to the angular distribution of the electrons is equivalent to integration of the emission of an individual electron in all directions, expression (4.22) differs from the spectral distribution of the power of the total emission (in all directions) of an individual electron only in the factor $N_e(k)$:

$$p(v) = \sqrt{3}\,\frac{e^3 H \sin\theta}{mc^2}\,\frac{v}{v_c}\int_{v/v_c}^{\infty} K_{5/3}(\eta)\,d\eta. \qquad (4.24)$$

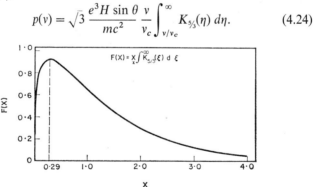

Fig. 8. Spectral distribution of total emission (in all directions) of a charged particle in a magnetic field (see expression (4.24)).

A graph of the function

$$F(x) = x\int_{x}^{\infty} K_{5/3}(\eta)\,d\eta$$

which reflects the spectral distribution of the emitted power is shown in Fig. 8. Its values with the values of the function $F_p(x) = xK_{2/3}(x)$

are given in Appendix 3 at the end of the book (as can be seen from (4.23) the polarisation is $\Pi = F_p(x)/F(x)$). We should point out that the maximum in the spectrum of a single electron's synchrotron emission occurs at the frequency

$$\nu_m \simeq 0{\cdot}29\nu_c = 0{\cdot}07\,\frac{eH_\perp}{mc}\left(\frac{E}{mc^2}\right)^2 = 1{\cdot}2 \times 10^6 H_\perp\left(\frac{E}{mc^2}\right)^2$$

$$= 1{\cdot}8 \times 10^{18} H_\perp(E_{\mathrm{erg}})^2 = 4{\cdot}6 \times 10^{-6} H_\perp(E_{\mathrm{ev}})^2. \quad (4.25)$$

Here the frequency ν is expressed in cycles per second. For the maximum frequency (4.25) the spectral density of the total emission power of an individual electron is

$$p(\nu_m = 0{\cdot}29\nu_c) \simeq 1{\cdot}6(e^3 H_\perp/mc^2) = 2{\cdot}16 \times 10^{-22} H_\perp \ \mathrm{erg \cdot sec^{-1} \cdot (c/s)^{-1}}. \quad (4.25a)$$

The energy spectrum of the electrons along the line of sight can be approximated over a limited energy range by an exponential function of the form

$$N_e(E, k)\,dE = K_e(k)E^{-\gamma}\,dE \qquad (E_1 \leqslant E \leqslant E_2). \quad (4.26)$$

Here $N_e(E, k)$ is the number of electrons moving towards the observer per unit solid angle and unit energy range along the line of sight.

This approximation, as we shall see below, is generally valid over a sufficiently wide energy range for the electrons responsible for cosmic radio emission. At the same time the boundaries E_1 and E_2 of the spectrum (4.26) can often be considered to be such that the emission of electrons with energies of $E < E_1$ and $E > E_2$ is insignificant in the range of energies of interest to us. Upon this assumption the spectrum (4.26) in the integrals in (4.20) and (4.21) can be extended to the whole energy range and use made of the relationships:

$$\int_0^\infty dE E^{-\gamma}\,\frac{\nu}{\nu_c}\,K_{2/3}\!\left(\frac{\nu}{\nu_c}\right) = \tfrac{1}{4}\Gamma\!\left(\frac{3\gamma-1}{12}\right)\Gamma\!\left(\frac{3\gamma+7}{12}\right)\left(\frac{3eH\sin\theta}{2\pi m^3 c^5 \nu}\right)^{(\gamma-1)/2},$$

$$\int_0^\infty dE E^{-\gamma}\,\frac{\nu}{\nu_c}\int_{\nu/\nu_c}^\infty K_{5/3}(\eta)\,d\eta$$

$$= \frac{1}{4}\frac{\gamma+7/3}{\gamma+1}\,\Gamma\!\left(\frac{3\gamma-1}{12}\right)\Gamma\!\left(\frac{3\gamma+7}{12}\right)\left(\frac{3eH\sin\theta}{2\pi m^3 c^5 \nu}\right)^{(\gamma-1)/2}, \quad (4.27)$$

where $\Gamma(x)$ is a gamma-function. In this case (4.20) reduces to the following expression for the emission intensity of a system of electrons with energy spectrum (4.26) in a homogeneous magnetic field H:

$$I_0(k) = \frac{\sqrt{3}}{\gamma + 1} \Gamma\left(\frac{3\gamma - 1}{12}\right) \Gamma\left(\frac{3\gamma + 19}{12}\right) \frac{e^3}{mc^2} \left(\frac{3e}{2\pi m^3 c^5}\right)^{(\gamma - 1)/2}$$

$$\times K_e(k)[H \sin \theta]^{(\gamma + 1)/2} v^{-(\gamma - 1)/2}. \quad (4.28)$$

Here $K_e(k)$ is the coefficient in the spectrum (4.26). Let us assume that the electron distribution can be considered homogeneous and isotropic, i.e., $N(E, r, k) = (1/4\pi)N_e(E)$, where

$$N_e(E) \, dE = K_e E^{-\gamma} \, dE \quad (4.29)$$

is the number of electrons per unit volume with arbitrary directions of motion and with energies in the range E, $E + dE$. Then

$$K_e(k) = \frac{1}{4\pi} K_e L, \quad (4.30)$$

where K_e is the coefficient in the energy spectrum (4.29) and L is the extent of the emitting region along the line of sight. We notice that in the general case $K_e(k)$ depends on the angle θ between the direction of the magnetic field and the line of sight.

In the case of a homogeneous field the degree of polarisation of the emission depends only on the index γ of energy spectrum (4.26) and, as can be checked from (4.16) and (4.27), is equal to

$$\Pi_0 = \frac{\gamma + 1}{\gamma + 7/3}, \quad (4.31)$$

which amounts to 75 per cent at $\gamma = 3$ and 69 per cent at $\gamma = 2$.[166, 171]

When applied to magnetic bremsstrahlung of cosmic electrons formulae (4.28) and (4.31), generally speaking, are of no use since the observed emission is collected from a large region of space with the magnetic field differentially orientated in various parts of it. It is more appropriate to consider that on the average the directions of the magnetic fields on the line of sight are random. In this case there is no emission polarisation and the intensity can be found easily by averaging (4.28) over all directions of the magnetic field.[172, 173] Since

$$\frac{1}{2} \int_0^\pi (\sin \theta)^{(\gamma + 1)/2} \sin \theta \, d\theta = \frac{\sqrt{\pi}}{2} \cdot \frac{\Gamma\left(\frac{\gamma + 5}{4}\right)}{\Gamma\left(\frac{\gamma + 7}{4}\right)}, \quad (4.32)$$

the aforementioned averaging leads to the following expression for the intensity of emission of a homogeneous and isotropic electron distribution with an energy spectrum (4.29) in a random magnetic field†:

$$I = a(\gamma)\frac{e^3}{mc^2}\left(\frac{3e}{4\pi m^3 c^5}\right)^{(\gamma-1)/2} H^{(\gamma+1)/2} K_e L v^{-(\gamma-1)/2}. \quad (4.33)$$

Here K_e is the coefficient in the spectrum (4.29) per unit volume, $H^{(\gamma+1)/2}$ is taken to be the mean value of this quantity in the emitting region and $a(\gamma)$ is a coefficient depending on the energy spectrum index γ:

$$a(\gamma) = \frac{2^{(\gamma-1)/2}\sqrt{3}\Gamma\left(\frac{3\gamma-1}{12}\right)\Gamma\left(\frac{3\gamma+19}{12}\right)\Gamma\left(\frac{\gamma+5}{4}\right)}{8\sqrt{\pi}(\gamma+1)\Gamma\left(\frac{\gamma+7}{4}\right)}. \quad (4.34)$$

The values of the coefficient $a(\gamma)$ are given in Table 6.

TABLE 6

γ	1	1·5	2	2·5	3	4	5
$a(\gamma)$	0·283	0·147	0·103	0·0852	0·0742	0·0725	0·0922
$y_1(\gamma)$	0·80	1·3	1·8	2·2	2·7	3·4	4·0
$y_2(\gamma)$	0·00045	0·011	0·032	0·10	0·18	0·38	0·65

It can be seen from expressions (4.28) and (4.33) that the power-law energy spectrum of emitting particles with an exponent γ corresponds to the power-law emission frequency spectrum.

$$I_\nu \sim \nu^{-\alpha}, \qquad \alpha = \frac{\gamma-1}{2}. \quad (4.35)$$

Because of the importance of formula (4.35) we shall also derive it by a simple approximate method. We do, in fact, ignore the width of the emission spectrum of one electron, assuming that all the emission occurs at a frequency $\nu = \nu_m$ (corresponding to the maximum in the spectrum (formula (4.25)). The energy of an electron

† Formula (4.33) is given in section 6 (see (6.1)) in a form which is convenient to use (with numerical values for the constant coefficient).

can then be expressed by the frequency v with $E^2 = (1/0.29)(4\pi m^3 c^5/eH_\perp)v$. Further, the total emission power of an ultra-relativistic electron is given by the well-known expression (see formula (8.12) below)

$$-\frac{dE}{dt} \equiv P = \tfrac{2}{3}c\left(\frac{e^2}{mc^2}\right)^2 H_\perp^2\left(\frac{E}{mc^2}\right)^2.$$

Upon these assumptions for spectrum (4.29) the intensity of emission collected from a path L is

$$I_v \, dv = \frac{L}{4\pi} PK_e E^{-\gamma} \, dE$$

$$= a'(\gamma)\frac{e^3}{mc^2}\left(\frac{3e}{4\pi m^3 c^5}\right)^{(\gamma-1)/2} H^{(\gamma+1)/2}LK_e v^{-(\gamma-1)/2} \, dv,$$

(4.33a)

where $a'(\gamma) = 0.31(0.24)^{(\gamma-1)/2}$ and it is taken that for a random field on the average $H_\perp^2 = \tfrac{2}{3}H^2$. Formula (4.33a) differs from (4.33) only in the replacement of the factor a (γ) by $a'(\gamma)$, these factors not differing by a factor of more than two for values $1 < \gamma < 4$.

It was assumed above that the electron energy spectrum follows a power law (see (4.26) and (4.29)) over a certain fairly wide energy range. We shall now give a quantitative estimate of this range. The error introduced as the result of replacing the finite integration limits in (4.20) and (4.21) by 0 and ∞ respectively do not exceed 10 per cent for a given frequency γ for each of the limits if

$$E_1 \leqslant mc^2\left[\frac{4\pi mcv}{3eHy_1(\gamma)}\right]^{\frac{1}{2}} \simeq 2.5 \times 10^2\left[\frac{v}{y_1(\gamma)H}\right]^{\frac{1}{2}}\text{eV},$$

$$E_2 \geqslant mc^2\left[\frac{4\pi mcv}{3eHy_2(\gamma)}\right]^{\frac{1}{2}} \simeq 2.5 \times 10^2\left[\frac{v}{y_2(\gamma)H}\right]^{\frac{1}{2}}\text{eV}.$$

(4.36)

The values of the factors $y_1(\gamma)$ and $y_2(\gamma)$ for different γ are given in Table 6. It can be seen that the range of energies which make the basic contribution to the emission at a given frequency depends essentially on the nature of the spectrum. This dependence, as is to be expected, is such that with a hard spectrum (small γ) there is a considerable increase in the part played by large energies, whilst the contribution of electrons with small energies is considerably less significant even with a very soft spectrum (large γ). This is caused by the exponential drop in the emission intensity in the high-frequency region when compared with the slower power-law variation in the region below the maximum of the spectral distribution (4.24).

From the results given the conclusion can be drawn that if the observed emission spectrum in the frequency range $v_1 \leqslant v \leqslant v_2$ follows a power law in form and can be characterised by an index α, then the energy spectrum of the emitting electrons with an accuracy of not less than about 10 per cent also follows a power law in the energy range†

$$\left[\frac{1}{y_1(\gamma)}\frac{4\pi mc}{3e}\frac{v_1}{H}\right]^{1/2} \leqslant \frac{E}{mc^2} \leqslant \left[\frac{1}{y_2(\gamma)}\frac{4\pi mc}{3e}\frac{v_2}{H}\right]^{1/2}, \qquad (4.37)$$

and the spectrum index is $\gamma = 2\alpha + 1$.

We gave above the expressions for the intensity of magnetic bremsstrahlung in the two limiting cases normally looked at: for a homogeneous field and a completely random field. The first of them is characterised by the maximum possible polarisation, whilst there is no polarisation in the second. The question of the applicability of one or other expression can be solved in the first place on the basis of polarisation measurements. However, in the well-known cases when polarisation of cosmic magnetic bremsstrahlung is being observed it generally turns out to be considerably less than in the case of a homogeneous field (4.31). This may mean basically that the magnetic field in the emitting region is not strictly homogeneous. The degree of polarisation in this "intermediate" case has been calculated by Korchak and Syrovatskii[170] for two magnetic field models.

The first of them assumes that on the homogeneous field H is

---

† Strictly speaking, it is only true to say that with a power-law electron spectrum more than 80 per cent of the emission in the frequency range $v_1 < v < v_2$ is caused by electrons with energies from the range (4.37). It is obvious that with an arbitrary electron spectrum the emission spectrum over a limited range can always be approximated by a power law function. In particular the emission spectrum of a single electron in the range below the maximum is always of the form $I_v \subset v^{1/3}$ (see (4.24) and Appendix 3), but condition (4.37) in this case ($\alpha = -\frac{1}{3}$, $\gamma = \frac{1}{3}$) is deprived of meaning. This value of the spectral index α is the minimum permissible for magnetic bremsstrahlung.

As for the values $\alpha > 0$ (see (4.35)), with a wide enough frequency range $v_1 < v < v_2$ the emission spectrum can follow a power law over this range only if the electron energy spectrum follows a power law in the energy range defined by conditions (4.37).

It is to this case that the conclusion drawn in the text relates.

superimposed a certain random (isotropic, when averaged, over the emitting region) field H_c, the absolute value of whose strength is constant. It is possible that this situation is approximated near the galactic plane and in the spiral arms of the Galaxy in particular. If H_1 is the projection of the strength of a homogeneous magnetic field onto the plane of projection and $\beta = H_1/H_c$, then in the two limiting cases of weak and strong homogeneous fields the degree of polarisation is

$$\Pi = \frac{(\gamma + 3)(\gamma + 5)}{32} \Pi_0 \beta^2 \qquad (\beta \ll 1), \qquad (4.38)$$

$$\Pi = \left(1 - \frac{2}{3\beta^2}\right)\Pi_0 \qquad (\beta \gg 1), \qquad (4.39)$$

where Π_0 is defined by expression (4.31).

The second model corresponds to the situation when there is no homogeneous field but due to the more or less regular nature of the field (for example, due to a mixture of dipole or toroidal fields) certain directions are encountered more frequently than others. This may be the case in discrete sources of cosmic radio emission. If the directional distribution of the magnetic fields is almost isotropic and the strength of the field H can be considered to be approximately constant in absolute value, then, as was shown by Korchak and Syrovatskii,[170] the degree of polarisation is

$$\Pi = \frac{15}{8} \frac{\gamma + 5}{\gamma + 7} \Pi_0 \frac{\overline{\Delta H^2}}{\overline{H^2}}, \qquad (4.40)$$

where $\overline{\Delta H^2} = \max (\overline{H_1^2} - \overline{H_2^2})$, H_1 and H_2 are the projections of the magnetic field onto two arbitrarily orientated directions at right angles to each other in the plane of projection and averaging is carried out over the whole volume of the source.

Polarisation has been found of the Galaxy's general non-thermal emission[174–176, 435] (see section 5) and also of the optical magnetic bremsstrahlung and radio emission in the centrimetric band for the Crab Nebula.[177–180, 163] Polarisation has also been found in the optical magnetic bremsstrahlung of the "jet" in the radio galaxy NGC 4486 (radio source Virgo A)[161, 181] and slight polarisation ($\Pi = 3 \pm 1.5$ per cent) of the non-thermal radio emission of this radio galaxy in the $\lambda = 21$ cm band.[182]

In the case of Cygnus A on wavelength of 3·15 cm the polarisation is $\Pi = 8 \pm 1$ per cent but at wavelengths of about 10 cm it is $\Pi < 1$ per cent.[183] Polarisation has been found[184] in a whole series of extragalactic radio sources at a wavelength of $\lambda = 20$ cm; for the radio galaxy Centaurus A it is as much as $\Pi = 38$ per cent.

When use begins to be made of equipment with high angular resolution permitting reliable measurements of low polarisation, polarisation measurements, in all probability, will become particularly important (see also in this connexion some recent articles[185–187] and the remarks made below when discussing formula (4.41)).†

Influence of the medium

Up to now we have paid no attention to the medium in which the magnetic bremsstrahlung appears and is propagated. At the same time in certain cases the medium may have a significant effect on the generation of magnetic bremsstrahlung and also alter its properties on its way from the source to the observer. Let us now examine these effects more closely.

In connexion with the magnetic bremsstrahlung polarisation which has just been discussed it should be borne in mind that during propagation in the ionised interstellar gas the direction of polarisation and its degree may change due to Faraday rotation of the plane of polarisation.[161, 162, 178, 187, 190, 191] It is well known that when a wave travels a distance L at an angle θ to the magnetic field H the wave's plane of polarisation is rotated by the angle‡

$$\phi = \frac{e^3 n_e H \cos \theta}{2\pi m^2 c^2 v^2} L = 2{\cdot}36 \times 10^4 \frac{n_e L H \cos \theta}{v^2}, \qquad (4.41)$$

where n_e is the medium's electron concentration.

Under cosmic conditions rotation of the plane of polarisation

---

† These possibilities were apparent as early as 1953[4, 151, 158, 160] but attention has been drawn to them only recently. This is not by chance since for a long time all the magnetic bremsstrahlung theory of cosmic radio emission remained unacknowledged beyond the U.S.S.R. A typical example of this was the paper devoted to magnetic bremsstrahlung theory sent to the Manchester Radio Astronomy Symposium in 1955 which was not even published in the transactions of the Symposium. At the same time these transactions which appeared in 1957 contained an article connecting non-thermal cosmic radio emission with the hypothesis of the existence of an enormous number of radio stars.[188, 189, 279]

‡ Here no account is taken of the fact that the propagation of radio waves ($\lambda < 10$ km) in the interstellar medium ($H \lesssim 10^{-5}$ oersted) can in practice be taken always as "quasi-longitudinal" (see reference 192, section 37).

leads to a depolarisation of the emission as a result of the following two effects.

The first effect is linked with the inhomogeneity of the magnetic field in the plane of projection leading to different rotations of the plane of polarisation in the different elements of the detector's solid angle. This effect can be eliminated by increasing the angular resolution of the receiving aerial until only sections with a homogeneous field come within the polar diagram at each distance.

The second possible cause of depolarisation, even in the case of a homogeneous magnetic field, is the finite depth of the emitting region. The point is that emission occurring at different distances from the observer will be subjected to different rotations. As a result the total emission received is to a greater or lesser degree depolarised. For example for $H = 3 \times 10^{-6}$ oersted, $\cos \theta = \frac{1}{3}$, $n_e = 1$ cm^{-3}, $v = 10^8$ c/s ($\lambda = 3$ m) and a depth of the emitting region of $L = 1pc = 3 \times 10^{18}$ cm the angle of rotation of the plane of polarisation of the emission coming from the further edge of the emitting region will be about 2π times greater than for emission coming from the nearer edge. Since the intermediate layers of the source will give all the intermediate angles of rotation the emission in the present case is practically entirely depolarised.

The question of the part played by Faraday depolarisation in actual observations can be solved by measuring the degree of polarisation at two adjacent frequencies. Due to the strong dependence of the rotation on the frequency the transition region from polarised to fully depolarised emission occupies a very narrow band of frequencies. For instance in the example above at a frequency of 3×10^8 c/s ($\lambda = 1$ m) the maximum difference in the angles of rotation is only $2\pi/9$ and the depolarisation will be insignificant. In this case it is assumed, of course, that the emission is generated in one region with a homogeneous field. If, however, as must be the case in a number of examples, there is a number of emitting regions along the line of sight (with different projections of the field H onto the plane of projection the polarisation of the observed emission may be considerably less than the polarisation of the emission from an individual region.†

In addition, the Faraday rotation on the way from the emitting region to the observer leads to rotation of the plane of polarisation

† We shall not discuss here the depolarisation of the received emission connected with the finite width of the pass band of the receiving device.[174]

of radio emission. This last effect can be used, as is clear from formula (4.41), to estimate the average value of the product of $n^e H \cos \theta$ along the line of sight. This possibility is particularly interesting when it is a question of measuring the polarisation of the radio emission of extra-galactic discrete sources (in this case we may hope to obtain valuable information on the galactic halo and metagalactic space[185, 187]).

Faraday rotation of the plane of polarisation is not the only effect of the medium. The expressions given above for the intensity of magnetic bremsstrahlung in the low-frequency region must be made more precise by allowing for a difference between the medium's refraction index and unity.[4, 193, 194] For an ionised gas the refractive index is†

$$\tilde{n} = \left(1 - \frac{n_e e^2}{\pi m v^2}\right)^{1/2} = \left(1 - \frac{0.8 \times 10^8 n_e}{v^2}\right)^{1/2} \tag{4.42}$$

and in the conditions of interest to us ($n_e < 10 \text{ cm}^{-3}$, $v > 10^6$ c/s) differs very little from unity. The refraction of the emission in the interstellar clouds can therefore be completely ignored. For the actual process of emission by ultra-relativistic particles, however, even a slight deviation from unity in the refractive index may be significant, as is well known for example in the case of Cherenkov emission.

The point is that in a medium with a refractive index $\tilde{n}$ instead of the factor (4.1) there appears in the denominators of the expressions for the field strengths and the emission intensity powers of the factor

$$1 - \left(\frac{v\tilde{n}}{c}\right) \cos \psi. \tag{4.43}$$

It follows in particular from this that if $\tilde{n} > c/v > 1$ instead of being concentrated in the direction of the instantaneous velocity the emission is concentrated near the surface of the Cherenkov cone

$$\cos \psi = \frac{c}{\tilde{n}v}.$$

† Even in a field $H \sim 10^{-2}$ oe which may be found in nebulae the gyro-frequency is $\omega_H = eH/mc \sim 10^5$ c/s and in the radio-band is therefore $(\omega_H/\omega)^2 \lesssim 10^{-4}$ (for $\lambda \lesssim 100$ m). Therefore the effect of the magnetic field on the refractive index $\tilde{n}$ can be ignored unless it is a question of the rotation of the plane of polarisation discussed above.

In the case of a rarefied ionised gas which we are interested in (the interstellar gas and gaseous nebulae which are sources of cosmic radio emission) $\tilde{n} < 1$ and if $\tilde{n}$ is different enough from unity the relativistic effect leading to the appearance of strong directional emission will as a whole be absent. In actual fact in this case the denominator of (4.43) even for a particle velocity v very close to the velocity of light c will not be small unless $1 - \tilde{n} < 1 - v/c \ll 1$. It is clear from this that the effect of the medium can be ignored only when

$$1 - \tilde{n}^2 \ll \left(\frac{mc^2}{E}\right)^2. \tag{4.44}$$

In this case the fact that $\tilde{n}$ differs from unity can be ignored and the expressions given above for emission in a vacuum be used. At first glance condition (4.44) establishes the upper limit of the permissible energies at which emission does not differ from emission in a vacuum. In actual fact this is not the case for an ionised gas: the emission starts to differ from emission in a vacuum when the particle energy decreases; this corresponds to the low-frequency section of the magnetic bremsstrahlung spectrum. This can be easily confirmed if we bear in mind that the refractive index (4.42) itself depends on the frequency which in its turn is determined by the energy of the emitting particle. Condition (4.44) can be put into a more convenient form by means of expressions (4.42) and (4.25) for the characteristic emission frequency of an electron with an energy E. What we do is to write inequality (4.44) in the form of a condition for the range of emitted frequencies for which the difference between the refractive index and unity is insignificant:

$$v \gg v_n = \frac{ecn_e}{H_\perp} \simeq 15 \frac{n_e}{H_\perp}. \tag{4.45}$$

The qualitative estimates which have been given are confirmed by an exact calculation[193, 194] which for a medium with a refractive index of $\tilde{n} < 1$, $1 - \tilde{n} \ll 1$ leads to the following expression for the power emitted by an electron per unit frequency range (compare expression (4.24)):

$$p(v) = \sqrt{3}\frac{e^3 H_\perp}{mc^2}\left[1 + (1 - \tilde{n}^2)\left(\frac{E}{mc^2}\right)^2\right]^{-\frac{1}{2}} \frac{v}{v'_c} \int_{v/v'_c}^{\infty} K_{5/3}(\eta)\, d\eta, \tag{4.46}$$

where

$$v'_c = v_c\left[1 + (1 - \bar{n}^2)\left(\frac{E}{mc^2}\right)^2\right]^{-\frac{3}{2}}. \qquad (4.47)$$

It can be seen from this that when condition (4.44) is fulfilled the difference between (4.45) and (4.24) really can be ignored.

In the Galaxy $n_e \lesssim 1$ cm^{-3} and $H_\perp \gtrsim 10^{-6}$ oe and we have $v_n = ecn_e/H_\perp \lesssim 10^7$ c/s, $\lambda_n = c/v_n \gtrsim 30$ m. Generally $\lambda_n > 100$ m since in the halo $n_e \sim 10^{-2}$ cm^{-3}, $H_\perp \sim 1$–3×10^{-6} oe and in the disk $n_e < 1$ cm^{-3}, $H_\perp \sim 3$–6×10^{-6} oe. The position may change in certain nebulae and condition (4.45) must, of course, not be forgotten.[195]

An important characteristic of the medium is the absorption coefficient. The interstellar gas, despite its rarefaction, can noticeably absorb the radio waves of interest to us in the $v \sim 10^6$ to 10^{10} c/s band as the result of the collision of electrons with the ionised atoms of the medium (in quantum language so-called free-free transitions occur in the continuous energy spectrum in this case). The collisions of electrons with neutral atoms in the interstellar gas are completely insignificant since even in the so-called neutral hydrogen clouds (HI-regions) the degree of ionisation is fairly large (about 10^{-3} to 10^{-4}) so electron-ion collisions are a determining factor. In the regions of ionised hydrogen (HII-regions) and also in the highly rarefied gas between the clouds and far from the galactic plane there is practically total ionisation.

Due to the high rarefaction of the interstellar gas the radio frequencies of interest to us are significantly greater than the Langmuir frequency of the interstellar plasma:

$$v_0 = \left(\frac{e^2 n_e}{\pi m}\right)^{\frac{1}{2}} \simeq 9 \times 10^3 \sqrt{n_e}. \qquad (4.48)$$

Under these conditions the coefficient of absorption of the radio waves is defined by the expression (see, e.g., reference 192, section 37)

$$\mu = 10^{-2} \frac{n_e^2}{T^{\frac{3}{2}}v^2}\left[17\cdot7 + \ln\frac{T^{\frac{3}{2}}}{v}\right], \qquad (4.49)$$

where T is the temperature of the medium (more precisely T in (4.49) is the electron temperature) which for the regions of the ionised interstellar gas is of the order of magnitude of $T \simeq 10^4$ °K. Knowing the absorption coefficient μ we can calculate the optical thickness of the gas in a certain direction:

$$\tau = \int \mu \, dr, \qquad (4.50)$$

where the integration is carried out along the line of sight. If $\tau \gtrsim 1$ then a gas with a temperature $T \sim 10^4$ °K must be a source of noticeable thermal radio emission. If the intensity at $\tau \gg 1$ is equal to the intensity of the emission of a black body

$$I_\nu = \frac{2k\nu^2}{c^2} T \infty \nu^2, \qquad (4.51)$$

i.e., in the range of frequencies of interest to us ($h\nu \ll kT$) it is proportional to the square of the emission frequency (the spectral index of the thermal radio emission is $\alpha = -2$). At an arbitrary optical thickness the emission will have an intensity

$$I_\nu = \frac{2k\nu^2}{c^2} T_{\text{eff}} = 3 \cdot 07 \times 10^{-37} \nu^2 T_{\text{eff}} \text{ erg/cm}^2 \cdot \text{sec} \cdot (\text{c/s}) \cdot \text{sterad.} \quad (4.52)$$

Here

$$T_{\text{eff}} = T(1 - e^{-\tau}). \qquad (4.53)$$

If $\tau \ll 1$ the effective emission temperature is $T_{\text{eff}} \simeq T \cdot \tau \infty \nu^{-2}$ so the intensity is

$$I_\nu = \frac{2k\nu^2}{c^2} T\tau = \text{const}, \qquad (4.54)$$

i.e., it does not depend upon the frequency. Therefore for the thermal emission of the interstellar gas the spectral index α characterising the relationship of the intensity to the frequency

$$I_\nu \sim \nu^{-\alpha} \qquad (4.55)$$

varies within the limits $-2 \leqslant \alpha \leqslant 0$, whilst the effective emission temperature cannot be higher than the gas temperature T. These two circumstances allow us in principle, by means of observations at different frequencies, to pick out with certainty the magnetic bremsstrahlung of interest to us from the medium's thermal radio emission.

The absorption of radio waves in the interstellar medium can significantly alter the spectrum of the long-wave cosmic radio emission received on Earth.[154, 196] For example for waves with a wavelength of $\lambda = 1$ km the absorption is significant even with the limits of the solar system (in the interplanetary medium we can evidently put on average† $n_e \sim 10^2$ cm^{-3} so according to formula (4.49) with $T \sim 10^4$ °K the optical thickness is $\tau = \mu L \sim 1$ for a path $L \sim 5 \times 10^{13}$ cm). For $n_e \sim 10^{-2}$ cm^{-3} and $T \sim 10^4$ °K we have $\tau \simeq 2 \times 10^{-11} L/v^2$ and the absorption over the whole path of radio waves in the halo ($L \sim 3 \times 10^{22}$ cm) becomes significant for frequencies $v \lesssim 10^6$ c/s ($\lambda \gtrsim 300$ m).

It is therefore clear that it is absolutely necessary to allow for absorption in the interplanetary and interstellar medium in the field of long-wave radio astronomy based on satellites.[196] Absorption in the interstellar gas must also be allowed for in the $v \lesssim 10$ Mc/s ($\lambda \gtrsim 30$ m) region. According to available data[464] there is a "gap" in the non-thermal Galactic emission spectrum at frequencies of $v \lesssim 3$ Mc/s which can clearly be explained by absorption in the ionised interstellar gas.[465, 187] As for the band of waves shorter than 10 m which are generally used in radio astronomy the absorption in question is generally slight since it is inversely proportional to the square of the frequency (for example even for $n_e \sim 1$ cm^{-3}, $T \sim 10^4$ °K and $\lambda = 10$ m the thickness is $\tau \sim 2 \times 10^{-22} L$, i.e., the absorption is effective only in very low galactic latitudes; in actual fact the galactic plane evidently averages to $n_e \ll 1$ cm^{-3} due to the low degree of ionisation of the interstellar medium in the HI-regions).

Let us finally examine the possible reabsorption of magnetic bremsstrahlung by the relativistic particles themselves.[194, 197] If the energy distribution of the emitting electrons were an equilibrium (Boltzmann) distribution with a certain temperature T, then for a sufficiently large optical thickness of the emitting medium ordinary thermal emission corresponding to this temperature would be observed as the result of reabsorption. However, due to the non-equilibrium (power law) nature of the relativistic electron spectrum the frequency dependence of the emission will differ from that of the emission of a black body (4.51) even if the optical thickness is great when compared with the self-absorption (reabsorption).

In order to calculate the coefficient of absorption caused by reabsorption we can use Einstein's relations between the probabilities of

† The question of the concentration of the gas and electrons in interplanetary space is unclear particularly with respect to the contribution made by solar corpuscular fluxes. In periods when the flux power is at a minimum the concentration is $n_e < 10^2$ cm^{-3}. At the same time even with $n_e \simeq 5$ cm^{-3} absorption may still play a part within the solar system.

emission and absorption of quanta in the radio frequency band. The change in the number of quanta in an emission flux with an intensity I_v connected with transitions of electrons from state 1 with an energy $E - hv$ to state 2 with an energy E and back is $B_{21}N_e(E)I_v - B_{12}N_e(E - hv)I_v$, where B_{12} and B_{21} are the Einstein coefficients of absorption and stimulated emission, whilst $N_e(E)\,dE$ is the number of electrons in a unit volume with energies in the range $E,\ E + dE$. Therefore, allowing for all possible transitions, the coefficient of absorption μ_r is

$$\mu_r = -\frac{1}{I_v}\frac{dI_v}{dx} = \int \{B_{12}N_e(E - hv) - B_{21}N_e(E)\}hv\,dE. \quad (4.56)$$

Let us now use Einstein's relations $B_{12} = B_{21} = A_{21}(c^2/2hv^3)$, where the probability of spontaneous emission A_{21} is equal to the number of quanta emitted by an electron in a unit solid angle per unit time and thus is equal to $A_{21} = p(v)/4\pi hv$ (see (4.24)); here we shall consider that the emission takes place in a vacuum. As a result, if we bear in mind that only transitions with $hv \ll E$ proceed with noticeable intensity so that we can put $N_e(E - hv) - N_e(E) = -hv(\partial N_e/\partial E)$, we obtain the following expression for the absorption coefficient due to reabsorption:

$$\mu_r = -\frac{c^2}{8\pi v^2}\int \frac{\partial N_e}{\partial E}\,p(v, E)\,dE \quad (4.57)$$

Using ratios (4.24) and (4.27) in the case of a power-law spectrum of the form $N_e(E) = K_e E^{-\gamma}$ (see (4.29)) we obtain from expression (4.57)

$$\mu_r = f(\gamma)\frac{e^3}{6\pi m}\left[\frac{3e}{2\pi m^3 c^5}\right]^{\gamma/2}K_e H_\perp^{\gamma/2+1}v^{-(\gamma/2+2)}. \quad (4.58)$$

Here the coefficient $f(\gamma)$ is defined by the expression

$$f(\gamma) = \frac{3\sqrt{3}}{4}\frac{\gamma}{\gamma + 2}\Gamma\left(\frac{3\gamma + 2}{12}\right)\Gamma\left(\frac{3\gamma + 22}{12}\right). \quad (4.59)$$

In the range of values $\gamma = 1$ to 5 the coefficient $f(\gamma)$ varies between $f(1) = 0.96$ and $f(5) = 1.77$. Substituting the numerical values of the constants in (4.58) we obtain

$$\mu_r = f(\gamma) \times 0.65 \times 10^{-2}[3.5 \times 10^9]^\gamma K_e H_\perp^{\gamma/2+1}v^{-(\gamma/2+2)}. \quad (4.60)$$

If the depth of the emitting region is $l \gg 1/\mu_r$, i.e., the optical thickness with respect to self-absorption is greater than unity, then there will be emission only from a layer about $1/\mu_r$ thick and the spectral dependence of the observed emission will take the form

$$I_v \infty v^{-(\gamma-1)/2}v^{\gamma/2+2} = v^{5/2} \tag{4.61}$$

unlike the frequency dependence of the equilibrium emission (4.51).

As will be shown in section 6 the reabsorption of magnetic bremsstrahlung by relativistic electrons in the Galaxy is completely insignificant. For certain nebulae, however, which are sources of strong magnetic bremsstrahlung and where the relativistic electron concentration is high, reabsorption of magnetic bremsstrahlung may play an important part in the low frequency part of the radio band.

5. SOME RADIO ASTRONOMY DATA

The rapid development of radio astronomy, particularly in recent years, has led to the accumulation of a large amount of material which cannot be covered in any detail in this book. Therefore for details we shall refer the reader to the corresponding sources, pausing here on a few points which are particularly important for what is going to be said. We are mainly interested in radio astronomy data relating to the spatial distribution, intensity and spectrum of the non-thermal emission of the Galaxy, the galactic nebulae and extragalactic objects (galaxies, clusters of galaxies, and the intergalactic medium).

Non-thermal radio emission of the Galaxy

It is well known that most of the matter in the Galaxy is in the form of stars, clouds of interstellar gas and dust concentrated in a relatively thin disk with a radius of 12 to 15 kpc and a thickness of about 300 pc. The distribution of the matter within this disk is by no means even. The concentration of stars rises considerably near the centre of the Galaxy where the so-called galactic core is (a very dense region only a few parsec in size). In addition, the hot (young) stars and clouds of interstellar gas are concentrated largely in the spiral arms of the Galaxy.

The first studies of the Galaxy's non-thermal radio emission have already shown that although its intensity decreases with the distance away from the galactic plane the decrease is too small for us to be able to consider the emission sources to be concentrated only within the thin galactic disk. This circumstance was a fresh independent argument[156] in favour of the existence of a galactic "corona" or "halo" which was initially postulated as a reservoir of cosmic rays and whose necessity also proceeded from considerations of a dynamic nature.[200, 201] A halo was later found[202] in the spiral galaxy M31 (in the constellation of Andromeda) as well whose structure is like that of our Galaxy and in a number of other galaxies.

However, as has recently become clear,[466] it is by no means all galaxies that have a noticeable radio halo. For example the spiral galaxies NGC 253, NGC 4945 and NGC 5236 which are bright in the optical waveband do not have a noticeable radio halo and their radio emission comes chiefly from a comparatively small region clearly surrounding the central part of these galaxies.[466] In this connexion it must be stressed that the absence of a radio halo still does not prove the absence of a halo. In fact, if there is a gaseous halo in a galaxy, then with a weak magnetic field and a low concentration of relativistic electrons in this halo it will be extremely dim or even unnoticeable in the radio band.

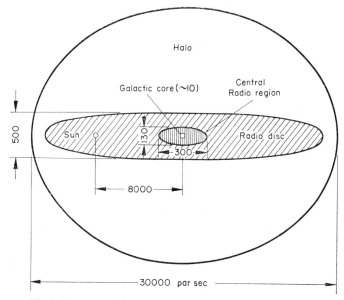

Fig. 9. Structure of the Galaxy according to radio astronomy data in the metric waveband. The drawing is schematic and the dimensions are given in parsec.

We note also that reports on the revision of the data on the halo of our Galaxy have been published in the form of a conference report.[467] Considerable flattening and possibly even complete absence of a galactic halo were indicated in that report. The corresponding results have not yet been published, not to mention the fact they contradict all earlier results and therefore need careful checking. Bearing in mind the presence of a large halo in the M31 galaxy, which is like our Galaxy and evidently genetically close to it, and also all the known data and arguments, we cannot see at present any reason to reject the idea of the existence of some halo in the Galaxy. All that is possible is that this halo (or even not the halo but its radio brightness) is less than has heretofore been accepted and less than is indicated below (we later use the picture that had been called the most probable before the appearance of the above-mentioned conference report).

The use of highly directional aerials has made possible a considerable clarification and addition of detail to the information on the non-thermal galactic radio emission. Here particular mention must be made of measurements[203, 204] at wavelengths of 22 cm and 3·5 m with an angular resolution of about 1°. From these and subsequent measurements we can pick out three basic regions in space where there is emission; these are shown diagrammatically in Fig. 9.

1. *The galactic corona or halo*, which is a quasi-spherical region embracing the Galaxy with a mean radius of the order of 10 to 15 kpc = (3 to 5)10^{22} cm. The majority of recent estimates[163, 205] lead to a value of the mean radius of the halo of $R = 10$ kpc so the volume of the halo is $V = 10^{68}$ cm^3. Within the limits of measurement accuracy achieved (and, what is most important, of the certainty of picking out the meta galactic component) the halo can also be considered to be an ellipsoid of rotation with a ratio of the axes of 1·5.[206] The majority (80 to 90 per cent) of all cosmic radio emission comes from the halo. A feature of the halo's radio emission is the weak dependence of its intensity on the direction of and also the distance to the galactic centre.

A large number of papers have been devoted to determining the spectral index α of the Galaxy's total non-thermal radio emission but there are unfortunately considerable discrepancies in their results.

For example some authors[5, 161] take the value $\alpha = 0·82$ ($\gamma = 2\alpha + 1 = 2·64$); in later works[163, 207] the value $\alpha = 0·7 \pm 0·1$ is used.

According to Adgie and Smith[208] $\alpha = 0\cdot5 \pm 0\cdot1$ and according to Costain[209] the value $\alpha = 0\cdot37 \pm 0\cdot04$ was obtained for the $1\cdot7 \leqslant \lambda \leqslant 7\cdot9$ m range of wavelengths.

Komesaroff[216] has compared the available data for the frequency range 19·7 to 1390 Mc/s and obtained the average spectral index value $\alpha = 0\cdot6 \pm 0\cdot1$. This takes into account only measurements in directions not less than 4 to 5° from the galactic plane (in directions closer to the galactic plane a significant part may be played by absorption and thermal emission caused by the clouds of ionised hydrogen).

Recent careful measurements of the intensity of the halo's radio emission at several frequencies in the $v = 26$ to 404 Mc/s band have shown[210] that the spectral index α does not remain constant but varies smoothly from $\alpha = 0\cdot35$ at the bottom end of this band to $\alpha = 0\cdot8$ in the high-frequency region. The inconstancy of the spectral index found in this work may also explain the discrepancy mentioned above in the values obtained in different papers. We shall discuss

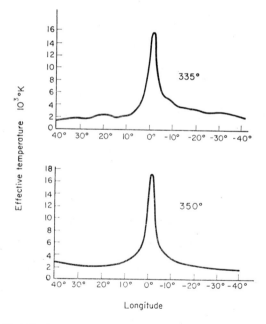

Fig. 10. Effective temperature of non-thermal cosmic radio emission at a wavelength of $\lambda = 3\cdot5$ m as a function of the galactic latitude (for the two galactic longitudes of 335° and 350°).

the possible reasons for the variation in the spectral index in sections 6 and 17.

2. *The "radio disk"* of the Galaxy, which is a region near the galactic plane in which the intensity of radio emission is significantly higher (by a factor of about 6 to 10) than in the halo and drops off quite sharply as one moves away from the galactic plane. The thickness of the radio disk is about 500 pc = 1.5×10^{21} cm, whilst the thickness of the plane sub-system of clouds of interstellar gas and young stars in the optical spiral (this region may be called the optical disk) is $\lesssim 300$ pc. The nature of the transition from the radio disk to the halo can be clearly seen in Fig. 10 which shows the effective temperature of the radio emission T_{eff} at a wavelength of 3·5 m as a function of the galactic latitude for two galactic longitudes.[204]

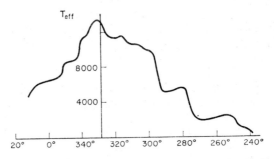

Fig. 11. Variation of T_{eff} in the disk as a function of the galactic longitude.

Along the galactic plane the intensity varies irregularly with the galactic longitude: near directions tangential to the spiral arms a faster rise is observed in the intensity[163, 207] (Fig. 11). This is some indication of a spiral structure in the radio disk, the radio disk embracing, as it were, an optical spiral which is a third or half as thick. The question of the spiral structure of the radio disk is still, however, largely unclarified.[212-215]

Measurements on the neutral hydrogen line ($\lambda = 21$ cm) have led to considerable progress in elucidating the arms of the Galaxy's optical spiral.[181, 217-221] The general picture is clear from Fig. 12 where a cross marks the centre of the Galaxy, a circle with a dot in the middle the solar system and the light patches correspond to observed accumulations of neutral hydrogen (it should be borne in mind that the observational conditions did not make it possible to investigate

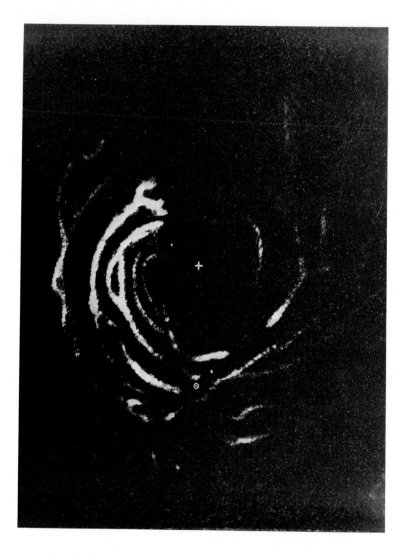

Fig. 12. Structure of the arms of the Galaxy according to data on the neutral hydrogen concentration (measurements of the 21 cm line). Cross—centre of the Galaxy; dotted circle—solar system; white patches—neutral hydrogen accumulations (no observations on the line from the centre to the Sun).

the region lying on or near the line from the Sun to the centre of the Galaxy). It follows from Fig. 12 and a fuller analysis of the data that the arms of the spiral are formed only at a distance of the order of 3 kpc from the centre of the Galaxy (the solar system is 8200 pc from the centre of the Galaxy). In addition, there are many separate arms, they are inhomogeneous with respect to the density of the gas and the thickness along their axis and are interrupted in many places.[217]

At a wavelength of 3·5 m the total emission of the disk is about a tenth of the total emission of the halo although the intensity of the emission in the disk is almost an order of magnitude larger. This can be explained by the small volume of the disk when compared with the volume of the halo. It is curious that, despite the considerable difference in intensitites, the spectrum of the disk's radio emission, at least in the direction of the galactic anti-centre, differs little or not at all from the halo's spectrum.[210, 211] According to recent measurements[210] the spectral index of the radio disk in the 100 to 300 Mc/s frequency range varies smoothly between $\alpha = 0·8$ for the higher frequencies and $\alpha = 0·35$ for the lower ones.

3. The "central radio region" of the Galaxy, which is the region surrounding the galactic centre. The dimensions of the source of non-thermal radio emission here, whose intensity rises towards the centre, are about 300 pc (major axis) and 130 pc (minor axis).[203, 222] Much of interest has also been found out in recent years[181, 217, 223, 224, 468, 469] about the distribution (in the central region) of neutral hydrogen from radio observations in the neutral hydrogen line ($\lambda = 21$ cm). The hydrogen is concentrated in a layer about 100 pc thick and its mean concentration is $n \sim 1$ to 2 cm^{-3}. All this mass of neutral hydrogen and, evidently, the stars contained in this region (their concentration is 500 to 1000 times greater than in the region of the Sun) rotate rapidly (the velocity is about 200 km/sec at a distance of about 100 pc from the centre).

A galactic nucleus with a diameter of about 8 pc has been found[223-225] in the central part of the Galaxy under discussion (from the thermal radio emission of ionised hydrogen). There is a similar nucleus composed of a dense stellar cloud with a mass of about $1·3 \times 10^7 M_\odot$ ($M_\odot = 2 \times 10^{33}$ g is the mass of the Sun) and of about the same size in the M31 (Andromeda) Nebula.[226] The nucleus of the M31 nebula rotates as a whole at an enormous velocity, making a complete revolution in $0·5 \times 10^6$ years. The nuclei of galaxies contain ionised hydrogen and must be sources of thermal radio emission (this emission has been as yet found only from the core of the Galaxy). In the centre of the Galaxy's nucleus (which, of course, has no sharply defined boundaries) the concentration reaches a value of $n \sim 3$ to 10×10^2 cm^{-3}.

Magnetic fields in the Galaxy

The high intensity and isotropy of cosmic rays even of very great energies can be explained only on the assumption that the cosmic rays are held within the Galaxy for a long time. In this connexion the opinion has been expressed[200, 227] that there is a large-scale galactic magnetic field which is also this retaining factor. After the discovery in 1949 of a polarisation of the light of distant stars, which can be explained by the non-isotropic absorption of the light by particles of interstellar dust orientated by a magnetic field, practically no doubts remained about the existence of galactic magnetic fields.† An additional argument in favour of the existence of these fields is the specific shape of certain galactic nebulae[229] not to mention the general considerations of ionised gas dynamics.[230] This is without speaking of the Galaxy's non-thermal radio emission itself which can be explained naturally only within the framework of the magnetic bremsstrahlung theory.

Estimates of the strength of the galactic magnetic field based on an analysis of the polarisation of stellar light, on considerations of the balance of the magnetic field energy and the energy of the motion of the gas masses in the Galaxy, and also on the condition of gravitational stability of the spiral arms lead to closely agreeing values of $H \simeq 1 \ \gamma = 10^{-5}$ oersted.[231] The magnetic field in the spiral arms of the Galaxy is evidently stronger than outside them.[232] Measurements of the Zeeman splitting of the $\lambda = 21$ cm line in the spectrum of powerful sources of radio emission (the absorption line is formed as the result of passing through a layer of the interstellar medium) gave, according to Ref. 233, a value of 0·5 to 1 γ as the upper limit of the magnetic field strength. According to recent data[234] (bearing in mind their subsequent increase in accuracy), however, a field $H \sim 10^{-5}$ oersted $= 1 \ \gamma$ has been found by this method in the spiral (in a cloud of neutral hydrogen). For the sake of comparison we should point out that the magnetic field strength in the solar system as measured directly by a satellite with a very elongated orbit

† A review of work on the polarisation of the light of stars was given by Pikel'ner.[228]

beyond the geomagnetic field averaged about 20 γ in the period of the corresponding observations.[235,199]

It is generally considered that the magnetic field in the arms is ordered to a considerable degree. This conclusion is made on the basis of information on the polarisation of the light of stars whose direction remains more or less constant over large sections of the sky. An analysis of the shape of a number of galactic nebulae leads to the same conclusion.[218,229] Nevertheless all these data relate only to a certain average field with averaging generally carried out over a fairly large region. The fact that such an ordered average field exists is clearly fully compatible with the presence in the spiral of random, unordered fields as well or, in any case, of noticeable local deviations in the direction of the field from the average. Hoyle and Ireland[236,237] in particular give certain arguments in favour of the magnetic field in the arms not being homogeneous but rather being helical in nature.

Radio astronomy observations can provide definite information on the nature of the magnetic field in the spiral. This relates firstly to measurements of the intensity as a function of the direction. In actual fact, as is clear from formula (4.28), when the emitting electrons are distributed isotropically the intensity of the radio emission I_v is proportional to the value of $H_\perp^{(\gamma+1)/2} = (H \sin \theta)^{(\gamma+1)/2}$ along the line of sight. Therefore, when observing along a homogeneous field, for example, the intensity is equal to zero. Unfortunately this effect is smoothed out for the spiral arms even with a fully ordered field because of the curvature of the arm. Nevertheless careful measurements at different frequencies and with a high angular resolution may reveal the nature of the deviations of the magnetic field in the arms from strict ordering and will also make it possible to determine the role of the non-thermal emission in the region of the optical spiral and the contribution made by the arms' radio emission to the total emission of the radio disk. Although the available data do not yet permit a definite interpretation the conclusion that there is noticeable lack of ordering of the field in the arms is the most natural one.[212-214,435] It is also probable that the mean specific emission from the arms is slightly higher than the mean emissivity in the radio disk. This may be connected with an increase in the field strength and possibly in the cosmic ray concentration in the arms.

The question of the nature of one characteristic feature in the radio sky, which is sometimes called the "radio belt", is also connected with the problem of the radio emission of the arms. In an article by Tunmer[238] the existence of the radio belt is linked with an ordered field in the arm in which the Sun is. This hypothesis, however, has not stood up to close enquiry.[6, 163, 239-231] The radio belt evidently is not related to the ordering of the field in the arm but is linked either with structural formations in the halo[163] (this possibility is more probable in the light of recent data[247]) or with a local inhomogeneity in the galactic spiral or with the existence of the shell of a supernova which has exploded near the solar system.[239, 246]

Measurements of the radio emission polarisation may also provide very important data on the magnetic field in the halo and in the arms. Measurements of this kind known to date have referred to the general galactic radio emission and their results have been highly contradictory. According to Razin[174] the polarisation of the general galactic radio emission on a wavelength of $\lambda = 1.45$ m ($\nu = 203$ Mc/s) in directions with a galactic latitude greater than $5°$ is about 1 per cent (according to Razin's corrected data). At the same time Thompson[242] and Pawsey and Harting[243] found no polarisation greater than a possible measurement error of the order of 1 per cent at wavelengths of $\lambda = 1.87$ m ($\nu = 159.5$ Mc/s) and $\lambda = 1.5$ m ($\nu = 215$ Mc/s) respectively. Polarisation was not found by Pauling-Toth et al.[241] either. Although these measurements related to different sections of the sky and a final conclusion cannot therefore be drawn, we should nevertheless bear in mind the following two circumstances which make a negative result, i.e., the absence of noticeable polarisation in the metric wave band, quite possible.

Firstly the polarisation of the general galactic radio emission may be extremely slight or be practically entirely absent due to the irregularity of the field in the halo (unlike the arms there is no reason here to expect the existence of a magnetic field which is to any extent ordered over the whole volume).

Secondly, Faraday depolarisation of the emission may play an important part in the range under discussion due to the finite depth of the emitting region. For example for an electron concentration $n_e \sim 10^{-2}$ cm^{-3} in a field $H \sim 3 \times 10^{-6}$ oe the emission is totally depolarised for an emitting region depth of about 100 pc $= 3 \times 10^{20}$ cm (see (4.41)). For $n_e \sim 10^{-3}$ cm^{-3}, however, the polarisation of the halo's radio emission for wavelengths of 1 to 2 m may nevertheless be as much as several per cent.[244] Therefore the question of the polarisation of the general galactic radio emission can be solved only on the basis of reliable and sufficiently extensive experimental data.

What has been said is well illustrated by the example of polarisation measurements in the galactic plane (i.e., in the region of the radio disk). Both from measurements[174] and from theoretical considerations (allowing for the Faraday rotation of the plane of polarisation) it might be expected that in the direction of the galactic plane there is no polarisation of the radio emission or in any case it is less than the polarisation in the medium and high galactic latitudes. This conclusion, however, contradicts the results of measurements[175] of the polarisation of different sections of the sky at a wavelength of $\lambda = 73$ cm ($v = 408$ Mc/s) with an angular resolution of $2°$ and a pass band of $1·9$ Mc/s.[176, 435] The data obtained point to a fairly considerable polarisation of the emission which in one of the directions of the galactic plane reaches a value of $\Pi = (I_1 - I_2)/(I_1 + I_2)$ $\simeq 5$ to 10 per cent.

More and fuller data will make it possible to obtain a more detailed picture of the directional distribution of the interstellar magnetic fields; at present only a rough estimate can be made of the degree of homogeneity of the magnetic field in the arms. We shall not allow for rotation of the plane of polarisation in the interstellar medium at first. Then for a degree of polarisation of $\Pi = 10$ per cent and a spectral index of $\alpha \simeq 0·8$, which corresponds to the frequency range $v \simeq 400$ Mc/s in question, it follows from formulae (4.31) and (4.38) that the ratio of the squares of the regular H and random H_c fields in the galactic plane is $\beta^2 = 0·1$; hence the regular field is $H \lesssim 0·3 H_c$. If, however, the field is ordered only in the arms and they provide about half the total intensity of the radio disk's emission the degree of polarisation of the arms' emission must be about 20 per cent. In this case $\beta^2 = 0·2$ and in the arms $H \lesssim 0·5 H_c$. Only in the case when the intensity of the arms is only about 1/8 of the total intensity of the radio disk can the polarisation of the arms' emission be considered to be total ($\Pi_0 = 73$ per cent at $\alpha = 0·8$, see (4.31)) so the field is quite regular. In this case the observed decrease in the degree of polarisation to 10 per cent could be explained by a considerable ($\gtrsim 80\%$) contribution from the non-polarised emission of the rest of the radio disk. This possibility, however, is not very probable since the arms account for not less than 1/5 of the distance along the line of sight in the galactic plane and the field strength in the arms is generally considered to be two or three times greater than outside the arms (in this case the ratio of the emission intensities of the arms and the rest of the disk is $I_{arm}/I_{disk} \gtrsim (1/4)$ $(2 \text{ to } 3)^{1 \cdot 8} \gtrsim 1$, see formula (4.33)).

In addition, it should be borne in mind that the observed polarisation of the order of 10 per cent corresponds to small areas in the sky where the field may be more homogeneous than it is on the average in the arm.

No allowance has been made above, as we indicated, for the possibility of Faraday depolarisation of the emission in the estimates given. This could lead to a local degree of radio emission polarisation, as it were, in the arms being greater than that observed and the field being more homogeneous than would follow from the estimates given. In this connexion it should be pointed out that the observations point to the absence of any significant Faraday rotation of the plane of polarisation. It is sufficient to say that the strong dependence of the Faraday rotation on the frequency and a correspondingly narrow transition region from a fully polarised to a fully depolarised emission makes it highly improbable that the frequency $v = 408$ Mc/s falls just into this region. In any case this can be easily checked by measuring the polarisation at a frequency which differs by a factor of two or three from that in question.

For a radio arm thickness of about 500 pc, a field strength of $H = 3 \times 10^{-6}$ oe and $\cos \theta \simeq 1$ the absence of Faraday depolarisation means that the electron concentration in the arms does not exceed a value of $n_e \simeq 3 \times 10^{-3}$ cm^{-3} (using formula (4.41) with $H = 3 \times 10^{-6}$ oe, $v = 408$ Mc/s, $\cos \theta = 1$ and $L = 1 \cdot 5 \times 10^{21}$ cm we see that the angle $\phi = 2\pi$ for $n_e \simeq 10^{-2}$ cm^{-3}). By virtue of the nature of this estimate† it can still be taken that in the arms $n_e \sim 10^{-2}$ cm^{-3} but the degree of ionisation in the arms can by no means be considered to be close to unity (the gas concentration in the arms[231] is $n \sim 1$ cm^{-3}). Since a high degree of ionisation is observed only in the HII regions and the hydrogen in most of the disk is not ionised (HI regions) the values $n \sim 1$ cm^{-3} and $n_e \sim 10^{-2}$ cm^{-3} are apparently compatible as average values for the whole arm.

In the light of what has been said the halo model in which on the average $n_e \sim 10^{-3}$ cm^{-3} (which would allow observations of slight polarisation of the halo's radio emission in the metric band[244] also does not seem improbable.

---

† In particular the possibility has not been excluded that on the average $\cos \theta \ll 1$ in the directions in question.

Discrete galactic sources—supernova shells

Even before radio astronomy observations became an effective means of studying the distribution of relativistic particles in space the suggestion was made that supernova flares are a powerful mechanism for the generation of cosmic rays.[245] This suggestion was based in essence only on energy considerations since it was known that at present supernovae are the most significant energy-producing process in the Galaxy and can provide the observed cosmic ray intensity as far as energy goes. At that time there were no other arguments in favour of this point of view.

Of course, the enormous amount of energy given off in the form of light, although it drew attention to supernovae as a possible source of cosmic rays, did not itself guarantee the simultaneous appearance of a considerable number of relativistic particles. A decisive step in this direction was made as the result of identifying a number of discrete sources of cosmic radio emission with gaseous nebulae which had appeared at the position of supernova flares and of elucidating the magnetic bremsstrahlung nature of the non-thermal cosmic radio emission. After this no doubt remained as to whether the shells of supernovae were powerful sources of relativistic particles.

At present practically all the known galactic supernovae have been identified with discrete sources of non-thermal radio emission. There is reason for supposing, on the other hand, that almost all the discrete galactic sources of non-thermal radiation† have appeared as the result of supernova flares.[161] The fact that, in fact, there are known to be many more (several thousand) discrete radio sources than there are identified remains of supernovae can be explained in many ways. Firstly by far the majority of discrete radio sources are linked with extragalactic objects (we shall speak about these later). Secondly it is possible to record supernova explosions in the Galaxy only in the narrow confines of the solar system where interstellar absorption of light does not make its effect felt; what is more this recording can be carried on more or less systematically for only a very limited space

† There are published indications[372, 436] of the existence of galactic radio sources of a special type which may be stars (radio stars). According to present information, however, these sources are distant radio galaxies connected with "super-stars" (see below).

We note that in 1963 the first report[470] appeared of the observation of a flare of radio emission from the non-stationary star V371 Orionis (a radio flare lasts about 15 min, just like an optical flare).

of time. For example it has been necessary to use chronicles and manuscripts from the Middle Ages even to identify a number of fairly bright and comparatively young discrete radio sources with galactic supernovae[161] e.g., the Crab Nebula with the shell of the 1054 supernova.

Supernovae can be divided into two types according to their optical characteristics, the general release of energy and distribution in space. Supernovae of the first type belong to the spherical sub-system of the Galaxy's star population concentrated towards the galactic centre. An exploding star has a comparatively small mass and the explosion occurs in the final stage of the star's slow evolution; basically they are old stars. The masses of the gas shells thrown off are approximately $\gtrsim 0.1 M_\odot$, whilst the velocity at which they are moving away is 1000 to 3000 km/sec which corresponds to the liberation of an energy of 10^{48} to 10^{49} erg in the explosion.

Supernovae of the second type are concentrated towards the galactic plane and thus belong to the plane sub-system of the Galaxy's star population. They are massive young stars whose evolution is proceeding rapidly. The masses of the shells thrown off are $\lesssim 10 M_\odot$ and they are moving away at a velocity of 5 to 10 thousand km/sec. The energy liberated in an explosion reaches a value of about 10^{52} erg.[269]

Table 7 on p. 112 lists some of the discrete galactic radio sources which have been identified with gas nebulae (supernova shells). The first ten of them are remains of the second type of supernova. The most powerful of these sources is Cassiopeia A; according to available data this explosion took place only about 250 years ago.[248] The velocity at which the shell of this supernova is spreading out exceeds 7000 km/sec.

The filament nebula in Cygnus is the shell of a supernova that exploded about 10^5 years ago. Certain other extensive shells are also fairly old: IC 443, Puppis A, Velum X, the filament nebula in Auriga, and so on.[249, 250]

The last three radio sources of those given in Table 7, which have been identified with the shells of the A.D. 1054 (Taurus A—Crab Nebula, see Fig. 13), the A.D. 1572 (Tycho Brahe supernova) and the A.D. 1604 (Kepler supernova) supernovae, are generally included among the type 1 supernovae.

In our Galaxy type 2 supernovae explode on the average once in 50 to 100 years, whilst type 1 supernovae may be slightly rarer—once

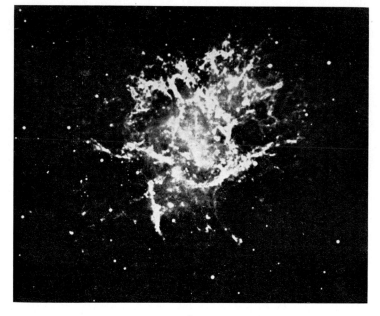

a

b

Fig. 13. Crab Nebula (radio source Taurus A): *a*—photograph
in one of the strong spectral lines; *b*—photograph in the full
(continuous) spectrum.

in 100 to 200 years. These figures, it is true, are only approximate; a lower explosion frequency is not excluded. Since the frequency of supernova explosions determines the energy of cosmic rays it is highly desirable to determine these figures more precisely. It follows from the frequency of explosions and the lifetimes of shells that many supernova remnants (of the order of thousands) can be found in principle.[162] The majority of these extensive radio sources almost merge with the background, however, and in the optical part of the spectrum they are very weak objects. Therefore, at least at present, the estimate given for the frequency of explosions does not contradict the number of supernova shells found.[248, 214]

The question of the nature and magnitude of the magnetic field in supernova shell nebulae is of great interest. There are no direct data in this respect yet and the estimates of the field strength are made indirectly with certain simple assumptions (see section 6). Only in the case of the Crab Nebula, for which polarisation of the magnetic bremsstrahlung has been found in both the optical and centimetric bands,[163, 177–180] can certain conclusions be drawn on the magnetic structure and an independent estimate be made of the magnetic field strength.[170] This estimate is based on the well-known acceleration value of $1 \cdot 1 \times 10^{-3}$ cm/sec^2 with which the nebula is expanding along the major axis and on the measured degree of polarisation of the nebula's total emission which is $\Pi = 7$ per cent at a wavelength of $\lambda = 3$ cm. We shall give this estimate here.

If the accelerated expansion of the nebula along one of the axes is caused by an anisotropic magnetic pressure, then using formula (4.40) the excess magnetic pressure $\Delta p = \overline{\Delta H^2}/8\pi$ can be expressed by the degree of polarisation and the mean square of the magnetic field strength in the source. With $\Pi = 0 \cdot 07$ and $\alpha = 0 \cdot 35$ ($\gamma = 1 \cdot 7$) this gives $\overline{\Delta H^2} = 0 \cdot 073 H^2$ and hence $\overline{H^2} = 3 \cdot 4 \times 10^2 \Delta p$. Estimating the value of $\Delta p \simeq nmLa$ from the observed acceleration $a = 0 \cdot 0011$ cm/sec^2, the size (semi-major axis $L \simeq 2 \cdot 8 \times 10^{18}$ cm) and the density of the nebula (atomic mass $m \simeq 1 \cdot 7 \times 10^{-24}$ g, concentration $n \sim 0 \cdot 1$ to 1 cm^{-3}) we obtain $H = \sqrt{\overline{H^2}} = 0 \cdot 4$ to $1 \cdot 3 \times 10^{-3}$ oersted. Other estimates also lead to values which are close to this.[177]

The spectral distribution of the intensity is an important characteristic of the non-thermal emission of supernovae. The emission spectrum has been measured reliably enough for a number of sources and over a wide range of frequencies is characterised by a constant spectral index α. For example for the source Cassiopeia A in the frequency range $3 \times 10^7 \leqslant \nu \leqslant 10^9$ c/s the spectral index is $\alpha = 0.8$ (with a high degree of accuracy). The emission intensity of Cassiopeia at different frequencies is often used as a reference standard for determining the intensity of other sources. The spectrum of the Crab Nebula has also been fairly well studied although here there is a certain indefiniteness in the extrapolation of the spectrum from radio to optical frequencies. For example in the radio frequency range the frequency dependence of the intensity is clearly best described by the spectral index $\alpha = 0.25$ although the data do not contradict a value of $\alpha = 0.35$ which leads to the intensity observed in the optical band.[251]

The data on the spectra of certain other sources such as Puppis A, W 44, IC 443 and the supernovae of A.D. 1604 and A.D. 1572 are also more or less reliable. At the same time there are large discrepancies in the published values of the spectral index for a number of sources. Table 7 uses the values given by Korchak.[252] In particular a value of $\alpha = 0.5$ is accepted for the filament nebula in Cygnus, whilst Harris[253] took the spectral index of this source as $\alpha = 0.1 \pm 0.1$. We should point out that Harris[253] considered the spectra of a number of sources to be considerably flatter than is generally accepted, even negative values of α are met with, i.e., spectra for which the intensity rises with the frequency. In that paper a study of the available data is used to draw the conclusion that the spectral index decreases as the age of the supernova shells increases.[276]

However the accuracy of measuring the spectral indices and determining the age of shells is not yet high enough for us to be able to consider this conclusion as convincing.

The average for galactic sources is $\alpha = 0.6$, there being a considerable scatter in the values from $\alpha = 0.2$ to $\alpha = 1.2$ although in the majority of cases $0.4 \leqslant \alpha \leqslant 0.8$.[163]

Extragalactic sources. Radio galaxies

Many other "normal" galaxies, chiefly irregular and spiral ones, are sources of non-thermal radio emission like our Galaxy.

Table 8 on p. 113 lists a number of extragalactic sources of the type in question ("normal" galaxies). With respect to their power of radio emission the "normal" galaxies are close to our Galaxy or weaker. A typical and one of the most studied objects of this type is the M31 galaxy (the large nebula in the constellation of Andromeda) which is similar in structure to our Galaxy. Radio measurements with high angular resolution[202] have found that a halo exists in the M31 galaxy which has been an independent argument in favour of the existence of a halo in our Galaxy as well. The spectral index of the radio emission of M31 is $\alpha = 0.5 \pm 0.1$ in the metric band[254] and rises to $\alpha = 1.1$ in the $\nu = 1400$ Mc/s range.[255]

For extragalactic sources the spectral index averages $\bar{\alpha} = 0.9$,[163] the value varying between $\alpha = 0.4$ and $\alpha = 1.9$. Apart from the sources which have been successfully identified with optical objects there is a number of unidentified radio sources (basically extragalactic objects) for which the spectral index averages $\bar{\alpha} = 1.2$, values up to $\alpha \simeq 2$ being met.

Apart from the "normal" galaxies the extragalactic radio sources also include the rarer "anomalous" objects which, apart from having a high power of radio emission, are characterised by certain structural features. These are the so-called "radio galaxies". If the explosions of supernovae are the most awesome explosive phenomena observed in galaxies (an energy of up to 10^{52} erg is released), then the "explosions" of galaxies (birth of radio galaxies) in which the energy

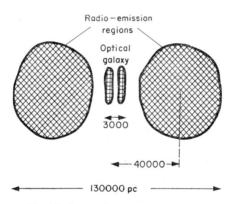

Fig. 14. Source Cygnus A (schematic).

released reaches 10^{61} erg have no equal in scale in the whole of the known Universe unless we consider the observed expansion of the Metagalaxy.

The radio galaxy Cygnus A is one of the most characteristic examples of discrete radio sources and, what is more, was the first to be found (1946). This source is located at a distance of 220 Mpc and consists of two parts (clouds) between which there is a galaxy which is visible in the optical spectrum and also consists of two parts close to each other or separated by a dark band of dust in the middle (see Fig. 14; not to scale). The spectrum of this radio galaxy has a characteristic break at a frequency of $v = 1500$ Mc/s near which the spectral index changes from a value of $\alpha = 0.75$ for the lower frequencies to a value of $\alpha = 1.25$ at the higher frequencies.[256-258] With the exception of the comparatively close supernova Cassiopeia A this extremely remote radio source has no equal in brightness in the whole radio sky.

Table 9 on p. 114 gives some data on the radio galaxies. The radio galaxy Centaurus A is also a twin source reminding one of the Cygnus A radio galaxy;[259] its size, however, is almost an order larger and there is a difference in the structure of its central (optical) part when compared with the Cygnus A radio galaxy.

The radio galaxy Virgo A (this galaxy is elliptical) is the only known representative of another type of radio galaxy; this object has a bright jet on one side whose optical emission is polarised and must have a magnetic bremsstrahlung nature (Fig. 15).

In 1963 the presence was established of a new type of object in the Universe which we, like a number of other authors, shall call "super-stars". This discovery[471-474] is connected with the finding of a considerable red shift and variations of the brightness of star-like sources linked with radio sources 3C273-B, 3C48 etc. (as has already been pointed out in the footnote to page 91 these sources were first considered to be radio stars).[372, 436] Super-stars are, according to some suggestions, gigantic non-stationary stars with masses of the order of $10^5 - 10^8 M_\odot$. For example the size of super-star 3C273-B (i.e.,the optical object located in radio source 3C273-B) apparently does not exceed 10^{16} to 10^{18} cm, whilst the total power (brightness) of its optical emission is two orders greater than the brightness of the Galaxy (because of this the brightness of super-star 3C273-B is the greatest known for any object in the Universe). The question of the optical, radio and gamma emission of object 3C273 is discussed by Ginzburg et al.[475] Some remarks will be made on the nature of super-stars in section 11 (see also some recent papers[471-476, 481]).

The method of estimating the energy of the relativistic particles and the magnetic field strength in sources of cosmic radio emission will be discussed in section 6. To conclude this section we should like to remark that the suggestion[260] that there is noticeable radio emission coming from intergalactic space has not been con-

Fig. 15. Galaxy NGC 4486 (radio source Virgo A).

firmed.[163, 261, 262] This result agrees with the fact that an impermissibly large value was used by Shklovskii,[260] in all probability, for the energy of the cosmic rays in intergalactic space (for more details on the radio emission of intergalactic space see section 13).

6. COSMIC RAYS IN THE UNIVERSE

We shall make use of radio astronomy observations chiefly for determining the concentration, spectrum and energy of relativistic particles in the Galaxy and also in galactic and extragalactic discrete sources. The radio astronomy data relating to the intensity of the non-thermal cosmic radio emission allow us to estimate directly only the spatial distribution, spectrum and energy of the relativistic electrons. There is therefore a certain undefined element, whose nature will become clear, in all the conclusions relating to cosmic rays consisting basically of atomic nuclei. Nevertheless the present state of the question of cosmic rays in the Universe is not in the least comparable with the situation existing before the establishment of a connexion between the radio emission and relativistic electrons in the Universe, when the completely different assumptions about the sources of cosmic rays were more or less equally possible.

Electron component of cosmic rays in the Galaxy

It follows from (4.33) that the spectral intensity of the electron emission at a frequency v in a magnetic field H, which in future we shall consider to be isotropic (averaged along the line of sight), can be defined by the expression

$$I_v = 1 \cdot 35 \times 10^{-22} a(\gamma) L K_e H^{(\gamma+1)/2} \left(\frac{6 \cdot 26 \times 10^{18}}{v} \right)^{(\gamma-1)/2}$$

$$\text{erg/cm}^2 \cdot \text{sterad} \cdot \text{sec} \cdot (\text{c/s}), \quad (6.1)$$

where L is the extent of the emitting region along the line of sight and K_e is the coefficient in the power electron spectrum (4.29) with respect to a unit volume.

Radio astronomy methods allow a direct measurement to be made of the frequency dependence of the emission intensity thus enabling a determination of the exponent $\gamma = 2\alpha + 1$ and the coefficient K_e in the electron spectrum.

Using formula (6.1) we can express† for the coefficient K_e in terms of the intensity I_ν or the effective emission temperature $T_{\text{eff}} = (c^2/2k\nu^2)I_\nu$ for a frequency ν:

$$K_e = \frac{7\cdot4 \times 10^{21} \times I_\nu}{a(\gamma)LH}\left(\frac{\nu}{6\cdot26 \times 10^{18}H}\right)^{(\gamma-1)/2}$$

$$= \frac{8\cdot9 \times 10^{22}HT_{\text{eff}}}{a(\gamma)L}\left(\frac{\nu}{6\cdot26 \times 10^{18}H}\right)^{(\gamma+3)/2}. \qquad (6.2)$$

As we have already seen in section 5, in the $\nu \gtrsim 300$ Mc/s frequency range the spectral index of the non-thermal galactic radio emission is $\alpha = 0\cdot8$ so the emitting electrons have an energy spectrum with an exponent $\gamma = 2\cdot6$. If, as Baldwin's data[210] indicate (see section 5), the spectral index α changes its value in the frequency range $\nu \lesssim 300$ Mc/s the value of $\gamma = 2\cdot6$ given for the electron spectrum component relates only to the energy range (see (4.36))

$$E \gtrsim 2\cdot5 \times 10^2\left(\frac{\nu_1}{y_1(\gamma)H}\right)^{\frac{1}{2}} \text{eV}, \qquad (6.3)$$

i.e., $E \gtrsim 10^9$ eV $= 1$ GeV for $H \simeq 10^{-5}$ oersted.

In order to determine the coefficient K_e in the electron spectrum we shall use the data of Shklovskii[156] and Westerhout[263] according to which in the direction of the galactic pole, where the contribution made by the thermal emission of clouds of ionised gas can be ignored, the effective emission temperature at a wavelength $\lambda = 75$ cm ($\nu = 400$ Mc/s) is $T_{\text{eff}} = 25$ °K. Putting $L \simeq 10$ kpc $= 3 \times 10^{22}$ cm and $H \simeq 10^{-5}$ oersted in expression (6·2) we obtain $K_e = 2\cdot6 \times 10^{-17}$. The electron spectrum in the Galaxy averaged over the line of sight thus takes the form

$$N_e(E)\,dE = \begin{cases} 2\cdot6 \times 10^{-17}E^{-2\cdot6}\,dE & (E \text{ in ergs}), \\ 7\cdot8 \times 10^{-13}E^{-2\cdot6}\,dE & (E \text{ in GeV}). \end{cases} \qquad (6.4)$$

It is easy to determine from this the concentration of electrons with an energy greater than a certain given energy:

$$N_e(\geqslant E) = \int_E^\infty K_e E^{-\gamma}\,dE = \frac{K_e}{\gamma - 1}E^{-(\gamma-1)}. \qquad (6.5)$$

† We should point out once more that unless anything is said to the contrary the absolute Gaussian system of units is used (for example in (6.2) the frequency ν is measured in cycles per second, the field H in oersteds, the path L in centimetres and T_{eff} in degrees absolute).

It follows, in particular, from (6·4) and (6·5) that $N_e(E \geqslant 2\cdot5 \text{ GeV}) \simeq 1\cdot1 \times 10^{-13} \text{ cm}^{-3}$ and $N_e(E \geqslant 1 \text{ GeV}) \simeq 5 \times 10^{-13} \text{ cm}^{-3}$.

The value $H = 10^{-5}$ oersted taken above is evidently slightly too high if we bear in mind the average value of the field strength in the halo. If we bear in mind that according to (6.2) and (6.5) $N_e(\geqslant E) \infty H^{-(\gamma+1)/2}$ then for the value $\bar{H}_{\text{halo}} = 3 \times 10^{-6}$ oersted the electron concentration in the halo should be $(10^{-5}/3 \times 10^{-6})^{1\cdot8} = 8\cdot7$ times greater, i.e.,

$$N_e(E \geqslant 2\cdot5 \text{ GeV}) \simeq 9\cdot7 \times 10^{-13} \text{ cm}^{-3},$$

$$N_e(E \geqslant 1 \text{ GeV}) \simeq 4\cdot4 \times 10^{-12} \text{ cm}^{-3}. \tag{6.6}$$

At the same time the relativistic electron concentration at the Earth[57] (see also section 2) is $N_e(E > 7 \times 10^8 \text{ eV}) \lesssim 1\cdot3 \times 10^{-12} \text{ cm}^{-3}$; the measurements were made at a period of high solar activity and it may be thought that a long way from the Sun the value of N_e is higher. Within the limits of achievable accuracy, therefore, the radio astronomy data and the measurements on Earth lead to one and the same conclusion: the concentration of electrons with an energy of $E > 1$ GeV in cosmic rays is of the order of magnitude of a hundredth of the concentration of all the cosmic rays (see sections 1 and 2 and in particular the values (1.5)).

In the $E < 1$ GeV energy range the spectrum of galactic relativistic electrons evidently becomes steeper or simply breaks (see below); therefore the energy density of the relativistic electrons can be considered equal to $w_e = N_e \cdot \bar{E} \sim 10^{-12} \text{ cm}^{-3} \cdot 3 \times 10^9 \text{ eV} = 3 \times 10^{-3}$ eV/cm³, which is a value of the order of one per cent of the energy density of all cosmic rays $w \simeq 0\cdot3$ to 1 eV/cm^3. Taking the volume of the halo to be $V \simeq 1$ to $5 \times 10^{68} \text{ cm}^3$, for the total energy of all the cosmic rays and electrons in the Galaxy we obtain the respective values $W \sim 10^{56}$ erg and $W_e \sim 10^{54}$ erg. These values may be several times too high if as we move away from the plane of the Galaxy the cosmic ray energy density w decreases and, for example, averages $w \sim 0\cdot1 \text{ eV/cm}^3$ for the halo. When using the diffusion picture (see section 10) the more probable assumption is that the energy density of the cosmic rays varies comparatively little over the whole region they occupy with a radius $R \lesssim 10$ to 15 kpc, i.e., $w \sim 0\cdot3$ to $1\cdot0$ eV/cm³.

The variation found in the spectral index of the emission at $v < 300$ Mc/s does not allow us to extend spectrum (6·4) to the $E < 10^9$ eV energy range. Moreover there is no foundation here for considering the electron energy spectrum a power-law one since the spectral index[210] $\alpha \simeq 0.35$ relates only to the small range of frequencies $v = 20$ to 100 Mc/s. In actual fact by virtue of (4.37) the spectrum can be considered to follow a power law with an exponent $\gamma = 1.7$ only if the spectral index α remains constant and equal to 0·35 at least when the frequencies change by two orders (see Table 6 with $\gamma = 1.7$). It is true that one could think that the electron spectrum (6·4) occurs over the whole energy range and the observed variation of the radio emission spectrum in the 20 to 100 Mc/s range is caused by the effect of the medium: by the difference of the refractive index from unity, by absorption in the interstellar plasma or reabsorption in the gas of the relativistic electrons themselves. Let us therefore give some estimates of the possible part played by these effects.

It follows from (4.45) that the difference of the refractive index from unity could be significant in the frequency range $v \simeq 10^8$ c/s in question only for an electron concentration

$$n_e \geqslant \frac{vH_\perp}{15} \simeq 7 \text{ cm}^{-3}, \tag{6.7}$$

where $H_\perp$ is taken as 10^{-6} oersted. Even in this case of the minimum permissible field value the medium's electron concentration is evidently too high if we bear in mind that it is a question of the mean concentration of electrons in the halo.

Absorption in the interstellar gas may significantly alter the curve of the emission intensity if the optical thickness τ of the emitting region is comparable with unity. In this case (see (4.49))

$$\tau = \int \mu \, dr = \frac{10^{-2}\left[17.7 + \ln\left(\dfrac{T^{3/2}}{v}\right)\right]}{T^{3/2}v^2} \int n_e^2 \, dr, \tag{6.8}$$

where in the transition to the last expression the temperature is considered to be constant along the line of sight (or a certain mean value of the corresponding factor is taken); the quantity $\int n_e^2 \, dr$ is called the measure of emission and is usually measured in $\text{cm}^{-6} \cdot \text{pc}$. For a frequency $v = 3 \times 10^7$ c/s ($\lambda = 10$ m) and $T \simeq 10^4 \,^\circ$K we obtain

$$\tau \simeq 5 \times 10^{-4} \int n_e^2 \, dr$$

if $\int n_e^2 \, dr$ is measured in $\text{cm}^{-6} \cdot \text{pc}$. For a typical HII region (ionised hydrogen region) the measure of emission is[164] 3400 cm^{-6}·pc and in the example under discussion $\tau \simeq 1.7$; this corresponds to a decrease in intensity by a factor of $e^\tau \simeq 5.5$. For the halo with $n_e = 10^{-2}$ cm^{-3} and $R = 15$ kpc the measure of emission is 1.5 cm^{-6}·pc and the absorption of emission with $\lambda = 10$ m can be ignored. It follows from these estimates that at wavelengths $\lambda \sim 10$ m the absorption can be ignored only for sufficiently high galactic latitudes (lat. $b \gtrsim 4$ to 5°) and on the condition that there are no HII regions along the line of sight.

Lastly, reabsorption in the relativistic gas of electrons would be significant only on the condition (see (4.60) with $H_\perp \sim 3 \times 10^{-6}$ oe and $\gamma = 2.6$) that the coefficient K_e in the electron spectrum satisfies the condition $K_e \gtrsim 2 \times 10^{-8}$. There is no possibility at all of this concentration of relativistic electrons in the halo (compare (6.4)).

The conclusion can thus be drawn that the observed change in the radio emission spectrum in the $\nu < 10^8$ c/s range cannot be explained only by the effect of the medium on the radio emission or by reabsorption and evidently reflects a genuine change in the energy spectrum of relativistic electrons in the Galaxy. The possible reasons for the change will be discussed in sections 7 and 17.

Radio emission of the galactic disk and halo

Let us now examine in greater detail the question of the connexion between the radio emission of the Galaxy's halo and disk. This question is one of the most important ones in the theory of the origin of cosmic rays since it is closely linked with the question of the nature of the motion of relativistic particles in the Galaxy and the regions in space where these particles accumulate. There are two essentially different points of view here.

One of them consists in that the halo and spiral arms, which make the basic contribution to the disk's radio emission, are looked upon as individual, spatially isolated regions of the Galaxy, free exchange of relativistic particles between them being prevented by virtue of the nature of the magnetic field of the arms. In this case the particles responsible for the radio emission of the halo and the disk differ not only in their spatial distribution but also to a considerable degree in their origin with all the consequences resultant on this.

According to the second point of view the cosmic rays, including relativistic electrons, penetrate more or less freely from the disk into the halo and vice versa so in the final event the same particles are responsible for the emission of both the disk and the halo depending on which of these regions of space they are in at a given moment. A number of arguments will be given below in favour of the second point of view which is taken in this book.

The cosmic rays on the Earth are isotropic to a high degree (see section 3); this isotropy, at least as regards the high-energy particles, cannot be considered to be local or to relate only to the region near the Sun. From this alone it can be concluded that the cosmic rays enter the arms fairly freely from both ends and highly probably through the walls as well. This assumption is particularly natural if one bears in mind that there are many arms, they are relatively short and are, as it were, "submerged" in an enormous reservoir of cosmic rays—the halo. In addition, a closer analysis of the motion of cosmic rays in the interstellar magnetic fields (see section 10) allows us to consider that this motion, provided we are speaking of lengthy periods of time, proceeds considerably more freely than follows from the simple consequences of the theory of the motion of a charge in a given magnetic field.

We must also bear in mind the greater thickness of the radio disk when compared with the optical disk. There are two possible causes for this. Firstly it may be assumed that the concentration of radio-emitting electrons in the optical arms is higher than in the halo and the electrons from the arms diffuse into the halo. In other words the expansion of the radio disk can be ascribed to a smooth variation in the electron concentration.[249] But in this case the electrons should be able to leave through the walls of the arms and pass into the halo. The ordering and even the quasi-homogeneity of the field in the arms are compatible, at least in principle, with this picture. In actual fact the ordering of the field is fully capable of being accompanied by considerable scatter (departure) of the magnetic flux from the arm (see diagram in Fig. 16; the corresponding situation can be even more easily imagined in an actual three-dimensional case). The indications given in section 5 of considerable irregularity in the field of the arms and the features of diffusion of cosmic rays in the galactic magnetic fields (see section 10) make this possibility even more probable.

In the second place the cause of the thickening of the radio disk may be the gradual attenuation of the magnetic field in the transition from the spiral to the halo. Frequently, for example, for each of these regions the respective values $H = 7$ to 10×10^{-6} oersted and

Fig. 16. Configuration of the field in an arm (schematic representation of one of the possibilities).

$H = 3$ to 5×10^{-6} oersted are taken. Then, even when the relativistic electron concentration is constant, the intensity will decrease in proportion to $H^{(\gamma+1)/2}$.† When H is halved and $\gamma = 2.6$ the intensity of emission is reduced by a factor of 3·5. In actual fact the intensity drops by a factor of 6–10 (see section 5) in the transition from the disk to the halo. But, on the other hand, there are regions in the disk with a stronger field.[214] There is therefore no basis for assuming that the relativistic electron concentration in the disk differs significantly

---

† Here the electron distribution is considered to be isotropic both in the disk and in the halo. If we assume that when electrons move from the disk into the halo the adiabatic invariant $\sin^2\theta/H = $ const. is maintained a twofold variation in the field strength leads to a reduction in the emission intensity proportional to

$$H_\perp^{(\gamma+1)/2} = H^{(\gamma+1)/2} (\sin \theta)^{(\gamma+1)/2} \infty H^{3(\gamma+1)/4},$$

i.e., by a factor of about 6·5. By virtue of the limitations imposed by Liouville's theorem (see section 12) the questions of maintaining the adiabatic invariant and of the variation in the electron concentration are interlinked. However we shall not discuss this problem here since we wish only to stress the existence of a connexion between the disk and the halo.

from that in the halo. The important thing is, in the framework of the question under discussion, that the greater thickness of the radio disk when compared with the optical disk can hardly be explained if there is no close connexion between the cosmic rays in the optical spiral and in the halo, since if the optical spiral were isolated it would be natural to expect a sharp difference in the relativistic electron concentration in the halo and in the disk and the thicknesses of the optical and radio disks to be the same. It can therefore be concluded from radio observations either that the walls of the optical spiral are "transparent" to cosmic rays or that, in any case, there is great freedom of exchange of cosmic rays between the halo and the spiral. This means that the arms differ from the other regions in the halo only in a quantitative respect and if, for example, the halo regions with a quasi-homogeneous field are characterised by a certain size $l \sim 10$ pc (see section 10), then the arms are elongated regions with a thickness of $d \approx 250$ pc and a length of $L \simeq 1$ to 10 kpc. In this model, with isotropy of the cosmic rays in the halo, an isotropic directional distribution of the cosmic rays in the spiral should also be expected.

We should point out that Hoyle and Ireland[265] also suggest a model according to which the magnetic field in the disk and particularly in the halo is highly chaotic and for example in the halo consists of, as it were, individual loops (rings) of lines of force. Finally, there is the fact that there are weighty considerations of a dynamic nature[266] which speak in favour of considerable lack of ordering of the magnetic field in the Galaxy.

It has already been remarked that the spectra of the Galaxy's non-thermal radio emission within the limits of accuracy achieved are identical in the halo, in the radio disk and in the central radio region. This circumstance is also the most natural one if there is rapid exchange of cosmic rays between the different spatial regions of the Galaxy.

The volume of the radio disk is about 5 per cent of the volume of the halo and the volume of the central radio region about 3×10^{-4} per cent. It can be taken that under conditions of free particle exchange in the first approximation the share of the total energy of cosmic rays and relativistic electrons in the Galaxy appropriate to these regions is about the same or slightly higher (the total energy of the cosmic rays in the Galaxy is $W \simeq 3 \times 10^{56}$ erg; see Table 8). Here, perhaps, we need definite, although quite natural, clarifications. For example a particularly large number of type 1 supernovae explode in the central region of the Galaxy, so it may be assumed that these supernovae supply cosmic rays largely to the central region. This may be the reason for a certain higher cosmic ray concentration in the central region when compared with the mean value for the whole Galaxy. Type 2 supernovae may play a similar part in the spiral arms of the Galaxy.

Cosmic rays and magnetic fields in discrete sources

The angular sizes of galactic and extragalactic nebulae which are discrete sources of non-thermal radio emission are generally small and the measured value is generally not the intensity but the spectral density of the emission flux F_ν. This quantity is defined as the emission energy flux per unit frequency range incident along the normal per unit area:

$$F_\nu = \int I_\nu \, d\Omega, \tag{6.9}$$

where integration is carried out over the whole solid angle occupied by the source. If the source's linear dimension L is small compared with the distance to it, R, and the absolute magnitude of the magnetic field strength and the relativistic electron concentration can be considered approximately to be constant over the volume of the source, then from (6.9) and (6.1) we have

$$F_\nu = 1\cdot35 \times 10^{-22} a(\gamma) \frac{K_V H^{(\gamma+1)/2}}{R^2} \left(\frac{6\cdot26 \times 10^{18}}{\nu}\right)^{(\gamma-1)/2}, \tag{6.10}$$

where $K_V = K_e V$ is the coefficient in the electron energy spectrum with respect to the total volume of the source $V = \pi L^3/6$. Here it is assumed, as it was before, that the electron energy spectrum is of the form

$$N(E) \, dE = K_V E^{-\gamma} \, dE \tag{6.11}$$

in the energy range

$$2\cdot5 \times 10^2 \left(\frac{\nu_1}{H y_1(\gamma)}\right)^{\frac{1}{2}} \leqslant E_{(eV)} \leqslant 2\cdot5 \times 10^2 \left(\frac{\nu_2}{H y_2(\gamma)}\right)^{\frac{1}{2}} \tag{6.12}$$

(compare 4.37)), where ν_1 and ν_2 are the frequency extremes of the observed radio band in which the spectral index $\alpha = (\gamma - 1)/2$ has a constant value.

Relation (6.12), which connects the frequency and energy ranges, and the formulae given below which are based on this relation are valid only for $\alpha > 0$, i.e., $\gamma = 2\alpha + 1 > 1$ (see footnote on page 70). For a rough estimate of the energy range for $\alpha > -\frac{1}{3}$ in (6.12) and also in formulae (6.14 to 17) we can put $y_1(\gamma) = y_2(\gamma) = 0\cdot29$; this corresponds to the assumption that all the emission of an electron with an energy E is at the frequency ν_m corresponding to the maximum in the emission spectrum of an individual electron (see (4.25)).

Expressing K_V by the spectral density of the emission flux F_ν observed at a certain frequency ν we obtain

$$K_V = \frac{7\cdot4 \times 10^{21}R^2}{a(\gamma)H}\, F_\nu \left(\frac{\nu}{6\cdot26 \times 10^{18}H}\right)^{(\gamma-1)/2}. \qquad (6.13)$$

This can be used to determine the total number of relativistic electrons in this energy range:

$$N_e = \int_{E_1}^{E_2} K_V E^{-\gamma}\, dE$$

$$= \frac{7\cdot4 \times 10^{21}}{(\gamma-1)a(\gamma)}\, \frac{R^2F_\nu}{H}\left[\frac{y_1(\gamma)\nu}{\nu_1}\right]^{(\gamma-1)/2}\left\{1 - \left(\frac{y_2(\gamma)\nu_1}{y_1(\gamma)\nu_2}\right)^{(\gamma-1)/2}\right\}. \qquad (6.14)$$

This formula is, of course, approximate since inequalities (6.12) have been used in the transition from E_1, E_2 to ν_1, ν_2; these inequalities, when the electron spectrum follows a power law, define each of the limits only with an accuracy of up to 10 per cent. Since generally $\Lambda_1 \ll \nu_2$ and $y_2(\gamma) < y_1(\gamma)$ at $\gamma > 1$ the number of electrons is defined in practice only by the lower limit of the frequency range and is

$$N_e(>E) = \frac{7\cdot4 \times 10^{21}}{(\gamma-1)a(\gamma)}\, \frac{R^2F_\nu}{H}\left[\frac{y_1(\gamma)\nu}{\nu_1}\right]^{(\gamma-1)/2}. \qquad (6.15)$$

The values of the factors $a(\gamma)$ and $y_1(\gamma)$ are given in Table 6 on p. 68.

In a similar way we can express the total energy of the electrons in the source responsible for the emission in the observed frequency range $\nu_1 \leqslant \nu \leqslant \nu_2$:

$$W_e = \int_{E_1}^{E_2} K_V E^{-\gamma+1}\, dE = A(\gamma, \nu)\,\frac{R^2F_\nu}{H^{3/2}}, \qquad (6.16)$$

where

$$A(\gamma, v) = \begin{cases} \dfrac{2\cdot96 \times 10^{12}}{(\gamma - 2)a(\gamma)} v^{\frac{1}{2}} \left[\dfrac{y_1(\gamma)v}{v_1}\right]^{(\gamma-2)/2} \left\{1 - \left[\dfrac{y_2(\gamma)v_1}{y_1(\gamma)v_2}\right]^{(\gamma-2)/2}\right\} \\ \qquad\qquad\qquad\qquad\qquad\qquad\qquad\qquad (\text{if } \gamma > 2), \\[4pt] 1\cdot44 \times 10^{13} v^{\frac{1}{2}} \ln\left[\dfrac{y_1(\gamma)v_2}{y_2(\gamma)v_1}\right] \quad (\text{if } \gamma = 2), \\[4pt] \dfrac{2\cdot96 \times 10^{12}}{(2 - \gamma)a(\gamma)} v^{\frac{1}{2}} \left[\dfrac{y_2(\gamma)v}{v_2}\right]^{(\gamma-2)/2} \left\{1 - \left[\dfrac{y_2(\gamma)v_1}{y_1(\gamma)v_2}\right]^{(2-\gamma)/2}\right\} \\ \qquad\qquad\qquad\qquad\qquad\qquad\qquad\qquad (\text{if } \gamma < 2). \end{cases} \qquad (6.17)$$

For a known distance to the source R and an emission flux F_v at a certain frequency v expression (6.16) allows us to determine the total energy of the relativistic electrons in the source if the magnetic field strength H is known. Unfortunately there are as yet no reliable independent methods of estimating the magnetic field strength in the sources so certain additional assumptions must be made in the calculation of W_e.

The basic assumption generally made is that the magnetic field energy in the source and the energy of the relativistic particles (cosmic rays) have one and the same order of magnitude or, in the first approximation, are simply equal to each other. In actual fact this corresponds to the minimum total energy of the system of the field and the particles for a given magnetic bremsstrahlung emission power.† In addition, a magnetic field with an energy density considerably less than the relativistic particle energy density would not be able to keep the relativistic particles in the limited volume of the source and as a result of their leakage the system itself would come to a state close to a state of quasi-equilibrium of energy between the magnetic field and the relativistic particles. It is therefore fairly sensible to consider that in sources as to the order of magnitude

$$W_H = W_{cr}, \qquad (6.18)$$

where $W_H = (H^2/8\pi)V$ is the total energy of the magnetic field and W_{cr} is the total energy of the relativistic particles (cosmic rays and electrons) in the radio emitting nebula.

† The total energy of the particles and the magnetic field in the source as a function of the field strength for a given emission power by virtue of (6.16) is $W = W_H + W_{cr} = C_1 H^2 + C_2 H^{-3/2}$, where C_1 and C_2 do not depend on H. Determining the minimum of this expression with respect to H we find that the total energy minimum is reached at $W_H = \frac{3}{4} W_{cr}$.

Radio observational data allow us to estimate only the number and energy of the electrons in the source so that, in order to determine the total energy of all the relativistic particles, it is further necessary to establish the connexion between this quantity and the energy of the relativistic electrons W_e. There are no reliable methods at present for estimating the share of relativistic electrons in the total relativistic particle energy so the second significant assumption is usually made that the energy of all the cosmic rays in the source is simply proportional to the energy of the relativistic electrons:

$$W_{cr} = \kappa W_e, \qquad (6.19)$$

where the coefficient of proportionality κ usually is as to an order of magnitude put equal to $\kappa = 100$. The selection of this value is to a certain degree arbitrary but there is a basis for it in the ratio between cosmic rays and electrons as a whole in the Galaxy and in certain considerations connected with the process of particle acceleration to relativistic energies.[4, 5] In addition, Pikel'ner[427] obtains the value $\kappa \sim 100$ from the condition that the magnetic field and cosmic ray pressure in the shell of Cassiopeia A and the gas pressure in the gas filaments observed in this nebula are equal. However, as will be stressed below, it is more likely that $\kappa \lesssim 1$ for the Crab Nebula; according to Shklovskii[477] the value of κ is also low in the radio galaxy Virgo A.

With these assumptions the observed radio emission flux can be used to make a direct determination of the magnetic field strength and the total energy of the cosmic rays and electrons in a source if the source's spectrum, angular size and distance away are known. Indeed, it follows from (6.16), (6.18) and (6.19) that

$$W_H \equiv \frac{H^2}{8\pi} V = \kappa A(\gamma, v) \frac{R^2 F_v}{H^{3/2}},$$

hence

$$H = \left[48\kappa A(\gamma, v) \frac{F_v}{R\phi^3} \right]^{2/7}, \qquad (6.20)$$

where $A(\gamma, v)$ is defined by expressions (6.17) and $V = \pi L^3/6$ is the volume and $\phi = L/R$ is the angular size of the source. In this case the total energy of the cosmic rays in the source is

$$W_{cr} = \kappa W_e = W_H = 0 \cdot 19 [\kappa A(\gamma, v) F_v R^2]^{4/7} (R\phi)^{9/7}. \qquad (6.21)$$

Because of the rapid expansion of some radio emitting nebulae (the shells of supernovae in particular) their magnetic bremsstrahlung flux may change fairly rapidly with time.[267] When there is no "pumping" of relativistic electrons the dependence of the emission flux upon the radius of the expanding nebula can be estimated as follows. The expansion of a nebula is accompanied by a decrease in the relativistic particle energy and a decrease in the magnetic field strength. In this case the relativistic particle energy varies adiabatically in accordance with the law $E \infty V^{-\frac{1}{3}} \infty L^{-1}$, where V is the volume of the nebula and L is its linear size (see section 9). The corresponding dependence of the coefficient K_V in the energy spectrum (6.11) on the size of the nebula takes the form $K_V \infty L^{-\gamma+1}$. To confirm this it is sufficient to substitute in expression (6.11) $E = E_0 L_0/L$, where E_0 and L_0 are certain initial values of E and L. Further, from the maintenance of the total magnetic flux in the nebula we have $H \infty L^{-2}$ (the total magnetic flux is maintained with a high degree of accuracy since the conductivity of the medium is very great.[231] Therefore, in accordance with (6.10), the dependence of the magnetic bremsstrahlung flux on the linear size of the expanding nebula is of the form

$$F_\nu \sim L^{-2\gamma}. \tag{6.22}$$

For example for radio source Cassiopeia A (a type 2 supernova) whose rate of expansion is $v \simeq 7000$ km/sec and whose diameter is $L \simeq 1 \cdot 2 \times 10^{19}$ cm the flux's rate of decrease should be

$$\frac{1}{F_\nu} \frac{\partial F_\nu}{\partial t} = -2\gamma \frac{1}{L} \frac{\partial L}{\partial t} = -2\gamma \frac{2v}{L} \simeq 6 \times 10^{-10} \text{ sec}^{-1}, \tag{6.23}$$

i.e., approximately 1·8 per cent per annum.[267] This effect was recently established[268] from the data of a series of observations made from 1949 to 1960, the radio emission flux of Cassiopeia A at a frequency $\nu = 81 \cdot 5$ Mc/s decreasing by $1 \cdot 06 \pm 0 \cdot 14$ per cent per annum. There is no cause for surprise in the discrepancy between this value and the estimate given above. It suffices to say that in (6.23) we put $\partial L/\partial t = 2v$, as should be the case with isotropic expansion of the shell. In the case of Cassiopeia A, however, the expansion is not isotropic. In addition, other factors may also be significant: "pumping" of electrons, disturbance of the relationship $H \infty L^{-2}$ due to the presence of chaotic velocities, etc.).

Values of W_{cr} and H for individual sources

Tables 7 to 9 give the values of the magnetic field strength and the relativistic particle energy for a number of sources calculated by means of relations (6.20) and (6.21).† These calculations are based on the known data on the angular size, spectral density of the emission flux, spectral index and distance for each of the sources listed. The first two of these quantities can be determined fairly reliably from radio observations and the errors in the measurement of these quantities can be ignored, particularly if we bear in mind that by virtue of a series of simplifying assumptions (isotropy, constant spectral index, spectrum outside the observed range, and so on) expressions (6.20) and (6.21) themselves are approximate.

The possible error in the determination of the spectral index is not very significant either since expressions (6.20) and (6.21) depend fairly weakly on its value (see (6.17)). In the case when the spectral index of the source is unknown (this is true of sources HB 3 and S 147 in Table 7) an arbitrary value of $\alpha = 0.5$ is taken in the calculations and the corresponding results must be looked upon as only approximate.

More significant is a certain arbitrariness in the determination of the limits v_1 and v_2, for which the values $v_1 = 10^7$ c/s and $v_2 = 10^{10}$ c/s are taken in the calculations; this corresponds to the range in which most radio astronomy observations are being made at present. In the case of the Crab Nebula whose emission spectrum evidently continues with a constant spectral index[251] $\alpha = 0.35$ up to frequencies of $v \simeq 10^{15}$ c/s Table 7 also gives the results for $v_2 = 10^{15}$ c/s (see row No. 11 for $\alpha = 0.35$). In this case the magnetic field strength and the particle energy are 1.5 to 2 times greater than at $v_2 = 10^{10}$ c/s and the same α. In all the calculations it is assumed that the relativistic electron energy is 1 per cent of the total energy of all the cosmic rays, i.e., a coefficient $\kappa = 100$ is taken in formula (6.19). This assumption is not absolutely necessary, as is clear from what has been said before, but in the majority of cases it is probably approximately correct. Type 1 supernovae and the Crab Nebula in particular are a possible exception (in the latter case it is desirable to reduce the field H to a value of about 10^{-4} oe in order to avoid the assumption that energy is being pumped continuously into the electron component; the field $H \sim 10^{-4}$ oe corresponds to the value $\kappa < 1$).

† The basis of the tables, with certain changes, are the data and results collected by Korchak.[252] Fresh information on the structure of extragalactic sources and estimates of the magnetic field strength and relativistic particle energy are given in recent papers[437, 478].

If the coefficient κ is fixed the maximum error is introduced by the uncertainty in the values of the distances to the sources. Out of the sources listed in Table 7 (type 2 supernovae) the distances are actually known only for Cassiopeia A, the filament nebula in Cygnus and IC 443. No reliable measurements of the distances of the other seven sources are known to us. Therefore a conventional distance of 1000 pc is taken for these sources in Table 7 which should not differ greatly from the true value in order of magnitude. Since the relativistic particle energy W_{cr} is proportional to $R^{17/7}$ (see (6.21)) the values given for W_{cr} in Table 7 can be easily recalculated as the distances become known more precisely: a twofold error in the distance to the source leads to an error of a factor of 5·4 in the estimate of its energy. The scale of distances to radio-emitting remnants of type 2 supernovae suggested by Shklovskii[269] gives close values from 1000 to 2000 pc for all these unknown distances. This scale of distances is based on the assumption that for all explosions of type 2 supernovae the initial conditions and subsequent history are identical, whilst the observed differences are caused simply by the different ages of the corresponding expanding shells. Also, we assume that the spectral emission indices of all such shells are in the first approximation constant and identical ($\alpha = 0·5$). This last assumption is the weakest point in the arguments and should be generalised somehow in order to allow for the observed differences in the spectral indices and their possible dependence on time (in this connexion see a paper by Kellerman et al.[270]).

With the above reservations the values given in the last column of Tables 7 to 9 give an idea of the total energy of all the relativistic particles in the shells of supernova, in normal and in radio galaxies (see a recent paper by Ginzburg et al.[475] for the corresponding data for object 3C273).† By virtue of the assumptions made the same is true of the value of the total magnetic field energy.

---

† The values of the total energy W_{cr} given in Tables 7 to 9 differ as a rule from corresponding values obtained previously by Burbidge[271] and discussed by us elsewhere.[6] This can be explained by the stricter allowance in (6.21) for the energy spectrum limits and the use of more recent initial data. With respect to the Galaxy the values given in Table 8 for H, W_{cr} and P were obtained from formulae (6.20), (6.21) and (6.24) by replacing $R^2 F_\nu$ in the latter by $V I_\nu / L$. Here the volume of the Galaxy V is taken as 3×10^{68} cm^3, the value taken for I_ν is the radio emission intensity in the direction of the galactic pole ($T_{eff} = 25$ °K at $\nu = 400$ Mc/s) and $L \simeq 10$ kpc is the extent of the halo in this direction. Other estimates of the energy for the Galaxy are given in section 11.

TABLE 7

SUPERNOVA SHELLS

No.	Radio source	Angular size ϕ, min	Distance R, pc	Spectral index α	Emission flux density F_ν for $\nu = 10^8$ c/s, W/m²(c/s)	Emitted power P in range 10^7–10^{10} c/s, erg/sec	Field strength H, oersted	Total energy of relativistic particles W_{cr} erg
1	Cassiopeia A	4	3400	0·8	$1·9 \times 10^{-22}$	$2·5 \times 10^{35}$	$1·3 \times 10^{-3}$	$6·6 \times 10^{49}$
2	Velum X	120	(1000)	0·7	$1·2 \times 10^{-23}$	$1·6 \times 10^{33}$	$4·5 \times 10^{-5}$	$5·1 \times 10^{49}$
3	W44, 3C392, 2C1607	22	(1000)	0·5	$7·1 \times 10^{-24}$	$1·6 \times 10^{33}$	$1·7 \times 10^{-4}$	$4·8 \times 10^{48}$
4	Puppis A, 08S4A	50	(1000)	0·7	$5·6 \times 10^{-24}$	$7·8 \times 10^{32}$	$7·5 \times 10^{-5}$	$1·1 \times 10^{49}$
5	HB21, 3C420, 2C1725	80	(1000)	0·9	$5·1 \times 10^{-24}$	$4·8 \times 10^{32}$	$5·3 \times 10^{-5}$	$2·1 \times 10^{49}$
6	Filament nebula in Cygnus	170	770	0·5	$4·2 \times 10^{-24}$	$5·8 \times 10^{32}$	$2·8 \times 10^{-5}$	$2·6 \times 10^{49}$
7	IC443, 3C157, 2C537	50	2000	0·5	$4·0 \times 10^{-24}$	$3·7 \times 10^{32}$	$6·0 \times 10^{-5}$	$5·3 \times 10^{49}$
8	HB9, 2C437, 05N4A	80	(1000)	0·8	$1·4 \times 10^{-24}$	$1·6 \times 10^{32}$	$3·6 \times 10^{-5}$	$1·0 \times 10^{49}$
9	HB 3	120	(1000)	0·5	$1·0 \times 10^{-24}$	$2·4 \times 10^{32}$	$2·3 \times 10^{-5}$	$1·4 \times 10^{49}$
10	S147	180	(1000)	0·5	$4·6 \times 10^{-25}$	$1·1 \times 10^{32}$	$1·3 \times 10^{-5}$	$1·5 \times 10^{49}$
11	Taurus A (Crab Nebula, A.D. 1054 supernova)	5	1100	0·35 0·25	$1·7 \times 10^{-23}$	$1·3 \times 10^{37}$ $1·0 \times 10^{34}$	$1·4 \times 10^{-3}$ $1·0 \times 10^{-3}$	$5·3 \times 10^{48}$ $2·7 \times 10^{48}$
12	Kepler supernova (A.D. 1604 supernova)	2	1000	0·6	8×10^{-25}	$1·4 \times 10^{32}$	$6·9 \times 10^{-4}$	$5·7 \times 10^{46}$
13	Tycho Brahe supernova (A.D. 1572 supernova)	5·4	360	0·6	$2·4 \times 10^{-24}$	$5·5 \times 10^{31}$	$5·4 \times 10^{-4}$	$3·2 \times 10^{46}$

Note: For radio source Taurus A (Crab Nebula) the values of P, H and W_{cr} corresponding to the spectral index $\alpha = 0.35$ are calculated with $\nu_2 = 10^{15}$ c/s. The names (indices) of certain sources are given according to different catalogues.[198]

TABLE 8

EXTRAGALACTIC SOURCES—NORMAL GALAXIES

No.	Galaxies	Angular size ϕ, min	Distance R, Mpc	Spectral index α	$F_{p=10^8 c/s}$ W/m² (c/s)	P, erg/sec	H, oersted	W_{cr}, erg
1	The Galaxy	—	—	0·8	—	4.4×10^{38}	6.0×10^{-6}	3.0×10^{56}
2	NGC 1068, M77	2·5	10	0·6	2.4×10^{-25}	4.3×10^{39}	2.9×10^{-5}	1.9×10^{56}
3	NGC 5236, M83	23	4·0	0·9	4.0×10^{-25}	6.1×10^{38}	6.8×10^{-6}	5.4×10^{56}
4	NGC 3034, M82	36	2·3	0·2	1.5×10^{-25}	4.7×10^{38}	5.7×10^{-6}	2.7×10^{56}
5	NGC 4631	19	5·3	0·7	1.0×10^{-25}	3.9×10^{38}	4.7×10^{-6}	3.4×10^{56}
6	NGC 224, M31	200	0·73	0·5	2.7×10^{-24}	3.3×10^{38}	2.9×10^{-6}	4.0×10^{56}
7	NGC 5194/95, M51	16	4·2	1·0	2.2×10^{-25}	3.2×10^{38}	8.2×10^{-6}	3.1×10^{56}
8	NGC 4490	10	5·3	1·0	1.0×10^{-25}	2.3×10^{38}	9.2×10^{-6}	1.9×10^{56}
9	NGC 5457, M101	36	4·2	1·3	1.7×10^{-25}	2.1×10^{38}	4.9×10^{-6}	1.2×10^{57}
10	NGC 253	35	2·4	0·7	2.5×10^{-25}	2.0×10^{38}	4.5×10^{-6}	1.8×10^{56}
11	IC 342	30	2·2	1·1	4.7×10^{-25}	1.7×10^{38}	8.0×10^{-6}	2.8×10^{56}
12	NGC 4258	25	3·3	0·8	1.1×10^{-25}	1.4×10^{38}	4.5×10^{-6}	1.7×10^{56}
13	NGC 2403	30	2·3	1·0	1.1×10^{-25}	4.8×10^{37}	4.7×10^{-6}	1.1×10^{56}
14	NGC 55	60	2·4	0·7	4.1×10^{-26}	3.3×10^{37}	1.7×10^{-6}	1.3×10^{56}
15	IC 1613	80	0·69	0·6	1.6×10^{-25}	1.4×10^{37}	2.8×10^{-6}	2.0×10^{55}
16	NGC 598, M33	105	0·69	1·0	2.3×10^{-25}	9.1×10^{36}	2.8×10^{-6}	4.4×10^{55}

Note: The angular sizes of the sources are taken as the arithmetic mean of the radio sizes along the major and minor axes given by Hanbury Brown and Hazard[272]; the distances and fluxes are taken from Korchak's data.[252] It should be pointed out that galaxies NGC 1068 and NGC 5457 are often included among the radio galaxies.

TABLE 9

RADIO GALAXIES

No.	Radio source	Angular size ϕ,	Distance R, Mpc	Spectral index α	$F_{\nu=10^8 c/s}$ W/m^2 (c/s)	P, erg/sec	H, oersted	W_{cr}, erg
1	Cygnus A, C3 405 (twin)	$2 \times 38''$	220	0.75	1.3×10^{-22}	7×10^{44}	1.9×10^{-4}	3×10^{60}
2	3C295, HBH 18, 14N5A	4.5''	2000	0.6	1.8×10^{-24}	1.3×10^{45}	2.3×10^{-4}	2.7×10^{60}
3	Hercules A (twin)	$2 \times 47''$	300	0.93	6×10^{-24}	5×10^{43}	7×10^{-5}	1.7×10^{60}
4	Perseus A, NGC 1275: extensive source	26'	70	0.7	6×10^{-25}	4×10^{41}	3×10^{-6}	8×10^{59}
	central source	1'	70	0.7	6×10^{-25}	4×10^{41}	5×10^{-5}	1.1×10^{58}
5	Hydra A,	42''	200	0.9	5×10^{-24}	2×10^{43}	9×10^{-5}	3.5×10^{59}
6	3C338, NGC 6166	1.5'	130	1.2	1×10^{-24}	1.2×10^{42}	4×10^{-5}	2×10^{59}
7	Centaurus A, NGC 5128: extensive source (twin)	$2 \times 180'$	3.8	0.77	7.6×10^{-23}	1.3×10^{41}	4×10^{-6}	1.7×10^{59}
	central source	4.5'	3.8	0.77	1.8×10^{-23}	3×10^{40}	8×10^{-5}	5×10^{56}
8	Fornax A, NGC 1316: non-symmetrical twin source	30'	15.8	0.77	5.6×10^{-24}	1.7×10^{41}	8×10^{-6}	9×10^{58}
		25'	15.8	0.77	2.8×10^{-24}	8×10^{40}	7×10^{-6}	5×10^{58}
9	Virgo A, NGC 4486, M87: extensive source	10'	11	0.8	6×10^{-24}	8×10^{40}	2.2×10^{-5}	1×10^{58}
	"jets" in centre	$2 \times 23''$	11	0.8	9×10^{-24}	1.2×10^{41}	3.3×10^{-4}	2.5×10^{56}

Note: In the case of twin symmetrical sources the angular size of one of them is shown and this is indicated by $2\times$ in column 3. The values of ϕ, R, α and F_ν are taken from papers by Shklovskii[198] and Korchak.[252] The distance R was determined for a number of sources by using the value of Hubble's constant $h = 75$ km/sec·Mpc. At present $h = 100$ km/sec·Mpc is more generally used and it is this value which is taken in section 13. The latest data known to us on the distances are those in an article by Davies and Verschuur[372] where the following values are taken for R: Cygnus A 170 Mpc, 3C295 1380 Mpc, Hercules A 460 Mpc, Perseus A 53 Mpc and Virgo A 12 Mpc.

Tables 7 to 9 also give the values of the integral power of sources of radio emission in the frequency range $v = 10^7 - 10^{10}$ c/s; the power is defined (for $F = \text{const} \cdot v^{-\alpha}$) by the expression

$$P = 4\pi R^2 \int_{v_1}^{v_2} F_v \, dv = 4\pi R^2 F_v \frac{v^\alpha v_2^{1-\alpha}}{1-\alpha}\left[1 - \left(\frac{v_1}{v_2}\right)^{1-\alpha}\right]. \quad (6.24)$$

The values given for the integral power P characterise the energy loss rate of sources to emission in the radio band. For example, for the radio galaxy Cygnus A the rate of the energy losses by radio-emitting electrons is $P \simeq 7 \times 10^{44}$ erg/sec (see Table 9) whilst the total energy of these electrons is evidently $W_e = 3 \times 10^{58}$ erg (i.e., 1 per cent of the energy of all the cosmic rays W_{cr}). When there is no electron "pumping", therefore, the duration of the radio-emitting phase cannot exceed $T \sim W_e/P \simeq 10^6$ years in order of magnitude. The conclusion that the radio galaxy Cygnus A is young (about 10^6 years) also follows from an analysis of the shape (presence of a break) of the radio emission spectrum of this source.[257]

CHAPTER III

MOTION OF COSMIC RAYS IN THE INTERSTELLAR MEDIUM

THE basic characteristics of primary cosmic rays such as concentration, energy spectrum and chemical composition depend in the first place on the properties of the cosmic ray sources. When discussing the question of the origin of cosmic rays, therefore, particular attention is generally paid to their sources. However, the medium in which the cosmic rays move on their way from the sources plays a no less important part, and one that to a considerable extent does not depend on the sources, in the formation of the observed characteristics of the cosmic rays. For example, the cosmic ray intensity, just like the power of the sources, is determined also by the life-time of cosmic rays in the Galaxy. In addition, during motion in the interstellar medium the chemical composition of the cosmic rays undergoes considerable changes and so does their energy spectrum (in the regions of very high and non-relativistic energies at least).

The question of the change in the properties of the cosmic rays in the interstellar medium on their way from the sources is particularly important since very little is as yet known about the sources themselves. When discussing the question of the origin of cosmic rays, therefore, we are in many cases obliged to base ourselves not on any concrete information about their sources but, on the contrary, to draw conclusions about the properties of the sources proceeding from data about cosmic rays on the Earth and on the nature of their motion and interaction in the interstellar gas.

In the present chapter we shall discuss the basic processes accompanying the motion of the cosmic rays in interstellar space. These processes include nuclear and electromagnetic interactions of cosmic rays with particles of the medium, the possible mechanisms for the acceleration of charged particles in a moving magnetised plasma filling interstellar space, and also the effect of the interstellar magnetic fields on the nature of the cosmic ray motion itself in the Galaxy. These processes occur to a greater or lesser degree also as the cosmic rays move through metagalactic space and in the actual cosmic ray sources.

The material discussed in this chapter is therefore of fairly general significance from the point of view of the sphere of applicability of the results. In addition, since it is chiefly a question of phenomena which have been carefully studied under laboratory conditions and the corresponding results are not connected with actual considerations of the sources of cosmic rays they should be borne in mind in any theoretical considerations relating to the field of cosmic ray astrophysics.

7. ENERGY LOSSES AND FRAGMENTATION OF THE NUCLEAR COMPONENT

In this section we shall discuss the interaction of protons and heavier nuclei in cosmic rays with the matter filling the Galaxy and the Metagalaxy. This interaction leads to energy loss, fragmentation and absorption of the nuclear component which is reflected in the concentration, energy spectrum and chemical composition of the cosmic rays observed on Earth. However, before passing to a discussion of this circle of questions we shall pause briefly to consider the available data on the distribution of matter in the Universe.

Distribution of matter in the Galaxy and Metagalaxy

In the Galaxy the basic mass of matter is contained in the stars, the mass of all the stars being about $10^{11} M_\odot = 2 \times 10^{44}$ g (the Sun's mass $M_\odot = 1 \cdot 99 \times 10^{33}$ g). The interstellar gas is the next in decreasing order of magnitude. The total mass of interstellar gas in the Galaxy is estimated to be approximately equal to $10^9 M_\odot$ (for a more precise value see below). The basic component of the interstellar gas is hydrogen with helium coming second; the contribution of heavier elements to the total mass of the interstellar gas can be ignored within the limits of present accuracy. In accordance with the cosmic distribution of the elements the number of hydrogen atoms accounts for about 90 per cent of the interstellar gas, the remaining 10 per cent being helium (according to Suess and Urey[49] the percentage contents of hydrogen and helium in the Universe are 93 and 7 per cent, whilst Cameron[50] takes, respectively, values of 87 and 13 per cent. More than 90 per cent of the interstellar hydrogen is in the neutral state, but the degree of ionisation of the interstellar hydrogen, and also its spatial distribution, is extremely inhomogeneous (the hydrogen is ionised in the so-called H II regions surrounding hot stars; these clouds account for about 5 per cent of all the gas clouds in the optical disk of the Galaxy which is about 300 pc thick).

In what follows the most important characteristic of the interstellar matter will be the concentration n of the gas in the region of space occupied by cosmic rays. In this case, of course, the selection of the region for averaging the concentration plays a determinative part. As has already been pointed out, cosmic rays in the Galaxy occupy a quasi-spherical volume $V = 1$ to 5×10^{68} cm^3. For a number of reasons (see sections 6 and 10) it can be taken that the cosmic rays are exchanged fairly freely between the different parts of this volume and leave the spiral for the halo and vice versa, in particular. There is also reason for assuming that the cosmic rays also penetrate the dense clouds of interstellar gas; this is mentioned again below. Therefore the simplest, and at the same time most natural, assumption about the mean concentration n is that the value of n is determined simply by the ratio of the whole mass of gas in the Galaxy (including the halo) to the volume of the system $V = 1$ to 5×10^{68} cm^3. The mass of the neutral hydrogen in the Galaxy without allowing for the halo, i.e., only near the galactic plane, is[203] $2 \cdot 8 \times 10^{42}$ g.† For a mixture of 93 per cent hydrogen and 7 per cent helium we hence obtain the minimum value for the mean density

$$\rho = \frac{3 \cdot 6 \times 10^{42}}{(1 \text{ to } 5) \times 10^{68}} = 0 \cdot 7 \text{ to } 3 \cdot 6 \times 10^{-26} \text{ g/cm}^3,$$

and for the mean concentration $n = 0 \cdot 4$ to $1 \cdot 8 \times 10^{-2}$ cm^{-3}. The most probable value $V = 10^{68}$ cm^3 which we used earlier clearly corresponds to the larger value for the concentration $n = 1 \cdot 8 \times 10^{-2}$ cm^{-3}.

The question of the mean concentration of the gas in the halo $\bar{n}_{halo}$ is still open. According to Pikel'ner and Shklovskii[266] $\bar{n}_{halo}$

† The accuracy of the determination of the total mass of gas in all probability allows us to use with just as much justification a value of 3×10^{42} g for the mass. However, in order not to introduce unnecessary uncertainty, here and in a number of other cases we use the available published values without rounding them off even if this seems entirely justified.

$\sim 10^{-2}$ cm^{-3} but this result was obtained theoretically and from the same considerations we cannot exclude a value $\bar{n}_{halo} \sim 10^{-3}$ cm^{-3}.

Kahn and Woltjer[282] assumed that at a distance $R \simeq 15$ kpc from the Galactic centre $n \simeq 3.6 \times 10^{-4}$ cm^{-3} which still does not contradict the value $\bar{n}_{halo} \sim 10^{-2}$ cm^{-3}. Although an analysis based on the application of the virial theorem to the halo[277] is not unambiguous it is nevertheless compatible with a halo model with $\bar{n}_{halo} \simeq 10^{-2}$ cm^{-3}. Observations[278] indicate that the clouds of comparatively dense interstellar gas ascend to distances of $z \simeq 1$ kpc from the Galactic plane. For a cloud to reach such an altitude the projection of its velocity at right angles to the plane of the Galaxy must be of the order of 50 km/sec at $z = 0$. Unfortunately the estimates of the density of the gas in the clouds are very uncertain but, probably, 1 cm$^{-3} < n_{cloud} < 10$ cm^{-3}. If the clouds occupy a volume of about 5 per cent in a layer 2 kpc thick and 10 kpc in diameter ($V \sim 10^{67}$ cm^3) and $n_{cloud} \sim 1$ cm^{-3} the mean concentration in this layer is of the order of 5×10^{-2} cm^{-3} and in the whole halo ($V \sim 10^{68}$ cm^3) is $\bar{n}_{halo} \sim 5 \times 10^{-3}$ cm^{-3} when the gas outside the clouds is ignored. An examination of the influence which the gas in the halo would have on the form of the spectral lines leads us to conclude[278] that we cannot take the values $\bar{n}_{halo} \sim 0.1$ cm^{-3} and $T \sim 10^4$ °K for the halo. In this connexion Munch and Zirin[278] are inclined to favour a halo model with $\bar{n}_{halo} \sim 5 \times 10^{-4}$ cm^{-3} and $T \sim 10^6$ °K. However the halo model with $\bar{n}_{halo} \sim 10^{-2}$ cm^{-3} evidently does not contradict the data of Munch and Zirin.

As for radio astronomy data, they have not yet thrown any light on the gas concentration in the halo. We have earlier[279] made an attempt to explain the "break", present according to some data[280] in the galactic radio emission spectrum at a frequency $v_c \simeq 10^7$ c/s by the effect of ionisation losses. In this case, however, too high a value is obtained for the density ($\bar{n}_{halo} \sim 0.1$ cm^{-3})[281]. At the same time it is clear that further elucidation of the long-wave part of the cosmic radio emission spectrum may be very significant for estimating the gas concentration in the halo.[196]

The question of the value of $\bar{n}_{halo}$ thus remains open but there are evidently no weighty arguments against the estimate $\bar{n}_{halo} \sim 10^{-2}$ to 10^{-3} cm^{-3}, whilst there are a number of considerations in favour of such values. In addition, it is clear that the value of n for the whole region occupied and penetrated by cosmic rays which is particularly significant for us is known to be greater than $\bar{n}_{halo}$ and for $\bar{n}_{halo} \lesssim$

10^{-2} cm^{-3} may not differ much from the above estimate of the lower limit of n which allows only for the interstellar gas near the plane of the Galaxy.

Comparing all the above arguments it can be said that at present the most probable values on the average for the Galaxy (for the region where the cosmic rays are) are

$$n \simeq 10^{-2} \text{ cm}^{-3}, \qquad \rho \simeq 2 \times 10^{-26} \text{ g/cm}^3. \qquad (7.1)$$

In the case of the gas concentration in intergalactic space the situation is even more uncertain than in the case of the Galactic halo. The value $\bar{n}_{Mg} = 10^{-5}$ cm^{-3} is generally taken for the mean gas concentration in the Metagalaxy, corresponding to a mean density $\rho_{Mg} \simeq 10^{-29}$ g/cm^3; these figures are, however, only a guide (see also sections 12 and 13).

Absorption of cosmic rays by stars and interstellar dust

Despite the fact that the majority of the matter in the Galaxy is concentrated in the stars their part in the absorption of cosmic rays is negligibly small. The explanation of this is that the length of the nuclear path is much less than the radius of the star so only a thin surface layer takes part in the absorption. Since the calculated effect is small it may be taken for a rough estimate that there are about 10^{11} stars in the Galaxy with a radius $r_{st} \sim 10^{11}$ cm and a concentration $n_{st} \sim 10^{11}/10^{68} = 10^{-57}$ cm^{-3}. The mean life of a relativistic particle before hitting a star is $T = (\pi r_{st}^2 n_{st} c)^{-1} \simeq 10^{24}$ sec $= 3 \times 10^{16}$ years. This time is many orders greater than the age of the Galaxy ($\sim 10^{10}$ years) so the rôle of stars in the absorption of cosmic rays can be completely ignored.

Considerably more frequent are collisions of cosmic rays with the interstellar dust whose total mass in the Galaxy is evidently not more than 0·01 of the total mass of the interstellar gas. The mean radius of the dust particles r_d is approximately 4×10^{-5} cm and the mass of a particle is $\frac{4}{3} \pi r_d^3 \rho_d \simeq 3 \times 10^{-13}$ g; the density of the matter in the dust particles, which are crystals of ice, ammonia or methane, is generally taken as $\rho_d \simeq 1$ g/cm^3. In order of magnitude interstellar space therefore contains not more than $N_d \simeq 10^7 \times 2 \times 10^{33}/ 3 \times 10^{-13} \simeq 10^{53}$ dust particles with a mean cross section of $\pi r_d^2 \simeq 5 \times 10^{-9}$ cm^2. Hence the average time between collisions with the interstellar dust is $T \simeq (\pi r_d^2 c [N_d/V])^{-1} \simeq 10^{13}$ sec $\simeq 3 \times 10^5$ years (here $V \simeq 10^{68}$ cm^3 is the volume of space in the Galaxy occupied by cosmic rays). Collisions of cosmic rays with interstellar dust thus occur relatively frequently. But the thickness of the matter in a dust particle which a relativistic particle passes through in any such collision averages only $\frac{4}{3}r_d \simeq 5 \times 10^{-5}$ g/cm^2. Since the nuclear interaction path of cosmic ray protons in matter is about 100 g/cm^2, in order of magnitude, an average of about 10^6 collisions with dust particles are necessary for such a proton to undergo one nuclear interaction.

The life of cosmic rays with respect to nuclear interactions with the interstellar dust is thus approximately not less than 3×10^{11} years, i.e., greater than the age of the Galaxy. Moreover nuclear collisions with the interstellar gas occur considerably more often (see below) and in comparison with these the nuclear interactions in the interstellar dust are insignificant (the losses due to collisions with the dust particles are not more than 1 per cent of the losses caused by nuclear collisions in the interstellar gas, as should be the case if we bear in mind that the mass of the interstellar dust is $\lesssim 1$ per cent of the mass of the interstellar gas).

Ionisation losses

During the motion of a particle (nucleus) with a mass M and a charge Z in atomic hydrogen the losses to excitation and ionisation of the medium's atoms are

$$-\left(\frac{dE}{dt}\right)_i = \frac{4\pi e^4 Z^2 n}{mv}\left\{\ln\left[\frac{2mv^2}{I}\left(\frac{E}{mc^2}\right)^2\right] - \frac{v^2}{c^2}\right\}$$

$$= 7\cdot62 \times 10^{-9}Z^2 n\,\frac{c}{v}\left\{22\cdot2 + 4\ln\frac{E}{mc^2} + 2\ln\frac{v^2}{c^2} - 2\frac{v^2}{c^2}\right\}$$

$$\text{eV/sec.} \quad (7.2)$$

It is assumed here† that the total energy of a particle is $E \ll (M/m)Mc^2$, v is the velocity of the particle, e and m are the charge and mass of an electron, $I \simeq 15$ eV is the effective (mean) excitation (ionisation) energy and n is the concentration of hydrogen atoms (and atomic electrons simultaneously). In the case of a medium of other light atoms formula (7.2) can also be used as a good approximation, taking n to be the concentration of all the atomic electrons.

---

† If $E \ll (M/m)Mc^2$ the maximum energy transmitted by the particle in question to an electron is $W_{max} = 2mv^2(E/Mc^2)^2$: this circumstance is also used in (7.2).

In the non-relativistic case (with $E_k = E - Mc^2 \simeq Mv^2/2 \ll Mc^2$)

$$-\left(\frac{dE}{dt}\right)_i = 7 \cdot 62 \times 10^{-9} Z^2 n \sqrt{\frac{2Mc^2}{E_c}} \left\{11 \cdot 8 + \ln \frac{E_k}{Mc^2}\right\} \text{ eV/sec.} \quad (7.3)$$

In the ultrarelativistic case with $E \gg Mc^2$ but nevertheless with $E \ll (M/m)Mc^2$

$$-\left(\frac{dE}{dt}\right)_i = 7 \cdot 62 \times 10^{-9} Z^2 n \left\{20 \cdot 2 + 4 \ln \frac{E}{Mc^2}\right\} \text{ eV/sec.} \quad (7.4)$$

This formula can be used in practice for protons in the region $10^{12} \text{ eV} > E > 2$ to $3 \times 10^9 \text{ eV}$. If $E \gg (M/m)Mc^2$, then a particle can transfer to an electron any energy up to its own energy E. In this case

$$-\left(\frac{dE}{dt}\right)_i = \frac{2\pi e^4 Z^2 n}{mc} \left\{\ln \frac{2mc^2}{I^2} \frac{E^3}{(Mc^2)^2} - 2\right\}$$

$$= 7 \cdot 62 \times 10^{-9} Z^2 n \left\{3 \ln \frac{E}{Mc^2} + \ln \frac{M}{m} + 19 \cdot 5\right\} \text{ eV/sec.} \quad (7.5)$$

We notice that this formula does not allow for the so-called density effect which is permissible at energies of $E/Mc^2 < 3 \times 10^{11}/\sqrt{n}$ (see section 8; at an atomic hydrogen concentration of $n \simeq 1 \text{ cm}^{-3}$ the density effect need not be taken into account for protons right up to energies of $E \simeq 10^{20}$ eV).

In a completely ionised medium with an electron concentration n, in the non-relativistic case

$$-\left(\frac{dE}{dt}\right)_i = \frac{2\pi e^4 Z^2 n}{mv} \ln \frac{m^3 v^4}{\pi e^2 n \hbar^2}$$

$$= 7 \cdot 62 \times 10^{-9} Z^2 n \sqrt{\frac{2Mc^2}{E_k}} \left\{\ln \frac{E_k}{Mc^2} - \tfrac{1}{2} \ln n + 38 \cdot 7\right\} \text{eV/sec.}$$

$$(7.6)$$

This formula is obtained from (7.2) with $E_k = (Mv^2/2) \ll Mc^2$ and $I = \hbar\omega_0 = \hbar\sqrt{(4\pi e^2 n/m)} = 3 \cdot 7 \times 10^{-11} \sqrt{n}$ eV. A more consistent calculation[284] leads to the same result. At the ultra-relativistic energy $E \gg Mc^2$ the losses in a completely ionised gas are

$$-\left(\frac{dE}{dt}\right)_i = \frac{2\pi e^4 Z^2 n}{mc} \ln \frac{m^2 c^2 W}{4\pi e^2 n \hbar^2}$$

$$= 7.62 \times 10^{-9} Z^2 n \left\{ \ln \frac{W}{mc^2} - \ln n + 74.1 \right\} \text{ eV/sec}, \qquad (7.7)$$

where W is the maximum energy transferred to an electron by a particle ($W = E$ for $E \gg (M/m)Mc^2$ and $W = 2mc^2(E/Mc^2)^2$ for $Mc^2 \ll E \ll (M/m)Mc^2$)†. We should point out that to obtain the losses in eV/cm the values of (7.4), (7.5) and (7.7) for relativistic particles should be divided by $c = 3 \times 10^{10}$ cm/sec; losses in hydrogen in eV/g·cm^{-2} are obtained by multiplying the losses in eV/cm by $6 \times 10^{23}/n = 1/1.67 \times 10^{-24}n$.

Braking of slow ions

From the point of view of injection and studying the initial stage of cosmic ray acceleration the nature of the energy losses for ions with comparatively low velocities is of considerable significance. The expressions (7.2), (7.3) and (7.4) given above for the ionisation losses are valid only for particles whose velocities are high when compared with the characteristic velocity of the medium's electrons. In the case of atomic hydrogen this characteristic velocity is the orbital velocity of the electrons $v_0 = e^2/\hbar = 2.19 \times 10^8$ cm/sec. In a completely ionised gas the characteristic velocity is the mean thermal velocity of the electrons $v_T = \sqrt{(3kT/m)} = 6.8 \times 10^5 T_e^{1/2}$ cm/sec.

If the ion velocity is less than the velocity of the electrons (but the energy, of course, is greater than the mean thermal energy of the medium's electrons or atoms), then the dependence of the energy losses on the velocity of the ion is qualitatively of a different nature from that for high velocities: if $v < v_0$, the losses rise as the velocity increases in proportion to its square. In this energy range ($v < v_0$) the energy losses of an ion with a charge Z in a gas consisting of atoms with a concentration n with an atomic number Z_c, where $\frac{1}{4}Z \lesssim Z_c \lesssim 4Z$, are defined by the expression[235, 286]

$$-\frac{dE}{dt} = 2.34 \times 10^{-23} n(Z + Z_c)v^2 \text{ eV/sec}. \qquad (7.8)$$

† According to more precise calculations[284] the term 74.1 in formula (7.7) should be replaced by 73.1 for $W = 2mc^2(E/Mc^2)^2$. At $W = E$ the difference between the precise formula and formula (7.7) lies beyond the limit of accuracy of the significant figures (the precise formula for this case can be obtained from (8.2) by replacing E by $2E$).

In a completely ionised gas the corresponding expression takes the form[287]

$$-\frac{dE}{dt} = 1 \cdot 8 \times 10^{-12} \frac{Z^2 n}{AT_e^{3/2}} E_k \text{ eV/sec.} \qquad (7.9)$$

In the intermediate velocity range when the ion's velocity is comparable with the velocity of the medium's electrons v_0 the losses reach a maximum and then drop inversely proportional to the velocity (see (7.2)). The general nature of the losses as a function of the velocity is shown in Fig. 18 (see section 9). There are no exact expressions for the ionisation losses in the $v \sim v_0$ velocity range. The value of the maximum losses in neutral hydrogen can be estimated approximately by determining the maximum of expression (7.3) as a function of the velocity. This gives

$$-\left(\frac{dE}{dt}\right)_{i,\,\text{max}} \simeq 2 \cdot 9 \times 10^{-6} n Z^2 \text{ eV/sec} \qquad (7.10)$$

for an ion velocity $v = 1 \cdot 4 v_0 = 3 \cdot 2 \times 10^8$ cm/sec. Bearing in mind the approximate nature of formula (7.10) we must consider that this agrees well with experiment[288] which gives the maximum proton losses in hydrogen as $6 \cdot 5 \times 10^{-15} n$ eV/cm for a proton velocity $v = 3 \cdot 4 \times 10^8$ cm/sec ($E_k \simeq 60$ keV).

In ionised hydrogen the maximum losses are for an ion velocity close to the mean thermal velocity of the medium's electrons v_T. For a rough estimate of the maximum losses it can be taken that their value is v_0/v_T times greater than the maximum losses in neutral hydrogen (7.10).

When using formula (7.10) for estimating the maximum losses of multiply charged ions it should be borne in mind that this formula always gives too high a value for the losses if Z is taken to be the atomic number of the braking ion. The point is that for an ion velocity of $v \sim v_0$ the recharging process (capture and loss of electrons by the moving ion, see below) plays an important part. As a result of this the effective ion charge which is part of the expression for the losses is considerably less than its atomic number which is denoted by Z_0 below. The dependence of the maximum losses on the atomic number Z_0 is much weaker than the dependence of (7.10) on the effective charge Z. According to available data[286] the maximum losses are approximately proportional to the first power of Z_0.

Provided that collisions of the ion in question with particles of the medium occur often enough, the mean ion charge Ze determining the magnitude of the losses has a certain equilibrium value depending on the velocity. This value is determined by the relative effectiveness of the processes of electron loss and capture and, according to Bohr,[289] in the velocity range $1 < v/v_0 < Z_0^{1/3}$ (here $v_0 = e^2/\hbar = 2 \cdot 19 \times 10^{-3}$ cm/sec) depends on the ion velocity as follows:

$$Z = Z_0^{1/3} \frac{v}{v_0}. \qquad (7.11)$$

For velocities greater than Zv_0 and with sufficiently frequent collisions the ionisation can be considered practically complete.

Relationship (7.11) is a reflection of the following picture of the ionisation of a multi-electron atom at low velocities. The loss of the next least bound electron occurs when the ion velocity is comparable with the orbital velocity of this electron and the energy transferred during collisions is sufficient to strip it off. If the ionisation potential of the corresponding shell is equal to I, electrons begin to be lost from this shell for a kinetic energy of the ion $E_k \simeq (M/m)I$, where M is the mass of the braking ion. The effective ionisation cross section is defined well enough by the relationship.[287]

$$\sigma_i = k \frac{\pi e^4}{I} \frac{M}{mE_k} \ln \frac{mE_k}{MI}, \qquad (7.12)$$

where k is a coefficient of the order of unity which is constant for each element. If $E_k \simeq 3(M/m)I$, the ionisation cross section is at its maximum and is

$$\sigma_{i,\,max} = \frac{k}{3} \frac{\pi e^4}{I^2}. \qquad (7.13)$$

The ionisation cross section given for a moving ion relates to a collision with one electron of a medium at rest. The ionisation cross section has approximately the same value in collisions with nuclei of the interstellar hydrogen; therefore when considering the ionisation of particles moving in the interstellar hydrogen the concentration of the medium's particles must be taken as $2n$ (n is the interstellar hydrogen concentration).

The characteristic cross section of the loss of the first electron ($I \sim I_H = 13 \cdot 5$ eV), according to (7.13), is the same in order of magnitude as the gas kinetic cross section, i.e., is several times 10^{-16} cm^2.

At the same time the effective cross section of the loss of the last electron from the atom's K-shell depends strongly on the atomic number Z_0 (the ionisation potential of the K-shell is $I = I_H Z_0^2 = 13 \cdot 5 Z_0^2$ eV) and for example for iron has a maximum not greater than about 10^{-21} cm^2.

Magnetic bremsstrahlung losses for protons and nuclei

A nucleus with energy E, atomic number Z and mass M in the ultra-relativistic case ($E \gg Mc^2$) is subjected to magnetic bremsstrahlung losses:

$$-\left(\frac{dE}{dt}\right)_m = \tfrac{2}{3}c\left(\frac{e^2}{mc^2}\right)^2 \left(\frac{Z^2 m}{M}\right)^2 H_\perp^2 \left(\frac{E}{Mc^2}\right)^2$$

$$= 0 \cdot 98 \times 10^{-3} H_\perp^2 \left(\frac{Z^2 m}{M}\right)^2 \left(\frac{E}{Mc^2}\right)^2 \text{ eV/sec.} \quad (7.14)$$

When compared with the magnetic bremsstrahlung losses for electrons (see (8.12)) the losses (7.14) are $\xi = (Zm/M)^4$ times less (for the same E and $H_\perp$). For protons $\xi \simeq 10^{-13}$ and for nuclei $\xi \simeq 10^{-14}$ since in the majority of cases $Z/M = Z/AM_p \simeq \tfrac{1}{2}M_p$ approximately (A is the atomic weight or, to be more precise, the mass number). The characteristic time for magnetic bremsstrahlung losses during which the energy is halved for nuclei is

$$T_m = \frac{3M^3 c^5}{2e^4 Z^4 H_\perp^2} \frac{Mc^2}{E} \simeq \frac{3 \cdot 2 \times 10^{18} A^3}{H_\perp^2 Z^4} \frac{Mc^2}{E} \text{ sec.} \quad (7.15)$$

The maximum energy observed in cosmic rays is $E \simeq 10^{20}$ eV. Even if these particles are protons in a field $H_\perp \simeq 10^{-6}$ oe we find $T_m \simeq 10^{12}$ years (for heavy nuclei with the same values of E and $H_\perp$ the time T_m is about 10 times greater). In actual fact the mean field $H_\perp$ on the trajectory of particle with such a high energy is probably close to the metagalactic field, i.e., does not exceed the value $H \simeq 10^{-7}$ oe. It is clear, therefore, that the magnetic bremsstrahlung losses of protons and nuclei in a time of the order of the "cosmological time" $T \simeq 10^{10}$ years (or the life of a nucleus T_{nucl} in the Galaxy) can be considered as small for all the particles observed. It may be necessary to allow for these losses only, for example, for protons with an energy $E \simeq 10^{22}$ eV in a field $H_\perp \simeq 10^{-6}$ oe or for protons with a slightly lower energy in radio galaxies with a relatively strong magnetic field.

During accelerated motion, in particular during motion in a magnetic field, emission occurs not only of electromagnetic waves (photons) but also of gravitational waves (gravitons) and other particles (π-mesons, electrons, etc.). It is well known[165] that in the non-relativistic region the gravitational emission is incomparably weaker than the electromagnetic emission (we are dealing here with electrons, protons and nuclei). It has been shown[290] that in the ultra-relativistic case also the gravitational emission is negligibly small when compared with the electromagnetic emission. If we have in mind, for definiteness, ultra-relativistic protons, then during their motion in a magnetic field they should lose energy (apart from losses due to photon emission) also as the result of the processes[291]

$$p \to p + \pi^0, \qquad p \to n + \pi^+, \qquad p \to n + e^+ + \nu. \qquad (7.16)$$

At high enough energies these magnetic bremsstrahlung losses may be of interest. However the energies at which the losses due to processes (7.16) are significant under cosmic conditions are considerably higher (by many orders)[291] than the maximum energy $E \sim 10^{20}$eV observed in cosmic rays.

Photonuclear reactions

Photo-fission on thermal photons emitted by the Sun and stars may be significant for primary nuclei with energies of about 10^{16} eV/nucleon. This effect has been discussed[292, 293] for the Sun and leads to the possibility of the formation of correlated extensive atmospheric showers caused by fission products of the initial nucleus (basically a photonucleon and the residual nucleus) hitting the atmosphere. According to some estimates[293] the frequency of these correlated showers, if the cosmic rays in the high energy region consist largely of heavy nuclei, is 10^{-4} to 10^{-3} km^{-2}·hr^{-1}·sterad^{-1}. The mean separation of cores in a shower observed on Earth caused by the transverse momentum acquired in the nuclear photoeffect will be about 1 km.† A study of correlated showers could

---

† G. T. Zatsepin informs us that the estimate of the mean distance between cores changes significantly if allowance is made for the effect of the interplanetary magnetic field and the difference of the A/Z ratios and thus also of the radii of curvature $r_H = E/300ZH$ of the fission products of the initial nucleus, for example of a residual nucleus with $A = 2Z$ and a photoproton with $A = Z = 1$. In this case the mean separation of fragments at a distance of 1 a.u. $= 1\cdot5 \times 10^{13}$ cm in a field $H \simeq 10^{-5}$ oersted is about 400 km. This circumstance considerably complicates the possibility of detecting correlated extensive atmospheric showers.

provide information on the chemical composition of cosmic rays in the very high energy region but the experimental possibilities in this respect are not yet obvious.

The nuclear photo-effect on Galactic and Metagalactic photons has been discussed.[294] It has been shown[294] that the fission of complex nuclei caused by this effect may lead to "erosion" of the nucleus spectrum in the range of energies near 10^{16} eV/nucleon corresponding to resonance in the nuclear photo-effect. If the density of emission in the Metagalaxy, as is assumed by Gerasimova and Rozental'[294] is about 0·1 eV/cm³ at a mean photon energy of about 1 eV the life of the nuclei with respect to photo-fission is $T_{nucl,ph} \simeq 10^9$ years. In a time of the order of 10^{10} years, therefore, heavy nuclei with energies $E \simeq 10^{17}$ to 10^{18} eV would be largely broken down. In other words heavy nuclei with energies $E \simeq 10^{17}$ to 10^{18} eV could, evidently, not arrive in the Galaxy under these conditions. However, as we shall see in section 8, the emission density in the Metagalaxy at present is considerably less than 0·1 eV/cm³ and, apparently, $w_{ph, Mg} \simeq 10^{-3}$ eV/cm³. It is true that the effective mean value of $w_{ph, Mg}$ in the evolutionary cosmological model is an order of magnitude larger even for $w_{ph, Mg} \simeq 10^{-2}$ eV/cm³, however, the effect of heavy nucleus fission is of little significance.

Nuclear interactions

The basic factor in the absorption of photons and heavier cosmic ray nuclei is their nuclear interactions with the interstellar hydrogen and helium. The mean free path Λ_i (in g/cm²) with respect to inelastic nuclear interactions in the interstellar gas is defined as

$$\Lambda_i = \rho/n\sigma_i = M/\sigma_i, \tag{7.17}$$

where σ_i is the effective cross section of the inelastic interaction of a nucleus of a kind i with a nucleus of the interstellar hydrogen (helium), n and ρ are the mean concentrations of the atoms and the density of the medium in the path of the particle and $M = \rho/n$ is the mean mass of the gas nuclei in the medium.

The values of the inelastic cross sections σ_i and the interaction paths Λ_i in hydrogen and interstellar gas are given for different nuclei in Table 10. In accordance with the cosmic distribution of the elements it is assumed that the interstellar gas contains, apart from hydrogen, 10 per cent helium (10 per cent of the number of atoms).

The cross section of the inelastic p-p interaction is taken from a paper by Kalbach et al.[295] For the determination of the inelastic interaction cross sections of nuclei with $Z > 2$ with hydrogen use is made of the formula.[296]

$$\sigma = \pi r^2, \qquad r = 1\cdot 26 \times 10^{-13} A^{\frac{1}{3}} \text{ cm}, \qquad (7.18)$$

which describes satisfactorily enough the results obtained from accelerators and in the cosmic ray flux. This formula apparently gives a value which is slightly too high for α-particles. In Table 10,

TABLE 10

CROSS SECTIONS AND PATHS IN HYDROGEN AND THE INTERSTELLAR GAS

Group of nuclei	$\bar{A}$	$\sigma \times 10^{26}$ cm^2		Λ, g/cm^2		Absorption in interstellar gas	
		hydrogen	interstellar gas	hydrogen	interstellar gas	λ, g/cm^2	T_{nucl}, yr
p	1	2·3	3	74	72	72	$3\cdot 6 \times 10^9$
α	4	9·3	11	18	20	34	$1\cdot 7 \times 10^9$
L	10	23	25	7·3	8·7	10	$5\cdot 0 \times 10^8$
M	14	29	31	5·8	6·9	7·8	$3\cdot 9 \times 10^8$
H	31	48	52	3·5	4·2	6·1	$3\cdot 0 \times 10^8$
H_3	24	41	44	4·1	4·9	7·1	$3\cdot 5 \times 10^8$
H_2	36	54	58	3·1	3·8	5·5	$2\cdot 7 \times 10^8$
$H_1 \equiv VH$	51	69	73	2·4	3·0	4·4	$2\cdot 2 \times 10^8$
Fe	56	73	78	2·3	2·8	2·8	$1\cdot 4 \times 10^8$

therefore, the inelastic interaction cross section for protons on α-particles is taken from a paper by Riddiford and Williams.[297] The cross sections for the interaction of different nuclei with helium are calculated by the formula[298]

$$\sigma = \pi(R_1 + R_2 - 1\cdot 7 \times 10^{-13})^2 \text{ cm}^2, \qquad (7.19)$$

where R_1 and R_2 are the "radii" of the colliding nuclei defined as $R = 1\cdot 45 \times 10^{-13} A^{\frac{1}{3}}$ cm and A is the atomic weight of the nucleus (in the case of He we put, of course $R_2 = 1\cdot 45 \times 10^{-13} \times 2^{\frac{1}{3}}$ cm). Table 10 lists, apart from the groups of nuclei already discussed, sub-groups of the H group which covers a wide range of atomic numbers. These sub-groups are: H_1 ($Z \geqslant 20$), $H_2(Z = 16$ to $19)$ and $H_3(Z = 10$ to $15)$. For unity of notations the VH sub-group is called H_1 here. The average atomic weights $\bar{A}$ for these sub-groups in accordance with the relative distribution of the elements in the sub-groups in question (see Table 2) are taken as 51, 36 and 24 respectively.

The seventh column in Table 10 gives the values of the absorption paths λ_i in the interstellar medium.† The absorption paths are obviously greater than the inelastic interaction paths for the groups of nuclei. This difference arises because there is a finite probability P_{ii} of the formation of a new nucleus of the same group in the inelastic collision of a nucleus of a given group i. In this case the absorption path λ_i is connected with the interaction path Λ_i by the relationship

$$\lambda_i = \frac{\Lambda_i}{1 - P_{ii}}. \tag{7.20}$$

We shall discuss the values of the "fragmentation probabilities" P_{ik} below.

Finally, in the last column of Table 10 the values are given for the nuclear life in the Galaxy

$$T_{\text{nucl}, i} = \frac{\lambda_i}{\rho c} \tag{7.21}$$

for the relativistic cosmic rays belonging to the corresponding groups. These values are calculated at a mean concentration of the gas in the Galaxy of $n = 10^{-2}$ cm^{-3} (see (7.1)) and a mean interstellar gas density (allowing for 10 per cent of helium) of $\rho = 2 \cdot 2 \times 10^{-26}$ g/cm^3 respectively. It is assumed here, as was indicated at the beginning of this section, that the cosmic rays penetrate freely into the clouds of interstellar gas and in general the mean gas concentration n is at the same time the concentration determining the nuclear life. Another assumption is also conceivable, however, in which the cosmic rays could be largely in regions with a gas concentration less than the average. But this would mean that the cosmic rays do not "mix" in the Galaxy and, for example, move only along the lines of force in which they land when injected from the sources. As we shall see in section 10, this assumption is not only without base but is evidently unacceptable on a number of counts. Here we would draw attention to the part played by time averaging since over a period of the order of about 10^9 years the motion of the clouds and the differential galactic rotation lead to great changes in the field

† For protons Table 10 gives the actual values of λ and T_{nucl} for interaction and not for absorption (for this see pages 25 and 137 and section 17).

configuration. In actual fact the field probably changes its configuration noticeably even in one revolution of the Galaxy which takes about 2×10^8 years in the region of the solar system. Moreover, as is pointed out by Vorontsov-Vel'yaminov,[299] there is a continuous mixing of the gas within the Galaxy connected with the flow of gas from the core along the Galactic plane and its reflux into the core from the halo. This mixing of the gas must definitely lead to mixing of the cosmic rays as well. As a result it can be assumed that deviations of the concentration n determining the nuclear life from the average value of n over the whole volume should not be reflected noticeably in our estimates.

Fragmentation probabilities

The motion of cosmic rays in interstellar space is accompanied by a change in their chemical composition due to fragmentation (fissions) of the heavy nuclei in nuclear interactions with the interstellar gas. For a quantitative estimate we must know the so-called fragmentation probabilities P_{ik} (or p_{ik}) defined as the number of nuclei of a kind k formed on the average in each nuclear interaction (or absorption) of a nucleus of kind i in the interstellar medium. Since the main component of the interstellar gas is hydrogen we shall be interested below largely in the fragmentation probabilities of different nuclei in interactions with hydrogen nuclei in an energy range of the order of several GeV/nucleon corresponding to the majority of the observed cosmic rays.

The fragmentation probabilities can be determined experimentally from an analysis of the interactions of cosmic rays or protons obtained in accelerators in nuclear photo-emulsions. In the first case the difficulty is to pick out the interactions with hydrogen of interest to us from among all the interactions of cosmic rays with the different nuclei making up the emulsions. In the second case, when protons obtained from accelerators are used, difficulties arise when identifying the slow fragments appearing from fissions of the nuclei by the protons.

Because of the experimental difficulties and the insufficient statistical accuracy of the measurements the available data on fragmentation probabilities are not yet reliable enough and, what is most important, are not detailed enough. For example the present known data on the fragmentation probabilities of the H group are based on an analysis of only about 100 H-nucleus fissions which have been studied.[33, 36, 44, 300, 301]   This comparatively small amount of statistical material does not allow any reliable further detail on the fragmentation probabilities for the sub-groups of the H group although this would be very important for a more precise determination of the thickness of matter passed through by the cosmic rays and the chemical composition of the cosmic rays in the sources.

It should be borne in mind that the direct application to cosmic rays of fragmentation probabilities determined from an analysis of the nuclear interactions in photographic emulsions may lead to a certain systematic error. The point is that the life of the cosmic rays is sufficiently great for practically only stable isotopes to be observed in them, these having been accelerated directly in the cosmic ray sources or formed during fragmentation and the subsequent radioactive decay. On the other hand, when the fragmentation probabilities in photographic emulsions are determined, the fragments of a given charge group cover both stable and unstable isotopes with the atomic numbers corresponding to this group. As a result of the subsequent decay the charge group to which a fragment may belong may change. In the interpretation of the observed chemical composition of the cosmic rays, therefore, we must use not only directly observed fragmentation probabilities but also fragmentation probabilities with respect to the final stable products of the fissions. This difference is small for charge groups covering several elements but it is very significant when determining the composition within groups, for example the relative distribution of Li, Be and B nuclei in the group of L nuclei.[302]

The values of the fragmentation probabilities P_{ik} with respect to the path of the inelastic interaction of a nucleus of a kind i in hydrogen are given in Table 11. These values, with the exception of $P_{\alpha\alpha}$, are based on the results of several authors[33, 36, 44, 300, 301] in which an analysis is given of the interactions of cosmic rays with individual nucleons in a photographic emulsion (see the summary of data by Aizu et al.[44]). It is considered that the interaction takes place with an individual nucleon if not more than one track of a heavy slow particle is observed (i.e., the number of "grey" and "black" tracks $N_h < 1$). In this kind of sampling some of the spallations examined occur in peripheral interactions of cosmic rays with the heavy nuclei of the photographic emulsion. It can be assumed, however, that the values obtained are sufficiently close to the true fragmentation probabilities in hydrogen. This is indicated by the available data on the spallation of certain elements in a beam of artificially accelerated protons [303] (see also below).†

TABLE 11

FRAGMENTATION PROBABILITIES P_{ik} IN AN INELASTIC INTERACTION

$i \backslash^{k}$	H	M	L	α
H	$0 \cdot 31 \pm 0 \cdot 07$	$0 \cdot 36 \pm 0 \cdot 07$	$0 \cdot 12 \pm 0 \cdot 04$	$1 \cdot 35 \pm 0 \cdot 18$
M		$0 \cdot 11 \pm 0 \cdot 02$	$0 \cdot 28 \pm 0 \cdot 04$	$1 \cdot 22 \pm 0 \cdot 11$
L			$0 \cdot 15 \pm 0 \cdot 05$	$1 \cdot 09 \pm 0 \cdot 17$
α				$0 \cdot 41 \pm 0 \cdot 03$

The value $P_{\alpha\alpha} = 0 \cdot 41$ given in Table 11 is determined in accordance with the results of Riddiford and Williams[297] where a study was made of the interactions of protons with an energy of 970 MeV with helium. In the calculation of $P_{\alpha\alpha}$ it is assumed that the α group contains nuclei of the helium isotope He^3 as well as α-particles.

The values of P_{ii} in Table 11 were used with formulae (7.20) and (7.21) to determine the absorption paths λ_i and nuclear life-times of cosmic rays in the Galaxy $T_{\text{nucl}, i}$ given in the last two columns of Table 10. It is arbitrarily assumed here that the probabilities P_{ii} for the groups H_1, and H_2 and H_3 coincide with the probability $P_{HH} = 0 \cdot 31$.

Of particular importance for the following are the probabilities of the formation of group L nuclei from heavier ones, i.e., the coefficients P_{HL} and P_{ML}. The available data on the spallation of carbon nuclei by protons with an energy $E = 1 \cdot 6$ GeV obtained from an accelerator[303] agree closely with the value $P_{ML} = 0 \cdot 28$ in Table 11.

According to Zhdanov and Fedotov[303] for a total absorption cross section of 227 ± 12 mb the cross section of the direct formation of L-nuclei from carbon is 63 mb so $p'_{CL} = 0 \cdot 28$. In addition, allowance should be made for the cross section of the formation of the radionuclei C^{10} and C^{11} from which boron is formed as the result of

† The results have recently been published[479] of determining the parameters p_{ik} for hydrogen by comparing the fragmentation of nuclei with $Z > 2$ in polyethylene $(CH_2)_n$ and teflon $(CF_2)_n$. Although the accuracy of the results is low the method used is very promising. The values $p_{HM} < 0 \cdot 25$, $p_{HL} = 0 \cdot 85 \pm 0 \cdot 44$ and $p_{ML} = 0 \cdot 42 \pm 0 \cdot 14$ obtained by Friedlander et al.[479] differ significantly from the data of earlier papers used in our calculations (see Table 12). These results still lack confirmation and we have not used them. The problem of the chemical composition in the light of the values by Friedlander et al.[479] are discussed by Syrovatskii.[480]

β-decay. This cross section, according to Zhdanov and Fedotov[303] is 31 mb. The total cross section of L-nucleus formation during the spallation of carbon by a proton and the subsequent radioactive decay of the fragments is therefore 94 mb and the corresponding probability is $p_{CL} = 0.41$. The formation of Li in the β-decay of He^6 can be ignored since the effective cross section for the appearance of the He^6 isotope in the spallation of carbon by protons is only about 0.5 mb.[304]

As can be seen, allowing for the radioactive decay of unstable fragments leads to a considerable change in the fragmentation probability p_{CL}. On the average, however, this change should evidently be less significant for the M group of nuclei, i.e., with respect to the probability p_{ML}. In addition, it should be borne in mind that the values of P_{ML} given in Table 11 are with respect to the interaction path. Recalculation for the absorption path λ_i is carried out by formulae

$$p_{ik} = \frac{P_{ik}}{1 - P_{ii}}, \qquad (7.22)$$

where p_{ik} is the number of nuclei of a kind k formed in the absorption of a group i nucleus.

Since the reliability of the available data on fragmentation probabilities is low we shall in future use several variants of possible sets of values for the fragmentation probabilities p_{ik} and the absorption paths λ_i for the groups of nuclei. These variants are shown in Table 12.

TABLE 12

	p_{HM}	p_{HL}	$p_{H\alpha}$	p_{ML}	$p_{M\alpha}$	$p_{L\alpha}$	λ_H	λ_M	λ_L	λ_α
a	0.52	0.17	2.0	0.31	1.4	1.3	6.1	7.8	10	34
b	0.38	0.10	1.5	0.26	1.2	1.0	5.5	7.6	9.7	32
c	0.69	0.26	2.5	0.37	1.5	1.6	6.8	7.9	11	36
d	0.7	0.1	3.0	0.4	1.5	1.5	7	8	11	36

The sets of values of p_{ik} and λ_i corresponding to variants a, b and c are determined by formulae (7.22) and (7.20) using the values of P_{ik} from Table 11 and the interaction paths in the interstellar gas Λ_i from Table 10. In this case the a variant corresponds to the mean values of P_{ik} given in Table 11 and variants b and c are determined from the minimum and maximum values of P_{ik} respectively permitted by the statistical limits of error given in Table 11.

We notice that the probability P_{HL}, according to experimental data, is comparatively low in photographic emulsions.† This would mean that the L-nuclei are chiefly formed from the heavier nuclei within a narrow range of atomic number as the result of their losing several nucleons or α-particles and the direct formation of group L nuclei from very heavy nuclei hardly plays any part at all. Moreover, on the average, on the way from the source, due to the more rapid stripping of the heavy nuclei, the cosmic ray composition must differ from that observed on Earth in that there is an increase in the number of heavy nuclei even within the H group nuclei. Under these conditions the probability P_{HL} determined for the H group with the relative element composition observed on Earth may differ noticeably from the effective value of P_{HL} on the whole path from the source. On the basis of what has been said above it may be assumed that the effective value of P_{HL} averaged over the path from the source will be slightly less and the probabilities of the formation of elements next in order of decreasing atomic numbers of the groups will be slightly higher then than those in Table 11, as will also the probabilities for protons and α-particles. To allow for this effect Table 12 also lists variant d in which, in accordance with what has been said, the value of p_{HL} is slightly reduced and the other probabilities are slightly increased. These changes, however, do not in essence go outside the limits of error of the available data, as can be seen from a comparison of variant d and the others listed in Table 12.

A stricter analysis of the question of the composition of cosmic rays requires more detailed information on the fragmentation probabilities particularly for the H group nuclei. In actual fact the H group covers a large number of elements from Ne and at least up to Fe which differ strongly in their atomic weights, interaction paths and nuclear structure. As we shall see below, the mean thickness of matter which cosmic rays pass through before hitting the Earth is considerably greater than the absorption path of the heaviest nuclei of this group. The composition of the H group therefore undergoes noticeable changes on the way from the source. This means that the mean characteristics for the group as a whole such as the absorption path λ_H and the fragmentation probabilities p_{Hi} also vary with the distance from the source and depend on thickness of matter passed through.

† For the sake of comparison we should point out that earlier works[4, 8] took values of 0·23 to 0·48 for P_{HL}.

In order to allow for this effect we must replace the H group by several sub-groups of nuclei with closely similar atomic numbers, for example the sub-groups H_1, H_2 and H_3 (see Table 10). However, the practically complete absence of data on the fragmentation probabilities for these sub-groups does not allow us at present to make any reliable generalisation. Attempts to estimate the fragmentation probabilities for sub-groups of the H group proceeding from theoretical considerations and the available scattered experimental data have been made by several authors.[44, 302] The values taken for the fragmentation probabilities in these papers are shown in Table 12 but these values are only by way of a guide.

TABLE 13

k	H_1	H_2	H_3	M	L	References
H_1	0·40	0·55		0·05	0·0	44
	0·44	0·16	0·14	0·09	0·12	302
H_2			0·28	0·32	0·48	

Secondary electrons appearing in nuclear interactions

Neutral and charged π-mesons are formed in the nuclear interactions of cosmic rays in the interstellar gas as well as the heavy fragments which contribute to the nuclear component of cosmic rays. The neutral π°-mesons decay with the formation of γ-quanta whose intensity was estimated in section 2. The charged π^+-mesons contribute as a result of $\pi \to \mu \to e$ decay to the electron component of cosmic rays. At a high enough interstellar gas density this process could be basic from the point of view of the appearance of relativistic electrons (and positrons) in the Galaxy.[62, 283, 305, 306] Let us now examine this process in greater detail.

An analysis of the generation of π-mesons by cosmic rays in the atmosphere leads to the following expression for the spectral intensity of the electrons that appear as the result of the $\pi \to \mu \to e$ decay of π-mesons formed by the cosmic ray flux over the whole of its path in the atmosphere[67]:

$$I_{e,\,\text{atm}}(E) \, dE = 0 \cdot 020 E^{-2 \cdot 64} \, dE \text{ electrons/cm}^2 \cdot \text{sterad} \cdot \text{sec} \qquad (7.23)$$

(the electron energy E is expressed in GeV). Spectrum (7.23) relates to the $E \gtrsim 1$ GeV energy range.

The path of cosmic rays in which their energy decreases $e = 2 \cdot 72$ times is $\lambda_E = 180$ g/cm^2 (see sections 2 and 17), whilst the mean density of the interstellar gas is $\rho = 2 \times 10^{-26}$ g/cm^3. Therefore after multiplying (7.23) by $4\pi\rho/\lambda_E$ we find that per unit volume the mean power of relativistic electron generation in the Galaxy is†

$$q_e(E) \, dE = 2 \cdot 8 \times 10^{-29} E^{-2 \cdot 64} \, dE \text{ electrons/cm}^3 \cdot \text{sec.} \quad (7.24)$$

Hence we can determine the total number of electrons with an energy $E \geqslant 1$ GeV that appear each second in a unit volume in the Galaxy:

$$q_e(E \geqslant 1 \text{ GeV}) = 1 \cdot 7 \times 10^{-29} \text{ electrons/cm}^3 \cdot \text{sec.} \quad (7.25)$$

If the life of the electrons in question in the Galaxy is $T \simeq 3 \times 10^8$ years (see section 10), then by virtue of (7.25) their concentration should be

$$N_e(E \geqslant 1 \text{ GeV}) = 2 \times 10^{-13} \text{ electrons/cm}^3. \quad (7.26)$$

This concentration is an order less than value (6.6). For more detail on the secondary electron concentration see Section 17.

The spectral intensity $I_e(E)$ of the electrons formed in nuclear interactions of cosmic rays with the interstellar gas can also be determined by another method, namely by taking as a basis the data available on the generation of secondary particles in high-energy p-p collisions.

Let the fraction of primary energy transferred to the electrons in a p-p interaction and the subsequent $\pi \to \mu \to e$ decay be

$$\kappa_e(E) = \kappa E^\alpha, \quad (7.27)$$

and the average number of π-mesons (and electrons respectively) arising from each collision be

$$n_\pi(E) = \nu E^\delta. \quad (7.28)$$

† Here, of course, the additional assumption has been made that it is possible to transfer the data of (7.23) for air to the interstellar medium. Since we are dealing with the generation of π-mesons over the whole path of a particle this assumption is natural. In addition, the cosmic ray flux is considered to be the same everywhere in the Galaxy as it is on Earth.

Then the energy E of the primary proton corresponds to a secondary electron energy

$$E_e = \frac{\kappa_e(E)}{n_\pi(E)} E = \frac{\kappa}{\nu} E^{1+\alpha-\delta}. \tag{7.29}$$

Corresponding to the primary spectrum of the cosmic rays $I(E)dE = KE^{-\gamma}dE$ we thus have the following intensity of the electrons formed over the inelastic interaction path λ:

$$I_e(E_e)\, dE_e = K_e E_e^{-\gamma_e}\, dE_e = n_\pi(E)I(E)\, dE, \tag{7.30}$$

where

$$K_e = \frac{\nu}{1+\alpha-\delta}\left(\frac{\kappa}{\nu}\right)^{\frac{\gamma-1-\delta}{1+\alpha-\delta}} K, \qquad \gamma_e = \frac{\gamma+\alpha-2\delta}{1+\alpha-\delta}. \tag{7.31}$$

From an analysis of the available experimental data[307, 312] it follows that the mean degree of inelasticity of the collisions at high energy hardly depends on the energy (i.e., we can put $\alpha = 0$) and the multiplicity of π-mesons in the $E \gtrsim 10$ GeV range can be represented in the form

$$n_\pi(E) = 2E^\delta, \qquad \delta = 0{\cdot}15 \text{ to } 0{\cdot}25. \tag{7.32}$$

Assuming that approximately 5 per cent of the energy of the primary nucleon is transferred to the electrons (see below), i.e. $\kappa = 0{\cdot}05$, and making the index γ and the coefficient K in the primary spectrum $\gamma = 2{\cdot}5$ and $K = 1$ (see (7.31)), we obtain

$$I_e(E)\, dE = (7 \times 10^{-3} E^{-2{\cdot}59} \text{ to } 6 \times 10^{-3} E^{-2{\cdot}67})\, dE$$

$$\text{electrons/cm}^2 \cdot \text{sterad} \cdot \text{sec.} \tag{7.33}$$

Upon these assumptions the secondary electron spectrum thus proves to be fairly close to the spectrum (7.23) obtained from an analysis of the experimental data on the generation of π-mesons in the atmosphere (to change from (7.33) to (7.23), i.e., from $I_e(E)$ to $I_{e,\,\text{atm}}$, $I_e(E)$ must be multiplied by the ratio $\lambda_E/\lambda = 180/72 = 2{\cdot}5$ since the spectrum (7·33) is the spectrum of the electrons formed over the length of the interaction path λ).

A power-law spectrum occurs for π-mesons (and decay electrons respectively) with an index $\gtrsim 2{\cdot}5$ (cp. (7.23) and (7.33)) only in the energy range $E_\pi \simeq 1{\cdot}4$ GeV.[308, 309] At lower energies, in the range $E \simeq 250$ to 1400 MeV, the π-meson spectrum takes the form[308, 310, 311] $N_\pi(E)\, dE \sim E^{-(1{\cdot}4 \text{ to } 1{\cdot}5)}\, dE$. This change in the spectrum may prove to be significant for interpreting the observed frequency spectrum of the Galaxy's non-thermal radio emission in the low-frequency range (see sections 5 and 6) if the radio-emitting electrons in the Galaxy are really of secondary origin (see, however, section 17).

Let us estimate the electron energy corresponding to the "break" in the π-meson spectrum at $E_\pi \simeq 1\cdot4$ GeV. The kinetic energy of a μ-meson formed in a $\pi \to \mu$ decay in the rest system of a decaying π-meson is $E_{k,\mu}^* = 4\cdot18$ MeV.[71] Since this energy is much less than the rest energy of a μ-meson $m_\mu c^2 = 105$ MeV a decay μ-meson moves in fact at the same velocity as the initial π-meson so the mean energy of the μ-meson formed in the laboratory system is

$$E_\mu = \frac{E_\pi}{m_\pi c^2} E_\mu^* \simeq \frac{E_\pi}{m_\pi c^2} m_\mu c^2 = \frac{1}{1\cdot32} E_\pi, \qquad (7.34)$$

where E_π and m_π are the total energy and rest mass of the initial π-meson.

The mean energy of the electrons formed in a $\mu \to e + v + \bar{v}$ decay is $E_e^* = 34$ MeV. In the laboratory system, therefore, the mean energy of the decay electrons is linked with the energy of the initial π-meson by the relationship

$$E_e = \frac{E_\mu}{m_\mu c^2} E_e^* \simeq 34 \frac{E_\mu}{m_\mu c^2} \text{ MeV} = 0\cdot24 E_\pi. \qquad (7.35)$$

Since the "break" in the π-meson spectrum corresponds to an energy $E_\pi \simeq 1\cdot4$ GeV or $E_\pi/m_\pi c^2 \simeq 10$ the corresponding change in the electron spectrum should occur in the $E_e \simeq 0\cdot34$ GeV energy range.† In this case even a very sharp break in the π-meson spectrum is reflected in the electron spectrum in the form of a smooth transition since in the laboratory system there is a considerable scatter of energies around the mean value of (7.35). In actual fact when a μ-meson decays the maximum energy of the decay electrons is $E_{e, \max}^*$ = 53 MeV. Since in the system fixed at the μ-meson the decay electron distribution is isotropic on the average in the laboratory system the energy scatter of electrons arising from the decay of a μ-meson with an energy $E_\mu \simeq 1$ GeV is

$$E_e = \frac{E_\mu}{m_\mu c^2} E_{e, \max}^* \pm \frac{p_\mu c}{m_\mu c^2} c p_{e, \max}^* \simeq 4 \text{ to } 700 \text{ MeV.} \qquad (7.36)$$

† We should point out here that for an inelasticity coefficient (the fraction of energy transmitted to all the π-mesons) of $0\cdot3$ and $N_\pi^\pm/N_{\pi^\circ} = 2$ the fraction of the nucleon's primary energy transferred to electrons during a collision is $\kappa = 0\cdot24 \times 0\cdot3 \times \frac{2}{3} = 0\cdot05$, i.e., 5 per cent (cp. (7.27)).

For electron energies of $E \lesssim 300$ MeV their spectrum should approach a power-law one with an index $\gamma_e = 1\cdot4$ to $1\cdot5$ corresponding to the π-meson spectrum in the corresponding energy range.

This energy blurring of the electrons, however, and the fact that for $E_\pi < 200$ MeV the π-meson spectrum should strongly change its form† (in particular, the spectrum passes through a maximum and near the threshold becomes zero (see Fig. 20)) does not allow us in general to approximate the secondary electron spectrum for $E_e < 1$ GeV by a power-law function. The qualitative discussions given allow us only to draw the conclusion that the secondary electron spectrum for $E_e < 1$ GeV should be steeper than in the region of higher energies.

As has already been pointed out in section 6 it is this behaviour of the electron spectrum in the Galaxy that is a consequence of the non-thermal Galactic radio emission spectrum. This can be looked upon as an argument in favour of the secondary nature of the radio-emitting electrons in the Galaxy. At the same time we should stress the necessity of obtaining more precise data on the π-meson spectrum and that of the decay electrons generated in nuclear interactions of cosmic rays particularly in the low energy region.

It follows from a more detailed calculation of the spectrum and intensity of the secondary electrons (see section 17) that the intensity of their magnetic bremsstrahlung is insufficient to explain the thermal radio emission of the Galaxy.

8. ENERGY LOSSES FOR ELECTRONS

During motion in the interstellar medium the electron energy is reduced due to ionisation, radiation (bremsstrahlung), "Compton" and magnetic bremsstrahlung losses. In the cases of interest to us the losses for electrons and positrons are identical (below, therefore, electrons will be taken to mean both electrons and positrons).

Ionisation and radiation losses

The ionisation losses of non-relativistic electrons are of no interest here and we shall limit ourselves to the remark that in this case we may in the first approximation use formulae (7.2) and (7.3) or (7.6)

---

† The minimum kinetic energy of $\pi^\pm$-mesons generated on fixed nucleons is 11 MeV.

with $Z = 1$ and $M = m$. In the ultra-relativistic case (for an electron energy $E \gg mc^2$) the ionisation losses in atomic hydrogen are as follows:

$$-\left(\frac{dE}{dt}\right)_i = \frac{2\pi e^4 n}{mc}\left\{\ln\frac{E^3}{mc^2 I^2} - 2\right\} = 1\cdot53 \times 10^5\left\{3\ln\frac{E}{mc^2} + 18\cdot8\right\}$$

$$\frac{eV\cdot cm^2}{g}$$

$$= 2\cdot54 \times 10^{-19} n\left\{3\ln\frac{E}{mc^2} + 18\cdot8\right\} eV/cm$$

$$= 7\cdot62 \times 10^{-9} n\left\{3\ln\frac{E}{mc^2} + 18\cdot8\right\} eV/sec. \qquad (8.1)$$

Here n is the concentration of hydrogen atoms and the effective ionisation energy I is assumed to be 15 eV. Formula (8.1) differs from (7.5) with $M = m$ only in the absence of the factor 2 under the sign of the logarithm (this difference is connected with the fact that the maximum energy transferred by an electron to an electron must be made equal to $E/2$).

Since the energy I in formula (8.1) is theoretically not defined it may be said that this formula is true only with an accuracy up to a certain factor under the logarithm sign (with the value $I = 15$ eV taken the inaccuracy of formula (8.1) clearly does not exceed a few percent and decreases as E/mc^2 rises). In addition, formula (8.1) relates only to the case when the density effect can be ignored. This is permissible as long as $v/c < 1/\sqrt{\varepsilon(0)}$, where v is the velocity of the particle and $\varepsilon(0)$ is the dielectric constant at a frequency $\omega = 0$. In atomic hydrogen $\varepsilon(0) = 1 + 4\pi\alpha n$, $\alpha = (9/2)(\hbar^2/me^2)^3 \sim 10^{-24}$ cm^3 and the density effect can be ignored at values of E/mc^2 less than $1/\sqrt{4\pi\alpha n} \sim 3 \times 10^{11}/\sqrt{n}$. Even with $n \sim 100$ cm^{-3} this means that formula (8.1) can be used for an electron energy of $E < 10^{16}$ eV.

The ionisation losses on non-hydrogen atoms can in the first approximation be determined by the same formula (8.1) where n must be taken as the concentration of all the atomic electrons. For a mixture containing 90 per cent H and 10 per cent He the ionisation losses are approximately 10 per cent greater than in pure hydrogen (for the same total concentration of the atoms). The contribution made by elements heavier than He does not exceed 1 per cent.

Therefore, allowing for the inaccuracy of determining the gas concentration in the cosmos, the interstellar medium can be replaced by hydrogen when calculating the ionisation losses.

In a completely ionised gas the ionisation losses are (n is the electron concentration)[†]

$$-\left(\frac{dE}{dt}\right)_i = \frac{2\pi e^4 n_e}{mc}\left\{\ln\frac{m^2 c^2 E}{4e^2 n\hbar^2} - \frac{3}{4}\right\}$$

$$= 7.62 \times 10^{-9} n\left\{\ln\frac{E}{mc^2} - \ln n + 73.4\right\} \text{ eV/sec.} \qquad (8.2)$$

For $n = 0.1$ cm^{-3} and $E = 5 \times 10^8$ eV losses (8.2) are twice as much as losses (8.1).

Radiation (or bremsstrahlung) losses are caused by the formation of bremsstrahlung γ-quanta in collisions of electrons with the medium's nuclei and electrons. When there is no screening (in the fully ionised interstellar plasma in particular[74]) we have for the radiation losses[70]

$$-\frac{1}{E}\left(\frac{dE}{dt}\right)_r = \frac{4e^6 nZ(Z+1)}{m^2 c^4 \hbar}\left[\ln\frac{2E}{mc^2} - \frac{1}{3}\right]$$

$$= 2.74 \times 10^{-3}\left\{\ln\frac{E}{mc^2} + 0.36\right\}\text{g}^{-1}\cdot\text{cm}^2$$

$$= 1.37 \times 10^{-16} n\left\{\ln\frac{E}{mc^2} + 0.36\right\}\text{ sec}^{-1}, \qquad (8.3)$$

where n is the concentration of atoms with atomic number Z and when changing to numerical values we have put $Z = 1$ (hydrogen). In a non-ionised gas with $E \gtrsim 10^9$ eV a good approximation is the formula corresponding to total screening[70]:

[†] We should recall that ionisation losses are all energy losses going not only into the excitation and ionisation of the atoms but also into Vavilov–Cherenkov emission and the formation of δ-electrons. In a completely ionised plasma the ionisation losses are made up of the losses in the formation of δ-electrons ("near collisions") and the losses connected with the Cherenkov emission of plasma waves ("distant collisions").

We should also point out that previously[4, 5] an expression was used differing from (8.2) by a small factor under the logarithm sign. This factor was determined more precisely by Tsytovich[284] and was reduced to the appearance (in the last expression of (8.2) for example) of the term 73.4 instead of the earlier[4, 5] 74.6.

$$-\frac{1}{E}\left(\frac{dE}{dt}\right)_r = \frac{4e^6 nZ(Z+1)}{m^2 c^4 \hbar}\left[\ln(191Z^{-\frac{1}{3}}) + \frac{1}{18}\right]$$

$$= 7 \cdot 26 \times 10^{-16} n \ \text{sec}^{-1}. \tag{8.4}$$

Losses (8.3) and (8.4) are comparable at $E/mc^2 \simeq 10^4$, whilst for $E/mc^2 \simeq 10^3$ (i.e., for $E \simeq 5 \times 10^8$ eV) losses (8.3) are approximately two thirds of losses (8.4). The value given for the logarithm in (8.4) is inaccurate for the light elements and it must be increased by 10 per cent.[70] As a result for non-ionised hydrogen

$$-\frac{1}{E}\left(\frac{dE}{dt}\right)_r = 1 \cdot 6 \times 10^{-2} \ \text{g}^{-1} \cdot \text{cm}^2 = 8 \cdot 0 \times 10^{-16} n \ \text{sec}^{-1}. \tag{8.5}$$

The "shower" or t-unit of length in which the electron energy on the average is reduced due to radiation losses by a factor of $e = 2 \cdot 72$ is 62 g/cm^2 in accordance with (8.5). In helium with the same concentration n the radiation losses are 3 times greater than in hydrogen. Therefore in a mixture of 90 per cent H and 10 per cent He the radiation losses are 1·2 times greater than in hydrogen. Inaccuracy in determining the concentration n under cosmic conditions generally makes it superfluous to introduce the corresponding correction (see, however, the footnote on page 29 and section 19). It must be stressed that the radiation losses are not continuous since the energy of a bremsstrahlung γ-quantum is generally of the order of the energy of an electron. Roughly speaking it may therefore be taken that there are no radiation losses in general on a particle's path but as it passes through a 62 g/cm^2 layer the electron at once loses all its energy (it is more correct to consider that all the energy is lost in one event but the probability of an electron passing over a path of L g/cm^2 without losses is $e^{-L/62}$).

"Compton" energy losses

Electrons also lose energy in collisions with thermal photons located in interstellar and intergalactic space (the stars are the main source of thermal emission). This effect—the scattering of electrons on photons—is sometimes called the "inverse Compton effect" and the corresponding losses "Compton" losses.[313, 207]

In a coordinate system fixed at the electron the photon energy $\varepsilon' = (E/mc^2)\varepsilon(1 - \beta\cos\alpha)$, where $\beta = v/c$; v is the velocity of the electron; ε and E are the energies of the photon and the electron in a "fixed" ("laboratory") system of reference—in the present case in a system fixed in the Galaxy; the angle between the directions of motion of the electron and photon in the "fixed" system is denoted by α. On the average for isotropic emission or isotropic directional distribution of the electrons

$$\bar{\varepsilon}' = \frac{E}{mc^2}\,\bar{\varepsilon} \quad \text{and} \quad \bar{\varepsilon}' \ll mc^2,$$

if

$$\frac{E}{mc^2}\cdot\frac{\bar{\varepsilon}}{mc^2} \ll 1, \tag{8.6}$$

where $\bar{\varepsilon}$ and $\bar{\varepsilon}'$ are appropriate mean energies.

With this condition the scattering cross section of non-polarised photons by an electron is the Thomson cross section:

$$d\sigma_T = \frac{1}{2}\left(\frac{e^2}{mc^2}\right)^2 (1 + \cos^2\theta)\,d\Omega;$$

$$\sigma_T = \int d\sigma = \frac{8\pi}{3}\left(\frac{e^2}{mc^2}\right)^2 = 6{\cdot}65 \times 10^{-25}\ \text{cm}^2, \tag{8.7}$$

where θ is the scattering angle; $d\Omega = 2\pi \sin\theta\,d\theta$.

In practice cross section (8.7) can be used with sufficient accuracy as long as $(E/mc^2)(\bar{\varepsilon}/mc^2) \lesssim \frac{1}{4}$ which at $\bar{\varepsilon} \simeq 1$ eV occurs for electrons with an energy $E \lesssim 5 \times 10^{10}$ eV. Under cosmic conditions it is generally these electrons which are of interest but in individual cases (the Crab Nebula, the "jet" in Virgo A) electrons of greater energies are also found. Under the inverse conditions to (8.6), i.e., when

$$\frac{E}{mc^2}\cdot\frac{\bar{\varepsilon}}{mc^2} \gg 1, \tag{8.8}$$

we must use the cross section[70, 72] (see Heitler's monograph[72] for the cross section in the general case)

$$\sigma = \frac{3}{8}\sigma_T \frac{mc^2}{\varepsilon'}\left(\ln\frac{2\varepsilon'}{mc^2} + \frac{1}{2}\right). \tag{8.9}$$

In the case of (8.6) and (8.7) the mean energy and longitudinal momentum transmitted by a photon to an electron in the reference system, where the electron has come to rest before scattering, are

$$\bar{E}' = \frac{\overline{(\varepsilon')^2}}{mc^2} \quad \text{and} \quad \bar{p}'_v = \int \frac{\bar{\varepsilon}'}{c}(1 - \cos\theta)\frac{d\sigma_T}{\sigma_T} = \frac{\bar{\varepsilon}'}{c}$$

respectively. Therefore in the fixed system the mean energy transferred to a thermal photon by relativistic electrons is

$$\Delta \bar{E} = -\frac{(\bar{E}' + v\bar{p}'_v)}{\sqrt{1 - v^2/c^2}} \simeq -\frac{c\bar{p}'_v}{\sqrt{1 - v^2/c^2}} = -\frac{\bar{\varepsilon}'E}{mc^2},$$

or finally†

$$\Delta E = -\bar{\varepsilon}\left(\frac{E}{mc^2}\right)^2. \tag{8.10}$$

Hence we obtain the approximate expression for the Compton losses

$$-\left(\frac{dE}{dt}\right)_c \simeq c\sigma_T \bar{n}_{ph} \Delta E = c\sigma_T w_{ph}\left(\frac{E}{mc^2}\right)^2 = 2 \times 10^{-14} w_{ph}\left(\frac{E}{mc^2}\right)^2$$

$$\text{eV/sec,} \quad (8.11)$$

where $\bar{n}_{ph}$ is the average number of photons; $w_{ph} = \bar{n}_{ph}\bar{\varepsilon}$ is a certain mean density of the emission energy measured in eV/cm^3.

In the case of (8.8) and (8.9) at each collision an electron loses the energy $\Delta E \approx E^{313, \ 314}$. Therefore

$$-\left(\frac{dE}{dt}\right)_c \simeq c\sigma \bar{n}_{ph}E \simeq \tfrac{3}{8}c\sigma_T w_{ph}\left(\frac{mc^2}{\bar{\varepsilon}}\right)^2 \ln\left(\frac{2E\bar{\varepsilon}}{m^2c^4} + \frac{1}{2}\right)$$

$$\simeq 10^{-14}\left(\frac{mc^2}{\bar{\varepsilon}}\right)^2 w_{ph} \ln\left(\frac{2E\bar{\varepsilon}}{m^2c^4}\right) \text{ eV/sec.} \tag{8.11a}$$

For $(E/mc^2)(\bar{\varepsilon}/mc^2) \simeq 1$ the values of (8.11) and (8.11a) are of the same order, as should be the case. Formula (8.11a) is valid for $\bar{\varepsilon} \simeq 1$ eV if $E \gg 2 \cdot 5 \times 10^{11}$ eV.

Under conditions (8.8) electron-positron pairs may be generated in collisions of electrons with photons. The corresponding energy losses,[313, 314] however, differ from the losses (8.11a) by a factor of the order of $2 \times 10^{-3} \ln (E\bar{\varepsilon}/m^2c^4)$ which in the majority of cases is considerably less than unity.

Magnetic bremsstrahlung losses

When moving in a magnetic field an electron with an energy $E \gg mc^2$ loses the energy:‡

† A more accurate calculation (see section 19) leads to the appearance of the factor 4/3 in (8.10) and (8.11).

‡ This expression can, of course, be obtained by integrating (4.24) with respect to all frequencies. It is simpler, however, to derive formula (8.12) directly.[165]

$$-\left(\frac{dE}{dt}\right)_m = \tfrac{2}{3}c\left(\frac{e^2}{mc^2}\right)^2 H_\perp^2\left(\frac{E}{mc^2}\right)^2 = 0{\cdot}98 \times 10^{-3}H_\perp^2\left(\frac{E}{mc^2}\right)^2 \text{ eV/sec,}$$

$$(8.12)$$

where $H_\perp$ is the magnetic field component at right angles to the electron's velocity (in the second expression the field $H_\perp$ is measured in oersteds).

Integrating equation (8.12) we obtain

$$\frac{mc^2}{E} - \frac{mc^2}{E_0} = \frac{2e^4H_\perp^2}{3m^3c^5}\,t;$$

$$(8.13)$$

$$E = E_0\left(1 + 1{\cdot}9 \times 10^{-9}\,\frac{E_0}{mc^2}\,H_\perp^2 t\right)^{-1}.$$

Here E is the energy at time t and E_0 is the energy at time $t = 0$.

The characteristic "life" of electrons with respect to magnetic bremsstrahlung losses is

$$T_m = \frac{3m^3c^5}{2e^4H_\perp^2}\frac{mc^2}{E} = \frac{5 \times 10^8}{H_\perp^2}\frac{mc^2}{E}\text{ sec.}$$

$$(8.14)$$

The energy of an electron is halved in the time T_m.

The part played by different types of losses for electrons moving in the Galaxy and Metagalaxy

Let us now compare the energy losses which electrons undergo as the result of the various processes.

The Compton losses (8.11) and the magnetic bremsstrahlung losses (8.12) depend in exactly the same way on the energy and their ratio is

$$\zeta = \frac{(dE/dt)_c}{(dE/dt)_m} \simeq \frac{2 \times 10^{-11}w_{\text{ph}}}{H_\perp^2},$$

$$(8.15)$$

where $H_\perp$ is measured in oersteds and the emission energy density w_{ph} in eV/cm^3. When the magnetic bremsstrahlung and Compton energy losses of an electron are allowed for, its energy decreases in accordance with

$$E = \frac{E_0}{1 + (3{\cdot}8 \times 10^{-15}H_\perp^2 + 7{\cdot}7 \times 10^{-26}w_{\text{ph}})E_0 t},$$

$$(8.16)$$

where E_0 is the electron's energy (in eV) at $t = 0$; w_{ph} is measured in eV/cm^3, t in seconds and $H_\perp$ in oersteds.†
    According to Allen[315] in the Galaxy $w_{ph} \simeq 1\cdot2 \times 10^{-12}$ $erg/cm^3 = 0\cdot75$ eV/cm^3. According to other data[224] in the region of the Galactic disk $w_{ph} = 0\cdot2$ eV/cm^3 (the interstellar absorption of light is significant in the disk) and in the halo $w_{ph} = 0\cdot4$ eV/cm^3 (at a distance of 9 kpc above the galactic plane). In view of the great importance of the question of the value of w_{ph} we shall give here the corresponding estimates for the halo and metagalactic space.
    The optical emission of our Galaxy is $L \simeq 4 \times 10^{43}$ erg/sec (for the Sun $L = 3\cdot86 \times 10^{33}$ erg/sec). In the case of a point source at a distance r from it the emission flux is $S = L/4\pi r^2$ and the energy density is $w_{ph} = S/c = L/4\pi r^2 c$. Hence at $r = 3$ kpc $\simeq 10^{22}$ cm the density is $w_{ph} \simeq 10^{-12}$ $erg/cm^3 \simeq 0\cdot6$ eV/cm^3. It is clear that the mean value of w_{ph} in a spherical region with a radius R_0 is

$$\frac{3}{4\pi R_0^3} \int_0^{R_0} w_{ph} 4\pi r^2 \, dr = \frac{3L}{4\pi c R_0^2}$$

and for $L = 4 \times 10^{43}$ erg/sec, $R_0 = 10$ kpc we have $w_{ph} \simeq 0\cdot2$ eV/cm^3. For a luminous disk and not a point a value is obtained which is close to this. Averaged over the halo, therefore, there is complete justification for the estimate

$$w_{ph, halo} \gtrsim 0\cdot3 \ eV/cm^3; \qquad w_{ph, halo, max} \simeq 1 \ eV/cm^3. \qquad (8.17)$$

    † In the case in question, when $\bar{\varepsilon}E/(mc^2)^2 \ll 1$ (condition (8.6)), the magnetic bremsstrahlung and Compton losses are very alike in nature and are identically determined by the energy density of the electromagnetic field. In actual fact for a magnetic field that is isotropic on the average $H_\perp{}^2 = \frac{2}{3}H^2$ and the magnetic bremsstrahlung losses are (see (8.12))

$$-\left(\frac{dE}{dt}\right)_m = \frac{32\pi}{9} c \left(\frac{e^2}{mc^2}\right)^2 \left(\frac{E}{mc^2}\right)^2 \frac{H^2}{8\pi}.$$

The Compton losses in case (8.6) are

$$-\left(\frac{dE}{dt}\right)_k = \frac{32\pi}{9} c \left(\frac{e^2}{mc^2}\right)^2 \left(\frac{E}{mc^2}\right)^2 w_{ph}$$

(see (8.11) with the addition of the factor 4/3 obtaining in the more accurate calculation made in section 19). Therefore the total magnetic bremsstrahlung and Compton losses are really proportional to the sum of the field's magnetic energy density and the electromagnetic energy density of the photon field, i.e., the sum $(H^2/8\pi) + w_{ph}$.

For the Local Group of galaxies the density w_{ph} of the emission leaving the group's galaxies can be estimated as follows. The mass of all the galaxies of the group is approximately 7 times greater than the mass of the Galaxy and the radius of the group is 2×10^{24} cm (for further details see section 12). In the first approximation, therefore, we can use the estimate $w_{ph} = 3L/4\pi c R_0^2$, considering the luminosity L to be 7 times greater than for the Galaxy (in actual fact the luminosity L is only 3 to 4 times greater than for the Galaxy) and the radius R_0 to be 2×10^{24} cm. Hence $w_{ph, \text{Loc. Group}} \simeq 3 \times 10^{-4}$ eV/cm^3. This value is less than the value of $w_{ph, Mg}$ for the Metagalaxy so within the Local Group the value of $w_{ph, Mg}$ can be used for the estimates.

In order to determine $w_{ph, Mg}$ in the Metagalaxy let us introduce the mean value LN_G of the product of the galaxies, luminosity L and their concentration N_G. The photometric radius of the Metagalaxy is

$$R_{ph} \simeq \int_0^{cT_{Mg}} \left(1 - \frac{r}{cT_{Mg}} \right) dr = \frac{cT_{Mg}}{2}$$

(here $cT_{Mg} = c/h$; the introduction of R_{ph} is connected with the red shift in the spectrum of the galaxies when in the first approximation for $r \lesssim R_{ph}$ we have the ratio $\Delta v/v = hr/c$; see section 13). In the centre of a sphere with a radius R_{ph} the emission intensity is $I = N_G L R_{ph}/4\pi$ and the isotropic emission energy density is

$$w_{ph} = \frac{4\pi I}{c} = \frac{N_G L R_{ph}}{c}. \tag{8.18}$$

The value of w_{ph} does not depend on the scale of distances since $N_G \sim l^{-3}$, $L \sim l^{-2}$ and $R_{ph} \sim l$ (l is a factor defining the scale variation). If we use the data given by Allen[315] (see section 13), then $w_{ph, Mg} \simeq 2 \cdot 5 \times 10^{-3}$ eV/cm^3 (Allen uses an old scale of distances and gives the value $L \simeq 5 \cdot 8 \times 10^{41}$ erg/sec which corresponds to a mean absolute stellar magnitude $M_0 = -15 \cdot 2$, $N_G = 10^{-73}$ galaxy/cm^3 and $R_{ph} = cT_{Mg}/2 = 2 \times 10^{27}$ cm). It is best, however, not to have recourse to any recalculations but to make direct use of the Metagalaxy's emission intensity I_{Mg}. Unfortunately there are no direct measurements of this quantity yet but as an initial value we can take the value of I_{Mg} obtained as a result of observing the visible brightness of the galaxies. According to Allen[315] $I_{Mg} = 0 \cdot 5$ for galaxies of the 10th photographic magnitude per square degree. Hence

$$w_{ph, Mg} \simeq 2 \times 10^{-3} \text{ eV/cm}^3. \qquad (8.19)$$

It is impossible to be dogmatic in stating that this value is too low and it is scarcely possible to increase it more than a few times; in this connexion it must be assumed that the value $w_{ph, Mg} = 0.25$ eV/cm^3 indicated by Allen[315] (see section 13) does not correspond to the facts (H. Bondi, who made this estimate[386], told one of the authors that he set himself the task of merely indicating the upper limit of $w_{ph, Mg}$; we would note that the calculations by McVittie[395] lead to a value of w_{ph} which is several times greater than the estimate (8.19)). It should also be pointed out that the estimate (8.19) by its very nature refers only to the emission observed from the Earth. If in metagalactic space there were emission concentrated in the region of the spectrum which is still inaccessible to observation its intensity could significantly exceed the value given. A reliable determination of $w_{ph, Mg}$ based on measurements outside the atmosphere is a very important problem that cannot be put off. It is most probable, however, that the estimate (8.19) is valid and we shall use it in the remaining parts of the book without further reservations.

Using the value $w_{ph, halo} = 0.3$ eV/cm^3 we see that the Compton losses in the halo are equivalent to the action of a field $H_\perp = \sqrt{H^2_\perp}$ $\simeq 2.5 \times 10^{-6}$ oe. In the case of the Metagalaxy the Compton losses for $w_{ph, Mg} \simeq 2 \times 10^{-3}$ eV/cm^3 are equivalent to the losses in a field $H_\perp \simeq 2 \times 10^{-7}$ oe (the values selected for $w_{ph, halo}$ and $w_{ph, Mg}$ here are evidently minimum values; see above).

The density w_{ph} and the field $H_\perp$ were considered not to be dependent on the time. Otherwise in (8.16) we must replace $H^2_\perp t$ and $w_{ph} t$ by

$$\int_0^t H_\perp(t) \, dt \quad \text{and} \quad \int_0^t w_{ph}(t) \, dt.$$

This fact is significant, for example, if the Compton losses are calculated in an expanding cosmological model. The value found for (8.19) above relates to the present epoch, the density $w_{ph, Mg}$ having been higher previously. With homogeneous expansion and constant brightness of the galaxies in the Einstein–de Sitter model (see section 13)

$$w_{\text{ph, Mg}}(t) = w_{\text{ph, Mg}}(T_{\text{Mg}}) \left[\frac{R(T_{\text{Mg}})}{R(t)} \right]^{3/2} = w_{\text{ph, Mg}}(T_{\text{Mg}}) \left(\frac{T_{\text{Mg}}}{t} \right);$$

$$\int_{T_0}^{T_{\text{Mg}}} w_{\text{ph, Mg}}(t) \, dt = w_{\text{ph Mg}}(T_{\text{Mg}}) \cdot T_{\text{Mg}} \cdot \ln \frac{T_{\text{Mg}}}{T_0}.$$

(8.20)

Since the galaxies were formed in the course of 10^8 years (we are speaking of the cosmological model used) we can put $T_0 \simeq 10^8$ yr and thus in the calculations of the Compton losses during the evolution of the Metagalaxy use the value $w_{\text{ph, Mg}} \simeq 5 \times 10^{-3}$ eV/cm^3 (this means that in formula (8.16) $w_{\text{ph, Mg}}t$ must be replaced by $5 \times 10^{-3} T_{\text{Mg}} \simeq 1.5 \times 10^{15}$).

The ratio of the radiation to the ionisation losses in atomic hydrogen in accordance with (8.1) and (8.5) is

$$\eta_\alpha = \frac{(dE/dt)_r}{(dE/dt)_i} = \frac{1.05 \times 10^{-7} E}{3 \ln E/mc^2 + 18.8}.$$

(8.21)

In the case of an ionised gas, bearing formulae (8.2) and (8.3) in mind,

$$\eta_i = \frac{1.8 \times 10^{-8} (\ln E/mc^2 + 0.36) E}{\ln E/mc^2 - \ln n + 73.4}.$$

(8.22)

In (8.21) and (8.22) the energy E is measured in eV. For $E = 5 \times 10^8$ eV $\eta_\alpha \simeq 3$ and $\eta_i \simeq 2$ (with $|\ln n| \lesssim 10$). Hence it is clear that for $E \gtrsim 10^9$ eV the ionisation losses are small when compared with the radiation losses and for $E \lesssim 10^8$ eV the opposite is the case. The ratio of the ionisation losses (8.1) to the magnetic bremsstrahlung losses (8.12) is

$$\xi = \frac{(dE/dt)_i}{(dE/dt)_m} = \frac{2.3 \times 10^{-5} n (\ln E/mc^2 + 6.3)}{H_\perp^2 (E/mc^2)^2}.$$

(8.23)

For a completely ionised medium the parameter ξ according to (8.2) is approximately twice the value of (8.23). For $E = 5 \times 10^8$ eV the parameter $\xi \simeq 3 \times 10^{-10} n / H_\perp^2$ and, for example, $\xi = 1$ for $n = 0.3$ cm^{-3} and $H_\perp \simeq 10^{-5}$ oe or for $n \simeq 10^{-2}$ cm^{-3} and $H_\perp \simeq 2 \times 10^{-6}$ oe.

9. ACCELERATION MECHANISMS AND COSMIC RAY INJECTION

After the energy spectrum and composition of cosmic rays had been elucidated in the first approximation as a result of the experimental study of primary cosmic rays on the Earth it became possible to define more closely the problem of the origin of cosmic rays. Here we shall examine two questions which are of great importance for any theory of the origin of cosmic rays.

The first of them—the question of the acceleration mechanisms—relates to the nature of the processes which result in the particles acquiring the very high energies observed in cosmic rays. This question could be evaded in a certain sense or, to be more precise, relegated to the sphere of as yet unsolved cosmological problems if it is assumed that the cosmic rays arose in the process of formation of the Galaxy or at early stages in the evolution of the Metagalaxy. In this case we can try to link all the properties of the cosmic rays with certain insufficiently known specific conditions which existed at these stages of the Universe's evolution. The cosmic rays, therefore, must be considered to be "remnants" preserved in the Galaxy (or Metagalaxy) from early stages of its development.

Not to mention the fact that it is hard to consider this point of view in any way constructive, it should be pointed out that the concept of cosmic ray remnants meets with very serious difficulties when interpreting the available data (see Chapter IV). In addition, this point of view can be scarcely justified because the generation of relativistic particles can be observed directly at present. One can point in particular to such phenomena as supernova flares, radio galaxies and the directly observable processes of cosmic ray generation on the Sun. There is every reason, therefore, for analysing the cosmic ray generation mechanism taking as a basis the existing physical and astrophysical considerations as applied in the first place to the actual conditions in the shells of supernovae, in galaxies.

The second problem is linked with the problem of injection and is as follows. Which of the particles in the region of action of an accelerating mechanism reach cosmic ray energies? What determines their share and chemical composition in relation to all the other particles in a source?

Both these questions are basic ones for the theory of the origin of cosmic rays in the narrow sense of the word, understood as the theory of the generation of relativistic particles under actual astrophysical conditions. We shall devote the present section to the discussion of these questions.

Basic types of acceleration mechanisms

At present the best developed and most firmly based concept is that of the electromagnetic nature of the acceleration of the particles making up the cosmic rays. There is a number of concrete mechanisms of this kind which will ensure the acceleration of particles to high energies under actual astrophysical conditions. The basic mechanisms of these will be discussed slightly later. Here we would stress that all the electromagnetic acceleration mechanisms are based on the action of an electric induction field appearing in the medium when the magnetic field strength varies in time. An induction field of this kind acts in a positive manner on a charged particle if the strength of the magnetic field in which it is moving rises in time and the characteristic scale of the field is not small when compared with the particle's radius of curvature.†

This is also valid for the acceleration of particles when they collide with moving magnetic "walls" (see below) if we bear in mind that the passage of a magnetic wall through a certain region of space is equivalent to a rise in the magnetic field strength in this region.

The most important distinctive feature of electromagnetic mechanisms is the smooth nature of the acceleration in which the high final energy is reached gradually (continuously or in small increments). This circumstance is particularly significant since it allows to explain the presence of ultra-relativistic heavy nuclei in cosmic rays. It is clear that a complex nucleus can be kept whole during the process of acceleration only if it acquires energy in sufficiently

---

† In actual fact the change in a particle's energy over the period of its rotation in a slowly changing magnetic field is

$$\Delta E = e \int (\mathscr{E} \cdot \mathbf{v})/dt = e \int (\mathscr{E} \cdot d\mathbf{l}) \simeq e \oint (\mathscr{E} \cdot d\mathbf{l}) = \frac{|e|}{c} \frac{\partial \Phi}{\partial t},$$

where $\mathscr{E}$ is the strength of the electric induction field and Φ is the magnetic field flux through the particle's orbit whose projection onto a plane at right angles to the direction of the magnetic field can in the first approximation be considered as closed; the appearance of $|e|$ in front of $\partial \Phi/\partial t$ is connected with allowing for the relative direction of the vectors $\mathbf{v}$ and $\mathscr{E}$ during the particle's motion in an alternating magnetic field. Acceleration by shock waves in an inhomogeneous magnetic field is discussed by Wentzel.[483]

small increments. This requirement, which proceeds from the presence of heavy nuclei in cosmic rays, is clearly fairly general. From this point of view it is natural to assume that the acceleration is macroscopic in nature and is not the consequence of a certain elementary event or collision process as would occur, for example, in ultra-relativistic shock waves.

Acceleration in shock waves is a mechanism which can be considered separately from the electromagnetic mechanism.† By the nature of the matter when particles are accelerated in shock waves it is a question of heating and macroscopic acceleration of a gas as the result of the passage of a shock wave front.

Normal shock waves formed in the collision of gaseous masses cannot lead directly to the formation of relativistic particles. For example, even with a gas velocity of about 10^4 km/sec the particle energy is only about 0·5 MeV/nucleon. However, in special cases such as when there are cumulative effects present or when very strong shock waves are being propagated in a medium with decreasing density the part they play could, in principle, be more significant.

For example Colgate and Johnson[316] discusses a concrete model of a supernova flare and assumes that the shock wave arising as the result of the sudden collapse of the star converts into cosmic rays the whole surface layer of the star starting from the level with a density of about 1 g/cm³. The theory of supernova flares has not yet been developed in any complete form. However, it is already possible to adduce a number of considerations which indicate that the generation of galactic cosmic rays in shock waves could hardly occur. In actual fact the presence of a considerable fraction of heavy nuclei in the composition of cosmic rays, as was pointed out above, indicates the gradual collection of energy by these particles. If the energy were collected in some rapid process of momentum transfer from one part of the gaseous medium to another, as occurs during the propagation of ultra-relativistic shock waves, then the collisions of particles with each other inevitable in this process and also with γ-quanta of the emission field (photofission) would lead to the destruction of the heavy nuclei at relativistic energies. In addition, Colgate and Johnson[316] had to make certain radical and as yet unfounded assumptions on the structure of a shock wave

† We are not thinking of magnetohydrodynamic shock waves here. In order to estimate the magnitude of the acceleration on the fronts of waves of this kind we can roughly use the adiabatic invariant theory (see below).[426]

front. Lastly, the formation of relativistic particles in this way is accompanied by the transfer to non-relativistic particles of energy of an order of magnitude larger and this involves definite difficulties of an energetic nature. All this allows us to assume that shock waves, if they play a part in the generation of cosmic rays, can act only as "injectors" of fast particles which are then accelerated to the observed energies by some other mechanism.† All such mechanisms which are known have, in essence, an electromagnetic nature.

Regular electromagnetic acceleration

There are two basically different forms of electromagnetic acceleration mechanisms: betatron acceleration in a homogeneous magnetic field that is increasing in time[317] and acceleration of particles in collisions with moving magnetic field inhomogeneities.[318] All known electromagnetic mechanisms can either be reduced to one of these types or are a combination of them.

Betatron acceleration is discussed most simply by using the adiabatic invariant of the motion of a particle in a slowly changing magnetic field. As is well known, if a magnetic field is slowly changing along the path of a particle during the period of its Larmor rotation $T_H = 2\pi/\omega_H = 2\pi E/eHc$ there is the approximate relationship (the adiabatic invariant)

$$\frac{p_\perp^2}{H} \equiv \frac{p^2 \sin^2 \theta}{H} = \text{const}, \tag{9.1}$$

where $p_\perp = p \sin \theta$ is the component of the particle's momentum at right angles to the magnetic field H, and θ is the angle between the direction of motion and the direction of H. Relationship (9.1) is valid with an accuracy up to at least terms of the second order of smallness[319] with respect to the ratios T_H/τ and $r_H|\nabla H|/H$, where τ and $|\nabla H|$ are the characteristic period and gradient of the magnetic field and r_H is the radius of curvature (of the Larmor orbit) of the particle.‡

† The hypothesis of the generation of cosmic rays in the shock wave arising from the explosion of a supernova has recently been developed further by Colgate and White.[482] This paper calculates a model for the explosion of a supernova including the assumption that after collapse an outward-moving shock wave appears (this occurs after the nuclear forces of repulsion at short distances have come into play). We find it hard to judge the degree to which this model corresponds to the truth and allows the above-mentioned difficulties to be overcome.

‡ If the field H depends only on time, this relationship being sufficiently smooth, the adiabatic invariant has exponential accuracy.[320, 321]

In betatron acceleration the longitudinal (with respect to the magnetic field) component of the particle momentum $p_{\parallel}$ is invariant and for the transverse component we have $p_{\perp}^2 \propto H$ from the adiabatic invariant (9.1). Expressing H in terms of the radius of the particle's Larmor orbit $rH = cp_{\perp}/ZeH$ we obtain $p_{\perp}^2 \propto 1/r_H^2$, $H \propto 1/r_H^2$.[†] An increase in the momentum and magnetic field is thus linked with a compression of the Larmor orbits.[‡] For an ionised gas this is equivalent to a transverse compression of the gas. With a compression of this kind the volume of one particle is $V \propto r_H^2$ and thus $p^2 \simeq p_{\perp}^2 \propto 1/V$, where we have ignored the invariant longitudinal component of the momentum (for a cylinder $V = \pi r_H^2 l$, where the length l remains constant during the transverse compression in question). Hence the kinetic energy of particles is connected with the volume they occupy by the relationship

$$E_k \propto 1/V^{\gamma-1}, \qquad (9.2)$$

where $\gamma = 2$ for non-relativistic energies[322] ($E_k \propto p^2$) and $\gamma = 3/2$ for ultrarelativistic energies ($E_k \simeq E \propto p$). Relationship (9.2) and the values given for γ correspond to the normal adiabatic heating law for a gas when it is compressed in the case of a gas of particles with two degrees of freedom. If the gas compression is isotropic on the average, i.e., $V \propto r_H^3$, then the values of γ, as can be easily confirmed, agree with their ordinary values for a monatomic gas: $\gamma = 5/3$ in the non-relativistic case and $\gamma = 4/3$ in the ultra-relativistic case (it must be borne in mind that

$$p_{\perp}^2 \simeq p^2 \sim \frac{1}{r_H^2}, \qquad r_H \sim V^{1/3}, \qquad E_k \sim V^{1-\gamma}).$$

When the magnetic field returns to its initial value the particles slow down to their initial velocities. The process is completely reversible and therefore, if the magnetic field in the medium is at a constant level on the average, the energy of the particles is also unvarying on the average. A resultant acceleration, on the contrary, occurs if, for example, the field is inhomogeneous and the particle succeeds in leaving the region of the increasing field before it starts to decrease.[317]

† We should point out that the relationship $H \propto 1/r_H^2$ obtained in this way corresponds to the usual one of a "frozen-in" magnetic field for the conducting medium, i.e., to the condition of preservation of the magnetic flux through the material contour.

‡ There is an analogous situation when a charged particle passes through the front of a magnetohydrodynamic shock wave. In this case, however, the adiabatic invariant is valid only as to an order of magnitude.[426]

The second class of electromagnetic acceleration mechanisms—acceleration in collisions with moving magnetic field inhomogeneities—is simplest to discuss with a model of collisions with a moving solid wall. The part of this wall, obviously, is played by a region of a strong magnetic field that reflects the particles incident upon it. From the law of the conservation of energy and momentum in each such collision it is easy to find the increment of the total energy E of the particle in one collision[5, 318]

$$\Delta E = -\frac{2E}{c^2}(u \cdot v), \qquad (9.3)$$

where the velocity of the wall u is considered to be small as compared to that of the particle v.

We notice that in a collision with a magnetic inhomogeneity the acceleration at the final count is caused by the electric induction field $\mathscr{E} = -(1/c)[u \wedge H]$ arising when the magnetic field "frozen" in the medium is transferred with a velocity u. In actual fact the change in a particle's energy after reflexion from a moving magnetic "wall" (Fig. 17) is just equal to expression (9.3)

$$\Delta E = Ze \int (\mathscr{E} \cdot ds) = 2Ze\mathscr{E}r_H \sin \phi$$

$$= 2Ze \frac{uH}{c} \frac{Ev_\perp}{ZeHc} \sin \phi = -\frac{2E}{c^2}(u \cdot v).$$

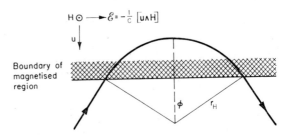

Fig. 17. Collision of a particle with a moving magnetized region (cloud). The magnetic field points towards the reader.

Here we have taken into account that the radius of curvature is $r_H = Ev_\perp/ZeHc$. At the same time we must stress that the result of

(9.3) does not depend on the actual mechanism of the collision of the particle with a wall. In other words, if this collision (and the transfer of energy and momentum connected with it) occurred by virtue of a non-electromagnetic interaction (for example due to gravitational forces) formula (9.3) would remain unchanged. Therefore by including the acceleration mechanism in question with the electromagnetic one we have in mind the fact that the collision of cosmic rays with a moving inhomogeneity takes place due to the action of electromagnetic forces.

During the spiral motion of a particle along a converging tube of lines of magnetic force the transverse component of the momentum first increases (due to the increase in the magnetic field just as in betatron acceleration) but after reflection it decreases to its initial value. Only the longitudinal component of the momentum (which is also subjected to the above-mentioned reflexion) receives a final change (if the tube is moving). A situation of this type may occur, for example, when particles are accelerated in a "magnetic trap" with "plugs" moving towards each other, i.e., with regions where the lines of magnetic force are concentrated. It is sometimes considered that this is the mechanism accelerating the particles forming the Earth's radiation belts.

If a particle is subjected to head-on collisions only, i.e., is located between converging magnetic "walls", then its energy, just as in betatron acceleration, varies in accordance with the law of adiabatic compression (9.2). Here, however, the particle has only one degree of freedom so in (9.2) $\gamma = 3$ for non-relativistic energies[322] and $\gamma = 2$ for ultra-relativistic energies. In actual fact in the time $\Delta t = 2l/v_\perp$, where l is the distance between the walls and $v_\perp$ is the particle's velocity component normal to the walls, the rate of change of the particle's energy is (see (9.3))

$$\frac{dE}{dt} \simeq \frac{\Delta E_1 + \Delta E_2}{\Delta t} = \frac{2Ev_\perp^2}{c^2}\frac{u_1 + u_2}{2l} = -\frac{Ev_\perp^2}{c^2}\frac{1}{l}\frac{dl}{dt}. \quad (9.4)$$

Here u_1 and u_2 are the absolute values of the velocity of each of the walls and, obviously, $u_1 + u_2 = -dl/dt$. If we ignore the velocity component parallel to the walls which is invariant for this acceleration and bear in mind the relationship $E^2v^2/c^2 = c^2p^2$, then from (9.4) we have

$$\frac{1}{p}\frac{dp}{dt} = -\frac{1}{l}\frac{dl}{dt}$$

so $p \infty 1/l$. Since in the one-dimensional compression in question $V \infty l$ this last relationship is equivalent to the law governing the variation of the particle's momentum $p \infty 1/V$. This also leads to the conclusion drawn above that law (9.2) for the adiabatic "heating" of a gas of particles when it is compressed is valid with the values of γ corresponding to the one-dimensional case.

If the walls are not strictly parallel and as a result of scattering all the velocity components become on the average equal, i.e., all the degrees of freedom of a particle take part in the acceleration, then, as should be the case in ordinary adiabatic compression, $\gamma = 5/3$ in the non-relativistic case and $\gamma = 4/3$ in the ultra-relativistic case. Isotropic distribution is apparently closest to that occurring under actual conditions, so in estimates of the effectiveness of regular acceleration we can generally use relationship (9.2) with the values $\gamma = 5/3$ and $\gamma = 4/3$.

Although the mechanisms discussed may ensure a high enough rate of energy pick-up determined by the rate of increase in the magnetic field or the velocity of the "walls" there are considerable limitations on the maximum energy achieved. For example in the case of converging magnetic walls it is clear that the particle cannot be squeezed into a volume smaller than its radius of curvature in the walls' magnetic fields. In the general case the maximum achievable energy is determined by the degree of compression of the medium permissible under actual conditions. For example for regular acceleration of particles from thermal energies of the order of 1 to 10 eV $\simeq$ 10^4 to 10^5 °K to relativistic energies of about 1 to 10 GeV, even in the most favourable case when $\gamma = 3$ in (9.3), the medium must be compressed 10^4 to 10^5 times. There is little probability of such compression under actual astrophysical conditions. The possibility of multiple acceleration of this kind, is, of course, not excluded. In this case the particle is accelerated in a certain converging region, then arrives in another converging region and so on. As the result of passing through k-regions with an increase in energy of x times in each of them the particle's energy is increased by a factor x^k. Very special conditions are necessary, however, for this kind of regular cascaded acceleration to occur. Regular acceleration is therefore most likely to play a part only at the initial stage of acceleration[323] and the acceleration to the high energies observed in cosmic rays is achieved by other mechanisms.

Statistical acceleration mechanisms

Depending on the sign of the change in the field in time or on the direction of motion of the magnetic inhomogeneities regular acceleration will lead either to an increase or a decrease in the particle energy.

If both of these processes take place on the average at more or less the same frequency the appearance of fast particles is nevertheless possible as the result of the following two effects.

The first of these is linked with the fact that a particle can be "carried" and arrives in the acceleration phase many times. Its energy will then rise rapidly (in the extreme case in the same way as in the regular "cascade" acceleration discussed above). However, the probability of such a fluctuating statistical acceleration is low and thus the number of accelerated particles is small.

Fluctuating acceleration will be discussed further in section 16. At present we shall examine the second effect which occurs if the probabilities of an increase and decrease in the energy to a given value are not equal. Therefore when averaging over a sufficiently large interval of time we shall observe a certain differential or, as we might say, average statistical acceleration. During betatron acceleration this resultant acceleration will occur, for example, if as the result of collections with magnetic field inhomogeneities the particle's energy is redistributed between the degrees of freedom corresponding to motions along (momentum $p_{\parallel}$) and at right angles to (momentum $p_{\perp}$) the field.[324-326] In this case after each collision (at $t = t_i$) the components of the particle's momentum p are on the average $p_{\perp}^2(t_i) = \frac{2}{3}p^2(t_i)$ and $p_{\parallel}^2(t_i) = \frac{1}{3}p^2(t_i)$. If the next collision occurs after a time τ then at the moment immediately before this collision

$$p^2(t_i + \tau) = \frac{1}{3}p^2(t_i) + \frac{2}{3}p^2(t_i)\frac{H(t_i + \tau)}{H(t_i)}$$

$$= \frac{1}{3}p^2(t_i)\left[1 + 2\frac{H(t_i + \tau)}{H(t_i)}\right],$$

where it is borne in mind that only $p_{\perp}$ changes in accordance with (9.1). Let the frequency of the collisions be twice as great as the frequency of the magnetic field oscillations, i.e., $H(t_i + \tau) = H + \Delta H$, $H(T_i + 2\tau) = H(t_i) = H$.   Then in the time of a complete cycle of the field the change in the momentum is

$$p^2(t_i + 2\tau) = \tfrac{1}{3}p^2(t_i + \tau)\left[1 + 2\,\frac{H(t_i + 2\tau)}{H(t_i + \tau)}\right]$$

$$\simeq \tfrac{1}{9}p^2(t_i)\left[9 + 2\left(\frac{\Delta H}{H}\right)^2\right].$$

Hence

$$\Delta p^2 \simeq \frac{2}{9}\left(\frac{\Delta H}{H}\right)^2 p^2. \tag{9.5}$$

In the general case of an arbitrary collision statistics the increment of the square of the total momentum, just as in (9.5), is a second order differential effect with respect to the amplitude of the oscillation field,† whilst the change in one half-cycle is an effect of the order of $\Delta H/H$.

In collisions with randomly moving magnetic field inhomogeneities the mean statistical acceleration is caused by the greater probability of head-on collisions than "overtaking" collisions in which the particle loses energy.[318] These probabilities for the simplest case of head-on collisions are $(v + u)/2v$ and $(v - u)/2v$ respectively. Therefore the mean change in a particle's energy in a collision is (see (9.3))

$$\overline{\Delta E} = \zeta\,\frac{u^2}{c^2}\,E, \qquad \zeta \sim 1. \tag{9.6}$$

If all the collisions are head on $\zeta = 2$; for the case of spherical elastically scattering inhomogeneities[329] $\zeta = 4/3$. As can be seen, in this case the energy increment is an effect of the second order of smallness with respect to u/c, whilst the change in energy as the result of one collision in regular acceleration is proportional to the first power of u/c (cp. (9.3)).

If the effective length of the free path of particles relative to their collisions with clouds is $1 = v\tau$ (τ is the time of free flight and v

† If the frequency of the collisons $1/\tau$ differs strongly from the frequency of the field's fluctuations the effectiveness of the acceleration is noticeably reduced. In the limit of $\tau \to 0$ the particle's energy has a well-defined connexion with the field strength (the momentum $p \propto H^{1/3}$) and if the latter remains on the average unchanged in time there is no resultant acceleration. As $\tau \to 0$ we return in fact to the adiabatic law (9.2) since for the transverse compression of a "frozen" field in question $H \propto V^{-1}$.

is the velocity of the particles) the mean rate of increase of the energy is defined by the equation.

$$\frac{dE}{dt} = \alpha \frac{v}{c} E, \qquad \alpha = \frac{u^2}{cl} = \frac{u^2}{cv\tau}. \tag{9.7}$$

For spherical clouds the length figuring here is

$$l = \frac{1}{\frac{4}{3}\pi r^2 N_{cl}},$$

where r is the radius of the clouds and N_{cl} their concentration.

This mechanism is the perfect equivalent of heating of a cold gas (cosmic rays) mixed with a hot gas (the "particles" of this hot gas are the macroscopic magnetised clouds of gas). Since the "temperature" of the magnetised clouds, i.e., the kinetic energy of their macroscopic motion, is infinite in practice from the standpoint of the scales of an individual accelerated particle this mechanism can in essence provide unlimited acceleration of cosmic ray particles. The limit is set by the life of a particle in the accelerating region (i.e., in the region with the intense gas motions and strong magnetic fields under discussion). In addition the coefficient α can be considered constant only if the cosmic ray concentration is low enough for their total energy in a given volume to be considerably less than the kinetic energy of all the clouds in the same volume. In the opposite case, it is necessary, of course, to allow for braking of the clouds by the cosmic rays and for the corresponding decrease in the coefficient α.

Electromagnetic mechanisms may thus firstly ensure a comparatively rapid, but limited in magnitude, regular acceleration which, when applied to the problem of the acceleration of cosmic rays, is reduced in all known cases simply to adiabatic heating of a gas upon compression. In the second place a slower† statistical acceleration may occur which, however, will act for the whole life of a particle in the accelerating region.‡

† The statement by Byakov and Avalov[327] that a statistical electromagnetic mechanism exists which ensures a rapid (in first order of u/c) collection of energy is linked with an error made in this work in determining the mean time of acceleration.

‡ We have not touched above on the question of the acceleration of particles by high-frequency electromagnetic waves. This includes acceleration by the pressure of light (in a vacuum) and the more interesting acceleration by radiation when the effect of the medium is allowed for.[328] Highly specific conditions are necessary for such acceleration to be effective.

The injection problem

Let us now examine in greater detail the initial stage of particle acceleration and the problem of injection connected with it. The importance of this problem is due to the fact that it is the initial stage of acceleration that determines to a considerable degree a characteristic property of cosmic rays like their chemical composition. As we know (see section 1), a considerable excess of heavy nuclei when compared with their natural distribution is observed in cosmic rays. We clearly cannot avoid the presumption that there is preferential acceleration of these heavy elements in the cosmic ray sources (see section 15) if we are to explain this fact. At the same time a simple comparison of the rate of energy collection (see, e.g., (9.7)) and the ionisation and collision losses in the medium can lead to the conclusion[4, 318] that there is considerable difficulty in the acceleration of heavy multiply-charged ions so their share should be noticeably reduced. In actual fact let the energy collection rate be defined by expression (9.7) which we can write in the form

$$\frac{dE}{dt} = \alpha\sqrt{E^2 - (Mc^2)^2},\tag{9.8}$$

where M is the mass of the particle being accelerated. As follows from the results given in section 7 the ionisation and collision losses in the medium can be represented in the form

$$-\left(\frac{dE}{dt}\right)_i = \frac{4\pi e^4 Z^2 nL}{mv}.\tag{9.9}$$

Here L is weakly (logarithmically) dependent on the energy; in future we shall consider this factor to be constant and equal to its mean value in the range of values of interest to us. If we define the kinetic energy of injection $E_{k,\,i}$ as the energy of a particle starting from which the increase in energy exceeds the losses, then by comparing expressions (9.8) and (9.9) we find for non-relativistic velocities ($E_k \ll Mc^2$)

$$E_{k,\,i} = \frac{2\pi e^4 Z^2 nL}{mc\alpha} \simeq 7 \times 10^9 \frac{Z^2 n}{c\alpha}.\tag{9.10}$$

In the substitution of numerical values here it is taken that $L = 20$. The strong dependence of expression (9.10) on the particle's charge just shows that for multiply-charged ions the injection threshold lies considerably higher with respect to energy so the share of heavy ions accelerated in ordinary decreasing energy distributions of particles will be considerably less than for light ions.

In the case of sufficiently effective acceleration this difficulty is eliminated when a more detailed analysis is made of the effect of losses on the acceleration in the non-relativistic region.[330] The point is that, as has already been pointed out in section 7, the ionisation losses reach a maximum at a particle velocity close to the velocity v_e of the electrons in the medium and decrease rapidly in the low energy region. Therefore when there is a sufficiently effective acceleration (i.e., a large enough value of α) a situation is possible when the energy

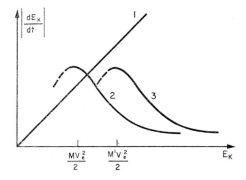

Fig. 18. Non-injection acceleration of heavy particles. The energy increase rate is shown by curve 1, the ionisation losses by curves 2 and 3. Curve 2 for a light particle intersects curve 1 and the point of intersection defines the injection energy. Curve 3 for a heavy particle runs below curve 1 everywhere, i.e., the energy losses are smaller than the gains everywhere in the accleration process.

collection rate is always greater than the loss rate. In other words the acceleration may be "non-injection" acceleration for particles with any initial energies. In this case it turns out that as the mass of the particle increases the requirements for effectiveness of acceleration become weaker: at one and the same rate of acceleration the *injection* threshold may be high enough for light nuclei and be practically absent for heavy ones. This situation can be seen qualitatively in Fig. 18 where the particle energy is plotted on the abscissa and the absolute values of the energy collection rate (curve 1) and the energy losses (curves 2 and 3) on the ordinate.

For the sake of simplicity we here assume that the law governing the energy variation is

$$\frac{dE_k}{dt} = \beta E_k,$$
(9.11)

and this can occur, for example, during regular acceleration (if the compression law is such that $dV/dt \infty V$; see (9.2)). For particles with masses M and $M' > M$ and identical initial ionisation† the loss curves may be of about the same magnitude at the maximum. In this case the maximum of the loss curve for the heavier particle will be shifted M'/M times to the right and the corresponding curve (curve 3 in Fig. 18), unlike the loss curve for the lighter particle (curve 2), cannot intersect the energy collection curve. Since the point of intersection defines the injection energy the heavier particles will be accelerated without injection, i.e., independently of their initial energy, whilst for the lighter particles the presence of an injection threshold makes acceleration difficult.

Similar arguments can be presented for an arbitrary acceleration mechanism and allowance can be made for the effect of loss of electrons by a particle as its velocity increases (see section 7).

This has been discussed in particular by Korchak and Syrovatskii[330] for statistical acceleration in accordance with the law (9.7), (9.8). In this case the value of the maximum losses can be estimated approximately with the aid of expression (9.9) for $v \simeq v_e$ which gives the correct order of magnitudes (see section 7). In addition, it is assumed that for $v < v_e$ the ionisation losses can be ignored when compared with the energy collection rate if the latter exceeds the losses at the maximum. With these assumptions it is not hard to determine a parameter $\alpha_c(A)$ such that for $\alpha > \alpha_c(A)$ non-injection acceleration will take place for all nuclei with mass numbers greater than or equal to A, whilst the lighter nuclei will be accelerated only beginning at a certain threshold energy.

If the particle's charge Z does not change during the acceleration process and corresponds to its initial ionisation the parameter $\alpha_c(A)$ is

---

† It is assumed here that the temperature, and thus the degree of ionisation as well, of the gas in the acceleration region are not too high ($T \simeq 10^4$ to 10^5 °K, $Z \simeq 1$ to 2). If the ionisation is amost complete, which may occur during injection by strong shock waves or when gas is ejected from the interior of a star, the strong dependence of the losses (9.10) on Z makes the acceleration of heavy nuclei practically impossible.

$$\alpha_c(A) = \frac{4\pi n e^4 L Z^2}{mc v_e^2 M} = \alpha_c(p)\frac{Z^2}{A}.$$ (9.12)

Here $\alpha_c(p)$ denotes the value of the parameter α_c for protons;

$$\alpha_c(p) = \frac{4\pi n e^4 L}{mc v_e^2 M_p},$$

where M_p is the mass of a proton.

If at each point in time an equilibrium charge succeeds in establishing itself $Z \simeq Z_0{}^{1/3}(v/v_0)$ (see (7.11)), then

$$\alpha_c(A) = \alpha_c(p)\left(\frac{v_e}{v_0}\right)^2 \frac{Z_0^{2/3}}{A}.$$ (9.13)

Expression (9.13) gives an upper estimate for the critical parameter α_c upon the condition that the mean velocity of the medium's electrons is $v_e > v_0 Z_0{}^{-1/3} Z$ (cp. (7.11)). In the region $v_e < v_0 Z_0{}^{-1/3} Z$, i.e., in a medium with a not very high temperature $T \lesssim 10^5 Z_0{}^{-2/3} Z^2$, we should use expression (9.12) as before with Z equal to the ion's initial charge.

At a density of the medium of $n = 10^3$ cm^{-3} and a temperature of 10^3 °K the values of α_c calculated by formulae (9.12) and (9.13) are 0.6×10^{-9} and 1.2×10^{-9} respectively for iron, whilst for hydrogen under the same conditions[331] $\alpha_c(p) = 8.1 \times 10^{-9}$. It has been shown by Ginzburg[5,332,333] that these values of the parameter α may be achieved in supernova shells.

Lastly, there is no reason to assume that the values of α fall within the required limits by chance. However, if at an initial point in time, for example immediately after a supernova flare, α were high enough non-injection acceleration of all the nuclei of the shell (i.e., simply heating of the gas) will lead to rapid dissipation of the turbulent motion and a corresponding decrease in α until acceleration becomes possible only for a comparatively small number of heavy elements.

It is clear from the foregoing that non-injection acceleration corresponds to a very rapid rise in energy during which the ionisation losses for a given kind of particle are generally not significant. All such particles start to be accelerated practically simultaneously at the moment the accelerating mechanism is "switched on". During less intense acceleration when the injection threshold is significant, only particles with energies exceeding this threshold will be accelerated, i.e., particles belonging to the "tail" of the energy (in the simplest case thermal) distribution of the particles. As a result the spectrum becomes poor in fast particles near the threshold. However, collisions between particles trying to restore the equilibrium distribution will lead to the appearance in space of energies of a certain particle flux from the pre-threshold region going into the region where the accelerating mechanism acts. During sufficiently slow acceleration when the majority of the particles have energies below the threshold this flux can be taken as stationary (to be more precise quasi-stationary). In this case, of course, we must speak not simply of the fraction of accelerated particles but of their flux, i.e., of the number of particles accelerated per unit time.

An attempt has been made[329, 335] to estimate this particle flux into the "superthermal" energy region during statistical acceleration (9.7) to (9.8). These papers, however, discuss only one kind of particle, whilst the decisive rôle in the problem of ion injection is played by electron–ion collisions. The problem is examined more strictly for the statistical acceleration mechanism (9.7), (9.8) by Gurevich[335] with an allowance made for the losses in electron–ion collisions. This discussion is valid at low enough values of the acceleration parameter α defined by expression (9.7) when a quasi-stationary approximation is valid. Basing ourselves on the results of Gurevich[335] we can show that if†

$$1 \ll \frac{E_{k,i}}{kT} \frac{m}{M_i} \ll \frac{M_i}{m} \qquad (9.14)$$

the flux of accelerated ions with a mass M_i, whose concentration is N_i, is

$$-\frac{dN_i}{dt} = N_i \sqrt{\frac{8M_i}{\pi kT}} \frac{c\alpha E_{k,i}}{kT} \exp\left\{-4 \frac{E_{k,i}}{kT} \frac{m}{M_i}\right\}, \qquad (9.15)$$

where m is the mass of an electron and T is the temperature of the medium. After substituting the values of the constants we find with the aid of (9.10)

$$-\frac{1}{N_i} \frac{dN_i}{dt} = 9 \times 10^3 \frac{N}{T^{3/2}} Z^2 A^{1/2} \exp\left\{-3 \cdot 7 \times 10^{-6} \frac{N}{T\alpha} \frac{Z^2}{A}\right\}. \qquad (9.16)$$

† These conditions are connected in particular with the possibility of using the quasi-stationary approximation in question.

Here N is the concentration of the electrons in the medium. The left-hand side of expression (9.16) defines the relative number of ions of a kind i accelerated per unit time. In view of the strong dependence of the exponential index on the mass of the ion (the mass number A) at one and the same degree of ionisation (ion charge Z) there will be considerably more accelerated particles among the heavy ions than among the light ones. Thus preferential acceleration of heavy nuclei is possible in this case also. However, the nucleus flux will be large enough only at a low injection threshold near the left-hand limit of those in (9.14). Let us estimate this flux by assuming that the exponential index in (9.15) to (9.16) has a value of -16 which is clearly still possible under conditions (9.14). In this case $\alpha = 2\cdot3 \times 10^{-7}(N/T)(Z^2/A)$ and with the values $N = 10\,\mathrm{cm}^{-3}$, $T = 10^{4\circ}\mathrm{K}$, $Z = 1$ and $A = 16$ we obtain $\alpha = 1\cdot4 \times 10^{-11}\ \mathrm{sec}^{-1}$ and $(1/N_i)(dN_i/dt) \simeq 10^{-8}\ \mathrm{sec}^{-1}$. With this rate of acceleration in a time of about 10^8 sec $\simeq 3$ yr practically all the nuclei with $A = 16$ will be accelerated in a source and in a time of the order of $1/\alpha \simeq 7 \times 10^{10}$ sec $\simeq 2000$ yr they will acquire relativistic energy if the acceleration rate remains unchanged. We notice that as early as $A = 12$ the relative number of accelerated particles will be about 2×10^2 times less for the same Z. The values of the parameter $\alpha \simeq u^2/cl \gtrsim 10^{-11}\ \mathrm{sec}^{-1}$ are fully achievable, for example, in the early stages of supernova flares when we can assume random velocities of $u \gtrsim 3 \times 10^7$ cm/sec and characteristic magnetic field inhomogeneity dimensions of $l \lesssim 3 \times 10^{15}$ cm.

The preferential injection of heavy nuclei discussed here relates directly only to the case when the particle charge remains unchanged during acceleration and the same for different ions. As we saw in section 7, this does not generally occur. Moreover in the case of non-injection acceleration the statement that there is preferential acceleration of heavy elements is valid even allowing for the stripping of electrons in the acceleration process. It can be assumed that there is an analogous situation for the particle flux over the injection threshold (at least when there is a sufficiently effective acceleration when a noticeable fraction of the ions does not succeed in being completely ionised). In this case, of course, the dependence of fluxes (9.15) and (9.16) on Z and A will be significantly different.

10. THE NATURE OF THE MOTION OF COSMIC RAYS IN THE GALAXY

The high degree of isotropy of cosmic rays has served as one of the indications that cosmic rays reach the Earth from the sources indirectly and after complex motion and scatter in the interstellar magnetic fields. This motion can be looked upon as a kind of "diffusion" of the cosmic rays in interstellar space during which the particles "forget" their initial direction of motion. The elucidation of the true nature of this diffusion, however, is a fairly complex problem. Before discussing it let us first examine the simplest cases.

Motion of an individual particle in a given magnetic field

In a given external magnetic field whose characteristic scale and characteristic time of change are large compared with the radius of curvature of the particle's trajectory and the period of its rotation in this field the motion of the particle proceeds in accordance with the adiabatic invariant (9.1). At the same time in the inhomogeneous field the centre of the Larmor orbit of the particle moves in practice along one and the same line of force, being subjected to only a slight shift (drift) in a direction at right angles to the direction of the magnetic field and its gradient. This drift, depending on the magnetic field inhomogeneity, may vary in nature[336] but its velocity v_d in order of magnitude must always be estimated from the condition

$$v_d \simeq \frac{r_H}{l} v. \tag{10.1}$$

Here v is the particle's velocity,† l is the characteristic scale of the magnetic field inhomogeneity and r_H is the radius of curvature (radius of the Larmor orbit), equal in the ultra-relativistic case to

$$r_H = \frac{E \sin \theta}{300ZH}; \tag{10.2}$$

here the energy E is measured in eV, the field H in oersteds and r_H in cm.

---

† If the field gradient is at right angles to the actual field, then v should be taken to mean $v_\perp$, i.e., the velocity at right angles to the field. If, however, it is a question of "centrifugal" drift connected with a twisting of the lines of force, then v in (10.1) is the particle's velocity along the field lines. In centrifugal drift l is the radius of curvature of the lines of force.

It follows from relationship (10.1) that in the time it takes to traverse a path of the order of the size of the field inhomogeneity, i.e., in the time $t \sim l/v$, the particle moves from the initial line of force a distance of the order of the radius of its Larmor orbit. For most of the cosmic rays with energies $E \simeq 10^9$ to 10^{10} eV the velocity is $v \simeq c$, so in an interstellar magnetic field with a strength $H \simeq 10^{-5}$ to 10^{-6} oersteds the radius of curvature is $r_H \simeq 10^{12}$ to 10^{13} cm. At the same time the characteristic scale of the interstellar magnetic field inhomogeneities, according to various estimates[5, 337] (see also section 16), lies within the limits 3 to 100 pc $= 10^{19}$ to 3×10^{20} cm. Therefore the drift velocity of the particles is relatively small ($v_d \simeq 10^3$ to 10^4 cm/sec) and, for example, for a proton the total distance travelled as the result of drift in the nuclear life $T_p \simeq 10^{17}$ sec is only 10^{20} to 10^{21} cm (we would remark that the total distance travelled in this time is 3×10^{27} cm $= 10^9$ pc).

Let us now examine the effects connected with the variation of the magnetic field in time. The electrical induction field $\mathscr{E}$ which appears when the magnetic field varies causes the particles to drift at a velocity

$$v_d = c \frac{[\mathscr{E} \wedge H]}{H^2}. \tag{10.3}$$

Moreover, if the interstellar gas is highly conductive any variation in the magnetic field in time (at a given point in space) is connected simply with the movement and deformation of the medium and the corresponding deformation of the "frozen in" magnetic lines of force in the medium. In this case it follows from the condition for being "frozen in" $\mathscr{E} = -(1/c)[u \wedge H]$, where u is the velocity of the medium, that the drift velocity (10.3) is just equal to the velocity of the parallel movement of the lines of magnetic force connected with the medium. Therefore, with this kind of drift a particle always remains on one and the same line of force.

When there is weak drift, therefore, it can be taken in the first approximation that the particles move along lines of force. This motion, in which the drift can in fact be ignored, will be called "adiabatic".

Diffusion in a given magnetic field (magnetic cloud model)

The adiabatic motion of the particle along the lines of force described above occurs, as has already been indicated, only if the radius of curvature of the trajectory of the particle is considerably less than the size of the magnetic field inhomogeneities, i.e., $r_H \ll l$. If this condition is not fulfilled everywhere on the particle's trajectory the motion may have the nature of ordinary diffusion. These regions, in which the condition of adiabaticity is broken, may be regions where there is a sharp change in the field (for example shock waves in a conducting medium if the width of their front is small enough) and also those regions of space in which the magnetic field strength becomes zero so $r_H = \infty$.

The simplest example of diffusion in a given magnetic field is the motion of particles in a magnetic field consisting of individual "clouds" or "loops" between which the field is very weak or completely absent (for the latter reason the adiabatic approximation in the motion between the clouds is invalid). These clouds could be in particular magnetised clouds† of ionised gas moving in a non-magnetic neutral gas. If l_0 is the mean size of the clouds in which the field is H_0 and l is the distance travelled by a particle before colliding with a cloud, the field H between the clouds being negligibly small ($l \ll r_H = E/300H$), then these clouds are ordinary scattering centres.

It is not difficult to determine the coefficient of diffusion for particles moving among such clouds[338]. If $r_{H_0} = E/300H_0 \lesssim l_0$ a particle with an energy E is subjected to scattering at a broad angle in each collision with a cloud. Therefore the effective length of the free path is the distance $l \simeq 1/l_0^2 N_{cl}$ travelled by the particle before collisions with a cloud (N_{cl} is the number of clouds with respect to unit volume) and the diffusion coefficient is

$$D_0 = \tfrac{1}{3}lv \simeq \frac{c}{3l_0^2 N_{cl}}, \qquad (10.4)$$

where the velocity v for cosmic rays is made equal to c (it is considered that between clouds a particle moves practically along a straight line).

If the opposite condition $r_{H_0} \gg l_0$ is fulfilled, then each time a particle passes through a cloud the particle undergoes only a small deflexion by an angle $\phi \sim l_0/r_{H_0}$. The mean square deviation after k collisions of this kind is $\overline{\phi^2} \sim k(l_0/r_{H_0})^2$. Therefore taking the

† The term "magnetised cloud" indicates that there is a "frozen" magnetic field in the cloud.

scattering length l_1 to be the distance over which $\overline{\phi^2} \sim 1$ we obtain $l_1 \simeq kl \simeq (r_{H_0}/l_0)^2 l$ and the corresponding diffusion coefficient will be

$$D(E) \simeq \tfrac{1}{3}lv\left(\frac{r_{H_0}}{l_0}\right)^2 = D_0\left(\frac{E}{E_0}\right)^2. \tag{10.5}$$

Here $E_0 = 300H_0l_0$ is the critical value of the particle's energy at which its radius of curvature is comparable in order of magntiude with the size of the scattering magnetic cloud and D_0 is defined by expression (10.4).

The cases of adiabatic motion and free diffusion discussed are in essence the two extreme cases for the possible types of motion of charged particles in given magnetic fields. Let us now turn to an examination of the actual situation for cosmic rays in the Galaxy.

Nature of the motion of cosmic rays in the Galaxy. The diffusion approximation

The small rate of drift when selecting the magnetic field inhomogeneity scales ordinarily used for the Galaxy allows us in principle to assume that cosmic rays move practically only along the lines of force of a certain quasi-stationary interstellar magnetic field. In this case the particles should remain all the time on the lines of force which they hit when injected in the actual source. This assumption is frequently made in published works but it leads to certain difficulties and, in our opinion, is inadequate for the real conditions for the motion of cosmic rays in the magnetic field of the Galaxy.

Above all it would be necessary with this kind of model to consider that on the Earth we observe cosmic rays only from sources located on a certain galactic line of force passing through the solar system. In this case such properties as the intensity, spectrum and chemical composition, generally speaking, should differ from the corresponding properties in the near regions of the Galaxy on other lines of force. At the same time radio astronomy data (see section 5) bear witness to a smooth enough variation in the intensity and spectrum of the relativistic particles in the Galaxy.

Further, certain additional assumptions are necessary to explain the high isotropy of the cosmic rays in this "adiabatic" model. It can be assumed, for example, that the sources are evenly distributed over the length of a line of force (at least that which penetrates the solar system). However, bearing in mind that the number of simultaneously active sources of cosmic rays in the Galaxy is small (see section 11), this possibility has a low probability. One could assume, on the other hand, that the solar system is located within a "magnetic trap" formed by interstellar lines of force and filled by cosmic rays from a nearby source, the cosmic rays already having been able to acquire isotropic distribution as the result of many reflexions.[339] However, it is difficult to ensure that the particles are held in such a trap for a long time and in particular to ensure their isotropy, which will be further spoken of below.† Lastly, in order to explain the isotropy during adiabatic motion along lines of force it is assumed sometimes[340] that while moving along the lines of force the particles from time to time undergo reflexions from sections of a stronger field. As a result, on the assumption that the reflexions are of a random nature the motion along the lines of force must be looked upon as one-dimensional diffusion. With a corresponding selection of the parameters this diffusion will be extremely slow and the expected degree of anisotropy sufficiently small. Moreover in this model, unless additional hypotheses are made, reflexions will occur only with particles moving at a sufficiently large angle to the field so the diffusion coefficient will depend considerably on the initial value of this angle. In actual fact, at a constant particle energy the following reflexion condition will follow from the adiabatic invariant (9.1): on a given line of force at a point with a field strength H_1 reflexions (sin $\theta_1 = 1$) will occur only for particles for which at a certain (initial) point of the same line of force with a field strength H_0 the pitch angle will be θ_0, where

$$\sin^2 \theta_0 = \frac{H_0}{H_1}. \qquad (10.6)$$

Particles with greater initial values of θ_0 are reflected earlier, whilst particles with small angles θ_0 pass through a strong field region without reflexion. As a result of this difference in the nature of the motion of the particles their angular distribution in the case of sources which are not evenly distributed in space and in time will not be isotropic. To preserve the isotropy in this kind of model we

---

† What has been said, of course, does not mean that the possibility is denied[246, 339] of the existence of individual regions with a high cosmic ray concentration. It is sufficient to say that in supernova shells (including very old shells) there is no doubt of the existence of a high cosmic ray concentration. The text deals with the distribution of cosmic rays in the Galaxy as a whole or in large regions of it.

must assume a certain mechanism for angular "mixing" of the particles. This, together with the assumption of the partial "leakage" of particles through sections of a strong field necessary in the one-dimensional diffusion under discussion, is equivalent to the assumption that the motion is not adiabatic or that it is impossible to discuss motion in a given field.† This model should therefore be discussed from the general premises of the assumption of non-adiabaticity of motion, a special analysis being necessary of the compatibility of this assumption with the requirement for strict motion along lines of force.

Certain difficulties therefore arise in the concepts of adiabatic motion of particles along lines of force of the interstellar magnetic field and these difficulties would require great care when using these concepts. On the other hand—and this should be looked upon as the main objection to unlimited use of the adiabatic approximation in the interstellar plasma—there is no foundation for discussing the motion of cosmic rays in interstellar space within the framework of the theory of the motion of an individual particle in a given magnetic field.

We shall discuss this question in greater detail a little later. For the moment we would stress the fact (which is of course quite obvious) that in order to elucidate the very important question of the nature of the motion of cosmic rays in the Galaxy we must first have complete enough information on the configuration and strength of the actual magnetic fields. In point of fact we know very little about them. This is why we must discuss the various possibilities in detail and adduce arguments of a theoretical nature instead of direct references to observational results.

The available information on the fields in the Galaxy has already been partly discussed. For example certain data on the field in the disk and spiral have been discussed in section 5. Here considerations were given which speak in favour of the assumption that there is

† In the region where the force tubes narrow, magnetic "plugs" are formed which may be practically impenetrable. Therefore one-dimensional diffusion along the force tubes is possible only if there are no plugs, if they appear only for a limited time or in the case of semi-transparency of the "plugs" by virtue of the inapplicability of the adiabatic approximation. In the conditions obtaining in the Galaxy (motion of the arms and gas clouds, differential, i.e. "not rigid body", rotation of the system) one can scarcely imagine a picture in which there are no constrictions and "plugs" on the force tubes. As a result we must allow for a change in the field configuration in time or reject the adiabatic approximation.

fairly free exchange of cosmic rays between the spiral and the halo.†
There are no direct data on the structure of the field outside the disk
and in the halo in particular. However, a number of considerations
allows us to consider the field in the halo to be basically random.
For example the radio emission of the halo is directionally fairly
evenly distributed as is to be expected for a random field after
averaging. Furthermore the halo rotates considerably more slowly
than the spiral (otherwise the halo would not be quasi-sperical).
If there were an ordered field in the halo somehow connected with
an ordered field in the spiral we would expect the halo and spiral
to revolve together. The random nature of the field is also accepted
in the most well-founded dynamic theory of the halo.[266, 224, 265]

For a random field it is natural to use the diffusion approximation
as we have done in earlier papers[4–6] and was done in a number of
other articles. This means that the motion of the cosmic rays is
equated with the diffusion of molecules in a gas whose velocity v
is equal to the velocity of motion along the lines of force ($v \sim c$;
below we generally take $v = 10^{10}$ cm/sec), whilst the effective length
of the mean free path l is determined by the structure of the magnetic
field (in the simplest case l is the size of the quasi-homogeneous
sections of the field).

In other words, the motion and diffusion are considered to be the
same as for the "magnetised cloud" model (10.4) discussed above but
with certain effective values of l and v in the expression for the
diffusion coefficient $D = lv/3$ or simply some effective value of D.

A possible objection to this diffusion model (as applied to a field
not having a cloud structure) is just that due to the smallness of the
ratio r_H/l the adiabatic approximation discussed above should be valid
for cosmic rays in the Galaxy with great accuracy, i.e., the particles
should be, as it were, glued to the lines of force and not be able to
diffuse in all directions. In this connexion we should point out that
even within the framework of the adiabatic motion concepts in the
case of a random field particles will arrive in a given sufficiently large
region of space along different lines of force. Therefore when averaging over such a region the concentration and other properties of
cosmic rays will also be determined by a certain effective "diffusion"
reflecting the degree of confusion of the lines of magnetic force of

† We note that for a spiral length of even 100 kpc = 3×10^{23} cm and with an
ordered field a relativistic particle moving along the lines of force with a velocity
$v \simeq 10^{10}$ cm/sec would take 3×10^{13} sec = 10^6 yr to traverse the whole spiral.

the random field. Let us explain this by an example. Let us assume that motion occurs only along force tubes but that these tubes themselves are tangled in a random manner, for example consist of rectilinear sections with an average length l, any angle between the directions of neighbouring sections being equally probable. The diffusion approximation is then fully applicable in an analysis of the question of the spatial distribution of particles (cosmic rays) averaged over large enough regions. For example it can be used for calculating the mean shift in a time t in any given direction (this shift is equal to $L = \sqrt{\frac{2}{3}lvt}$, where v is the velocity of the particle's motion along the tube). However, the diffusion approximation in this example is completely unsuitable for finding the concentration, chemical composition and degree of anisotropy of the particles within each force tube (there is considered to be no scatter in the tubes). It is thus clear that to calculate the average spatial distribution of the particles the requirements imposed on the model are less stringent than the conditions for the applicability of the diffusion approximation to all possible problems.† For example in order to use the diffusion approximation in calculations of the concentration, chemical composition and anisotropy at a given point (to be more precise in a region with dimensions of the order of the particle's radius of curvature) a departure from the framework of the adiabatic approximation is already very necessary. This difference is particularly significant for the problem of the origin of cosmic rays since such properties as the energy spectrum, chemical composition, etc. measured at the Earth's surface relate in the sense indicated

† What has been said need not be taken to mean that "tangling" of the lines of force guarantees the applicability of the diffusion approximation for calculating the spatial distribution of the particles. That this is not so is clear from the model discussed by Gemantsev.[340] Let us assume that motion occurs only along randomly tangled force tubes but that there is also scattering of the particles in the tubes themselves. For the latter reason we shall consider that the motion along the tube has the nature of one-dimensional diffusion with a diffusion coefficient D'. Then in a time t the particle moves an average distance of $L' = \sqrt{2D't}$ along the tube, i.e., will move at an average effective velocity $v' = L'/t = \sqrt{2D'/t}$. The general shift of the particle in space (as the result of diffusion along the tube and the tube's change in direction) is[340]

$$L = \sqrt{(D't)^{1/2}l/\pi^{1/2}} \, \infty \, \sqrt{\tfrac{2}{3}lv't} \, \infty \, t^{1/4}$$

instead of that which occurs during ordinary diffusion according to the law $L \infty t^{1/2}$. From this example (and moreover from other considerations) it is clear that tangling of the force tubes still does not guarantee the validity of the diffusion law $L = t^{1/2}$. We consider, however, that the actual circumstances and arguments provide good reason for using the diffusion model in the Galaxy and not, let us say, Getmantsev's model.[340]

to an individual point so the difference between the diffusion and adiabatic approximations is a major one.

The following considerations can, however, be adduced in favour of the applicability of the diffusion approximation to calculate all the quantities at a given point.

In the first place drift caused by inhomogeneity of the magnetic field may play an important part with respect to the transfer of a particle from one line of force to another. Although the shift due to drift is, as we have already seen, not large it may nevertheless lead to a considerably greater cosmic ray mixing effect in a random magnetic field.† In actual fact, in a strongly tangled field even a slight movement of a particle onto a nearby line of force may radically alter its later fate when compared with a particle which has not undergone shifting if the lines of force move away from each other quickly enough. The effectiveness of this process rises considerably in the presence of intense motions of the interstellar gas when each line of force while moving together with the gas alternately passes near different sections with another interstellar magnetic field. These processes combined with drift may, if we are dealing with a long enough period, ensure practically complete mixing of the cosmic rays in the Galaxy with a certain characteristic mean "free path length" which considerably depends on the structure of the galactic magnetic field.‡

Furthermore diffusion of the cosmic rays will be helped by disturbance of the adiabatic invariant (9.1) under definite conditions. One of the reasons for this may be the sharp magnetic field gradients on the fronts of magnetohydrodynamic shock waves in the interstellar gas. If the width of these fronts is of the order of the radius of curvature of the interstellar gas protons, i.e., much less than the radius of curvature of the cosmic rays, the adiabatic approximation is invalid and we can no longer speak of the motion of a particle along a definite line of force. We note in this connexion that even in the case of smooth enough shock waves, when the adiabatic invariant is valid for a particle's motion, there is considerable movement of

---

† In estimating the rôle of drift from the point of view of its effectiveness as a mixing mechanism we are diverging slightly from Davis' conclusions.[341] We must, however, not limit ourselves to the simple considerations given to this question and a more detailed study is necessary.

‡ In dense clouds the field may differ significantly from the field in the surrounding space.[232] The existence of sharp field gradients connected with this increase the part played by drift.

the particle across the lines of force. In actual fact, let us examine the case when a wave is propagated across the magnetic field at a characteristic magnetohydrodynamic velocity $u \simeq H/\sqrt{4\pi\rho}$ and leads to a rise in the magnetic field strength H ahead of its front to a value H_1 behind it. Then, for example, for a particle moving on the circumference (sin $\theta = 1$) by virtue of (9.1) we have $\Delta E = E_1 - E = E(\sqrt{H_1/H} - 1)$, where E is the initial energy of the particle ahead of the shock wave front. On the other hand this increase in energy is caused by the action of the electrical field in the wave $\mathscr{E} = (1/c)(uH) \simeq H^2/c\sqrt{4\pi\rho}$ (the field $\mathscr{E}$ is directed along the front at right angles to the magnetic field). If l is the movement of the particle along the front† then the change in its energy is $\Delta E = e\mathscr{E}l$. Comparing these two expressions for ΔE we find the value of the particle's shift along the front

$$l \simeq \frac{c\sqrt{4\pi\rho}}{eH^2} E\left(\sqrt{\frac{H_1}{H}} - 1\right). \tag{10.7}$$

Putting $\rho \simeq 10^{-25}$ g/cm^2 ($n \simeq 0.1$ cm^{-3}), $H \sim 3 \times 10^{-6}$ oe, $E \simeq 10^{-2}$ erg $= 10^{10}$ eV and accepting that the field in the wave rises by a factor of four we obtain $l \simeq 10^{17}$ cm.

Thus magnetohydrodynamic waves (particularly if they follow each other frequently enough) can ensure a very effective transfer of fast particles from one set of lines of force to another.

Apart from shock waves with a sharp front the adiabatic invariant also breaks down in regions with a zero field (i.e., at null points of the field). In regions of this kind the radius of curvature of a particle is infinite and its motion is determined only by the direction of arrival in this region. A similar part may be played by regions where the gas's degree of ionisation is low and the condition of "frozen-in" lines of magnetic force is not fulfilled. In this case although a particle moves along a line of force the line of force itself is not linked with the interstellar gas and during the motion of the latter passes through different regions of it. When a "neutral layering" of this kind is present and there is gas movement the unbroken continuation of the line of force loses meaning: particles arriving in this kind of "stratification" along one and the same line of force but at different points in time or at different angles to the field after passing through the

---

† The difference between the magnetic field strengths on both sides of the front, i.e., the presence of a field gradient, leads to a particle drift along the front. The electrical field acts in the same direction.

neutral region will arrive on different lines of force "frozen into" the next ionised region. Although the condition of being frozen in is fulfilled because of the high conductivity of the interstellar gas with greater accuracy, as a rule, nevertheless the presence of these neutral regions is not excluded and their investigation is of great interest.

The adiabatic invariant, generally speaking, also changes in nuclear collisions of cosmic rays and for electrons in bremsstrahlung. In the magnetic bremsstrahlung of relativistic electrons the frictional force is directed along the impulse so the angle θ hardly changes at all—only the particle's impulse changes. In nuclear collisions of high-energy particles the change in the angle θ is also small since all the particles formed move at practically the same angle θ as the initial particle. However for particles with an energy $\mathscr{E} \simeq 10^9$ to 10^{10} eV/nucleon which produce some radioemitting electrons with an energy $E \sim 10^8$ to 10^9 eV we can evidently consider that the secondary electrons are more or less evenly distributed over the angles θ independently of the angular distribution of the primary protons and nuclei.

Returning to the question of deciding between the adiabatic and diffusion models we shall now pause to discuss the following circumstance, which in our opinion is very important and has already been briefly mentioned. The adiabatic approximation is based on a theory of the motion of particles in a given external magnetic field independently of the spatial distribution and energy density of these particles. This approach is valid when the energy density of the particles is low when compared with the energy density of the magnetic field. In actual fact the energy densities in the Galaxy and the cosmic ray and magnetic field pressures are of the same order of magnitude ($w_{cr} \sim 10^{-12}$ erg/cm^3, $w_H = H^2/8\pi \sim 4 \times 10^{-13}$ erg/cm^3 for $H \sim 3 \times 10^{-6}$ oe). The kinetic energy density of the unordered motion of the gas and even the kinetic energy density of the gas connected with the galactic rotation is less than or of the order of w_{cr}.† Under conditions like these the magnetic field can in no way be considered to be invariable and given by external sources. On the contrary, the

---

† The characteristic velocity of the random motion of the gas is $u \sim 10^6$ cm/sec which for a total gas mass of about 3×10^{42} g leads to an energy $W_k \sim 10^{54}$ erg; the velocity of ordered motion (galactic rotation about the centre of the Galaxy) in the region of the Sun is $\sim 2 \times 10^7$ cm/sec which even for a gas mass of 3×10^{42} g corresponds to an energy $W_k \sim 5 \times 10^{56}$ erg. At the same time the total cosmic ray energy is $W_{cr} \sim w_{cr}V \sim 10^{56}$ to 10^{57} erg; the total field energy $W_H \sim (H^2/8\pi)V$ is of the same order of magnitude.

cosmic ray pressure and the motion of the gaseous masses lead simultaneously to a change in the configuration of the lines of force and to movement of the cosmic rays into new regions. Something of a like nature has long been known to be true of the Sun, or to be more precise its outer shells.[343, 344] Therefore in conditions when the magnetic energy density is comparable with the cosmic ray energy density we must take into account the reverse effect of the cosmic rays on the magnetic field. It is highly probable that the field configuration is conditioned to a considerable degree by the cosmic rays.

Therefore the cosmic ray pressure and the movement of gas in the Galaxy (we must also take into account the random motion of the clouds and the motions connected with the differential rotation) should lead to a change in the configuration of the magnetic fields, to the appearance of "stretching" of the lines of force and breaks in them, etc. In other words, there should be effective "mixing" of the cosmic rays if the period of time is long enough. Since the solar system makes one revolution around the galactic centre in 2×10^8 yr and a gas cloud with a velocity of $\sim 10^6$ cm/sec would travel a distance of $\sim 6 \times 10^{21}$ cm $\simeq 2000$ pc in the same time, it may be assumed that the characteristic mixing time is not more than 10^8 yr and is more likely to be $\sim 10^7$ yr. This time is still fairly small when compared with the characteristic lifetime of cosmic rays in the Galaxy of interest to us which is $T \sim 3$ to 10×10^8 yr. Therefore, provided we are dealing with times considerably longer than $\sim 10^7$ yr, it is hard to doubt that there is effective mixing of the cosmic rays.

We note that the numerous investigations in the field of plasma physics connected with the problem of controlled thermonuclear reactions also indicate how difficult it is to hold particles in a limited region largely because of the appearance of different kinds of instabilities (we are not considering cases when the magnetic pressure is several orders higher than the particle pressure).†

† As shown by Krall and Rosenbluth[345] an inhomogeneous plasma with a magnetic field is unstable however weak the inhomogeneity. This result is clearly still true for the relativistic "cosmic ray plasma"; in this case the characteristic scale of the disturbances that appear will be of the order of the particles' radius of curvature. It is still not clear what will be the amplitude of the oscillations appearing as the result of this instability. Nevertheless these small-scale oscillations and waves make diffusion of particles across the field easier and at the same time reduce the applicability of the diffusion approximation. In a long enough time this mechanism can ensure practically complete mixing of the cosmic rays in the Galaxy.

The convective mixing mechanism is analogous to turbulent diffusion. It can be assumed that in combination with drift effects this mechanism ensures the penetration of cosmic rays into all regions of the Galaxy and allows us to discuss and describe the process of this penetration within the framework of diffusion theory. By virtue of what has been said we come to the conclusion that the diffusion approximation is fully valid both in the halo and in the Galaxy as a whole (assuming, of course, that the field in the halo is randomly or weakly ordered). Moreover it should not be forgotten that the introduced parameter l or, what is better, the diffusion coefficient D has the meaning of a certain effective quantity and is an unknown parameter within certain limits (it should be determined from a comparison of calculations and observational data).

For "open" arms (i.e., in the case of the correctness of the conclusion drawn above on the free exchange of cosmic rays between the arms and the halo) their part in the general cosmic ray balance in the Galaxy should be small. Individual regions within an arm (the region of the solar system in particular) in this picture differ little from any other regions with a quasi-homogeneous field. Of course within the limits of such regions with dimensions of the order of the mean free path we should not speak of diffusion and the cosmic ray motion is ordered (we are ignoring for the moment possible scatter on shock wave fronts). Moreover the directional distribution of cosmic rays may be completely isotropic in a homogeneous field (this is the case near the Earth). At least for particles with a high energy this fact cannot be connected with the effect of the inter-planetary fields† and it is yet another argument in favour of the model used. As has already been mentioned if the cosmic rays in the arms were noticeably isolated from the cosmic rays in the halo and the field in the arms were quasi-homogeneous we should expect notice-able directional anisotropy of the cosmic rays. This could be con-nected, for example, with the fact that particles moving at small angles to the field would leave the system sooner and the particles left in the arm would be mostly ones revolving in a circle or along a helix with a small pitch.

The available data on solar cosmic rays are also clearly in favour

---

† The radius of the solar system is about 10^{15} cm and there is no foundation for assuming the existence beyond these limits of magnetic fields of solar origin with a strength greater than 10^{-6} to 10^{-5} oersted. At the same time a high degree of isotropy is possessed by cosmic rays with an energy greater than, say, 3×10^{13} eV for which the radius of curvature in a 10^{-5} oersted field is more than 10^{16} cm.

of the possibility of using the diffusion approximation for describing the motion of cosmic rays. For example cosmic rays accelerated during solar flares reach the Earth from different directions. In this case the process is described well by the diffusion equation.[2, 428]

All the arguments adduced still do not prove that we can limit ourselves to the diffusion approximation for quantitative purposes in the theory of the origin of cosmic rays. However, the assumption of the possibility of using the diffusion approximation (with a diffusion coefficient D that is not fixed beforehand) seems to us to be quite natural and probable. In any case nothing better can be suggested at present and any further step forward or allowance for smaller effects† is scarcely possible unless we pass the stage connected with the application of the diffusion approximation, comparing the corresponding results with observations, etc.

Therefore it is the diffusion picture that we shall use below (in section 15 calculations for a model with a regular field are also given for the sake of comparison). Quantitative calculations will be made in Chapter V. In the next sub-section and the whole of Chapter IV diffusion approximations are used only for estimates.

Cosmic rays leaving the Galaxy

In the framework of diffusion considerations the galactic cosmic rays formed largely near the galactic plane and the galactic centre diffuse towards the boundaries of the halo. If we ignore the reflexion at the boundaries the total flux at a distance R from the centre is of the order of magnitude of $S_0 = D \cdot dN/dr \cdot 4\pi R^2 \sim 4vlRN$ (since $D \simeq lv/3$ and $dN/dr \sim N/R$ where N is the cosmic ray concentration). Putting $R \sim 5 \times 10^{22}$ cm, the velocity of motion along the field $v \sim 10^{10}$ cm/sec, $l \sim 3 \times 10^{19}$ to 3×10^{20} cm and $N \sim 10^{-10}$ cm^{-3}, we obtain $S_0 \sim 10^{43}$ to 10^{44} particles·sec^{-1}.

Certain calculations using radio astronomy data and information on the chemical composition of cosmic rays (see Chapter V) also adduce evidence in favour of the value $l \sim 10$ pc $= 3 \times 10^{19}$ cm ($D \sim 10^{29}$ cm^2/sec).

The data on the gas clouds and the distance between them in the

---

† Among these effects we must first include the effect of the spiral arms on the degree of anisotropy δ calculated in the diffusion approximation in section 16. The presence of an ordered field in the arm containing the Sun could affect the value of δ and the direction of maximum intensity. As a result the corresponding parameters determined from terrestrial observations will not be characteristic for the mean distribution of cosmic rays in the Galaxy.

Galaxy resulting from observations indicate, rather, that the size of the regions with a quasi-homogeneous field is of the order of 100 pc. However, the effective length of the path l may be less so it is more correct to take the value $l \sim 10$ pc. Thus, despite the roughness of the estimate, there is reason to assume that the flux $S_0 > 10^{42}$ particles/sec and, probably, $S_0 \sim 10^{43}$ particles/sec. At the same time the total number of cosmic rays in the Galaxy is $NV \sim 10^{58}$ to 10^{59} which meets the necessity of injection for compensating the nuclear losses $NV/T_p \sim 10^{58}$ to $10^{59}/10^{17} \sim 10^{41}$ to 10^{42} particles/sec. This means that when reflexion from the Galactic boundaries is not taken into consideration the inequality $T_p > T_d$ is clearly valid, where $T_d \sim NV/S_0 \sim 10^{15}$ to 10^{16} sec $\sim 10^8$ yr is the characteristic time for departure of particles from the Galaxy. From energy requirements, therefore, the case when the departure of cosmic rays into meta-galactic space is limited is more favourable. This limitation, which is connected with the presence of strong cosmic ray reflexion at the "boundaries" of the Galaxy, would occur in the case of the "closed model" in which the Galaxy is a "clump" of closed lines and not a system with an "open" magnetic field.

There are objections to the "closed model" and it clearly does not correspond to reality. Nevertheless there is value in pausing to discuss the question of the departure of cosmic rays even in this model.

According to certain estimates (see section 13) the field in meta-galactic space is $H \sim 3$ to 10×10^{-8} oe; the field in the halo is $H \sim 3 \times 10^{-6}$ to 10^{-5} oe. Therefore in the closed model only about 1 per cent of the lines of force leave the halo, which corresponds (in the first approximation) to the departure of about 1 per cent of the cosmic rays reaching the edge. As a result† about $10^{-2}S_0 \sim 10^{41}$ to 10^{42} particles/sec leave the halo which is quite compatible with the estimate of the total life $T \simeq T_p$. We note that in a field $H \sim 10^{-5}$ oersteds the radius of curvature is $r_H \sim 20$ pc $\sim l$ for an energy $\mathscr{E} \sim 10^{17}$ eV/nucleon and therefore, at least when drift is not allowed for, the very heavy nuclei even with $E \sim 10^{19}$ eV will leave the halo in the closed model more slowly than they die in collisions. Independently of this moment, while $r_H \lesssim l$ the rate of diffusion changes but little (i.e., $D = \frac{1}{3}lv$ is weakly dependent on the energy).

---

† Strictly speaking we should also take into account the change in the flux S_0 itself in connexion with the change in the boundary conditions for the diffusion in question. This increase in accuracy is scarcely justified, however, because of the approximate nature of the estimates under discussion.

Thus if particles with an energy $E \lesssim 10^{18}$ to 10^{19} eV are heavy nuclei the assumption of their galactic origin does not meet with serious difficulties, at least in the question of the "transparency" of the Galaxy to particles with a high enough energy.

This conclusion is clearly also true when allowing for departure from the system under the influence of drift in the inhomogeneous magnetic field.[279, 346] The drift rate is defined by expression (10.1). The number of particles that leave due to drift can be estimated as

$$S_d \sim v_d N' 4\pi R^2 \xi \sim \frac{10^9 \mathscr{E} R^2 N' \xi \sin^2 \theta}{HL}. \tag{10.8}$$

Here N' is the concentration of the particles in question and $\mathscr{E}$ is their energy per nucleon in eV; the factor $\xi \leqslant 1$ allows for the fact that drift takes place at right angles to the field and its gradient and therefore cannot take a particle out of the system. Due to nuclear collisions in the system $S_{\text{nucl}} = (4\pi/3)(R^3 N'/T_{\text{nucl}})$ particles/sec disappear and so

$$\beta = \frac{S_d}{S_{\text{nucl}}} \sim 3 \times 10^8 \frac{T_{\text{nucl}} \xi \sin^2 \theta}{HRL}. \tag{10.9}$$

The maximum possible value of ξ is reached in practice with $\xi \sim 1$, $\sin^2 \theta \sim 1$, $H \sim 3 \times 10^{-6}$ oe and $L \sim l \sim 10^{20}$ cm, in which case $\beta_{\max} \sim 10^{-29} \mathscr{E} T_{\text{nucl}}$; for heavy nuclei $\beta_{\max} \sim 1$ at $\mathscr{E} \sim 10^{13}$ to 10^{14} eV/nucleon. In actual fact, however $\xi \ll 1$ (in an axial field, for example in a dipole field, $\xi = 0$; the value of ξ can be extremely small in more complex fields as well, as the example of the stellarator shows). It is no less significant that the characteristic dimension of the field L in (10.8) and (10.9) relates to the field of the halo as a whole and it is thus more likely that $L \lesssim R \sim 5 \times 10^{22}$ cm. Putting $L \sim 10^{22}$ cm, $\xi \sim 3 \times 10^{-2}$ and $\sin \theta \sim \frac{1}{3}$, we obtain $\beta \sim 10^{-33} \mathscr{E} T_{\text{nucl}}$; thus for heavy nuclei $\beta = 1$ at $\mathscr{E} \sim 10^{17}$ eV/nucleon and for protons $\beta = 1$ at $E \sim 10^{16}$ eV/nucleon. Therefore the number of particles with $E \lesssim 10^{18}$ to 10^{19} eV/nucleon that leave because of drift may be significant (for the values taken for L and ξ); this is the case for protons with $E \gtrsim 10^{16}$ eV/nucleon but not for heavy nuclei.

Above we have discussed the "closed model" of the Galaxy in which reflexion of the cosmic rays from the galactic boundaries takes place with a coefficient close to unity. In another conceivable case—the "open model"—the field drops smoothly to its metagalactic value and the cosmic rays diffuse freely into metagalactic space. In this case, as follows from the estimates given, $T_d < T_p$ or even $T_d \ll T_p \sim 3 \times 10^9$ years. In the latter case the life of the cosmic rays is $T \sim T_d \ll 3 \times 10^9$ years and probably $T \sim 3 \times 10^8$ years. When compared with the closed model an order of magnitude more of cosmic rays must be injected in this variant. From the energy point this is quite possible (see section 11).

A third possible model is an unstable halo with reflecting walls. Unlike the "closed model" in this case the halo is unstable[266] and when enough cosmic rays have accumulated they burst out of the system in some direction taking the gas and magnetic field along with them. This model from the point of view of the balance of the number and energy of the cosmic rays is close to the "open model".

It may be assumed that further radio astronomy investigations with instruments of high resolution will lead to a certain amount of progress in the question of the nature of the transition (boundaries) between galaxies and metagalactic space. It is highly significant that the coefficient of reflexion from the galactic boundaries has a strong influence on the chemical composition of cosmic rays. Moreover, in the framework of the diffusion approximation the observed chemical composition of the cosmic rays is by no means compatible with the "closed model"[6] (see also section 15).

It must also be pointed out that by its nature the "closed model" requires additional limitations for its realisation. In the conditions of the relatively very fast rotation of the Galaxy and its motion relative to the other galaxies of the Local Group it is hardly possible to ensure the existence of reflecting "boundaries" for a lengthy period. Below, therefore, we shall use the "open model" of the galactic magnetic field.

In the case of the open model the departure of particles from the system due to drift can hardly be discussed separately from the diffusion. The diffusion coefficient $D = lv/3$ is constant until the radius of curvature is $r_H \ll l$ and in practice also for $r_H < l$. With $l \sim 10$ pc and $H \sim 10^{-5}$ to 10^{-6} oe the radius is $r_H \sim l$ for particles with an energy $\mathscr{E} \sim 10^{16}$ to 10^{17} eV/nucleon. Therefore for an energy $\mathscr{E} < 10^{16}$ eV/nucleon the rate of departure of particles from the Galaxy is determined by the estimates made above. For $\mathscr{E} \gtrsim 10^{16}$ eV/nucleon the diffusion coefficient rises as the energy rises and the rate of departure of particles from the Galaxy increases. Therefore the spectrum of cosmic rays of galactic origin in the open model should change its form (become steeper) at a certain energy $\mathscr{E}_{cr} = E_{cr}/A \lesssim 10^{17}$ eV/nucleon. An attempt will be made in section 16 to make a quantitative examination of the question of the departure of cosmic rays from the Galaxy.

CHAPTER IV

THE ORIGIN OF COSMIC RAYS

THE problem of the origin of cosmic rays is a complex one and it is connected, as can be seen from the preceding chapters, with a number of questions of the most widely varying nature. Nevertheless two main lines can be distinguished in the theory of the origin of cosmic rays even though the distinction is somewhat arbitrary.

The first of these lines tries to indicate the sources of cosmic rays, in particular of primary cosmic rays on the Earth. The acceleration process and the phenomena in the sources themselves are not discussed. This approach can be successful to a greater or lesser degree by using various data of astrophysics and radio astronomy, e.g., information on the radio emission of supernova shells. Knowing the power of the cosmic rays sources it is possible to analyse independently of the processes in these sources the various models or, as is generally said, the theories of the origin of cosmic rays.

In other words it is possible to split the problem to a certain extent in two: into the "external" (cosmic rays outside the sources) and "internal" (cosmic rays in the sources). Both terminologically and to a certain degree in essence this division is analogous to division into external and internal ballistics. This approach has already fully justified itself—it has made it possible to move a long way forward in the solution of the "external" problem without any complete solution of the "internal" problem, i.e., without producing a source theory. But this, of course, by no means eliminates the question of producing a source theory and, most important, the necessity of analysing the mechanisms and features of the acceleration of cosmic rays in the sources. The "source theory" must also make up the basic content of the second approach mentioned above in the field of studying the origin of cosmic rays.

The source theory is closely connected with physical investigations into the acceleration mechanisms in a plasma, with the physics of the solar and stellar atmospheres, the theory of the explosion of stars, and so on. The acceleration mechanisms have already been discussed in section 9; a number of questions which can be included in the "source theory" have been touched upon in other parts of the book as well and are also discussed below. At present, however, there is still no possibility of giving a cosmic rays source theory in any sort of finished form. We shall therefore not devote a separate section to this problem. As for the first approach—the theory of the origin of cosmic rays without analysing the processes in the sources—it is this set of questions to which the present chapter is devoted.

The fairly large number of theories (models) of the origin of cosmic rays is most correctly classified depending on where the basic sources of primary cosmic rays reaching the Earth are localised. Four types of theory can be distinguished in this approach.

1. In the theories of the solar origin of cosmic rays their basic source is the Sun and the cosmic rays accumulate in a certain circumsolar region.

2. According to the Galactic theory the cosmic rays reaching the Earth are accelerated within our Galaxy (see section 11). Among the Galactic theories we shall also include the "expanded" galactic theory in which the cosmic rays are localised within the Local Group of galaxies (see section 12). This group is small and our Galaxy is one of its two basic members. Therefore, and also for a number of other reasons, it is best not to include this model among the metagalactic models.

3. The Metagalactic theory links the origin of cosmic rays with the Metagalaxy or such formations of the metagalactic scale as the Local Supergalaxy (see section 13).

4. In the "hierarchical" and similar theories the Sun, galactic objects (stars and supernova shells) and certain galaxies (radio galaxies in particular) are included as sources. In this case the part played by one source or another varies depending upon the range of energies under discussion and the spatial "capture region" of the cosmic rays.

There is no reason to doubt at present that the acceleration of cosmic rays is a universal phenomenon and takes place in a moving plasma with greater or lesser effect when only comparatively stringent conditions are observed. It has been established that cosmic rays are generated on the Sun, as the result of supernova explosions, and in radio galaxies (it is true that in the last case it has not yet been excluded that the acceleration is also a result of supernova explosions; it is far more likely that this is not so, however). It is difficult to doubt that cosmic rays are also generated in the atmospheres of a number of stars and nova explosions.

In this connexion it is natural to consider that the various sources make some sort of contribution to the cosmic rays on Earth. This, however, does not mean that we must stop at models (theories) of the fourth type since it is necessary to take into account only those sources whose contribution is large enough to be recognised in experiment. With this circumstance in mind it can be stated that the model of the solar origin of cosmic rays (in the $>10^9$ to 10^{10} eV range) is clearly unacceptable. It further turns out that the Galactic theory has a number of attractive features and in any case does not contradict the available data. In this case the basic source of cosmic rays is supernova explosions and possibly the explosion of the galactic core. At the same time the question of the metagalactic cosmic rays and their contribution to the cosmic ray flux on Earth is still not clear enough although, in all probability, this contribution is insignificant (except in the very-high energy region, probably).

Such is the present state of the question in general terms but any complete and clear characteristic of the situation naturally requires discussion at some length. For example section 11 will discuss the question of cosmic ray sources in the Galaxy and the foundations are laid for the theory of the galactic origin of cosmic rays which is discussed in greater detail in Chapter V. Section 12 discusses the "expanded" Galactic theory; section 13 which follows is devoted to cosmic rays of metagalactic origin.

11. COSMIC RAY SOURCES IN THE GALAXY AND THE GALACTIC THEORY OF THE ORIGIN OF COSMIC RAYS

The question of the sources of cosmic rays is connected in the closest possible way with another—the question of the region of space filled with the cosmic rays from the sources in question. It is therefore best to start not with a discussion of the data on the properties of one or another source but with a discussion of the models of the distribution of cosmic rays in the Galaxy and the question of the energy balance. In this way the requirements imposed on the sources will also become clear.

Cosmic ray distribution in the Galaxy (selection of a model)

By considering that the cosmic rays reaching the Earth are formed in the Galaxy we limit the number of possible models but are still a long way from selecting a more or less definite theory of the origin of cosmic rays. In fact we can point to two very different Galactic models (not to mention various models of an intermediate type).

1. A model in which the cosmic rays more or less evenly fill the whole volume of the Galaxy including the halo. In addition, it is assumed that practically complete mixing of the cosmic rays takes place in this volume. In other words, in this model there is, as it were, a single reservoir in which the cosmic rays are completely intermixed.

2. A model with various "capture regions". This means that the cosmic rays in the spiral or its individual regions are isolated to a considerable degree from the cosmic rays in the halo. Taking this point of view we can directly connect the data on the cosmic rays on the Earth only with the characteristics of the cosmic rays in the spiral arm in which the Sun is located. The cosmic ray sources in the spiral and the halo in this model may be different.

In essence we have already discussed in detail the question of choosing between these two models, particularly in section 10. Arguments were adduced which were against model No. 2 with isolated "capture regions". Both data of a radio astronomy nature and dynamic considerations indicate that cosmic rays cannot stay in the spiral for about 10^8 to 10^9 years or in parts of it (we recall, for example, that the spiral consists of individual "pieces" and is changing the whole time during the process of the galactic rotation). We therefore consider the Galactic model of a "single reservoir" (model No. 1) to be far closer to the truth provided that a large number of cosmic rays do not enter the Galaxy from outside. When analysing the finer points (for example calculating the chemical composition of the cosmic rays and their anisotropy) model No. 1 in its turn is greatly lacking in precision. For example we have to indicate the conditions at the galactic "boundaries", set a definite source distribution, select a diffusion coefficient, and so on. Bearing in mind that any such addition of detail is connected with some additional assumptions or estimates of limited accuracy it is best not to make the model precise from the start. This is possible since there are very important conditions for the discussion of which it is sufficient to know only the most general characteristics of the model. One of these conditions is the fulfilment of the energy balance.

In order to answer a very important question about the energy requirements of the sources in the first approximation we have to know only the volume of the reservoir V, the mean density of the cosmic ray energy in this volume $w_{cr} \equiv w$ and the mean life of the cosmic rays T (the index "cr" in w_{cr} will generally be omitted below).

As the volume V in the framework of the purely Galactic model it is natural to choose the volume of the halo $V \sim 4\pi R^3/3$ (the mean radius $R \sim 10$–15 kpc; see section 5):

$$V \sim 1 \text{ to } 5 \times 10^{68} \text{ cm}^3. \tag{11.1}$$

The mean energy density of the cosmic rays in the halo is evidently between 0·3 and 1 eV/cm^3 and we shall take

$$w_G \sim 0\cdot5 \text{ eV/cm}^3 = 8 \times 10^{-13} \text{ erg/cm}^3 \sim 10^{-12} \text{ erg/cm}^3. \tag{11.2}$$

Hence it is reasonable to assume that the total energy of the cosmic rays in the Galaxy is within the limits

$$W = w_G V \sim 1 \text{ to } 5 \times 10^{56} \text{ erg}. \tag{11.3}$$

The estimate of the energy W made in section 6 from slightly different considerations led to a value $W \simeq 3 \times 10^{56}$ erg (see Table 8).

The use of model No. 1 is, of course, connected with the assumption that the cosmic rays largely leave the Galaxy or are bent within it. In the "expanded" Galactic model, not to mention the metagalactic theories of the origin of cosmic rays, on the other hand, cosmic rays enter the Galaxy fairly freely. This possibility is not discussed in section 11 (see sections 12 and 13).

Energy balance and requirements for sources

The age of the Galaxy, T_G, is about 10^{10} years and it is generally assumed that the Galaxy has changed very little as a whole in the last 5 to 8×10^9 years. This circumstance allows us, within the framework of the Galactic model being used, to consider the distribution and energy of the cosmic rays in the Galaxy to be quasi-stationary.†

In actual fact even the longest nuclear life (the life of protons) is $T_p \simeq 4 \times 10^9$ years in the Galaxy (see Table 10). Actually the

† Here we are not considering the part possibly played by explosions of the galactic core which are dealt with later.

characteristic life of the cosmic rays in the Galaxy will probably be considerably less than T_p because of the departure of particles from the system ($1/T = 1/T_d + 1/T_{nucl}$, where T_d is the characteristic time for the departure of cosmic rays and T_{nucl} is the nuclear life). Estimates of T_d have already been made in section 10 and they will be mentioned again in section 15. Here we would mention that according to these estimates $T_d \sim 3 \times 10^8$ years so for protons $T \sim T_d \sim 3 \times 10^8$ years. This time is 1/30th of the age of the Galaxy which also allows the state of the cosmic rays in this model to be quasi-stationary.

The cosmic ray energy losses in nuclear collisions are determined by the life for protons T_p since the heavier nuclei transfer energy to the light nuclei in the collisions and in the final reckoning to the protons. The life $T_p \simeq 4 \times 10^9$ years estimated in section 7 is the time for interaction whilst the effective time for the loss of energy is about twice as long. If this difference were taken into account in the present case, however, the accuracy of the estimate would be exceeded so it can be taken that the nuclear losses of cosmic rays in the Galaxy (see section (11.3)) are

$$U_{nucl} \sim \frac{W}{T_{nucl}} \sim 3 \times 10^{38} \text{ to } 3 \times 10^{39} \text{ erg/sec;} \qquad (11.4)$$

the total energy losses determined by departure are

$$U \sim \frac{W}{T} \sim 3 \times 10^{39} \text{ to } 3 \times 10^{40} \text{ erg/sec} \qquad (11.5)$$

(for $T \sim 3 \times 10^8$ yr $\simeq 10^{16}$ sec).

More detailed calculations (see section 15) lead to values for U close to 3×10^{40} erg/sec and it is this value of U that we shall take in future (if the value of U is less it only reduces the requirements for sources). In a quasi-stationary state the power of the sources supplying cosmic rays to the Galaxy should evidently be equal to U, i.e.,

$$U_{source} \sim 3 \times 10^{40} \text{ erg/sec.} \qquad (11.6)$$

It is not easy to provide this source power, so considerations connected with taking the energy balance into account are very important. As an example let us examine the assumption frequently discussed in published works that the sources of cosmic rays are non-exploding stars. At first sight this hypothesis appears attractive since the generation of cosmic rays on the Sun has been established and many stars are indubitably more active than the Sun and probably emit more cosmic rays.

It is known from observations that the Sun on the average generates cosmic rays ($\mathscr{E}_k \gtrsim 10^9$ eV/nucleon) with a power $U_\odot \sim 10^{23}$ erg/sec. In order to allow for possibly more effective generation in the recent past we assume that

$$U_\odot \sim 10^{24} \text{ erg/sec.} \qquad (11.7)$$

Altogether in the Galaxy there are of the order of 10^{11} stars and if they all emitted cosmic rays just as the Sun does the total power of the total stellar emission would be 10^{35} erg/sec. But this is still 5 to 6 orders less than is required.

Various non-exploding stars as cosmic ray sources

The discrepancy of several orders of magnitude noted is difficult to overcome. Of course on many stars cosmic rays may be generated considerably more effectively than is the case on the Sun. But there are far fewer of these stars with special properties than other stars. For example there are about 10^9 of the relatively widely spread magnetic stars in the Galaxy, i.e., they account for about 1 per cent of the total number of stars.[347] The field on these stars is 10^3 times greater in order of magnitude. The magnetic energy is therefore about 10^6 times greater than the Sun's and it may be assumed that the activity of a star as a source of cosmic rays also exceeds that of the Sun by a factor of not more than 10^6. But for 10^9 stars this corresponds to a power of 10^{38} to 10^{39} erg/sec. This estimate cannot, of course, pretend to be to any degree proved but we see no reason to expect a greater evolution of energy, whilst a considerably lower effectiveness of acceleration for magnetic stars is quite possible.

Particularly effective cosmic ray generation may be expected of non-stationary stars particularly of stars like T Tauri and UV Ceti. The point is that on these stars there is evidently non-thermal emission. This emission may be connected with magnetic bremsstrahlung emission of relativistic electrons[348] and its presence in any case indicates stormy processes in a star's atmosphere. Stars like T Tauri, according to Gordon's data[348] are sources of relativistic electrons with a mean power of 10^{33} to 10^{34} erg/sec. In the Galaxy the number of such stars in an active state, according to Kholopov's data,[349] is 5×10^4. Hence we come to a generated energy of 10^{38} to

10^{39} erg/sec. In order to show how great this power is we would point out that the total light emission of the Sun is 3.86×10^{33} erg/sec. The thermal emission of stars like T Tauri is on the average less than the Sun's so the generation of cosmic rays (with a transfer in them of 10^{33} to 10^{34} erg/sec) will exceed all the thermal emission of these stars in power. Furthermore, even if the power of the sources of fast electrons is such, then it is still not clear what energy will be converted into the nucleons with $\mathscr{E}_k > 10^9$ eV/nucleon which are of interest to us. It is natural to assume that this energy is only a small part of the energy generated. But then either the emission power of nucleons with an energy $\mathscr{E}_k \gtrsim 10^9$ eV/nucleon is considerably less than 10^{33} to 10^{34} erg/sec or the total amount of energy turned into cosmic rays is still considerably higher than that given even though the value of 10^{33} to 10^{34} erg/sec is very high. This value therefore arouses great doubts particularly if one bears in mind that the estimate mentioned[348] for the power of stars of the T Tauri type as cosmic ray sources is based on indirect considerations. In other words, the extremely high effectiveness of particle acceleration on stars of the T Tauri type and the UV Ceti type is still hypothetical and therefore cannot be used as any kind of convincing argument in favour of the generation of a considerable number of cosmic rays on stars.

We therefore come to the conclusion that the various non-stationary stars should not supply more than 10^{38} to 10^{39} erg/sec to the cosmic rays (with $\mathscr{E}_k \gtrsim 10^9$ eV/nucleon). It is rather that the corresponding amount of energy generated is still less, i.e., several orders less than the necessary power $U \sim 3 \times 10^{40}$ erg/sec. It must be pointed out that Morrison[9] also accepts the value of 10^{35} erg/sec for the energy generated by non-exploding stars in the region of the galactic spiral. But this contribution can be significant only in the case of an isolated spiral which does not appear likely to us (see above).

We would also point out that the cosmic rays generated on the Sun have an energy spectrum[2, 350] $N(\mathscr{E}_k) = K\mathscr{E}_k^{-\gamma}$ with $\gamma \simeq 5$; this spectrum of the cosmic rays generated on the Sun, even independently of considerations of an energy nature, does not speak in favour of the assumption of the acceleration of galactic cosmic rays with $\gamma \simeq 2.5$ basically by non-exploding stars. What is more, solar cosmic rays clearly have a different chemical composition from the galactic cosmic rays in their sources (as will be shown in section 15 nuclei are preferentially generated in sources of galactic cosmic rays; the composition of solar cosmic rays is not less than about 90 per cent protons.)

To recapitulate, it may be said that the generation of the basic part of cosmic rays can be connected at present with non-exploding stars only if arbitrary and far-reaching hypotheses are adduced. But there is even less foundation for this since it has been reliably established that other, and at the same time more powerful, cosmic ray sources exist in the Galaxy.

Supernovae—the basic sources of cosmic rays in the Galaxy

Sections 5 and 6 have already given data which indicate with complete certainty the presence of cosmic rays in the shells of supernovae. In that way it is established, independently of any assumptions, that cosmic rays are generated as the result of explosions of supernovae. But this is only one side of the matter. It is no less important that the generation of cosmic rays in supernova explosions is an extremely powerful process.

For example the calculations given in section 6 show that in shells of type 1 supernovae there are cosmic rays with an energy W_{sn} reaching 10^{49} erg (according to Table 7 in the Crab Nebula $W_{sn} \sim 5 \times 10^{48}$ erg). In the shells of type 2 supernovae the cosmic ray energy reaches 10^{50} erg (for example for Cassiopeia A $W_{sn} \sim 7 \times 10^{49}$ erg; see Table 7). It is true that the calculation of the cosmic ray energy in the shells is connected with certain assumptions; the most important of them is the use of the coefficient 100 in the transition from the more or less directly measured energy of relativistic electrons to the energy of all the cosmic rays. However, both this assumption and the assumption of the approximate equality of the cosmic ray energy and the energy of the magnetic field in the shell are well enough founded for type 2 supernovae as long as it is only a question of estimates of order of magnitude. We should also point out that in order to explain the possible rôle of supernovae as sources of cosmic rays in the Galaxy it is important to know the cosmic ray energy in the shells at some stage of their evolution as to know the total energy of the cosmic rays formed as the result of an explosion and all the subsequent processes of acceleration and braking. Since the departure of particles from the shells is probably fairly significant this total energy may far exceed the energy of the cosmic rays retained in the shell. From this point of view it must be borne in mind that the total amount of energy generated by a number of supernovae exceeded 10^{50} erg and even reached[269] 10^{52} erg. Bearing in mind the general tendency to equal distribution of energy between the cosmic rays, magnetic field and kinetic energy and also the ideas of the magnetic bremsstrahlung nature of the optical emission in the actual explosions of certain supernovae[348] (clearly largely type 1 supernovae) certain conclusions can be drawn. As the upper boundary for the energy changing into cosmic rays in an explosion we come to the above-mentioned value of 10^{52} erg. This energy corresponds to a mass $M = W/c^2 \sim 10^{31}$ g $\sim 0.01 M_\odot$; if we bear in mind that the mass of type 2 supernovae may be tens of times the mass of the Sun ($M_\odot = 2 \times 10^{33}$ g) the energy generated corresponding to a mass 10^{31} g is still possible (in thermonuclear reactions the energy generated is of the order of 10^{-3} of the rest mass of the nuclei; the energy released during the neutron collapse of a star with a mass $\sim M_\odot$ also reaches 10^{52} erg).†

The conclusion which we can draw from what has been said is as follows. For the energy converted into cosmic rays in supernova explosions it is reasonable to take the average value

$$W_{sn} \sim 10^{49} \text{ to } 10^{50} \text{ erg.} \qquad (11.8)$$

This estimate may be slightly too high for type 1 supernovae but there are less explosions of these supernovae in the Galaxy than of type 2 supernovae (see below). Therefore from the point of view of making up the energy balance the value of (11.8) is not too large. The maximum value of the mean energy generated on a type 2 supernovae is probably even close to 10^{51} erg.

In order to judge the efficiency of supernova explosions as cosmic ray sources we must know still one more value—the average frequency of supernova explosions in the Galaxy $v_{sn} = 1/T_{sn}$ (T_{sn} is the average time between supernovae explosions). The time T_{sn} is different for different types of Galaxy and averaged over many galaxies is 300 to 400 years.[352] This figure relates more particularly to the brighter type 1 supernovae. The main thing is that the deviations of the time T_{sn} from the average value are so great that we

---

† Neutron collapse, which may occur in the explosions of certain supernovae, is understood as the formation of the neutron core of a star.[351] The energy released during the collapse is of the order $\kappa M^2/R$, where κ is the gravitational constant, M is the mass of the star and R is the radius of the neutron core. Since[351] $R \sim 10^6$ cm, $W_k \sim 10^{52}$ erg for $M \sim 0.2 \, M_\odot$.

should interest ourselves here in the value of T_{sn} determined for our Galaxy. According to Shklovskii[161] this time is 30 to 60 years, whilst in other papers[248, 269] it is assumed that for type 2 supernovae in the Galaxy $T_{sn} = 50$ years.

Therefore for the more powerful and more frequently exploding type 2 supernovae in the Galaxy we can say

$$T_{sn} \sim 50 \text{ yr}, \qquad v_{sn} = \frac{1}{T_{sn}} \sim 7 \times 10^{-10} \text{ sec}^{-1}. \qquad (11.9)$$

Combining the values of (11.8) and (11.9) for the mean power of supernovae as the sources of cosmic rays in the Galaxy we obtain

$$U_{sn} \sim \frac{W_{sn}}{T_{sn}} \sim 10^{40} \text{ to } 10^{41} \text{ erg/sec.} \qquad (11.10)$$

The closeness of this value to the necessary one from energy considerations of the source power $U_{source} \sim 3 \times 10^{40}$ erg/sec. (see (11.6)) literally leaps to the eyes. Of course, the estimates given cannot pretend to an accuracy of more than one or two orders of magnitude. For example, it would scarcely be possible to reject the estimate of $U_{sn} \sim 10^{39}$ erg/sec but this value is more likely a minimum one that is still compatible with the available data. It cannot therefore be stated that supernovae really supply just enough cosmic rays as are necessary to observe the balance. But, on the other hand, one can come with definite certainty to the conclusion that by identifying the basic sources of cosmic rays in the Galaxy with supernovae we can satisfy the very difficult requirements of an energetic nature.†

It has already been mentioned in section 5 that the possible efficiency of supernova explosions from the standpoint of cosmic ray generation was indicated[245, 261] even before the discovery of the powerful radio emission of supernova shells. The only argument for this was the enormous amount of energy generated in explosions. But, of course, the evolution of energy in the form of light or even in the form of kinetic energy still by no means guarantees its conversion into cosmic ray energy. Therefore the hypothesis of the generation of cosmic rays in supernova explosions has attracted serious

---

† Here it is necessary only to say that the necessity of choosing the value of (11.5) has not been strictly proved; if $U > 10^{41}$ erg/sec as would be so in the case of rapid departure of cosmic rays from the Galaxy ($T < 10^8$ yr), then it would scarcely be possible to ensure maintenance of the balance bearing only supernovae in mind. However, provided that the Galactic model is generally justified estimate (11.5) is not too low.

attention only in the light of radio astronomy data.[4, 154, 161, 354]

The assumption of the dominating rôle of supernovae as cosmic ray sources in the Galaxy becomes even more probable and attractive if one compares it with the alternative "hierarchical" hypothesis.[9, 355, 356]

We should mention that according to the "hierarchical" theory of the origin of cosmic rays particles with an energy of $E \lesssim 10^{12}$ eV are generated on non-exploding stars; in the $10^{12} \lesssim E \lesssim 10^{15}$ eV region the basic sources are supernovae and cosmic rays with $E > 10^{15}$ eV come from the Metagalaxy.

Since the cosmic ray spectrum drops, and rather quickly at that, the basic contribution to the total cosmic ray energy is made by particles with a relatively low energy. Hence it is clear that in the "hierarchical" theory practically all the energy must be supplied by non-exploding stars. But in the light of what has already been said this means that this theory is connected with the completely arbitrary assumption of the very high efficiency of many non-exploding stars (as has been pointed out, these stars should generate cosmic rays with a total energy several orders greater than follows from the available data and estimates). The other possibility, just as unfounded, is connected with the assumption of the absence of cosmic ray mixing between the spiral arms and the halo.

There are also other considerations against the "hierarchical" theory.

The chemical composition, and also the cosmic ray injection and acceleration conditions in supernova shells and for non-exploding stars, in all probability differ strongly. For this reason in the hierarchical theory we should expect a considerable change of the cosmic ray energy spectrum and chemical composition for a certain energy $E \sim 10^{12}$ eV. As far as is known there are no such changes (see Chapter I). It is true that the data relating to the chemical composition are still insufficient and the smoothness of the energy spectrum still does not prove that the sources are largely of one kind. But to reject the ideas of the dominating rôle of supernovae in favour of the hierarchical theory we must clearly have some weighty arguments and not only the possibility of the suggested theory in principle. For example if the energy or charge spectrum at $E \sim 10^{12}$ eV changed noticeably then this at least would be more natural in the case of two kinds of source. Since not one fact has been adduced that clearly indicates a plurality of sources we can see no convincing proof in favour of this assumption. In other words, there is still no reason to consider it even probable that non-exploding stars make a noticeable contribution to the cosmic ray flux in the Galaxy as a whole or even to the cosmic ray flux on Earth. Moreover this assumption is connected with definite difficulties largely of an energetic nature. There are no similar objections to the assumption of the dominant rôle of supernovae.

Despite what has been said definite care, of course, must be taken in conclusions and further analysis of the question of cosmic ray sources. A number of remarks will be made in this respect below.

We would now stress that no stars apart from supernovae are evidently capable of accelerating cosmic rays to energies greater than 10^{12} to 10^{13} eV. The point is that a particle can be accelerated to high energy only if it is held long enough close to a star and the accelerating mechanism is efficient enough. On the Sun, as is well known, cosmic rays are generated with an energy of up to 10^{10} eV, whilst a typical value for the magnetic field strength in the solar atmosphere is $H_\odot \sim 1$ oersted (considerably stronger fields are found in sunspots but we must allow for the rapid decrease in the sunspot field as we move away from the photosphere). In a field $H \sim 1$ oersted a proton with an energy $E \sim 10^{10}$ eV revolves on an orbit with a radius $r_H \lesssim E/300H \sim 3 \times 10^7$ cm, whilst the radius of the photosphere is $R_\odot = 7 \times 10^{10}$ cm. Thus for the Sun the characteristic parameter $\xi = r_H/R_\odot$ does not exceed 10^{-3}. It may be assumed that for other stars as well $\xi \lesssim 10^{-3}$ so the maximum cosmic ray energy is $E_{max} \sim 300 H r_H \sim 0.3 H R_{pht}$, where H is the characteristic value of the field and R_{pht} is the radius of the star's photosphere. Even for magnetic stars the value of HR_{pht}, and that also means E_{max}, scarcely exceeds (with rare exceptions) the corresponding values for the Sun by more than three orders. Hence we come to the estimate $E_{max} \sim 10^{13}$ eV. Of course, this estimate contains an element of arbitrariness but we know of no convincing counter-arguments that will allow us to make any great increase in the value $E_{max} \sim 10^{13}$ eV for non-exploding stars. Clearly, because of this, particles with an energy $E \gtrsim {}^{12}$ eV cannot be considered as being generated on non-exploding stars in the "hierarchical" theory either.

Let us now examine from this point of view the possibility of particle acceleration in the shells of supernovae. This question is still to a large degree open but certain conclusions can be drawn by

comparing the radii of the shells with the radius of curvature of the
particles.† According to Table 7 the radii of the shells R_0 of the
sources Taurus A (Crab Nebula) and Cassiopeia A are now about
1 to 2 pc ~ 3 to 6×10^{18} cm and the field strength in the shells is
$H_0 \sim 10^{-3}$ oersted. Hence we have

$$\xi = \frac{r_H}{R_0} \sim \frac{E}{300 H_0 Z R_0} \sim 10^{-18} \frac{E}{Z} \sim 10^{-18} \mathscr{E}, \qquad (11.11)$$

where eZ is the charge of the nucleus and $E = A\mathscr{E}$ is its total energy
($\mathscr{E}$ is the energy per nucleon).

If we assume that the maximum energy $E_{\max}$ is reached at a value
$\xi \sim 10^{-1}$ we come to the estimate

$$\mathscr{E}_{\max} \sim 10^{17} \text{ eV/nucleon}, \qquad E_{\max} \sim 10^{19} \text{ eV}. \qquad (11.12)$$

It is true that in the case of stars we have used the value $\xi \sim 10^{-3}$ but
the configurations of the fields in the stellar atmospheres and in the
shells differ considerably. Since the field in the shells is quasi-
closed the assumption that $\xi \sim 10^{-1}$ is still possible in principle. On
the other hand, if during the process of the shell's expansion $H_0 R_0^2$
$= $ const, then according to (11.11) at the earlier stages $\xi < 10^{-18}\mathscr{E}$.
Both for this reason and because of the extremely hypothetical
possibility of taking the value $\xi \sim 10^{-1}$ estimate (11.12) is clearly
the upper limit.

It follows from (11.12) that supernova explosions may result in
the generation of cosmic rays with $E \lesssim 10^{17}$ eV and if it is a question
of heavy nuclei then with $E \lesssim 10^{19}$ eV. Since the highest energy
recorded in cosmic radiation is $E_{\max} \sim 10^{19}$ to 10^{20} eV (only a few
particles with energies greater than 10^{19} eV have been recorded) it
can be assumed with a certain stretch of the imagination that supernovae supply cosmic rays over the whole energy range. This possibility would be refuted if it were established that in the $E \sim 10^{18}$ to
10^{19} eV energy range the cosmic rays consist not only of heavy nuclei
but also contain protons. Here, however, we are dealing with ordinary supernovae characterised by parameters (11.8) and (11.9).
The rarely met large supernovae and super-supernovae which may

† It is assumed here that particle acceleration occurs in the shell. If the
particles are accelerated by the shock wave in the actual explosion[316, 482] the
estimates must be made differently. According to Colgate and White[482] an
energy of $W \sim 10^{51}$ erg is transferred to the cosmic rays in the explosion of a
large supernova, the protons reaching an energy of 10^{16} to 10^{19} eV.

explode in the galactic core (see below) are quite capable of accelerating particles to an energy of 10^{19} to 10^{20} eV/nucleon. On the other hand protons with an energy of $\sim 10^{19}$ to 10^{20} eV very rapidly leave the Galaxy as well (for $H \sim 3 \times 10^{-6}$ oe, $Z = 1$ and $E = 10^{19}$ eV the radius of curvature $r_H = E/300H \sim 10^{22}$ cm which is only a few times less than the radius of the halo ~ 3 to 5×10^{22} cm; in addition, the field in the Galaxy is not homogeneous and the radius r_H is greater than the scale of the inhomogeneity; allowing for this circumstance considerably reduces the time that a particle stays in the Galaxy). We shall return to this question later (see section 16).

The possible rôle of novae

Exploding stars also include new stars (novae) as well as supernovae. In the explosion of novae an expanding shell is formed and in general the picture is in many ways close to that for supernovae. It is therefore natural to assume that cosmic rays are generated as the result of nova explosions.[4, 154, 161, 348]

It is true that radio emission of nova shells has not yet been observed but in the majority of cases it should be so small that there is still no contradiction here. In actual fact $\sim 10^{45}$ erg are emitted in the visible part of the spectrum in nova explosions (Payne–Gaposchkin[357] gives, for example, the average value of 6×10^{44} erg for the energy emitted). At the same time an average of 10^{49} erg is emitted in explosions of type 1 supernovae.[357] Other comparisons also lead to the conclusion that the power of novae is 3 to 5 orders less than that of supernovae. If this also relates to the cosmic ray generation power the radio emission from nova shells should be many orders weaker than the radio emission of supernova shells (apart from the lower concentration of radio emitting electrons the decrease in the magnetic field strength also has its effect here).†

Assuming that cosmic rays are generated as the result of a nova explosion whose energy is 4 orders less than for supernovae we come to the conclusion (see (11.8)) that

$$W_{nov} \sim 10^{45} \text{ to } 10^{46} \text{ erg.} \qquad (11.13)$$

The frequency of nova explosions in the Galaxy, according to various data, varies from[161] $\nu_{nov} \sim 200$ to $\nu_{nov} \sim 50$ explosions

---

† What we have said does not mean that nova radio emission cannot be found, particularly if it is a question of novae which are comparatively close to the solar system.

per annum.[357] Assuming that $v_{nov} = 1/T_{nov} \simeq 100$ yr$^{-1} \simeq 3 \times 10^{-6}$ sec^{-1}, we obtain for the power of cosmic ray generation in the Galaxy due to nova explosions

$$U_{nov} \sim \frac{W_{nov}}{T_{nov}} \sim 3 \times 10^{39} \text{ to } 3 \times 10^{40} \text{ erg/sec.} \qquad (11.14)$$

This value in essence agrees with the power U_{sn} for supernovae (see (11.10)). Therefore if we base ourselves only on energy considerations novae are fully capable of competing with supernovae as cosmic ray sources. One must bear in mind, however, that estimate (11.14) is much less well-founded than estimate (11.10) for supernovae. It is therefore by no means excluded that the power of cosmic rays from novae is $U_{nov} < 3 \times 10^{39}$ erg/sec and that these cosmic rays therefore play a comparatively small part in the overall balance. Furthermore in nova explosions particles indubitably cannot acquire as high an energy as in the case of supernovae. In other words, novae could make a contribution only to cosmic radiation with an energy that is not very high, for example in the $E \lesssim 10^{12}$ to 10^{14} eV range (according to formula (11.11) for $\xi \sim 0{\cdot}1$, $H_0 \sim 3 \times 10^{-5}$ oe and $R_0 \sim 3 \times 10^{15}$cm the maximum energy for an iron nucleus is 10^{14} eV).

In the extreme case, when the total energy contribution of novae would be basic (i.e., if $U_{nov} \gg U_{sn}$), they would play a part which would be challenged by the ordinary stars in the "hierarchical" theory (see above).† But we see no reason for this extreme assumption. All that can be concluded at present boils down to the following: the assumption of the generation of cosmic rays as the result of nova explosions is highly probable and at the same time it is not excluded that the contribution of these cosmic rays in the general balance of the Galaxy is significant (in the energy range $E \lesssim 10^{12}$ to 10^{14} eV). But it is also quite possible that this contribution is small and can be ignored.

It remains only to remark that the assumption that cosmic rays from novae play an important part alters practically nothing in the theory of the origin of cosmic rays since the dominant rôle as cosmic ray sources is ceded to supernovae. It suffices to say that the various

† Novae have considerable advantages when compared with ordinary stars in this respect. Not to mention the main, energy, side of the matter (see above), the closeness between novae and supernovae allows us to assume that both the chemical composition and the energy spectrum of the cosmic rays generated in both these cases are very close to each other.

supernovae are by no means identical and the amount of energy they generate and other parameters vary quite strongly even within one type. It is true that apparently there is no continuous transition between novae and supernovae but all these objects are closely inter-related. From this point of view the conclusion of novae as well as supernovae means only an increase in the dispersion of the para-meters which characterise the various individual cosmic ray sources among the exploding stars.

By virtue of what has been said we shall not always mention novae as well as supernovae below, considering this to be understood.

Cosmic ray acceleration in interstellar space

In interstellar space there is a moving gas into which magnetic fields are "frozen". Under these conditions there should be statistical acceleration of sufficiently fast particles and under certain conditions they may be accelerated systematically (see section 9). The question of interstellar cosmic ray acceleration has in the past attracted great attention.[318, 358] The assumption of the efficiency of interstellar acceleration has met, however, with great difficulties[4, 5, 74, 374] and has hardly been discussed at all of recent years. Nevertheless we must discuss it for a moment.

In regular (systematic) acceleration (first-order acceleration) a particle with a total energy E in each "collision" with a moving gas cloud receives energy of the order of uE/c (here u is the velocity of the gas; see section 9). The number of "collisions" per unit time for a relativistic particle is of the order of c/L, where $L(t)$ is the characteristic distance between two masses of gas coming to meet each other and the velocity of the forward motion of the particle is made equal to c (in actual fact this velocity is $v \leqslant c$ since v is the velocity of the motion along the lines of force; we generally take $v \sim 10^{10}$ cm/sec but in estimates the replacement of v by c is insignificant). Therefore during systematic acceleration $dE/dt \sim (u/c)(c/L(t))E$ and for $L = L_0 - ut$ the energy varies according to the law $E \sim EL_0/(L_0 - ut) = E_0L_0/L(t)$, where E_0 and L_0 are the initial values of E and L. This result is, of course, in complete agreement with the conclusion obtained in section 9; the approach of gas clouds leads to compression and a corresponding increase in pressure including the cosmic ray pressure. From this and a number of other considerations it is clear that under astrophysical conditions during systematic acceleration the energy E can scarcely increase by more than one or two orders. Excluded, of

course, would be the case when a particle, having finished acceleration in one compression region, enters another compression region
and so on. But there is no reason to consider that this is the situation
in the Galaxy even with a multiple repetition of the fortunate arrival
of particles all the time in the compression regions. If compression
is replaced by rarefaction or head-on collisions by "overtaking"
collisions, then the acceleration is statistical in nature and is a
second-order acceleration with respect to u/c. In this case (see (9.7))

$$\frac{dE}{dt} = \alpha E, \qquad \alpha = \frac{u^2 v}{c^2 l} \sim 10^{-11} \frac{u^2}{l}, \qquad E_{max} \sim E_0 \, e^{\alpha t_{max}}, \qquad (11.15)$$

where T_{max} is the maximum acceleration time and E_0 is the energy
at the beginning of the process.

In the region of the disk the velocity of the clouds in $u \sim 10^6$
cm/sec but sometimes $u \sim 3 \times 10^6$ cm/sec; for the free path lengths
(the sizes of the regions between accelerating clouds or fronts),
according to astrophysical data, we have values of tens or even a
hundred parsecs. But not all the fronts (inhomogeneities) can be
observed and from diffusion calculations for a quantity close in
meaning to l we obtain the value of about 10 pc. For $u \sim 3 \times 10^6$
cm/sec and $l \sim 10$ pc $\simeq 3 \times 10^{19}$ cm we have $\alpha \sim 3 \times 10^{-18}$ sec^{-1}. But
even for $\alpha \sim 10^{-17}$ sec^{-1} over the period of existence of the Galaxy
$T_G \sim 3 \times 10^{17}$ sec the maximum energy is $E_{max} \sim 10 E_0$, i.e., statistical
acceleration is clearly inefficient. The fact that statistical accelera-
tion could lead to the observed cosmic ray spectrum only with a
sharp increase in α is also clear from other considerations.

In actual fact statistical acceleration leads to the generation of
particles with a power-law spectrum $N(E) \, dE = K E^{-\gamma} \, dE$, for example, with the following assumptions (see section 16): it is assumed
that particles start to be accelerated with equal probability at any
point in time and the probability of finding a particle with an "age"
in the range t, $t + dt$ is $dW = (1/T) e^{-t/T} \, dt$. Then, according to
(11.15), $dt = dE/\alpha E$, $t = \ln(E/E_0)/\alpha$ and

$$dW \propto N(E) \, dE \propto E^{-(1 + 1/\alpha T)} \, dE, \qquad \gamma = 1 + \frac{1}{\alpha T}. \qquad (11.16)$$

The expression accepted for the probability dW is valid, for example,
in conditions when acceleration ceases as the result of nuclear collisions (at least in "catastrophic" nuclear collisions). However, if

$T = T_{\text{nucl}}$ in (11.16) the values of γ are different for different nuclei which completely contradicts the observations (it must not be forgotten that the time T_{nucl} for protons and iron nuclei differs by a factor of about 25 and the values of γ are identical with an accuracy of, say, 10 per cent). It must therefore be considered that the time T in (11.16) is determined by the departure of particles from the accelerating region (from the disk for example), T being considerably less than the nuclear life for the heaviest nuclei. Since for the Galaxy as a whole $T_{\text{Fe}} \simeq 1 \cdot 4 \times 10^7$ yr and for the region of the disk this life is noticeably even less it is hardly possible to make the time T more than 10^7 yr. But from experiment $\gamma \sim 2$ to 3 and thus $\alpha T \sim 1$, so that for $T \sim 10^7$ yr we have $\alpha \sim 3 \times 10^{-15}$ sec^{-1}. This value of α is three orders greater than that obtained for $u \sim 3 \times 10^6$ cm/sec and $l \sim 10$ pc. Since even these values of the parameters are probably far too high it is clear that a thousandfold increase in α would be absolutely unfounded and completely arbitrary.

We should remark that the interstellar acceleration with allowance made for the departure of particles from the accelerating region has been discussed by Morrison et al.[359] Here, on the one hand, the use of the probability $dW = (e^{-t/T}/T)\,dt$, where T is a parameter playing the part of the departure time from the system, was given a certain foundation (this foundation is necessary since during diffusion the expression for dW depends upon the boundary conditions and other factors). On the other hand, however, Morrison et al.[359] accept a value for α that is even slightly higher than the above-mentioned value of $\alpha \sim 3 \times 10^{-15}$ sec^{-1}. As we have said, we think this is not permissible.

It is appropriate to mention that the assumption of the acceleration of cosmic rays in interstellar space has also met with other difficulties. Apart from the assumption that the value of α is high it is necessary in the case of interstellar acceleration to replenish the kinetic energy of the clouds of interstellar gas rapidly.

In fact if the cosmic rays in the Galaxy receive energy from the clouds the latter should give off 3×10^{39} to 3×10^{40} erg/sec (see (11.5)). At the same time the total kinetic energy of the clouds' chaotic motion does not exceed 10^{54} to 10^{55} erg (the mass of all the gas in the disk is $M \sim 3 \times 10^{42}$ g, whilst the velocity of the clouds is less than 3×10^6 cm/sec and on the average is only 7 km/sec; hence $Mu^2/2 < 10^{55}$ erg). If the motion of the clouds were not maintained, then by giving off 10^{40} erg/sec they would be braked in a time of the order of 3×10^{14} sec $\simeq 10^7$ yr. Since the clouds have not been braked they should on this assumption receive about 10^{40} erg/sec from some source. Obviously it may here be a question of the internal energy of the stars, the potential (gravitational) energy in the Galaxy or the kinetic energy of the overall galactic rotation. From the purely energetic point of view all of these sources would be sufficient; but it is still not easy to ensure the necessary "pumping" power of the clouds' chaotic motion. Let it suffice to say that the time of 10^7 years (see above) is still 1000 times less than the age of the Galaxy and is more than an order less than the time for one revolution of the solar system around the galactic centre. The main thing is that, as far as we know, there is no indication of the existence of such a powerful transmission of energy to the clouds. The hypothesis of the acceleration of cosmic rays by the clouds therefore requires additional, far-reaching assumptions even if we ignore the great difficulty indicated above connected with the low rate of transfer of energy from the clouds to the cosmic rays.

With interstellar acceleration there also arises the problem of injection which is very awkward for low values of α (for example for $\alpha \sim 5 \times 10^{-17}$ sec^{-1} and a gas concentration of $n \sim 0\cdot1$ cm^{-3} the injection energy E_{inj} for Fe nuclei is $E_{inj} \sim 3 \times 10^{11}$ eV;[318] see also section 9). We shall not stop on this question since the picture as a whole is quite clear: interstellar acceleration is inefficient and, generally speaking, cannot compete with acceleration in the shells of supernovae.

In essence this conclusion is clear from very general considerations —from the very nature of the acceleration of particles in a moving gas. The greater the velocity of the gas and the smaller the scale l the more efficient the acceleration (we recall that $\alpha = u^2 v/c^2 l$). In interstellar space the scale l clearly exceeds the scales in supernova shells and the velocity u is hundreds of times less than the velocities of these shells. In section 13 we shall see that acceleration in intergalactic space is also inefficient.

In general it may be said that statistical acceleration, although it was adduced in application to interstellar space[318], is effective only in regions with stormy and relatively small-scale motion.[332] In this scheme, if we are speaking of the Galaxy, the region near the galactic centre draws attention to itself. Unfortunately the field configuration and the velocity distribution in this region are still unknown. Any lengthy (in the time scale $T_G \sim 10^{10}$ years) compression is impossible here as well (for example with $L \sim 100$ pc and a velocity $u \sim 3 \times 10^6$ cm/sec the compression time is $L/u \sim 3 \times 10^6$ years). In addition, observational data point rather to the fact that now gas flows out of the central region in the galactic plane. Influx and, possibly, compression of the gas in the case of the steady-state picture should then occur in the direction of the axis of the galactic rotation (the gas should not only flow out of but also into the central region since otherwise it would be emptied). When the gas is compressed in only one direction (or, in any case, not from all directions) the conditions for systematic particle acceleration deteriorate. If we say that in the central region[249] $u \sim 10^7$ cm/sec and $l \sim 0.3$ pc, then during statistical acceleration $\alpha \sim 10^{-15} \text{sec}^{-1}$ and $\alpha T \sim 1$ only, for $T \sim 3 \times 10^7$ years. It is very hard to keep particles in a region with a radius $R \sim 100$ pc for 3×10^7 years (for example the diffusion path $L \sim \sqrt{lvT} \sim 1000$ pc for the same values $l \sim 0.3$ pc and $T \sim 3 \times 10^7$ years). Lastly the gas's reserve of kinetic energy in the central region is comparatively small (with $\rho \sim 10^{-24}$ to 10^{-23} g/cm^3, $u \sim 10^7$ cm/sec and $V \sim 10^{61}$ to 10^{62} cm^3 the energy is

$$W \sim \frac{\rho u^2 V}{2} \sim 10^{51} \text{ to } 10^{53} \text{ erg}).$$

All this makes us consider that interstellar acceleration in the central region can play no part if we are speaking of the majority of cosmic rays in the Galaxy. But the central region could in principle be essential from the point of view of obtaining particles with the highest energy. In this region with a radius of about 100 pc the field is[249] $H \sim 10^{-4}$ oe which corresponds to a parameter value of $\xi \sim 10^{-19} \mathscr{E}$ (see (11.11)); hence with $\xi \sim 0.1$ for $\mathscr{E}_{max}$ we obtain the value $\sim 10^{18}$ eV/nucleon, which is an order greater than estimate (11.12) for supernovae. In the central region one type 1 supernova explodes in 10^4 years.[249] If in this case particles are formed with an energy $\mathscr{E}_{max} \sim 10^{16}$ to 10^{17} eV/nucleon an increase of one or two orders in their energy is still possible thanks to systematic and statistical acceleration in the central region. Yet another difficulty arises here. Both from energy considerations and from a comparison of the frequency of supernova explosions in the Galaxy and its central region it is clear that only about 10^{-3} or a maximum of 10^{-2} of all the galactic cosmic rays can come from this region. But this means that there would be very few particles with the highest energy even if they were accelerated in the central region. We can develop a similar argument but shall not stop to do this since we are speaking here of purely hypothetical structures. It is another matter if a new kind of phenomenon such as an explosion of the galactic core could occur in the centre of the galaxy. This possibility is discussed in the next sub-section.

To recapitulate, we can state that there is every reason to consider that interstellar acceleration of cosmic rays in the Galaxy is inefficient.† This kind of acceleration (and braking as well) probably plays no noticeable part at any energy. In principle, however, the assumption is permissible that in the region of the galactic centre interstellar acceleration increases by an order the energy of the comparatively small number of particles generated in this region in its present quiet period.

The possible part played by explosions of the Galactic core‡

Until recently it has been assumed that no processes occur in the Galaxy that are of an explosive type on a scale greater than that of a supernova explosion. In other words, the Galaxy as a whole was considered to be evolving slowly and to have changed comparatively little over several billions of years. It was by proceeding from such ideas that the Galactic theory of the origin of cosmic rays was developed up to 1963. The hypothesis was recently suggested,[438] however, of the possibility of explosions of galactic nuclei and the core of the Galaxy in particular.

There is not yet any direct proof that such explosions really occur in the Galaxy. But on the other hand, the assumption that there are explosions has a certain basis and deserves close attention.

In the first place, the actual phenomenon of explosions or vigorous activity of galactic cores does not arouse doubts in a number of cases (certain radio galaxies, the galaxy M82,[484] super-stars[471-476] and Seifert galaxies[438, 476]). In this connexion it is natural to assume that an explosion like the gigantic explosion of a supernova in principle is possible not only for stars but also for a condensing (and apparently collapsing) gaseous nebula with a mass of $M \sim 10^4$ to

---

† Allowing for the strong attenuation of magnetohydrodynamic waves in the interstellar medium[360-362] further strengthens the conviction that the effective statistical acceleration of particles leading to an increase in the cosmic ray energy of many orders can occur only in regions like supernova shells or stellar atmospheres.

‡ This sub-section has been added to the English edition of the book.

$10^8 M_\odot$.† The theory of such explosions has not yet been developed and the conditions necessary for their appearance are unknown. In this situation the assumption of the existence of explosions in spiral galaxies and the Galaxy in particular is quite permissible.

In the second place, the behaviour of the central region of the Galaxy, the question of the formation and evolution of its spiral structure and lastly the mechanism of the halo's formation are still not clear. In this connexion the assumption of the explosion of the galactic core opens up new possibilities and is a rather attractive hypothesis, at least until the completion of a more detailed analysis.

By virtue of what has been said let us assume that the galactic core can explode and let us discuss the question of these explosions as sources of cosmic rays which is the major one for us.

At present the core of the Galaxy, although gas is flowing from it, is clearly not an anomalously powerful source of cosmic rays (see the preceding sub-section of the present section 11). But in explosions of the core, just as in supernova explosions, cosmic rays could undoubtedly be generated in large numbers.‡ According to Burbidge and Hoyle's[438] estimate the kinetic energy K_e of an explosion in the core of the Galaxy is of the order of 3×10^{55} erg (mass $10^7 M_\odot$, velocity ~ 500 km/sec). The energy of the cosmic rays in the Galaxy is $W_{cr} \sim 3 \times 10^{56}$ erg. At the first glance, therefore, it appears that all the cosmic rays in the Galaxy, just like the halo, can be generated as the result of one explosion in conditions when the energy $W_{expl, cr} \sim K_{expl}$ is transferred to the cosmic rays (the discrepancy of an order of magnitude can be ignored if we bear in mind the roughness of the estimate of K_{expl} and $W_{expl, cr}$). In actual fact, however, the situation is far less favourable from the point of view of the possibility of accepting the non-stationary (explosive) model of the origin of the halo and the majority of the cosmic rays in the Galaxy. The point is that in the process of the halo's formation the cosmic rays ejected from the core together with

† Here we proceed from the assumption that the phenomena in the galactic cores under discussion are of the nature of an explosion of a single mass. Of course, this has not yet been proven and we cannot, for example, exclude multiple explosions such as explosions of a large number of supernovae. The assumption made that it is a single mass that explodes is in fact inessential to what follows.

‡ We speak of an explosion but it must be borne in mind that cosmic rays are more likely to be particularly efficiently accelerated not when the peripheral regions of the core are flying apart but at the stage of its formation and compression[411] (in this connexion see also section 13).

the gas and the magnetic fields expand and their energy decreases in proportion to $V^{-1/3} \propto R^{-1}$, where $V \sim 4\pi R^3/3$ is the volume of the region occupied by the cosmic rays (the expansion is considered isotropic but this assumption is not essential here; see section 9). As a result the energy of the cosmic rays from the explosion, even if we do not allow for their departure from the Galaxy, should be of the order

$$W_{\text{expl, cr}} \sim W_{\text{cr}} \frac{R_H}{R_{\text{expl}}} \sim 3 \times 10^{56} \frac{R_H}{R_{\text{expl}}} \text{ erg,}$$

where $R_H \sim 15$ kpc is the radius of the halo and R_{expl} is the radius of the region in which the cosmic rays were generated in the explosion. If we take it that $R_{\text{expl}} \sim 100$ pc the energy of the explosion should be more than $W_{\text{expl, cr}} \sim 3 \times 10^{58}$ ergs.

The theory of the explosion of actual galactic nuclei is still quite undeveloped so we cannot estimate R_{expl} reliably. We think, however, that the value of R_{expl} should be still less than that taken above. In actual fact the gravitational energy $|\Omega| \sim \kappa M^2/R_{\text{core}}$ for $M \sim 10^8 M_\odot$ and $R_{\text{core}} \sim 100$ pc is only of the order of 10^{55} ergs. This means that the compression of the core which explodes because of gravitational energy must reach considerably smaller radii: this is also indicated by other considerations.[473-475] But if $R_{\text{core}} \sim 10^{-2}$ pc (in this case $|\Omega| \sim 10^{59}$ erg for $M \sim 10^8 M_\odot$), then cosmic ray acceleration can be expected near the nucleus and not in a region with the radius $\sim 10^4 R_{\text{core}} \sim 100$ pc.

However, another point is more important at present. As has been indicated, even with $R_{\text{expl}} \sim 100$ pc the energy of the explosion is 3 orders of magnitude greater than that estimated by Burbidge and Hoyle[438] which agrees with the data on the central regions of the Galaxy. When the departure of cosmic rays from the Galaxy is allowed for this discrepancy becomes even larger.

Moreover, we can hardly take it that $W_{\text{expl, cr}} \sim 3 \times 10^{58}$ erg (we are talking of the kinetic energy of the gas) and the kinetic energy of the explosion is $K_{\text{expl}} \sim 10^{56}$ erg. To be more precise, if such a possibility were realised then we were dealing with a radio galaxy: the cosmic rays would largely leave the system, forming characteristic radio emitting clouds. Therefore if explosions occurred in the Galaxy it is far more natural to assume that $W_{\text{expl, cr}} \sim 3$ to 10×10^{55} erg, but the cosmic rays and the gas are injected into an already existing halo (this, of course, does not mean that explosions play no part in maintaining the halo particularly if they are repeated more than once). Then the decrease in the cosmic ray energy as they enter the halo may be insignificant and, at the same time, they will remain in the halo and not leave immediately for metagalactic space. If explosions occur on the average every 5×10^7 years (a lower value is highly improbable) with $W_{expl, cr} \sim 3 \times 10^{55}$ erg the mean power of the explosions as cosmic ray sources is $U_{expl, cr} \sim 10^{40}$ erg/sec. This value is of the same order as or only an order less than the probable power of cosmic ray generation in supernovae (see (11.10)). Moreover, in this model the explosions of cores (they can be called super-supernovae) play in general the same part as the explosions of a combination of 10^4 to 10^6 supernovae exploding in the central region of the Galaxy. In other words, when there are comparatively weak explosions in the core, each of which do not lead to great changes in the halo,† from the point of view of the origin of cosmic rays the Galaxy can as before be considered in the first approximation to be stationary.

Thus when discussing the part played by explosions of the galactic core we must distinguish between two possibilities or models. The first of these models is essentially non-stationary and corresponds to "large" explosions. In this case the halo is formed or altered significantly in only one explosion; in this explosion most of the cosmic rays now observed are formed. The second model corresponds to the assumption of "small" explosions which play the part, as it were, of a very powerful supernova (a super-supernova). With the above-mentioned considerations in mind we consider the second model to be far more probable as applied to the Galaxy.

We should remark that there is no clarity in the question of the maximum energy generated by supernovae. Values are found in published papers[269, 482] giving values for the energy generated as high as 10^{51} to 10^{52} erg. If we consider that the source of the explosion is the gravitational energy generated in a gravitational collapse a star with a mass M can generate as much energy as $W_{max} \sim Mc^2$

---

† Both the high isotropy of the cosmic rays and the comparatively symmetrical form of the halo are in favour of this variant. With a powerful explosion we would be inclined to expect considerable asymmetry, which is observed in many radio galaxies, and also noticeable cosmic ray anisotropy as the result of insufficiently complete mixing of the explosion products. We should also remark that an explosion that occurred more than 3 to 5×10^8 years ago would not have played any part from the point of view of the observed cosmic rays in the Galaxy since $T_d \lesssim 3$ to 5×10^8 years.

$\sim 10^{54}M/M_\odot$ erg. However, with a centrally symmetrical collapse no explosion (ejection of energy) occurs† so the explosion is evidently connected with a non-symmetrical shape and rotation of the collapsing mass of gas. In this case it may be assumed that the maximum energy of the explosion, let us say, is only an order less than the energy W_{max}, i.e., $W_{expl, max} \sim 10^{53}M/M_\odot$. In this case an energy of the order of 10^{56} erg (see above) may be generated in the explosion of a "star" with a mass of $10^3 M_\odot$. This value is only one or two orders greater than the mass of the large type 2 supernovae discussed up to now.

All this suggests that there is no great gap between supernovae and super-supernovae any more than there is a jump in the transition from novae to supernovae. In other words, it is quite possible that powerful type 2 supernovae and super-supernovae (like novae and supernovae) differ in the first place only in the scale of the phenomenon and its probability (frequency of occurrence).‡

Above we have considered that the energy generated by supernovae on the average is 10^{49} to 10^{50} erg (see (11.8)) and they explode in the Galaxy on the average once every 50 years (see (11.9)). But this from the point of view of the energy balance is the equivalent of less frequent explosions generating more energy, for example an explosion generating 10^{56} erg occurring once in 10^7 to 10^8 yr. In general if the energy is generated as the result of gravitational collapse the total observed change in the gravitational energy (it corresponds to compression to the gravitational radius $R_{gr} = 2\kappa M/c^2$) is of the order of Mc^2 and obviously does not alter when one

† We are speaking here of a sufficiently massive star when an equilibrium neutron core cannot be formed.[474] Below when we discuss the possible analogy between supernovae and super-supernovae we are thinking mainly of the external manifestation and not of the questions of the energy sources and the state of the remaining star or the collapsed mass.

‡ In addition, of course, it is quite natural that the duration of the active phase in super-supernovae may be considerably longer than in supernovae. In the latter the characteristic time of high optical brightness is, let us say, months, $\sim 10^{50}$ erg being converted into light. If we consider that the super-star 3C273-B is a powerful super-supernova at the explosion stage it must be assumed that this stage lasts 10^3 to 10^4 years;[475, 476] in this case an energy of $\sim 10^{56}$ to 10^{57} erg is emitted in the optical part of the spectrum (the luminosity of the super-star 3C273-B is $\sim 10^{46}$ erg/sec). We thus find that the duration of the optically active phase increases only comparatively slightly more slowly than the total amount of energy generated. Moreover, there is here most probably only an apparent analogy and the super-star shines not as the result of the explosion but in the process of the compression of part of its mass which is comparatively slow because of its non-vanishing angular momentum.

supernova is replaced by any number of collapsing stars with the same total mass M.

Everything that has been said supports the conclusion already drawn above that "small" explosions of the galactic core are to a large extent equivalent to supernova explosions. Because of this the theory of the origin of cosmic rays which we have taken as the basis of discussion and in which supernovae are major sources needs no alteration as a whole.

We can and must, nevertheless, pose the question of the possible consequences of the suggestion that there are explosions of the galactic core, i.e., that super-supernovae appear in this core. It is quite obvious in the light of the accepted ideas about the quasi-stationary nature of the picture as a whole that a powerful explosion leads only to certain deviations from the mean behaviour of the system. In this respect a super-supernova in the centre of the Galaxy is like a supernova that explodes a short distance from the solar system. In both cases we may expect variations in the cosmic ray intensity in the solar system.

Let us make, for example, the following extreme assumption: let an explosion of the galactic core (an explosion of a super-supernova in the core) have occurred 5×10^7 years ago leading to the generation of practically all the cosmic rays observed on Earth. The latter means that before the explosion the cosmic ray intensity was considerably less than it is now. The most straightforward method of analysing the question of the possibility of such a variation of intensity is the study of the radioactivity and isotope composition of meteorites. According to the available data[453] the cosmic ray intensity has not varied noticeably over the last few million years. For the 10^8 to 10^9 years range the results are less accurate but there is nothing to indicate any great change in the cosmic ray intensity (according to the data given by Burbidge[476] the flux has changed by a factor of less than 2 to 3 in 10^8 to 10^9 years). We thus obtain yet another argument against the "large" explosion model.

There is an interesting possibility[485] of obtaining information on the cosmic ray intensity 10^9 years ago from measurements of the flux of γ-rays with an energy of 0.51 MeV generated in the annihilation of electrons and positrons (apart from γ-rays we can in principle observe the optical lines of positronium[486]). The point is that it is largely slow positrons that are annihilated; moreover the deceleration of the positrons generated in the interstellar medium by the action of cosmic rays and subsequent $\pi^+ \to \mu^+ \to e^+$ decay takes about 10^9 years.[485,523]

We should lastly like to indicate a radio astronomy method for observing explosions of the galactic core[487] (see also section 17). If in the explosion enough electrons are generated that go to make up the cosmic ray electron component the spectrum of their radio emission should change fairly sharply at a certain frequency v_m. In actual fact the energy of an electron which at the time of the explosion ($t = 0$) was E_0 is at present (time T) equal to $E = E_0/(1 + bE_0T)$, where $b = 3.8 \times 10^{-15}H_\perp^2 + 1.0 \times 10^{-25}w_{ph}$ (see (8.16) where the Compton losses are increased by a factor of $4/3$ in accordance with what is said in section 19). Further, the spectrum of the electrons with an energy E has a maximum at the frequency

$$v_m = 0.07 \frac{eH_\perp}{mc} \left(\frac{E}{mc^2}\right)^2 = 1.2 \times 10^6 H_\perp \left(\frac{E}{mc^2}\right)^2$$

(see formula (4.25)). If $v \gg v_m$, the intensity of the emission of an electron with energy E drops exponentially. With $w_{ph} \simeq 1$ eV/cm^3, $H_\perp \simeq 3 \times 10^{-6}$ oe and $T \simeq 3$ to 5×10^7 years $\sim 10^{15}$ sec the energy of the electrons is $E(T) \leqslant 1/bT \simeq 10^{10}$ eV no matter what the value of E_0. Hence the frequency is $v_m \simeq 10^9$ c/s ($\lambda_m = c/v_m \simeq 30$ cm) and the spectrum of the magnetic radio bremsstrahlung at this frequency should have a break in it. Unfortunately the appropriate measurements are extremely difficult.

The finding of some way of checking the suggestion that there are explosions of the galactic core and, what is most important, the determination of the parameters of this explosion is an urgent and important problem. At the present state of knowledge in this field, however, we can only once more stress the conclusion drawn above that explosions of the core, if they have occurred in the Galaxy, are most likely to have been small explosions (super-supernova explosions) with an energy of $W_{expl, cr} \sim 3$ to 10×10^{55} erg being transferred to the cosmic rays and these rays being injected into an already existing halo. In this case the intensity variations of the cosmic rays on Earth connected with the explosion would scarcely exceed a few per cent or tenths of a per cent. The data on the composition of meteorites, as we have seen, confirm, or in any case by no means contradict, this picture. If it is valid all the other known methods (measurements of the flux of γ-rays with an energy of 0.51 MeV, radio astronomy observations) will not make it possible to notice the explosion of the core (we have in mind the fact that the last such explosion in the Galaxy, if one has occurred, would have been not later than 10^7, or rather 5×10^7, years ago). It is nevertheless obvious that such a negative result from gamma and radio astronomy observations would be just as important as the discovery of the results of an explosion.

The part played by cosmic rays formed at an early stage in the evolution of the Galaxy

According to modern ideas[363, 364] at early stages in the evolution of the Galaxy (for 0·5 to 1×10^9 years) violent formation and evolution of stars took place and the frequency of supernova explosions was one or two orders greater than at present. In this connexion it is natural to consider that at early stages of the evolution of the Galaxy a particularly large number of cosmic rays were generated.[363, 365] But can these "remnant" cosmic rays be still present in the Galaxy? At first glance it appears that this is quite possible since the nuclear life for protons is $T_p \simeq 4 \times 10^9$ years and the age of the Galaxy is $T_G \sim 10^{10}$ years. In fact, however, the assumption of the existence of cosmic ray "remnants" meets with the most serious difficulties (it is not a question here of the "expanded" Galactic model in which the cosmic rays fill the volume of the whole Local Group of galaxies; see section 12).

In the first place, in the Galactic model it is most probable that cosmic rays leave the Galaxy with a characteristic time of 3×10^8 years (see above). At early stages in the evolution this time was probably still less (the halo could have been missing, the cosmic ray pressure could have been greater and so on). The concentration of cosmic rays of remnant origin in the first approximation decreases in the Galaxy according to the law $N = N_0 e^{-t/T_d}$ so with $t \sim T_G \sim 10^{10}$ years and $T_d \sim 3 \times 10^8$ years $N \sim 10^{-14} N_0$, i.e., there can be no question of the preservation of cosmic ray "remnants".

In the second place, even if cosmic rays do not leave the Galaxy at all heavy nuclei could not be kept in the composition of the "remnant" component.[5, 366] For example for iron nuclei with $n = 10^{-2}$ cm^{-3} the life time is $T_{Fe} = 1·4 \times 10^8$ years (see Table 10). Hence $N_{Fe} = N_{Fe, 0} e^{-T_G/T_{Fe}} \sim 10^{-30} N_{Fe, 0}(!)$. Even with $n = 10^{-3}$ cm^{-3}, when $T_{Fe} \simeq 1·4 \times 10^9$ years, the flux of Fe nuclei would decrease by a factor of about 1000 in 10^{10} years. Thus it would be possible to consider that only protons have been formed at an early stage. There is no reason to doubt the general origin of protons and nuclei and that the protons are largely secondary (see section 15). It should also be borne in mind that in the past the density of the gas in the Galaxy was probably higher than it is now. Therefore even with the present concentration of 10^{-3} cm^{-3} we should take a larger value for the mean concentration over the time $T_G \sim 10^{10}$ years.[367]

Therefore, within the framework of the Galactic theory of the origin of cosmic rays we see no real possibility of linking the observed cosmic rays with those generated at an early stage in the evolution of the Galaxy.† It is a different matter if we consider that most cosmic rays enter the Galaxy from the region of the Local Group or from the Metagalaxy. Then cosmic rays accelerated at any stages of the galaxies' evolution that are effective from this point of view (in particular at early stages in their evolution) could depart into intergalactic space and then enter the Galaxy. We shall examine these theories in sections 12 and 13. Let it suffice to say here that the models discussed in sections 12 and 13 differ radically from the variant of the Galactic theory discussed above in which allowance is made for cosmic ray "remnants". A reference to other models need not therefore be taken as an argument in favour of the possible justifiability of the Galactic model which takes cosmic ray "remnants" into consideration.

Cosmic rays of solar origin

About ten years ago there was wide discussion of the theory of the solar origin of cosmic rays.[368, 369] It is now clear enough that the hypothesis of the solar origin of cosmic rays is unjustified for the majority of them. Nevertheless the theories of solar origin deserve a certain amount of attention since solar activity indubitably has a significant effect on low-energy cosmic rays (see section 3).

This effect largely takes the form of distortions (modulation) of the galactic cosmic ray flux as they move in the solar system. But apart

† The flux of iron nuclei could remain practically unchanged in the Galaxy for 10^{10} years for $n \lesssim 3 \times 10^{-4}$ cm^{-3} and $T_d \gtrsim 3 \times 10^9$ years. These values meet the assumption that the field in the halo is closed and is well isolated from intergalactic space and the region of the disk. If the first assumption is very doubtful and is now considered highly improbable, the second seems to us to be even more unlikely (see section 10). It should not be forgotten either that the solar system is located in the disk so when the cosmic rays in the halo are isolated from the rays in the disk the assumption of the existence of "remnant" particles in the halo still could not be used to interpret the data on cosmic rays on the Earth.

from this the Sun is a source of cosmic rays[2] with an energy which is sometimes as much as 10^{10} and even 10^{11} eV.

The mean flux of cosmic rays arriving directly from the Sun in the relativistic energy range ($E_k \gtrsim 10^9$ eV) does not exceed in order of magnitude 0·1 per cent of the total cosmic ray flux. Hence it is clear that solar cosmic rays may play a significant part in the general cosmic emission flux on the Earth only if it is accumulated in the solar system. An analysis of the question of the possibility of such accumulation is a basic point in the theory of the solar origin of cosmic rays.

If the mean flux of cosmic rays coming directly from the Sun is $F_\odot = I_\odot \Delta\Omega$ on the Earth's orbit ($I_\odot$ is the intensity and $\Delta\Omega$ is the solid angle at which the Sun is visible from the Earth) then the total number of particles emitted by the Sun per unit time is $S_\odot = 4\pi R_{\odot\oplus}^2 \times I_\odot \Delta\Omega$ ($R_{\odot\oplus} \simeq 1.5 \times 10^{13}$ cm is the distance from the Sun to the Earth). Let the solar particles fill a certain volume with a radius R, their concentration being $N = (4\pi/v)I$ (it is assumed that the particles are distributed homogeneously and isotropically, v is the velocity and I the intensity). Then if the life of the solar particles in the range in question is T, we obtain from considerations on the conservation of the number of particles

$$\frac{4\pi}{v} \cdot I \cdot \frac{4\pi}{3} R^3 = I_\odot \Delta\Omega T \cdot 4\pi R_{\odot\oplus}^2,$$

$$R \sim \left(\frac{vI_\odot \Delta\Omega}{4I} TR_{\odot\oplus}^2\right)^{1/3}.$$

Let us assume that the intensity of rays of solar origin I is of the same order as the observed total intensity on the Earth. Then if we put $F_\odot \sim 3 \times 10^{-4}F$, then $F = \pi I \sim 3 \times 10^3 I_\odot \Delta\Omega$ and for $v \sim 10^{10}$ cm/sec we obtain

$$R \sim 10^{11} T^{1/3} \text{cm}, \qquad T \sim 5 \times 10^6 \left(\frac{R}{R_{\odot\oplus}}\right) \quad \text{sec.} \qquad (11.17)$$

The radius of the "capture region" R can in no way be less than several radii of the Earth's orbit; otherwise the cosmic ray flux would not be isotropic. In addition, the data on the solar corpuscular fluxes and the structure of the solar system do not allow us to assume that $R < 5R_{\odot\oplus}$. Hence from (11.17) we obtain the estimate $T > 6 \times 10^8$ sec $\sim$ 20 years. But a particle with a velocity $v \sim 10^{10}$ cm/sec travels a distance $R \sim 5R_{\odot\hbar} \sim 10^{14}$ cm in a time of the order of 10^4 sec. A comparison of this time with the time $T > 6 \times 10^8$ sec shows how complete the isolation of particles inside the "capture region" must be.

Furthermore the value $R \sim 10^{14}$ cm is still very much too low. The assumption of the existence of a practically ideal reflector of cosmic rays at such a small distance from the Sun clearly contradicts the data on solar cosmic rays which appear in certain solar flares (the presence of a reflector would lead to definite effects on Earth[2]). In addition, the value $R \sim 5R_{\odot\hbar}$ taken is merely the orbit of Jupiter. The radius of Pluto's orbit, which can be considered as the radius of the solar system, is approximately $40R_{\odot\hbar}$. For this value of R the time is $T \sim 10^4$ years (see (11.17)). Even larger values of R and T are obtained when trying to explain the fact of the presence of fast Li, Be, B nuclei of which there are known to be very few in the solar atmosphere. Therefore group L nuclei can appear in the composition of cosmic rays of solar origin only as the result of the spallation of heavier nuclei; for this purpose the latter should traverse a layer of matter several g/cm^2 thick. Not to mention the fact that the Sun emits few nuclei with $Z \geqslant 6$, for such a nucleus to traverse a layer 5 g/cm^2 thick the time $T = x/\rho v \sim 10^5$ years is needed for $x \sim 5$ g/cm^2, $\rho \sim 10^{-22}$ g/cm^3 and $v \sim c$. Hence in accordance with (11.17) $R \sim 2 \times 10^{15}$ cm.

Solar origin theories generally take the even far greater values $R \sim 3 \times 10^{16}$ cm ~ 0.01 pc and $T \sim 10^{16}$ sec $\sim 3 \times 10^8$ years. Moreover the diffusion departure of particles for any reasonable values of the diffusion coefficient takes place comparatively rapidly (see for example Ginzburg's corresponding estimate). The formation around the solar system of a perfect magnetic trap for relativistic particles is extremely improbable (it is well known now how difficult it is to create an efficient trap as the result of researches in the field of thermonuclear fusion[370, 371]). We shall not speak of the fact that there is no basis of an independent nature for the assumption of the existence of a trap.

Moreover, even if we make the arbitrary assumption of the presence of an ideal trap the theory of the solar origin of cosmic rays would come up against serious difficulties. They are connected with the question of the chemical composition and the energy spectrum of the cosmic rays: the cosmic rays emitted by the Sun, as has already been indicated, have a completely different composition and spectrum from the cosmic rays observed on the Earth. The assumption of the conversion of the composition and the spectrum in the capture region is connected at best with very far-reaching additional assumptions. Furthermore, even if there were a very effective magnetic trap for particles with relatively low energies this trap would cease to work as the energy rose. Assuming that the trap still works well for $\xi = r_H/R \sim 10^{-3}$ ($r_H = E/300H$ is the radius of curvature of a proton and R is the radius of the trap) we find the maximum capture energy is $E_{max} \sim 0\cdot3HR \lesssim 10^{11}$ eV for $R \lesssim 3 \times 10^{16}$ cm and $H \lesssim 10^{-5}$ oe. At the same time no features are observed in the cosmic ray spectrum for $E \lesssim 10^{14}$ to 10^{15} eV which indicate a change in the nature of their sources. Lastly, the theory of the solar origin of cosmic rays would be clearly artificial in the light of radio astronomy data on the existence of cosmic rays throughout the Galaxy.

We should therefore not speak of the solar origin of the majority of cosmic rays on Earth. The position may change with respect to low-energy particles ($E_k \lesssim 10^9$ eV and particularly $E_k < 10^8$ eV), as has already been mentioned in section 3. Furthermore even in this region the situation is still by no means clear and there are no convincing data pointing to the great effectiveness of the capture of these particles.

The origin of the electron component of cosmic rays

Within the framework of the Galactic theory of the origin of cosmic rays the relativistic electrons responsible for the radio emission and forming the electron component of cosmic rays should reach interstellar space from the primary sources of cosmic rays (largely from supernova shells) or be generated directly in the interstellar medium. In the latter case (secondary origin) electrons are produced by the $\pi \rightarrow \mu \rightarrow e$ decay of charged π-mesons appearing as the result of nuclear collisions of cosmic rays with nuclei of the interstellar gas.† Let us assume that the electrons (and positrons) receive 10 per cent of the energy of the primary nucleon (a value of 5 per cent was taken in section 7 for one collision; bearing in mind

---

† The electrons formed in the β-decay of neutrons and unstable nuclei have a velocity approximately equal to the velocity of these neutrons and nuclei. Therefore for the majority of cosmic rays the energy of the β-electrons formed in nuclear interactions is $E \ll 10^8$ eV, i.e., lies outside the energy range $E > 10^8$ eV that is of interest to us in the case of general galactic radio emission.

the nature of the estimates we are here taking the value of 10 per cent although the corresponding difference lies outside the limit of accuracy of the following calculations; for further detail see section 17). Then in the whole Galaxy the electrons receive (see (11.4))

$$U_e \sim 0 \cdot 1 U_{nucl} \sim 3 \times 10^{37} \text{ to } 3 \times 10^{38} \text{ erg/sec.} \quad (11.18)$$

At the same time it follows from radio astronomy data that the electrons lose 10^{38} to 10^{39} erg/sec in the Galaxy to radio emission[5]; from another, more direct, estimate[365] the electrons lose $\sim 3 \times 10^{38}$ erg/sec. The calculations made in section 6 led to a value of the emitted power of $4 \cdot 4 \times 10^{38}$ erg/sec. A comparison of all these data shows that within the limits of rough estimates the assumption that radio-emitting electrons are of secondary origin is permissible. Because of this it is this hypothesis which has been predominant in published papers up to now (i.e., the assumption that secondary electrons play a decisive part). Very recently, however, a fairly convincing proof has been given by two different methods[446] (see also section 17) that the radio-emitting electrons are largely primary. This will be treated in more detail in section 17. The present section (section 11) has been only slightly changed and added to when compared with the text of the Russian edition of the book.

The radio emission energy of the electrons, if we have in mind only the consideration of balance, is fully capable of being filled up by primary sources as well. For example according to (11.10) some supernovae may cause the appearance of relativistic electrons with a mean power of 10^{38} to 10^{39} erg/sec (this value is obtained by dividing the power (11.10) by 100 in accordance with what was accepted when determining the total energy of the cosmic rays in the shells on the basis of data on the number of relativistic electrons in these shells). There thus arises the important problem of choosing between two possibilities since it is rather improbable that primary and secondary particles play approximately the same part (this possibility is not excluded in principle, of course).

The answer to the question of the origin of the electrons, provided we are not thinking of bringing more precision to the values used above for the power and the gas concentration n, can be sought along three lines of approach.

In the first place, the secondary electron component should consist approximately equally of electrons and positrons (there would be even slightly more positrons than electrons because of the positive charge of the primary particles—protons and nuclei). At the same time only electrons could leave the shells of supernovae—this will be the case if they are accelerated directly in the shells and are not generated as the result of nuclear collisions. Hence it follows that the discovery of electrons only in the composition of the primary electron component of the cosmic rays on the Earth (i.e., no positrons) would definitely be an indication against the assumption of their secondary origin. The determination of the number of positrons in the composition of the electron component of the cosmic rays on the Earth is one of the most urgent problems. The use of artificial Earth satellites and space probes obviously opens up new possibilities in the provision of the electron and positron flux measurements near the Earth and in the solar system which are being discussed.[43] It has already been shown in section 2 that the first measurements[446] of the number of positrons in the cosmic ray nuclear component on Earth have already been made. The result runs counter to the assumption of the secondary nature of the radio-emitting electrons.

In the second place, the solution of the question of galactic radio-emitting electrons can be sought by studying the conditions for the departure of electrons from the sources and the nature of their motion in the interstellar magnetic fields. It is well known that, at least in a field that changes slowly enough in time and in space, the motion of particles takes place with the adiabatic invariant maintained $p_\perp^2/H = p^2 \sin^2 \theta/H = \text{const}$ (see section 10), where $p_\perp$ is the component of the particle's momentum p at right angles to H and θ is the angle between p and H.

If the field's variation in time can be ignored, then $p = \text{const}$ and we have

$$\frac{\sin^2 \theta}{H} = \text{con t.} \tag{11.19}$$

The systematic variation in the energy of the particles as they wander through the Galaxy, according to the estimates given above, is very small. The same can evidently be said of the variation in energy at departure from supernova shells, at least in the period preceding their strong expansion and erosion. Accepting the conservation law (11.19) therefore we see that the angle θ decreases when we change from a region with a strong field to a region with a weak field. This is the situation during the departure of particles from the shells, where $H \sim 10^{-3}$ to 10^{-4} oersteds, into interstellar space with $H \sim 3 \times 10^{-6}$ to 10^{-5} oersteds. Therefore even if $\sin \theta \sim 1$ in the shells for the departing particles $\sin \theta \sim 0 \cdot 1$. The radio-emitting capability in its turn depends on $\sin \theta$ and in fact[4] $I_v = \text{const} \cdot H_{\perp}^{(\gamma+1)/2} = \text{const} \cdot H^{(\gamma+1)/2}(\sin \theta)^{(\gamma+1)/2}$ (see also (2.1)). With $\gamma = 2\cdot4$ and the invariant (11.19) preserved this means that the emission intensity is proportional to $(\sin \theta)^{3(\gamma+1)/2} = (\sin \theta)^{5\cdot1}$ or for a given field H is proportional to $(\sin \theta)^{(\gamma+1)/2} = (\sin \theta)^{1\cdot7}$.

It follows from this[373] that if the adiabatic invariant is preserved in interstellar space and if the electrons are primary their number must be one or two orders of magnitude higher than the value taken in section 6. This strong increase in the relativistic electron concentration still does not have to be connected with a large additional consumption of energy: although there are more electrons they emit the same power as before. In other words, the life of the electrons, which is connected with the magnetic bremsstrahlung losses, increases in the case in question just proportionally to the increase in the concentration of the emitting particles. As for the lifetime for bremsstrahlung losses, this is $T_r \sim 60/(2 \times 10^{-26}c) \sim 3 \times 10^9$ years for a mean gas density of $\rho \sim 2 \times 10^{-26}$ g/cm^2 (see section 8). Therefore if the total energy of the electrons is 10 per cent of the total energy of the cosmic rays $W \sim 10^{56}$ erg (see (11.3)) the radiation losses are $U_r \sim 0\cdot1 \times 10^{56}/10^{17} \simeq 10^{38}$ erg/sec. This value is of the order of the power emitted in the form of radio waves.

The Compton losses exceed the magnetic bremsstrahlung losses in the halo for $H_{\perp} \lesssim 2$ to 5×10^{-6} oe. In actual fact, probably, $H_{\perp} \sim 3 \times 10^{-6}$ oe and the Compton losses are significant but allowing for them does not alter the order of magnitude. It can thus be said that the total energy of the electrons, provided one proceeds only from energy considerations, is perfectly capable of being brought up to 10 per cent of the energy of all the cosmic rays. The corresponding electron flux, strictly speaking, does not contradict the data on relativistic electrons on Earth either. As has been pointed out in section 2, this flux may be as much as 3 per cent of the total cosmic ray flux on Earth. But the flux of comparatively soft cosmic rays on Earth (particularly when there is not a solar activity minimum) may be strongly attenuated within the solar system.

Therefore the increase in question (of about one order of magnitude) in the concentration of relativistic electrons in the Galaxy is still compatible with the model under discussion and the assumption that electrons are largely generated in the sources. It is another matter that the electron flux must clearly be increased by more than an order of magnitude if the adiabatic condition (11.19) is exactly satisfied. An increase of two orders of magnitude in the electron flux obviously contradicts all the data and must be accepted as inadmissible. These remarks show how important is the question of maintaining the adiabatic condition (11.19) from the point of view of analysing the motion and radio emission of relativistic electrons. If this condition were satisfied the requirements imposed on electron sources would clearly be increased and would possibly become incompatible with the Galactic model under discussion. By virtue of this (in the framework of this model) it would be necessary to rest only on the assumption of the secondary origin of the electrons. Unfortunately it is rather difficult to explain with enough definiteness the limitations imposed by the adiabatic condition (11.19) on the motion of particles in the Galaxy. In section 10 we discussed this question and came to the conclusion that in all probability there is fairly effective mixing with respect to the angle θ in the Galaxy so relationship (11.19) can be ignored. In supernova shells the adiabatic approximation will also probably be broken down. Under these conditions the electrons also remain isotropic when the shell expands, the field in it reaching the interstellar value of $H \sim 10^{-5}$ oersteds. The electrons departing into interstellar space at this stage (and there may be more of them than any others) preserve their isotropic distribution.

The third possible way of explaining the origin of galactic electrons is connected with the use of radio astronomy data.[5, 162, 279, 337] Secondary electrons are formed both in the disk and in the halo so their energy spectrum, and that also means the radio spectrum, should be approximately the same in the halo and in the disk. Primary electrons reach the halo only from the spiral and central regions of the Galaxy and lose energy on the way. As a result in the latter case we could expect a certain change in the radio emission spectrum in the transition from the centre to the periphery of the Galaxy. In this case we are thinking only of the quantitative effect since even the secondary electrons are generated in a significant, if not large, part of the disk and the central region where the gas density is considerably greater than the mean density for the whole system. As far as is known there are no changes in the spectrum in the transition from the disk to the halo but the accuracy of the measurements and the nature of the calculations here still do not allow us to draw any definite conclusions.

The same can be said with respect to the attempt to draw conclusions on the secondary origin of interstellar electrons on the basis of the closeness of the spectra of the overall galactic emission and the emission of the majority of discrete sources which proceeds from certain data.[365] If the electrons in supernova shells and in interstellar space were generated in the first stages of an explosion, but some "are captured" in the shell whilst others leave it, then similarity of the spectra is to be expected. On the other hand, if the electrons leave the shell only after its disintegration and their spectrum is of the form $N_{e0} = K_0 E^{-\gamma_0}$, then after long enough wandering in interstellar space they will have a spectrum $N_e(E) = KE^{-\gamma}$, when $\gamma = \gamma_0 + 1$ (it is this possibility which is accepted by Shklovskii[365] who decided to proceed from the assumption of the generation of radio-emitting electrons in discrete sources). In the general case, when particles are leaving the shells all the time intermediate results will, of course, be obtained. It must also be borne in mind that the field strength is different in the shells and in interstellar space so electrons of different energies will be responsible for the emission at a given frequency in both cases. From what has been said it is clear that the question of the radio emission spectrum is a very delicate one and only quantitative calculations can open up the way for using the form of the spectrum to judge the nature of the electrons. A similar attempt is made in section 17 where calculations are made of the spectrum of the overall galactic radio emission caused by secondary electrons.

The calculations made in section 17 are a definite indication against the secondary nature of the majority of radio-emitting electrons in the Galaxy.

In conclusion we would remark that Getmantsev[375] discusses the assumption of the "remnant" origin of at least some of the radio-emitting electrons in the halo (this means that the electrons were accelerated or generated at an early stage in the Galaxy's evolution). The basis indicated by Getmantsev[375] for this hypothesis (the nature of the galactic radio emission spectrum) does not of itself appear to us to be sufficient to draw any probable conclusion on the existence of a remnant electron component. On the other hand, it is clear that the presence of a remnant component could have a strong effect on the halo's radio emission spectrum. We shall now examine the conditions in which a remnant component could be preserved in the halo.

The life of electrons with respect to bremsstrahlung losses is $T_r \simeq 3 \times 10^7/n$ years (see section 8). For $n \simeq 10^{-2}$ cm^{-3}, therefore, $T_r \simeq 3 \times 10^9$ years and in the time $T_G \sim 10^{10}$ years the electron flux would be reduced only by one order of magnitude because of radiation losses. When only Compton and magnetic bremsstrahlung losses are taken into account an electron's energy decreases in accordance with (8.16). In the halo $w_{ph} > 0.3$ eV/cm^3 and at early stages in the evolution of the Galaxy was probably even greater. For $w_{ph} = 0.3$ eV/cm^3 the Compton losses are equal to the magnetic bremsstrahlung losses with $H_\perp \sim \sqrt{\overline{H_\perp^2}} \sim 2.5 \times 10^{-6}$ oersteds. For this value of $H_\perp$ radio waves with a wavelength of $\lambda = 1$ m are radiated largely by electrons with an energy $E \sim 3 \times 10^9$ eV and in any case greater than 10^9 eV (see (4.25) and (6.3)). But according to (8.16) in the conditions under discussion ($H_\perp \sim 2.5 \times 10^{-6}$ oe, $w_{ph} \sim 0.3$ eV/cm^3 with $t \sim T_G \sim 3 \times 10^{17}$ sec) the energy of remnant electrons is $E \simeq 10^8$ eV for $E_0 \gg 10^8$ eV. If the magnetic bremsstrahlung losses are completely ignored but $w_{ph} \simeq 0.3$ eV/cm^3 we have $E = E_0/(1 + 2.3 \times 10^{-26} E_0 t)$ and for $t \sim 3 \times 10^{17}$ sec the energy is $E \lesssim 1/(2.3 \times 10^{-26} t) \simeq 1.4 \times 10^8$ eV for any E_0.

It is possible to ignore the magnetic bremsstrahlung losses in (8.16) the present case only if $H_\perp \lesssim 1.5 \times 10^{-6}$ oe when the emission of an electron with an energy $E \simeq 1.4 \times 10^8$ eV is a maximum at the frequency $\nu_{max} = 4.6 \times 10^{-6} H_\perp E^2 \lesssim 1.4 \times 10^5$ c/s ($\lambda \gtrsim 2$ km). Even when the density w_{ph} is reduced by a factor of three (i.e., if $w_{ph} = 0.1$ eV/cm^3), for which we can see no foundation (see section 8), for $\sqrt{\overline{H_\perp^2}} \sim 10^{-6}$ oe and $t = 3 \times 10^{17}$ sec the energy is $E = E_0/(1 + 3.5 \times 10^{-9} E_0) \lesssim 3 \times 10^8$ eV, $\nu_{max} \simeq 4.6 \times 10^{-12} E^2 \lesssim 3.8 \times 10^5$ c/s ($\lambda \gtrsim 1$ km). Under the same conditions, if $t = 10^{17}$ sec, the wavelength is $\lambda = c/\nu_{max} \sim 100$ m. Finally if we use formula (6.12) for electrons with a power-law spectrum the effective frequency is $\nu \lesssim 3 \times 10^{-5} HE^2$ c/s; if $H = 10^{-6}$ oe and $E = 2 \times 10^8$ eV this frequency is $\nu \lesssim 10^6$ c/s and $\lambda \gtrsim 300$ m.

By virtue of what has been said we can see no possibility even with the greatest stretch of imagination of considering that electrons generated at an early stage in the Galaxy's evolution ($t \sim 10^9$ years, $T_G \sim 10^{10}$ years) can now be responsible for radio emission in the metric band. It should be added that the departure of electrons from the halo has not been considered above. Moreover $T_d \ll T_G$ most likely (see section 10) and we must not then think of cosmic ray remnants (we note that Getmantsev[340, 375] draws the conclusion that the cosmic rays leave the Galaxy slowly but we consider that this conclusion is highly improbable; see section 10). We shall say more about cosmic ray remnants and in particular electrons in the "expanded" Galactic model in section 12.

General remarks on the Galactic theory

The Galactic model (theory) of the origin of cosmic rays discussed above is the one which has been most worked upon at present. The basic point in this model is the assumption that the cosmic rays in the Galaxy have been formed within its limits and can only leave this system. The metagalactic model is the opposite: here the cosmic rays enter the Galaxy from metagalactic space and are generated for preference in this space or in other galaxies (basically radio galaxies). The "expanded" Galactic model, which is discussed in detail in section 12, is an intermediate model. This model is very close to the Galactic model in which the radius of the halo is increased by an order of magnitude. On the other hand the "expanded" model differs significantly from the Galactic model in that in the "expanded" Galactic theory the cosmic rays arrive in the Galaxy from the whole volume of the Local Group of galaxies and may be generated in all 15 to 20 galaxies forming this group.

These are the three basic possibilities which deal with the majority of cosmic rays. As for particles with the highest energy $\mathscr{E} \gtrsim 10^{17}$ eV/nucleon they are best discussed separately with the model considered to be galactic even in the case when these particles arrive from the Metagalaxy or the Local Group of galaxies.

The data and estimates given above are an indication in favour of the fact that the Galactic theory is at least quite possible and does not come up against any great difficulties. Supernovae and novae, not to mention hypothetical explosions of the galactic core may supply the necessary amount of cosmic rays thus satisfying the correspondingly very high requirements imposed on cosmic ray sources in the framework of the Galactic theory. All the known features of the cosmic emission can be explained by this theory (this will be shown in Chapter V).

Nevertheless the Galactic theory still cannot be considered proved. The point is that in the present state of astrophysics a quantitative check of the theory is very difficult. As for selecting parameters to satisfy agreement of the theory with experiment (e.g., in the question of the chemical composition of the cosmic rays) this still does not prove the necessity of making this selection of parameters (it is a question, say, of the diffusion coefficient). It must not be forgotten either that there is a great difference between disproving and proving any theory. One solidly established fact that clearly contradicts the theory is enough to disprove it. At the same time even complete agreement of the theory with experiment with respect to a series of effects still does not prove the correctness of the theory and only indicates that it is not contradicted or is probable. What has been said relates even to fundamental theoretical postulates and is particularly clear in the example of the general theory of relativity.[376] Because of this we should not be surprised at the conclusion that the best proof of the Galactic theory would be the disproving of the "expanded" Galactic or Metagalactic theories of the origin of cosmic rays. For this it is enough to prove that the cosmic rays largely flow from the Galaxy and do not return to it again, this having been the case in the past as well.

The Metagalactic theory would be practically disproved also by proving the smallness of the cosmic ray flux in the Metagalaxy (when compared with the cosmic ray flux in the Galaxy). The "expanded" Galactic theory can be disproved by showing that in the Local Group of galaxies the cosmic ray concentration is considerably less than in the Galaxy. Another possibility is to establish the absence of a closed magnetic field ("trap") preventing the departure of cosmic rays from the Local Group (see section 12). Unfortunately the available data do not yet permit us to make these statements with complete certainty. This is connected to a considerable degree with the fact that extragalactic astronomy, and cosmology in particular, is still in a number of respects at an early stage in its development and in any case does not give an answer to the most fundamental questions (for example we still do not know the density of the gas in intergalactic space).

The Galactic, the "expanded" Galactic and the Metagalactic theories of the origin of cosmic rays in our Galaxy will be compared to a certain extent at the end of section 12 and in section 13. We should like to stress here and now, however, that we consider the Galactic theory to be considerably more probable. The authors were occupied in developing it previously[4-7] and have continued this work in the present monograph. In particular, various quantitative calculations are given in Chapter V in the framework of the Galactic theory. The results of these calculations, in the same way as an analysis of the "expanded" Galactic theory and the Metagalactic theory, are indubitably in favour of the Galactic theory of the origin of the cosmic rays on Earth and in the Galaxy in general.

12. "EXPANDED" GALACTIC THEORY OF THE ORIGIN OF COSMIC RAYS

The "expanded" Galactic theory (model) of the origin of cosmic rays is what we call the model in which the cosmic rays are localised within the Local Group of galaxies (we are speaking, of course, only of the cosmic rays which can be observed in the Galaxy and on Earth in particular). The "expanded" model was suggested recently[377] and in many respects is still insufficiently worked out. Nevertheless it undoubtedly deserves attention and detailed discussion.

Local Group of galaxies

One of the basic conclusions of extragalactic astronomy is that galaxies very often form multiple systems, groups and accumulations. For example our Galaxy has two satellite galaxies. These satellites (the Large and Small Magellanic Clouds) are at a distance of 53 kpc $\simeq 1.5 \times 10^{23}$ cm from the centre of the Galaxy (we recall that the radius of the disk and the halo is $\sim 5 \times 10^{22}$ cm). The masses of the Large and Small Magellanic Clouds are $2.5 \times 10^{10} M_\odot$ and $1 \times 10^{10} M_\odot$, respectively, whilst for the Galaxy $M \simeq 1 \times 10^{11} M_\odot$ ($M_\odot \simeq 2 \times 10^{33}$ g). The closest large galaxy to us is the galaxy M31 (the Large Nebula in the constellation of Andromeda). This galaxy is very like ours and its mass is about four times greater ($M = 4 \times 10^{11} M_\odot$); the galaxy M31 is at a distance $R = 0.6$ Mpc $\simeq 1.8 \times 10^{24}$ cm from the centre of the Galaxy (we give the distances and masses as given by Godferson[378]). Our Galaxy, the Magellanic Clouds and the galaxy M31 with its three satellites (the galaxies M32, M33 and NGC 205) form, as it were, the skeleton of a small collection of galaxies (the Local Group). Altogether this group contains 15 to 20 galaxies† the majority of them are dwarfs. For

† This uncertainty is due in the first place to the fact that some galaxies are related to the Local Group only conjecturally.[315] Secondly for multiple galaxies there is a certain arbitrariness in counting the number of independent components,

example the mass of the galaxy NGC 6822 located at a distance of approximately 0·3 Mpc is only $4 \times 10^8 M_\odot$. The total mass of the Galaxy, the nebula M31 and their five satellites is approximately $6·2 \times 10^{11} M_\odot$, whilst the mass of all the remaining galaxies of the group is clearly $M \simeq 1$ to $3 \times 10^{10} M_\odot$. Therefore the mass of the galaxies in the whole group is $M \simeq 6·5 \times 10^{11} M_\odot$.

The relative velocity of the centres of the Galaxy and the nebula M31 is $u \sim 100$ km/sec (the precise determination of their velocity is made difficult by the necessity of allowing for the galactic rotation[378]). The relative velocities of the other members of the Local Group are $u \sim 200$ km/sec. The kinetic energy of the group's galaxies is $W_k \sim 1$ to 5×10^{58} ergs. The radius of the group is $R \sim 0·7$ Mpc $\simeq 2 \times 10^{24}$ cm. The question of the density of the intergalactic gas within the group clearly remains unanswered. Kahn and Woltjer[282] drew the conclusion that the Local Group can be stable (the total energy equal to the sum of the gravitational and kinetic energies be negative) only if there is a lot of gas between the galaxies. In fact they took the value $\rho \simeq 1·6 \times 10^{-28}$ g/cm^3 or the concentration $n \simeq 10^{-4}$ cm^{-3} (the temperature of the gas is $T \simeq 5 \times 10^5$ °K, the gas being practically completely ionised). Godferson,[378, 380] however, shows that the determination of the total energy of the group's galaxies is very inaccurate and the stability can quite possibly be ensured without any gas at all.† In general the question of the stability and the density of the gas in the group remains unanswered and this uncertainty is a clear enough indication of the present state of extragalactic astronomy.

The "expanded" Galactic model

The "expanded" model suggested by Sciama[377], who calls it the "open" model of the galactic magnetic field, is based upon a number of assumptions which will be indicated below.

We should also state that only the very close galaxies M32 and NGC 205 are generally called satellites of the galaxy M31; however, the galaxy M33 is located close to M31 so it also could be considered a satellite of the galaxy M31.

† At present an extensive discussion has started in astrophysics[474] of the question of the existence of collapsed masses whose radius is close to the gravitational radius $R_{gr} = 2\kappa M/c^2$. These masses make no contribution to the brightness of the system but, of course, have a gravitational field (if $R \gg R_{gr}$, their gravitational potential as usual is $\phi = -\kappa M/R$). In this connexion the stability of stellar accumulations in the cases when this question arises can in principle be connected with the presence of collapsed masses. Apart from a gravitational field these masses may have a magnetic field, which leads to a number of consequences.[492]

The magnetic field is considered to be closed within the Local Group, the field's lines of force leaving the Galaxy freely. In accordance with this the field is considered to be a large-scale one. The effective length of the free path of cosmic rays in the field is therefore considered to be $l \sim L/10$, where L is the size of the region in question: the arms, the disk, the halo and the whole group. It is assumed here that

$$L_{arm} \sim 10^{21} \text{ cm}, \qquad L_{disk} \sim 10^{22} \text{ cm}, \qquad L_{halo} \sim 10^{23} \text{ cm},$$

$$L_{gr} \sim 2 \times 10^{24} \text{ cm}. \qquad (12.1)$$

By using the diffusion picture to describe the motion of the cosmic rays we can estimate the time T necessary to travel the path L. This is

$$T \sim \frac{L^2}{lv} \sim \frac{10L}{v} \sim 10^{-9}L, \qquad l \sim \frac{L}{10}, \qquad v \sim 10^{10} \text{ cm/sec}. \qquad (12.2)$$

Hence we have

$$T_{arm} \sim 10^{12} \text{ sec}, \qquad T_{disk} \sim 10^{13} \text{ sec}, \qquad T_{halo} \sim 10^{14} \text{ sec},$$

$$T_{gr} \sim 2 \times 10^{15} \text{ sec} \simeq 6 \times 10^{7} \text{ yr}. \qquad (12.3)$$

It is further assumed that departure of particles from the Local Group plays no part; this is possible only if a very perfect magnetic trap exists.

We should note that Sciama[377] takes the following values for the field strength:

$$H_{arm} \sim 5 \times 10^{-6} \text{ oersteds}, \qquad H_{disk} \sim 2 \cdot 5 \times 10^{-6} \text{ oersteds},$$

$$H_{halo} \sim 10^{-6} \text{ oersteds}, \qquad H_{gr} \sim 5 \times 10^{-7} \text{ oersteds} \qquad (12.4)$$

The whole volume of the group is $V \sim 4\pi R^3/3 \simeq 3 \times 10^{73} \text{ cm}^3$ $(R \sim 2 \times 10^{24} \text{ cm})$† and the mean density of the gas in this volume is taken to be

$$\rho \sim 5 \times 10^{-28} \text{ g/cm}^3, \qquad n \sim 3 \times 10^{-4} \text{ cm}^{-3}. \qquad (12.5)$$

Thus the total mass of gas in the group is considered to be $M \sim 7 \times 10^{12} M_\odot$, i.e., an order more than the mass of all the galaxies in the group. The value of (12.5) is three times greater than that used by Kahn and Woltjer[282] (see above) and is also 50 times higher than

† Sciama[377] takes for the volume $V \sim 4 \times 10^{72} \text{ cm}^3$.

the most probable density of the gas $\rho \sim 10^{-29}$ g/cm^3 in metagalactic space (see section 13).

Because of the inefficiency of intergalactic acceleration and the established efficiency of acceleration in the shells of supernovae it is assumed by Sciama[377] that cosmic rays are generated only in galaxies of the group. On leaving a galaxy the particles fill the volume of the group V, where

$$w_{gr} \sim 5 \times 10^{-14} \text{ erg/cm}^3, \qquad W = V w_{gr} \sim 10^{60} \text{ erg.} \quad (12.6)$$

Here w_{gr} is the cosmic ray energy density within the group taken by Sciama.[377] From the point of view of obtaining the estimate (12.6) and in the calculation of the magnetic bremsstrahlung losses and those due to radio emission there is the very important question of the maintenance of the adiabatic invariant (11.19). Sciama[377] assumed that this occurs, i.e., $\sin^2 \theta / H = $ const. If the cosmic rays arrive in the space between galaxies only from these galaxies where they are isotropically distributed, then the density of w_{gr} is significantly less than the density of the cosmic rays in the spiral arm $w_G \sim 1$ eV/cm^3 (we consider the value of w_G to be close to the cosmic ray density near the Earth).

In actual fact in a constant magnetic field, according to Liouville's theorem, the cosmic ray intensity I is identical along the particles' trajectories. If now in region 1 with a field H_1 the intensity $I(\theta) = I_0$ is identical for all θ (isotropic radiation), then upon transfer to region 2 with a field H_2 the intensity $I(\theta) = I_0$ for all angles θ which a particle may have in region 2 according to the laws of motion. When the adiabatic invariant is maintained for the field $H_2 < H_1$ we have $\sin^2 \theta_{max} / H_2 = 1/H_1$ (this means that in region 2 for angles $0 \leqslant \theta \leqslant \theta_{max}$ the intensity is $I(\theta) = I_0$ and for $\theta \geqslant \theta_{max}$ the intensity $I = 0$). Hence for the energy densities in regions 1 and 2:

$$\left. \begin{aligned} \frac{w_2}{w_1} &= \frac{\displaystyle\int_0^{\theta_{max}} \sin \theta \, d\theta}{\displaystyle\int_0^{\pi/2} \sin \theta \, d\theta} = 1 - \cos \theta_{max}, \qquad \theta_{max} = \arcsin \sqrt{\frac{H_2}{H_1}}, \\[2mm] \frac{w_2'}{w_1} &\simeq \frac{\theta_{max}^2}{2} = \frac{H_2}{2H_1} \quad \text{if} \quad \frac{H_2}{H_1} \ll 1. \end{aligned} \right\} \quad (12.7)$$

Using the values $H_{gr} \sim 5 \times 10^{-7}$ oe and $H_{arm} \sim 5 \times 10^{-6}$ oe (see (12.4)) we obtain

$$\frac{w_{gr}}{w_{arm}} \sim \frac{1}{20} \quad \text{and} \quad w_{gr} \sim \frac{10^{-12}}{20} = 5 \times 10^{-14} \text{ erg/cm}^3.$$

The nuclear energy losses for the gas density (12.5) are approximately 30 times less than for the value $n \sim 10^{-2}$ cm^{-3} used in the Galactic model. Hence it is clear that even for Fe nuclei in the "expanded" model the nuclear life is $T_{Fe} \simeq 30 \times 1\cdot4 \times 10^8 \simeq 4 \times 10^9$ years. Under these conditions heavy nuclei may be preserved even for the time of the system's evolution $T_G \sim 10^{10}$ years. For protons the nuclear losses in a time of 10^{10} years are only $T_G/T_p \sim 10^{10}/30 \times 4 \times 10^9 \sim 10$ per cent of the initial energy. Hence and from (12.6) it is clear that to fill the whole volume V with cosmic rays an energy of $\sim 10^{60}$ erg has to be injected in the whole time T_G (it is assumed that no particles leave the group). In 10^{10} years a relativistic particle will traverse a layer of matter 5 g/cm^2 thick when moving in a medium with a density of 5×10^{-28} g/cm^3. In the expanded model, therefore, it is quite possible to rely on obtaining the correct cosmic ray chemical composition.

General requirements for the "expanded" model

When discussing any model, and the "expanded" model in particular, it is important to discover the limits of variation of the parameters. We shall now discuss this question.

For group L nuclei to be able to be formed in the necessary quantity the heavier nuclei must travel a path of 5 to 10 g/cm^2 (see section 15). Hence $\rho = 5$ to $10/cT$ g/cm^3, where T is the time of motion at a velocity c (relativistic particles). The maximum value is $T \simeq T_G \simeq T_{Mg} \simeq 3 \times 10^{17}$ sec, so $\rho_{min} \simeq 5$ to 10×10^{-28} g/cm^3. This value must be at least doubled if we consider that a considerable number of the cosmic rays were not generated at the earliest stages of the group's evolution. Therefore the value taken for (12.5) can in no way be reduced and in fact $\rho \simeq 1$ to 2×10^{-27} g/cm^3 is more appropriate. Hence it follows that the estimate $M \sim 7 \times 10^{12} M_\odot \simeq 1\cdot5 \times 10^{46}$ g for the mass of gas in the group is not too high (even if we assume a reduction in the volume $V \sim 3 \times 10^{73}$ cm^3 by a factor of 2 to 3). What has been said is no less true of the estimate of the gravitational energy Ω of the gas in the group. For a sphere with a constant density the gravitational energy is

$$-\Omega_{gas} = \frac{3\kappa M^2}{5R} \sim 4 \times 10^{60} \text{ erg.} \tag{12.8}$$

Here $\kappa = 6 \cdot 67 \times 10^{-8}$ g^{-1}cm^{3}sec^{-2} is the gravitational constant, the mass of the gas is $M = 1 \cdot 5 \times 10^{46}$ g and the radius is $R = 2 \times 10^{24}$ cm. On the assumption that the system (galaxies and gas) is stable and is in a quasi-equilibrium state we can use the virial theorem[381]:

$$2W_k + 3P + W_H + \Omega = 0,$$

$$W_k = \int \frac{\rho u^2}{2} \, dV, \qquad P = \int p \, dV, \qquad W_H = \int \frac{H^2}{8\pi} \, dV, \quad (12.9)$$

$$\Omega = \int \rho \phi \, dV,$$

where p is the total pressure, Ω is the gravitational energy, ϕ is the gravitational potential, u is the macroscopic velocity of the matter and it is assumed that the pressure at the boundaries of the system is zero; the pressure p is made up from the pressure of the gas $p_{gas} = nkT$ and the cosmic ray pressure p_{cr}. According to some estimates[378, 380] for the galaxies of the Local Group $W_{k,G} \sim |\Omega_g| \sim 10^{58}$ to 10^{59} erg so $|\Omega| \simeq |\Omega_{gas}| \sim 4 \times 10^{60}$ erg. This value must also be used for estimating the upper limits for u, H, p_{cr} and p_{gas} within the group. The estimate is possible because in (12.9) only the quantity Ω is negative so the maximum value is $W_k = -\Omega/2$ and the maximum value of W_H is $-\Omega$, and so on.

Assuming that $|\Omega| = 4 \times 10^{60}$ erg, we find

$$\left.\begin{array}{ll} u_{max} \sim 200 \text{ km/sec}, & H_{max} \sim 2 \times 10^{-6} \text{ oe}, \\[2mm] \multicolumn{2}{c}{p_{cr, max} \sim 3 \times 10^{-14} \text{ erg/cm}^3,} \\[2mm] \multicolumn{2}{c}{p_{gas, max} = nkT_{max} \sim 3 \times 10^{-14} \text{ erg/cm}^3,} \\[2mm] \multicolumn{2}{c}{T_{max} \sim 10^6 \, ^\circ\text{K} \quad (n \sim 3 \times 10^{-4} \text{ cm}^{-3})} \end{array}\right\} \quad (12.10)$$

In (12.9) the pressure is considered to be isotropic and in this case the cosmic ray energy density is $w = 3p_{cr}$, i.e., $w_{max} \simeq 10^{-13}$ erg/cm^3. In the "expanded" model when the adiabatic invariant is maintained the cosmic ray pressure is highly anisotropic and largely directed along the lines of force. In this case $w \simeq p_{cr}$ but the possibility of using estimate (12.10) is not clear. In one way or another, by allowing for the possible contribution of the gas pressure and the kinetic energy, we see that the value taken by Sciama[377] and above for the cosmic ray energy density of $w_{gr} \sim 5 \times 10^{-14}$ erg/sec (see (12.6)) is the maximum possible value. Hence it follows that maintenance of the invariant $\sin^2 \theta/H = $ const is a necessary condition for self-congruence of the model. In addition, the magnetic field H_{gr}, as is clear from (12.7), cannot be made greater than about 5×10^{-7} oersteds which corresponds to a magnetic energy density of $H^2/8\pi \sim 10^{-14}$ erg/cm^3. Hence it follows that the most favourable value taken $w_{gr} = 5 \times 10^{-14}$ erg/cm^3 should be $w_{gr} \gg H^2/8\pi$, i.e., the magnetic energy is small when compared with the cosmic ray energy (here, it is true, we are speaking of a comparatively small factor of the order of 5).

The cosmic ray energy within the group $W \sim 10^{60}$ erg (see (12.6)) should accumulate in 10^{10} years when no particles leave which corresponds to a mean source power of $U \sim 3 \times 10^{42}$ erg/sec. As we have seen, the supernovae in the Galaxy can ensure the injection of cosmic rays with a power of $U_{sn, G} \sim 10^{40}$ to 10^{41} erg/sec (see (11.10)). For all the galaxies of the group, taking the power to be proportional to the mass, this value must be multiplied by about 7. Then $U_{sn, gr} \sim 7 \times 10^{41}$ erg/sec which is 4 to 5 times too small (the values $w = 5 \times 10^{-14}$ erg/cm^3, $V = 3 \times 10^{73}$ cm^3 and $T_G = 3 \times 10^{17}$ sec give the value $U = 5 \times 10^{42}$ erg/sec so the difference can be considered to reach 7 at the maximum power $U_{sn, G} = 10^{41}$ erg/sec). Of course this difference is still not a serious objection and bearing in mind the possible rôle of early stages of the system's evolution maintenance of the energy balance can be counted upon. Moreover there is no doubt that we cannot reject the assumption that the boundaries of the region have a very good reflecting power, i.e., that there is a quasi-spherical volume with a radius $R \sim 2 \times 10^{24}$ cm. If we use estimate (12.3), i.e., select the time $T_{gr} \sim 6 \times 10^7$ years, then in a time $T_G \sim 10^{10}$ years a particle can cross the region of the group almost 200 times. This means that the departure of particles will be of little significance only for the "boundary's" pass factor, which is 1 per cent or an even smaller value in order of magnitude. The existence of such a perfect magnetic trap certainly requires a number of conditions and is not in any way easily achieved.

Unfortunately the work in which a concrete model of the field in the Local Group is developed has not yet been published (it is referred to by Sciama[377]). Within the framework of what has been said above we can increase the time T_{gr} and all the times in (12.3) at least by an order of magnitude and probably even by 30. In fact in the "expanded" Galactic model the cosmic rays should have time to fill the whole volume of the group and come back to the Galaxy. For this we must have $T_{gr} \ll T_G$, i.e., $T_{gr, max} \sim 1$ to 3×10^9 years. Then $T_{halo} \sim 10^8$ years (see (12.3)), whilst in the Galactic model used in section 11 $T_{halo} \sim 3 \times 10^8$ years.

It is obvious that by increasing the time T_{gr} to the value $T_G \sim T_{Mg}$ we come in essence to the Galactic model (without the halo boundaries) and perhaps should only allow for the cosmic ray flux from the galaxy M31. This moreover must be borne in mind with any Galactic theory particularly for particles with the highest energy.

Returning to the "expanded" model we see that for $T_{gr} \sim 10^9$ years the coefficient of transparency of the group's "boundaries" should not exceed about 10 per cent.

Conclusions

It would be possible to solve the question of the permissibility of the "expanded" model without any difficulty if there were information available even on the density of the gas within the Local Group or on the effective length of the free path in the halo, and so on. Unfortunately there are no completely reliable data here so it is impossible to reject the "expanded" model at present. However, as is clear from what has been said above, this model can match up to reality only if a number of conditions and far-reaching assumptions are made.

1. The density of the gas within the group should be close to 10^{-27} g/cm^3. This value is very large, there is as yet no proof of the existence of this mass of gas and even for the stability of the group's galaxies the presence of gas need not be considered necessary. Moreover, in Sciama's model[377] fairly strong rotation of the plane of polarisation of the radio emission of discrete sources should occur in the Local Group.[420] In actual fact such rotation does not apparently occur.[185, 372, 435]

2. The motion of the cosmic rays during the whole period $T \sim T_G \sim T_{Mg} \sim 10^{10}$ years should occur with the adiabatic invariant $\sin^2 \theta/H = \text{const}$ preserved. Moreover in this time the Galaxy makes tens of revolutions around its centre, considerable mixing of the group's galaxies takes place, and so on. Further, if the adiabatic invariant is preserved the cosmic ray pressure is highly anisotropic. The magnetic pressure in the model is significantly lower than the cosmic ray pressure. Under these conditions the cosmic rays themselves should, it would appear, change the field configuration and

strength in such a way that the pressure becomes isotropic, i.e., when sufficiently long time intervals are examined the adiabatic invariant cannot be considered constant. It is also doubtful whether it is possible that the condition $W_{gr} \gg H^2/8\pi$ remains valid and, generally speaking, the field will grow if this condition is observed (see section 13). This is not permissible in the "expanded" model (see above).

3. The requirements imposed on cosmic ray sources in the "expanded" model are more rigid than in the Galactic model. It is not easy to ensure maintenance of the energy balance and both from these and other considerations the Local Group must be considered to be enclosed in an extremely perfect magnetic trap. The realisation of this trap requires additional conditions and is clearly not at all simple.

4. The magnetic field in the halo is considered to be large-scale by Sciama[377] so the effective length of the free path for diffusion is $l_{halo} \sim L_{halo}/10 \sim 10^{22}$ cm = 3000 pc. As far as we know there are no indications of such a field. Moreover this point is the least significant of all those listed—the more so where the value of l_{halo} can clearly be significantly reduced without rejecting the "expanded" model.

A number of ways can be indicated for checking the model (determining the number of positrons in the primary cosmic rays, measuring the anisotropy, allowing for the Compton losses and their effect on the radio emission spectrum, ...). We think, however, that the fate of the "expanded" model should be decided in the first place not by analysing the fine effects. When there is significant uncertainty in a number of parameters and unavoidable roughness in some of the necessary calculations it is very difficult to reject in this way a model which is even rather far from the truth. Therefore the centre of the investigation should probably lie in revealing the actual foundation upon which the model is built. In the case in question the assumptions listed above are the foundation. The question of the gas density is particularly important here: it will be sufficient to show that $\rho \ll 10^{-27}$ g/cm^3 to refute the model.†

† A possible objection to the "expanded" model is also connected with the fact that the "normal" galaxies include both the galaxies of the Local Group and many other galaxies. Within the framework of ideas on the formation and holding of cosmic rays in galaxies this situation cannot cause surprise. If the characteristics of the cosmic rays in a given galaxy are determined by accumulation the position must clearly be otherwise. We should expect the radio astronomy characteristics of galaxies to depend strongly on the type (size) of the collection

As we have said already, the question of the possibility of using the "expanded" Galactic model is, strictly speaking, still open. But if it is permissible in such a case to speak of probability, then the "expanded" model seems to us to have little probability: too many far-reaching conditions have to be fulfilled for this model to be consistent and to be in agreement with the reliably established facts. The low probability of the "expanded" model becomes still clearer if we bear in mind that the Galactic theory of the origin of cosmic rays does not come up against any similar difficulties.

13. COSMIC RAYS OF METAGALACTIC ORIGIN

The question of metagalactic cosmic rays, i.e., cosmic rays located or generated outside the Galaxy, can be put under three heads. Firstly there are the various problems connected with cosmic rays in different types of galaxy and radio galaxies in particular. Secondly the cosmic rays located in metagalactic space are of interest. Thirdly we must find out the part played by metagalactic cosmic rays in the Galaxy and in the solar system in particular. It is clearly this last aspect of the problem that is significant from the point of view of the cosmic rays observed on Earth.

We have a fairly large amount of information on cosmic rays in different galaxies since the corresponding information is obtained by radio astronomy methods. Some data of this kind have already been given in Chapter II. In addition, the question of the nature of the radio galaxies will be discussed briefly below. It should also be borne in mind that a number of conclusions relating to our Galaxy can be naturally transferred to many other "normal" galaxies. However, we shall not discuss in detail the question of cosmic rays in other galaxies since at the present stage it is largely descriptive in nature and closely connected with all extragalactic astronomy (for the latest survey devoted to radio galaxies see a paper by Shklovskii[198]).

As for the information which is of particular interest to us on cosmic rays in metagalactic (intergalactic) space and their penetration into the Galaxy there are unfortunately no direct data unless we take account of certain estimates of the upper bound of the cosmic ray concentration, and so on. This situation is closely connected with

they belong to. Galaxies not forming part of a cluster would behave differently to galaxies from the collections, and so on. We know of no indication of this behaviour and the picture is more likely to be the opposite.

the fact that we still cannot at present indicate a number of very important parameters (for example the density of the gas in metagalactic space is unknown). In addition, the possible assumptions and estimates relating to metagalactic cosmic rays are closely connected with the selection of definite cosmological ideas. In this latter question, if we are speaking of reliably established data, there is a great area of uncertainty. As a result of what has been said we should not be surprised that the question of metagalactic cosmic rays in intergalactic space and in the Galaxy remains, strictly speaking, unclear (in essence we must limit ourselves in this respect to only indirect data and qualitative considerations). On the other hand the part played by metagalactic cosmic rays could in principle prove to be extremely important both for the theory of the origin of cosmic rays and for all extragalactic astronomy—and possibly cosmology as well. In this connexion the problem of metagalactic cosmic rays is not only the least fully studied but also the most difficult of all the problems of cosmic ray astrophysics. Therefore we shall try below to expound in sufficient detail all the information and estimates we know of, which relate to metagalactic cosmic rays.

Some data from the field of extragalactic astronomy

The region of the Universe which can be observed with the most powerful optical and radio telescopes is called the Metagalaxy and has a radius of less than 10^{10} light years. This whole region is at present (here and below we are thinking of clocks on Earth) in a state of expansion. Here in the first approximation the velocity of recession of the galaxies u is

$$u = hr, \tag{13.1}$$

where r is the distance (from our Galaxy) and Hubble's constant h according to present data is approximately 100 km/sec·Mpc $\simeq 3\cdot2 \times 10^{-18}$ sec^{-1}.† The characteristic time of the metagalaxy's evolution is

$$T_{Mg} = \frac{1}{h} \simeq 3 \times 10^{17} \text{ sec} \simeq 10^{10} \text{ yr.} \tag{13.2}$$

Relationship (13.1) is valid only as long as $u \ll c = 3 \times 10^{10}$ cm/sec.

† In evolutionary cosmology Hubble's constant (or, rather, parameter) depends on time. The value given in the text relates to our epoch. We should also stress that in recent years the value taken for h in published works has been very much reduced. When using different metagalactic parameters allowance must be made for the value of h at which they were obtained.

In this case the Doppler shift of the wavelength λ_0 towards the red end of the spectrum is

$$z = \frac{\lambda - \lambda_0}{\lambda_0} = \frac{u}{c} \ll 1.$$

The condition $z \ll 1$ must also be observed, generally speaking, so as to be able to use Euclidean geometry. Below, moreover, we shall use terminology corresponding to Euclidean space right up to $z \lesssim 0.5$ (the value $z \simeq 0.5$ corresponds to the maximum distance which can be reached by existing optical telescopes). There is even more reason to proceed in this way since there is still no clarity in the question of the terms that are non-linear with respect to z (i.e., outside the region where $z \ll 1$). The available preliminary data indicate that the curvature of the Universe is relatively small and is possibly non-existent (this fits in with Euclidean geometry allowing, of course, for the expansion of the system).† In the region with $z \leqslant 0.5$ there are approximately 3×10^9 galaxies,[387] which for $h = 100$ km/sec·Mpc corresponds to a galaxy concentration

$$N_G = \frac{3 \times 10^9}{\frac{4}{3}\pi \cdot R_{1/2}^3} \simeq 5 \times 10^{-75} \, \text{cm}^{-3}, \qquad R_{1/2} = \frac{0.5c}{h} \simeq 5 \times 10^{27} \, \text{cm}.$$

$$(13.3)$$

The value of (13.3) is probably close to the lower limit of N_G since the number of galaxies assumed may be too low because of an underestimate of the number of dwarf systems. As has already been indicated in section 12, the mass of the Galaxy is approximately $10^{11} M_\odot = 2 \times 10^{44}$ g. The mass of the galaxy M31 is 4 times greater but there are dwarf galaxies with a mass of only $4 \times 10^8 M_\odot$. It is difficult to give a modern mean value for the mass of the galaxies but in order of magnitude $\overline{M} \sim 3 \times 10^{10} M_\odot$ (according to Allen[315] $\overline{M} = 5 \times 10^{10} M_\odot$). With $N_G = 5 \times 10^{-75}$ cm^{-3} and $\overline{M} = 10^{44}$ g the mean density of the matter in the Metagalaxy is $\rho = 5 \times 10^{-31}$ g/cm^3. This value is, of course, a lower limit since only the matter concentrated in the galaxies is taken into account in obtaining it. There are no more or less direct data on the density of the gas in intergalactic

† The Einstein–de Sitter model is the name of a non-stationary, homogeneous and isotropic model with zero curvature (with no Λ-term either). We would also mention that the Λ-term is the name of the Λg_{ik} term in the gravitational field equation[165]

$$R_{ik} - \tfrac{1}{2} g_{ik} R + \Lambda g_{ik} = \frac{8\pi\kappa}{c^4} T_{ik}.$$

space, as has already been mentioned. However, it is often considered that the most reasonable value is

$$\rho \simeq 10^{-29} \text{ g/cm}^3, \qquad n \simeq 10^{-5} \text{ cm}^{-3} \qquad (13.4)$$

(the conversion to the concentration n is made upon the normal assumption that the gas consists largely of hydrogen). The bases for the estimate (13.4) are as follows. In relativistic cosmology a certain critical density $\rho_{cr} = 3h^2/8\pi\kappa$, where $\kappa = 6\cdot67 \times 10^{-8} \text{ g}^{-1}\text{cm}^3\text{sec}^{-2}$ is the gravitational constant, is of great importance. In a homogeneous cosmological model, when there is no Λ-term,[165, 382–386] the value $\rho = \rho_{cr}$ corresponds to a Euclidean metric, i.e., the Einstein–de Sitter model (if $\rho > \rho_{cr}$ space has a positive and if $\rho < \rho_{cr}$ a negative curvature). The available preliminary data are in favour of $\rho \sim \rho_{cr} \simeq 2 \times 10^{-29}$ g/cm^3 (for $h = 100$ km/sec·Mpc). The value of (13.4) thus corresponds to a density close to ρ_{cr}. As a guide Smorodinskii[384] gives the more definite value $\rho = (1 \text{ to } 3)\rho_{cr}$. Not to mention the inaccuracy of the observational data this estimate of ρ depends on the selection of the model (in the present case models without a Λ-term are under discussion).

We note that in stationary cosmology[386, 388, 389] (see also below) the gas density is $\rho = \rho_{cr}$ and does not depend on time. The density ρ in Euclidean expanding space changes in accordance with the law

$$\rho(t) = \rho(T_{Mg})\left[\frac{R(T_{Mg})}{R(t)}\right]^3, \qquad (13.5)$$

where $\rho(T_{Mg})$ is the present value of the density, R is the characteristic scale (the distance between remote galaxies) and the scale for the time t is selected so that now $t = T_{Mg}$ (see below). Law (13.5) corresponds simply to preservation of the total mass of gas in the system connected with this expanding gas.

An estimate of the emission energy density in the Metagalaxy was given in section 8 (the index 3/2 in (13.6) is obtained below; see (13.11))

$$w_{ph}(t) = w_{ph}(T_{Mg})\left[\frac{R(T_{Mg})}{R(t)}\right]^{3/2}, \qquad w_{ph}(T_{Mg}) \sim 10^{-3} \text{ eV/cm}^3. \qquad (13.6)$$

This calculation proceeds from the assumption of the continuous emission of light, the brightness of the sources not changing in time. As for the emission at the moment t_1 the density of its energy varies in accordance with the law $w_{ph}(t_2) = w_{ph}(t_1)[(R(t_1)/R(t_2)]^4$. The energy density of any ultra-relativistic gas, in particular cosmic rays and neutrinos,[384] varies in the same way—in accordance with the law $(R_1/R_2)^4$. The appearance of an extra term (R_1/R_2) when compared with the case of a non-relativistic gas (in the latter case the energy density $3nkT/2$ is proportional to the density of the mass $\rho(t_2) = \rho(t_1)[R_1(t_1)/R_2(t_2)]^3$) is connected with the change in energy of a relativistic particle as the result of the Doppler effect. The same thing (the appearance of $(R_1/R_2)^4$ in the expression for the energy density) occurs for cosmological models in which the pressure is determined by relativistic particles, i.e., $p = w/3$ (w is the energy density). Unlike a non-relativistic gas, when the pressure p is small when compared with the total energy density $w = \rho c^2$, the expansion of a relativistic gas is linked with so much work done by the pressure forces that the extra degree R_1/R_2 appears.[165]

In the case of cosmic rays (for a constant number of particles) the law

$$w(t) = w(T_{Mg})\left[\frac{R(T_{Mg})}{R(t)}\right]^4, \qquad (13.7)$$

by virtue of what has been said may also always be applicable. In actual fact this does not have to be so. Of course, if ultra-relativistic cosmic rays move in a straight line in the Metagalaxy like photons or neutrinos the relationship (13.7) is valid. The idea that cosmic rays diffuse in the intergalactic magnetic fields is probably closer to reality. In this case the change in their energy density w is not universal and depends on the actual conditions. However, for an isotropically and homogeneously expanding medium the energy of a particle is $E \infty V^{-1/3}$, where V is the volume (see section 10). Since the particle concentration is $N \infty V^{-1}$ the energy density is $w = NE$ and $V \infty R^3$ we come once again to formula (13.7).

Galaxies have a tendency to come into multiple systems and clusters. We have spoken about one such cluster—the Local Group—in section 12. Other clusters are generally considerably larger than the Local Group (it consists of approximately 15 galaxies) and on the average there are about 200 galaxies in a cluster; the mean diameter of a cluster is about 10^{25} cm. Larger clusters are also met with (the cluster in Virgo consists of 2500 galaxies and the cluster in Coma of 1000 galaxies). There are probably even larger combinations of galaxies—superclusters or supergalaxies. For example the Local Group together with our Galaxy, according to a series of data[387], are part of the Local Supergalaxy. The nucleus of the latter is the large cluster in Virgo already mentioned which is at a distance of 12 to 15 Mpc $\simeq 5 \times 10^{25}$ cm (1 Mpc $= 3 \times 10^{24}$ cm). The Local Supergalaxy takes the form of a disk or a very flattened ellipsoid with a diameter of about 30 Mpc and a thickness of about 6 Mpc. The volume of the system is $V \sim 10^{77}$ cm^3. The mass of all the galaxies in the supergalaxy is $M \sim 10^{14} M_\odot$, but for stability of the system, according to Burbidge[387], the mass M must be of the order of $10^{15} M_\odot$. If this estimate is true and the system is stable then there should be† an intergalactic gas with a density $\rho \sim M/V \sim 2 \times 10^{48}/10^{77} = 2 \times 10^{-29}$ g/cm^3. This value is in accordance with estimate (13.4) so is quite probable.

The relative velocities of the galaxies (without allowing for the rate of overall expansion) are of the order of 100 to 500 km/sec. The intergalactic gas probably has velocities of the same order. If $\rho = 2 \times 10^{-29}$ g/cm^3 and $u = 300$ km/sec, then

$$\frac{\rho u^2}{2} \sim 10^{-14} \text{ erg/cm}^3, \qquad H_{\text{eq}} = \sqrt{4\pi \rho u^2} \sim 5 \times 10^{-7} \text{ oersteds,}$$

$$\rho \sim 2 \times 10^{-29} \text{ g/cm}^3, \qquad u \sim 3 \times 10^7 \text{cm/sec.} \tag{13.8}$$

Here the field strength H_{eq} is estimated from the condition $H_{\text{eq}}^2/8\pi = \rho u^2/2$. The values in (13.8) are clearly the maximum ones which are reasonable at the present time.‡ For a gas velocity $u \sim 10^7$ cm/sec

† Another possibility is conceivable—the existence of some condensed invisible masses (neutron stars or collapsed masses).

‡ As has already been mentioned in section 4, we may succeed in obtaining some information on the gas concentration and the magnetic field strength in metagalactic space by using data on the polarisation of the radio emission of extragalactic discrete sources (recently polarisation of a number of such sources has been discovered including Cygnus A and Centaurus A[183-186]). In actual fact, as follows from (4.41), the rotation of the plane of polarisation of emission when propagated in a plasma is

$$\phi = \frac{2 \cdot 36 \times 10^4}{\nu^2} \int n_e H \cos \theta \, dl,$$

where integration is carried out along the line of sight from the Earth to the source. In the metagalactic medium $n_e \simeq n$, apparently, so from polarisation radio measurements we shall be able to estimate the magnitude or upper limit of the mean value of the product of $nH \cos \alpha$ along the line of sight and obtain other information also.[187, 488] we clearly have $\rho u^2/2 \sim 10^{-15}$ erg/cm^3 and $H_{eq} \sim 10^{-7}$ oe; in addition, even the quasi-equilibrium value of the field H may be slightly less than H_{eq} if it is connected with small-scale turbulent motions.[396]

In the Local Supergalaxy there are about 10^4 galaxies which corresponds to a concentration of $N_{superg} \sim 10^{-73}$ cm^{-3}. This value is 20 times higher than the mean concentration (13.3) but it is hard to judge how accurate this estimate of N_{superg} is.

Radio galaxies

The question of the number of radio galaxies, or by virtue of this concept the number of galaxies with different radio brightness, is very important. The corresponding data have been collected together in survey articles.[164, 198] Here we shall give only some.

The concentration of radio galaxies N_{rg} depending on their absolute radio star magnitude† M_r drops sharply as the absolute value of M_r increases (approximately $\log N_{rg} = 7 + aM_r$, where $a \simeq 0.5$ for large negative values of M_r and N_{rg} is measured in Mpc^{-3}). The brightest radio galaxies Cygnus A and 3C 295 have a value $M_r \simeq -35$ and radio galaxy is the name generally given to objects with $M_r < -22$, whilst for "normal" galaxies generally $M_r \sim -18$ or -19. As a result the basic contribution to the sky's integral radio brightness is made by "normal" galaxies and radio galaxies of low brightness. The concentration of the most powerful radio galaxies like Cygnus A and 3C 295 ($M_r \simeq -35$) per interval of one stellar magnitude is very low and does not exceed 10^{-10} Mpc$^{-3} \simeq 4 \times 10^{-84}$ cm^{-3}; this means that the average distance between such objects is somewhat more than 1000 Mpc (in this sense Cygnus A, which is at a distance of 220 Mpc, should be considered as being close to us by chance). By comparing the reduced density of the super-powerful radio galaxies with the density of the galaxies (13.3) we see that, roughly speaking, there is one super-powerful

---

† The radio star magnitude of a galaxy m_r is defined by the relationship $m_r = -53.4 - 2.5 \log F_\nu$, where F_ν is the emission flux at a frequency of 160 Mc/s expressed in Wm^{-2}(c/s)$^{-1}$. With this definition m_r for "normal" galaxies is close to their photographic magnitude m_p. Further, the absolute radio star magnitude is defined as $M_r = m_r + 5 - \log r$, where r is the distance to the galaxy in parsec. With non-astronomical readers in mind we would also mention that increasing the stellar magnitude by unity corresponds to reducing the flux by a factor of 2.512 ($\log 2.512 = 0.4$). Therefore $\log (F(m_1)/F(m_2)) = 0.4(m_2 - m_1)$, where $F(m_i)$ is the emission flux from an object with a stellar magnitude m_i.

radio galaxy per 10^9 galaxies. The concentration of galaxies with $M_r = -22$ (at an interval of one stellar magnitude) is 10^{-4} Mpc$^{-3} \simeq$ 4×10^{-78} cm^{-3}, i.e., there is one such galaxy to every 1000 galaxies. However, radio galaxies with $M_r = -22$ emit only an order of magnitude more than normal galaxies in the radio band. The concentration of radio galaxies with $M_r = -24$ is about an order less than for $M_r = -22$. At the same time for these galaxies ($M_r = -24$) the ratio of the radio brightness to the brightness of the "normal" galaxies is about 100. It is among these or even an order more powerful radio galaxies of "medium" radio brightness that the radio galaxies located near us are included:† M 87 $\equiv$ NGC 4486 $\equiv$ Virgo A ($m_r - m_p = -6$), NGC 5128 $\equiv$ Centaurus A ($m_r - m_p = -3\cdot9$) and NGC 1316 $\equiv$ Fornax A ($m_r - m_p = -4\cdot6$). The radio galaxies Virgo A, Centaurus A and possibly Fornax A lie within the Local Supergalaxy. In addition, the weaker galaxies NGC 4261, M84 and NGC 1068 are also located in this supergalaxy. The radio emission of these galaxies is 20, 4 and 0·02 per cent respectively of the radio emission of Virgo A[387]. As has been pointed out above there are about 10^4 galaxies in the Local Supergalaxy so there is one radio galaxy to about 2000 galaxies. This conclusion agrees with that drawn above on the basis of the function $N_{rg}(M_r)$.

We note that attempts have been made to discover some rise in the radio emission intensity connected with the local Supergalaxy and some structural formation. Observations[261, 403] indicate, however, that there is no such radio emission (this means that radio emission has been observed only from the galaxies making up the supergalaxy and not from the supergalaxy as a whole).

Cosmological models

Observational data are still quite inadequate to draw far-reaching cosmological conclusions based on them. At present, therefore, various models are being examined in cosmology and attempts are being made to compare the conclusions obtained in this way with the observations. The available models and cosmological theories can

---

† The difference between the radio and photographic stellar magnitudes is called the radio index ($m_r - m_p$) and directly characterises the ratio of the radio and light fluxes $A(F_{radio}/F_{light}) = 10^{-0\cdot4(m_r - m_p)}$ where the constant is selected so that $A(F_{radio}/F_{light}) = 1$ for a normal Sb-galaxy (i.e., in this case $m_r = m_p$). Approximately $A \simeq 10^5$.

be variously classified but here we shall deal with only three cosmo-logical models which differ in a qualitative respect. These are

(1) a model with a "singularity" at $t = 0$;

(2) an "oscillating" model;

(3) a stationary model.

The first two of these models can be called evolutionary (this term is frequently used in published work with respect to models with a "singularity"). Before making some remarks about these models we should stress that at the present time cosmological questions should, in our opinion, be analysed only on the basis of the general theory of relativity. This theory has fully stood up to a check[376] in the weak field range and should undoubtedly be the best known approximation to the truth in the strong gravitational field range with which we are dealing in cosmology.† The fact that we may need some generalisations or additions to the general scheme of the general theory of relativity is another matter. A well known example of such an addition is the introduction of the additional term Λg_{ik}, called the cosmological or Λ-term (see above), into the equation for the metric tensor g_{ik}. But both this and certain other conceivable (although considerably less natural) generalisations based on the general theory of relativity allow us at least to use and allow for the positive sides and formalism of this theory. Moreover, the most natural thing at present is applying the gravitational field equations in cosmology in the Einstein form without the Λ-term, not to mention some other changes. The possibilities opened up in this way are by no means exhausted since up until now people have limited themselves to analysing isotropic and homogeneous models. Recently it has at last been determined[165] that the rejection of isotropy and homogeneity leads, generally speaking, to the elimi-nation of singular points in solutions. For the same reason the necessity of studying more general models than has been done to date

† The gravitational field is weak as long as $|\phi|/c^2 \ll 1$, where ϕ is the Newton potential. In the case of a gravitating sphere with a radius r and a mass density ρ we clearly have

$$|\phi|/c^2 \sim \frac{\kappa(\frac{4}{3}\pi \cdot \rho r^3)^2}{rc^2} \sim \frac{4\kappa\rho r^2}{c^2}.$$

With $\rho \sim 10^{-29}$ g/cm³, $|\phi|/c^2 \ll 1$, as long as $r \ll 10^{28}$ cm ($t = r/c \ll 10^{10}$ years). Since cosmological distances, generally speaking, do not satisfy this inequality the fields in this case are strong.

is quite clear. Nevertheless homogeneous and isotropic models are still clearly of great importance over a wide range—when the values of the density of matter are not too high. In other words, it is possible that the detailed allowance for the inhomogeneity and lack of isotropy of the Metagalaxy is basically necessary only under conditions of strong compression.

Returning to cosmological models let us be more exact about their characteristic features. The properties of models 1 and 2 for values of t that are not too low can be reliably described approximately by the known solutions for isotropic and homogeneous cosmological models with a singularity at $t = 0$. As is well known, these models may have zero, constant positive, or constant negative curvature. However, in the region $z = (\lambda - \lambda_0)/\lambda_0 \ll 1$, and in practice for $z \lesssim 0.2$ to 0.5, the curvature can be considered zero (plane or Euclidean metric) for all these three cases. The homogeneous isotropic model with zero curvature, when there is no Λ-term (Einstein–de Sitter model), has the metric[165]

$$ds^2 = c^2 \, d\tau^2 - R^2(\tau)(dx^2 + dy^2 + dz^2). \qquad (13.9)$$

In regions of not too high a density the matter in the Metagalaxy can be considered to be non-relativistic and the pressure small (the contribution of photons and cosmic rays to the total energy density at this stage is negligibly small; we also consider that the part played by neutrinos is small). Under similar conditions the scale in (13.9) changes according to the law

$$R(\tau) = \text{const} \cdot \tau^{2/3}, \qquad (13.10)$$

where τ is the actual time at each point in space. At $\tau = 0$ the metric has a singular point but this is not at all essential for us since the model will be used only for large enough τ.

According to (13.10) $(dR/d\tau)/R = h(\tau) = 2/(3\tau)$, where $h(\tau)$ is Hubble's constant (or, more correctly, parameter) at the moment τ. If we pay no attention to the invalidity of (13.10) in a certain small region of small enough values of τ, then the time $\tau = 2/3h(\tau)$ can be expressed directly by Hubble's constant. At the present time $h(\tau_{Mg}) \equiv h = u/r$ since $(dR/d\tau)/R = u/r$, i.e., is equal to the observed ratio of the velocity of a galaxy to its distance away (the condition $u/c \ll 1$ is used). Obviously $h(\tau_{Mg}) = 2/(3\tau_{Mg}) = h = 1/T_{Mg}$, i.e., the "age" of the model is $\tau_{Mg} = \frac{2}{3}T_{Mg} \simeq 6 \times 10^9$ years. Instead of the time τ it is more convenient below to use the time $t = 3\tau/2$ and it is this time t that is called the "age" of the Metagalaxy (the nature of this choice is no more conventional than when using the time τ since both quantities are of the same order and the model itself can aim at nothing better).

Using relationship (13.10) and replacing τ by $\frac{3}{2}t$ we can write relationships (13.5), (13.6) and (13.7) in the form

$$\rho(t) = \rho(T_{\mathrm{Mg}})\left(\frac{T_{\mathrm{Mg}}}{t}\right)^2, \qquad w(t) = w(T_{\mathrm{Mg}})\left(\frac{T_{\mathrm{Mg}}}{t}\right)^{8/3};$$

$$w_{\mathrm{ph}}(t) = w_{\mathrm{ph}}(T_{\mathrm{Mg}})\left(\frac{T_{\mathrm{Mg}}}{t}\right), \qquad R(t) = R(T_{\mathrm{Mg}})\left(\frac{t}{T_{\mathrm{Mg}}}\right)^{2/3}. \qquad (13.11)$$

It is taken into account here that $w_{\mathrm{ph}} \infty N_G R_{\mathrm{ph}} \infty R^{-3} R_{\mathrm{ph}}$ (see (8.18)) and $R_{\mathrm{ph}}(t) \sim c/2h(t) \infty t \infty (R(t)^{3/2})$. Hence

$$w_{\mathrm{ph}} \infty R^{-3/2} \infty t^{-1}.$$

The average distance between galaxies is $r_{gg} \sim N_g^{-1/3} \sim 5 \times 10^{24}$ cm (see (13.3)). The characteristic dimension of the galaxies is $r_g \sim 5 \times 10^{22}$ cm but in the formation stage this dimension was probably larger. It follows from this that the formation of galaxies as independent units could occur at a compression of about 30 to 100 times. Another estimate of the duration of the galactic phase can be made if we start with the present density of the intergalactic gas $\rho_{\mathrm{Mg}} \sim 10^{-29}$ g/cm^3 (see (13.4)). The density of the matter in the Galaxy is $\rho_G \sim 10^{11} M_\odot/(4\pi/3)R_G^3 \sim 3 \times 10^{-25}$ g/cm^3 ($M_G \sim 10^{11} M_\odot \sim 10^{44}$ g is the mass of the Galaxy, $R_G \sim 15$ kpc its radius). It is clear that $\rho_{\mathrm{Mg}} \sim \rho_G$ when the radius (scale R) is altered by a factor of about 30, i.e., the time t is altered by a factor of about 150 (when using law (13.11)). It may therefore be taken that the beginning of the galactic phase corresponds to a time $t = T_0 \sim 10^{-2} T_{\mathrm{Mg}} \sim 10^8$ years and the compression is about 30 times. In this range (i.e., for $T_0 \lesssim t \lesssim T_{\mathrm{Mg}}$) the use of the simple law of expansion (13.10) to (13.11) and the assumptions of isotropy and homogeneity are probable. In addition it may be assumed that models 1 (with a "singularity") and 2 (oscillating model) are equivalent for $T_0 < t < T_{\mathrm{Mg}}$ at least in the first approximation. If $T < T_0$ in model 1, unless there is some singularity the density in any case reaches very high values and the regions $t < 0$ do not correspond to any realistic state of the system (to be more precise, values $t < 0$ in general must not be discussed in a model with a singularity). Such as these are models of a homogeneous and isotropic universe if we take them without limitations. In the oscillating model (model 2), on the other hand, compression at a certain point in time T_{min} reaches a maximum and for $t < T_{min}$ the density is starting to decrease.

Oscillating or, to be more precise, non-monotonic cosmological models have not been investigated in detail since this investigation is connected with allowing for inhomogeneity and anisotropy of the system. If we speak only of the qualitative side of the matter these models now appear extremely attractive. For our purposes, however, the whole of the possible difference between models 1 and 2 is linked with the question of "remnant" cosmic rays generated for $t < T_0 \sim 10^8$ years. In the oscillating model, in the case of not too great a maximum density ρ_{max} at the time of greatest compression, there could be cosmic rays remaining from the preceding phase (the region $t < T_{min}$). In the model with a "singularity" the cosmic ray remnants should be generated in the period $0 < t \leqslant T_0$. Since, however, we cannot follow the evolution of the universe at $t \lesssim T_0$ the two models 1 and 2 will be combined to a certain extent below. One new parameter will be introduced—the energy density of the metagalactic cosmic ray remnants $w_{Mg, r}$ at T_0.

The stationary model 3 differs sharply from the others. In this model space is considered to be Euclidean and to be expanding evenly so that $(dR/d\tau)/R = h = \text{const}$. The density of the matter ρ is considered to be constant and equal to $\rho_{cr} = 3h^2/8\pi\kappa \sim 10^{-29}$ g/cm^3. In the steady-state cosmology[386, 388, 389] the density is kept constant in the presence of expansion by introducing the assumption of the continuous creation of new matter, the matter having to be created at a rate $3\rho_{cr}/T_{Mg} = 3\rho_{cr}h \sim 10^{-46}$ g cm^{-3}sec^{-1}. This value is so small by terrestrial scales that the possibility of the appearance of new matter (let us say neutrons or hydrogen) in these quantities does not, of course, contradict any known data. Nevertheless the rejection of the laws of conservation in their ordinary form is a very far-reaching hypothesis. It is also by no means clear what form the new matter can or should take. Furthermore, although the birth of new matter may clearly be formulated in the framework of the general theory of relativity by introducing a new field,[389] nevertheless the resultant equations contain an arbitrary parameter and permit solutions with any density value ρ[390] (Hoyle[388, 389] affirms we must have $\rho = \rho_{cr}$ in the steady-state cosmology).†

Under these conditions it would appear that we should develop the steady-state cosmological model only when there are some convincing facts that speak in its favour and at the same time contradict the conclusions for the other models. But there have been no such facts. On the other hand, the cosmological models with singularities which have been widely discussed until recently by no means appear natural either and the transition from physics to cosmology may turn out to be connected with the introduction of completely new ideas. As a result one's approach to steady-state cosmology, unless one is comparing it with observations, becomes to a certain degree a matter of taste. Only a comparison with astronomical data can be decisive. However, radio astronomy observations[391] are against the steady-state model (it is a question of calculating the concentration of radio galaxies as a function of their distance; there should be more remote sources in evolutionary cosmology than in steady-state cosmology). Possibly by virtue of additional assumptions[392] this conclusion may be altered but as an idea the measurements[391] are very convincing[393, 439] and their confirmation and continuation may at last solve the question.‡ The optical data[299, 395] are also rather against the steady-state cosmology. Lastly the first experiments in γ-astronomy[68] led to a conclusion which, although not excluding the steady-state model, was nevertheless highly unfavourable for it (in the steady-state model probably equal numbers of particles and anti-particles should be generated; but in this case, if we are

---

† It should also be pointed out that in the steady-state cosmology a privileged coordinate system is introduced—a system in which the matter being born is at rest (or has a symmetrical distribution function). In this way covariance of the theory is disturbed. This circumstance is noted and discussed by Hoyle,[389] certain considerations being adduced in favour of the permissibility of rejecting covariance in the steady-state cosmological model. There is no doubt, however, that the rejection of general covariance makes the statement of the possibility of relativistic formulation of a law for the generation of matter to a considerable degree illusory (see also the critical remarks made by Zel'dovich[379]).

‡ According to Hanbury Brown[342] the treatment of Ryle and Clark's measurements[391] meets with an objection and the statement of the presence of contradictions between the conclusions of steady-state cosmology and radio astronomy data must be considered to be still premature. We think, however, that the conclusion drawn by Oort[439] in favour of the evolutionary models is very convincing. In addition, the work by Hanbury Brown et al.[239] has been strongly criticised.[489]

speaking of protons and anti-protons, we should expect the appearance of annihilation γ-rays and these are not observed).†

As far as we know the only factor which is in any way favourable for the steady-state model is the discovery that rapid evolution of the galaxies is continuing. The point is that in the framework of evolutionary cosmology (this is true also in the case of an oscillating model if there is a clearly defined protogalactic phase) the galaxies were largely formed 10^{10} years ago and, as has generally been assumed, are now in a state of slow "ageing". In reality the galaxies may be evolving rapidly at the present as well as can be clearly seen in the example of radio galaxies; in addition, galaxies have been found which may be young ones.[299, 388, 397] In the steady-state model galaxies should be appearing the whole time as the result of the condensation of the intergalactic gas. In general by virtue of the very nature of the steady-state model galaxies should be observed in it at all stages of their evolution. This argument, however, can still not be looked upon as in the least degree decisive or even a serious objection against the evolutionary cosmology. Within the framework of the latter the assumption of the impossibility of rapid evolution at the present stage of expansion by no means follows and is only the simplest hypothesis. It is well known that even now stars are being continuously formed in the Galaxy's spiral arms. However, there is clearly no doubt that the process of star formation proceeded considerably more rapidly at an early stage when the galaxies themselves were being formed. In just the same way in the framework of evolutionary cosmology we must expect the formation and change of galaxies to be largely during the time $t \lesssim T_0$ (see above), but there is no reason to exclude the possibility of the formation or rapid evolution of a relatively small number of galaxies at present as well. The available data on radio galaxies and certain other galaxies which are in a non-quasi-stationary state do not in any case contradict this point of view so we should not speak of the steady-state model being confirmed in this question either.

To recapitulate it must be admitted that there is still great uncertainty with respect to the possibility of giving definite answers to even the most basic cosmological questions. Nevertheless we can come out in favour of the evolutionary models, the oscillating

† It follows from this that the particles formed must be considered to be neutrons or protons and electrons, i.e., we must reject the idea of conserving the number of nucleons (baryons).

cosmological model appearing particularly attractive to us if it is a question of the qualitative side of the matter. Over a certain limited range (for $T_0 \lesssim t \leqslant T_{Mg}$, $T_0 \sim 10^8$ years, $T_{Mg} \sim 10^{10}$ years) this model and models with singularities can probably be described approximately by using relationships (13.11) for the Einstein–de Sitter model. The steady-state model is connected with postulating a new, far-reaching physical hypothesis (non-conservation of the amount of matter in its known forms) and is not supported by the astrophysical data. At present, therefore, we think it is quite possible and most natural not to pay much attention to this model.

Metagalactic cosmic rays

What is the energy density of metagalactic cosmic rays at present? This is the basic question on whose answer depends the part played by the metagalactic component of the cosmic rays in the Galaxy. If this density $w_{Mg}(T_{Mg})$ is much less than the density of the cosmic rays in the Galaxy $w_G \sim 0.3$ to 1 eV/cm$^3 \sim 10^{-12}$ erg/cm^3 the cosmic rays on Earth should be of galactic origin.

Strictly speaking this statement requires reservations. In the first place for estimating the concentration of metagalactic cosmic rays in the Galaxy all that is essential is their concentration in the region around the Galaxy with dimensions smaller than 10^8 pc $= 3 \times 10^{26}$ cm (see below). In the second place, under quasi-stationary conditions the concentration and energy density of the cosmic rays outside the Galaxy could be considerably less than inside the Galaxy if the adiabatic invariant is conserved and the metagalactic cosmic ray distribution function is strongly anisotropic (see section 12). This last possibility is, however, quite unrealistic if the density w_{Mg} is the slightest bit significant (the arguments here are similar to those given in section 12: the anisotropic cosmic ray pressure arising when they are anisotropically distributed cannot be balanced over a long period, thus leading to mixing and isotropy).

In order to discuss the question of metagalactic cosmic rays it is best first of all to examine the various possibilities and variants relating to their sources.

1. In the evolutionary cosmology two types of source can be distinguished: (a) "remnant" sources whose action has led to the appearance of cosmic rays with a density $w_{Mg, r}(T_0)$ at a certain point in time $T_0 \ll T_{Mg}$ (see above); (b) cosmic rays which have arrived

in intergalactic space from the galaxies or clusters of galaxies in the period $T_0 < t \leqslant T_{Mg}$.

In addition, we must determine how the cosmic rays (spectrum, composition) vary in metagalactic space.

Another aspect of the affair is the spatial distribution of the sources. Here three possibilities can be indicated: (a) the metagalactic cosmic rays are distributed approximately evenly throughout the Metagalaxy (at least if $z = u/c \ll 1$); (b) in the Local Supergalaxy the cosmic ray concentration is considerably higher than on the average outside it[387]; (c) the cosmic ray concentration is high $(w_{Mg} \sim 10^{-13} \text{ erg/cm}^3)$ within the limits of the Local Group of galaxies (see section 12).

2. In the steady-state cosmology we must not speak of "remnant" cosmic rays because of its very essence and a stationary value must be found for the density w_{Mg}. As far as we know there have not yet been any attempts to calculate the value of w_{Mg} on the basis of the stationary model. Moreover at present this calculation is probably impossible with sufficient accuracy. Gold and Hoyle's statements[398] can be understood as follows: in the steady-state model the value

$$w_{Mg} \simeq w_G \simeq 10^{-12} \text{ erg/cm}^3 \qquad (13.12)$$

is permissible and in Gold and Hoyle's opinion[398] even natural. If this relationship is accepted the cosmic rays in the Galaxy must be considered to be basically of metagalactic origin. This is assumed by Gold and Hoyle[398] and the value of (13.12) is selected from this.

In sections 11 and 12 we have already discussed the different aspects of the problem of the origin of cosmic rays. It was stressed that the most reliable method of basing the theory of the galactic origin of the majority of the cosmic rays is proof that they are not of metagalactic origin. This last problem, as is clear from what has been said, reduces to proving the inequality

$$w_{Mg} \ll w_G \simeq 10^{-12} \text{ erg/cm}^3. \qquad (13.13)$$

It will be possible to obtain valuable information on the metagalactic cosmic rays (the intensity I_{Mg}) by measuring the flux of γ-rays on the Earth. This question has been discussed in section 2 where the following is shown. The intensity of all the metagalactic γ-rays produced in the decay of π°-mesons is

$$I_\gamma = 2\sigma n I_{Mg} R_{ph} \simeq 4 \times 10^{-4} \frac{I_{Mg}}{I_g} \, \text{cm}^2 \cdot \text{sterad}^{-1} \cdot \text{sec}^{-1}, \quad (13.14)$$

where it is taken in the change to a numerical value that: the "photometric" radius is $R_{ph} \simeq \frac{1}{2} c T_{Mg} \simeq 5 \times 10^{27}$ cm, the cross section for π°-meson formation is $\sigma = 2 \times 10^{-26}$ cm^2, the concentration of the intergalactic gas is $n = 10^{-5}$ cm^{-3}, and the intensity of the isotropic metagalactic cosmic rays is $I_g = 0 \cdot 2$ cm$^{-2}\cdot$sterad$^{-1}\cdot$ sec^{-1} (it was indicated in section 2 that for galactic cosmic rays $I_\gamma = 8 \times 10^{-27} nR$, which also leads to estimate (13.14)). It is clear from (13.14) that measuring the γ-ray intensity will make it possible to determine the product $n I_{Mg}$ (of course, it is assumed here that γ-rays are generated from π°-meson decay). It may largely be a question of an integral effect here. For example in the only experimental work on this subject to date[68] the intensity I_γ was measured for γ-rays with an energy $E_\gamma \gtrsim 50$ MeV. In the future it will be possible also to find the γ-ray spectrum and thus the spectrum of the cosmic rays generating these γ-rays. According to Kraushaar and Clark[68] $I_\gamma = (3 \cdot 7 \text{ to } 11) \times 10^{-4}$ cm$^2 \cdot$sterad$^{-1} \cdot$sec^{-1} but even this value is a preliminary one and is evidently in the nature of an upper limit for the intensity of the γ-rays of extraterrestrial origin (the subsequent processing[447] of the same data has confirmed this remark: Kraushaar et al.[447] give the value $I_\gamma(E > 40 \text{ MeV}) \leqslant (3 \cdot 3 \pm 1 \cdot 3) \times 10^{-4}$ cm$^2 \cdot$sterad$^{-1} \cdot$sec^{-1}). In addition, an answer has still not been provided to the question of the directional γ-ray distribution (galactic γ-rays should be concentrated in directions close to the galactic plane). Bearing all this in mind we still cannot exclude from measurements of the γ-photon flux the possibility of the existence of a high concentration (close to the galactic) of cosmic rays in metagalactic space. But we can already state that there are no more cosmic rays in the Metagalaxy than in the Galaxy. In the future then, after a reliable metagalactic value or upper limit has been obtained for I_γ, it will be possible to estimate the maximum possible intensity of the metagalactic cosmic rays I_{Mg} but only by fixing values for n and R (R is the effective radius of the region occupied by the cosmic rays; in (13.8) it is taken that $R = R_{ph}$).†

† The selection of $R = R_{ph}$ assumes that the whole Metagalaxy is filled with cosmic rays with a mean intensity I_{Mg}. If, let us say, in the Local Supergalaxy with a radius $R_{LS} \sim 5 \times 10^{25}$ cm the intensity is $I = I_{LS}$ and everywhere outside

The following reservation must be made, however. The intensity of the metagalactic γ-rays can be identified with the γ-radiation coming from intergalactic space only if we ignore the intensity of the γ-rays generated in the galaxies.

If the cosmic ray intensity in a given galaxy is I_G and the total mass of interstellar gas in the Galaxy is M (hence the total number of nuclei in the gas is $N_{\text{tot}} \sim 5 \times 10^{23} M$) then the Galaxy emits $L_\gamma = \sigma 4\pi N_{\text{tot}} I_G \sim 0.1 I_G M$ photons/sec (we recall that $\sigma \sim 2 \times 10^{-26}$ cm^2). For the Galaxy $L_\gamma \sim 10^{41}$ photons/sec (the mass of the gas in the disk is $M \sim 3 \times 10^{42}$ g, $I_G \sim 0.2$ cm$^2 \cdot$sterad$^{-1} \cdot$sec^{-1}). In a similar manner to the way we dealt with the thermal emission in section 8 we have for the intensity of the γ-rays from all the galaxies $I_{G,\gamma} = N_G L_\gamma R_{\text{ph}}/4\pi$, where N_G is the concentration of the galaxies and $R_{\text{ph}} \sim 5 \times 10^{27}$ cm. Taking the values $N_G = 5 \times 10^{-75}$ cm^{-3} (see (13.3)) and $L_\gamma \sim 10^{41}$ photons/sec we obtain the intensity $I_{G,\gamma} \sim 10^{-7}$ photons/cm$^2 \cdot$sterad$\cdot$sec. Since this value is almost four orders less than the intensity (13.14) it may be taken that the part played by γ-rays generated in the galaxies is relatively small (if $I_{\text{Mg}} \sim I_G$). This conclusion is valid only in conditions when the part played by radio galaxies (from the point of view of their contribution to the total flux of the emission from all galaxies) is relatively small or, at least does not noticeably exceed the γ-radiation flux from all the other galaxies. Bearing in mind the estimates given below it must be assumed that this is the case, i.e., the contribution of the radio galaxies does not alter the conclusion on the lowness of the intensity $I_{G,\gamma}$.

Metagalactic γ-rays should be generated not only as the result of π°-meson decay, which has been spoken of above, but also generated by relativistic electrons by virtue of bremsstrahlung and scattering on thermal photons (i.e., as the result of the inverse Compton effect). This question is discussed in detail in section 19. The basic conclusion is as follows: for the γ-ray intensity not to exceed the upper limit indicated above[447] the intensity of the cosmic ray electron component in metagalactic space should be at least 30 to 100 times lower than in the Galaxy.

Another source of information on metagalactic cosmic rays (on their electron component, to be more precise) is the metagalactic

this Supergalaxy is $I = I_{\text{Mg}}$, then in (13.14) $I_{\text{Mg}} R_{\text{ph}}$ must be replaced by $I_{\text{LS}} R_{\text{LS}} + I_{\text{Mg}}(R_{\text{ph}} - R_{\text{LS}})$. Since $R_{\text{LS}} \sim 10^{-2} R_{\text{ph}}$ the contribution from the Supergalaxy may be significant only if $I_{\text{LS}} > (10 \text{ to } 30) I_{\text{Mg}}$.

radio emission. Its intensity I_ν and effective temperature T_{eff} are (see (6.1) and (6.2)):

$$I_\nu = \frac{2k\nu^2}{c^2} T_{\text{eff}} = 1.35 \times 10^{-22} a(\gamma) L K_e H^{(\gamma+1)/2}$$

$$\times \left(\frac{6.26 \times 10^{18}}{\nu}\right)^{(\gamma-1)/2} \text{erg} \cdot \text{cm}^{-2} \cdot \text{sterad}^{-1} \cdot \text{sec}^{-1} \cdot (\text{c/s})^{-1}, \quad (13.15)$$

$$K_e H^{(\gamma+1)/2} = \frac{8.9 \times 10^{22} T_{\text{eff}}}{a(\gamma) L} \left(\frac{\nu}{6.26 \times 10^{18}}\right)^{(\gamma+3)/2} .$$

Here the magnetic field is considered to be isotropic (on the path L along the line of sight) and the electrons to have a spectrum $N_e(E) = K_e E^{-\gamma}$. The values of $a(\gamma)$ are for example $a(2) = 0.103$, $a(2.5) = 0.085$ and $a(3) = 0.074$. The temperature T_{eff} in (13.15) is measured in degrees, the frequency ν in c/s, the path L in centimetres and the field H in oersteds.

Unfortunately we have only very approximate estimates of the upper limit of $T_{\text{eff, Mg}}$ (the effective temperature of the metagalactic radio emission). For example, according to Costain,[209] for a wavelength $\lambda = 3.7$ m ($\nu \simeq 80$ Mc/s) $T_{\text{eff, Mg}} < 240\,°\text{K}$ if $\gamma = 2.6$ (Kaplan and Pikel'ner[224] give the value $T_{\text{eff, Mg}} \simeq 250\,°\text{K}$ at a wavelength $\lambda = 3.5$ m). According to Westerhout[263] at a wavelength $\lambda = 75$ cm ($\nu = 400$ Mc/s), when the use of the value $\gamma = 2.6$ is far more justified, $T_{\text{eff}} \simeq 25\,°\text{K}$ in the direction of the galactic pole. Hence it is clear that in the present case $T_{\text{eff, Mg}} < 25\,°\text{K}$. Let us put $a(\gamma) = 0.085$, $L = R_{\text{ph}} = 5 \times 10^{27}$ cm and $\gamma = 2.6$ in (13.15). Then the values $T_{\text{eff, Mg}}$ ($\nu = 80$ Mc/s) $< 240\,°\text{K}$ and $T_{\text{eff, Mg}}$ ($\nu = 400$ Mc/s) $< 10\,°\text{K}$ give approximately the same result†

$$K_{e, \text{Mg}} H_{\text{Mg}}^{1.8} < (1.5 \text{ to } 5) \times 10^{-32}. \quad (13.16)$$

For the Galaxy, putting $\nu = 400$ Mc/s, $T_{\text{eff}} = 25\,°\text{K}$, $H = 10^{-5}$ oe and $L = 3 \times 10^{22}$ cm, we obtain the value $K_e \simeq 2.5 \times 10^{-17}$ and a spectrum $N_e(E)\,dE = 2.5 \times 10^{-17} E^{-2.6}$ (E is in erg; see (6.4)). Hence $N_e(E > 1 \text{ GeV}) \simeq 5 \times 10^{-13}$ cm^{-3}. For a field $H \sim 3 \times 10^{-6}$ oe the values of K_e and N_e are increased by about an order since $(10^{-5}/3 \times 10^{-6})^{1.3} = 8.7$. The value of $K_{e, \text{Mg}}$ in the Metagalaxy,

† The value of $T_{\text{eff, Mg}}$ can be determined not only from the metagalactic space radio emission of interest to us but also from the total emission of the galaxies. If $\nu = 400$ Mc/s this last component probably corresponds[439] to a temperature $T_{\text{eff}} \simeq 3$ to $5\,°\text{K}$.

it may be taken, is in any case less than the galactic value $K_{e,G} \sim 10^{-16}$. Hence and from (13.16) if $K_{e,Mg} = K_{e,G} \sim 10^{-16}$ we can obtain a certain estimate for the possible strength of the metagalactic field

$$H_{Mg} < \left(\frac{3 \times 10^{-32}}{K_{e,G}}\right)^{0.555} \sim 3 \times 10^{-9} \text{ oersteds.} \quad (13.17)$$

In other words the assumption of the presence in metagalactic space of electrons with a spectrum with the index $\gamma = 2.6$ and with a galactic concentration is compatible only with a field value $H_{Mg} \lesssim 3 \times 10^{-9}$ oe. In addition, the "equilibrium" field in the Metagalaxy reaches a value 5×10^{-7} oe (see (13.8)) and in any case it is rather hard to expect the presence of a field weaker than 3×10^{-8} oe (for a field $H \sim 10^{-8}$ oe the magnetic energy would be at least one or two orders of magnitude less than the density of the kinetic energy $\rho u^2/2$ for $\rho \sim 10^{-29}$ g/cm^3 and $u \sim 1$ to 3×10^7 cm/sec).† At the same time it must be stressed that even in the case of approximate equality of the concentrations of the cosmic ray nuclear component in the Galaxy and Metagalaxy the concentrations of the electron component in both cases could, in principle, be quite different. For example if the electron component is secondary (is formed as a result of nuclear collisions) all other things being equal (with an identical spectrum and "accumulation time") the electron concentration is proportional to the density of the gas. Putting for the Metagalaxy and Galaxy respectively $\rho_{Mg} \sim 10^{-29}$ and $\rho_G \sim 10^{-26}$ g/cm^3 we obtain for $w_{Mg} = w_G$ the value $K_{e,Mg} \sim 10^{-19}$ and instead of (13.17) the estimate

$$H < 10^{-7} \text{ oersteds.} \quad (13.18)$$

This value can still probably be made to agree with the estimate of the "equilibrium" field from the condition $\rho u^2/2 \sim H_{eq}^2/8\pi$. But even in the case of (13.18) the field H_{Mg} is small when compared with the "equilibrium" field determined from the value of the density and energy of the cosmic rays $w_{Mg} \sim w_G \sim 10^{-12}$ erg/cm^3:

$$H_{eq,cr} \sim \sqrt{8\pi w_{Mg}} \sim 5 \times 10^{-6} \text{ oersteds.} \quad (13.19)$$

Still more important is the fact that the "accumulation" time for

† The question of how widely we can use the equality $\rho u^2/2 \sim H^2/8\pi$ under cosmic conditions to estimate the equilibrium value of the field is still not very clear. In any case this estimate is now the most natural one.

electrons in the Metagalaxy is greater than in the Galaxy. In addition, the gas density was higher in the past than it is now; the important thing is also that the majority of radio-emitting electrons are not secondary. For all these reasons, as is shown below, there is no particular reason to consider the percentage of electrons in metagalactic cosmic rays to be much lower than in galactic cosmic rays. This means that estimate (13.17) is the basic one and not (13.18).

Thus if we assume that in the Metagalaxy the cosmic ray concentration and the density of their energy are the same as in the Galaxy the intergalactic magnetic field must be considered to be relatively very weak. Even upon the assumption that the electron concentration in the Metagalaxy is two or three orders less than in the Galaxy the metagalactic field should be at least two orders weaker than the field (13.19). This means that the cosmic ray energy ray density should be (for $w_{Mg} \sim 10^{-12}$ erg/cm^3) at least four orders greater than the density of the magnetic energy and at least two orders greater than the kinetic energy density $\rho u^2/2 \sim 10^{-14}$ erg/cm^3 (see (13.8)). We shall return again later to this very important question.

Diffusion, energy losses and cosmic ray acceleration in the intergalactic medium

In order to find out how cosmic rays move in intergalactic space we must have some idea of the configuration of the magnetic fields. There are no direct data here but it is most natural to consider that on the average over a large region (with a dimension $R \gg 10^{25}$ cm, i.e., a dimension much greater than the mean distance between galaxies) the field is random. The assumption of the existence of a quasi-regular field is scarcely permissible, for example, if we take into consideration the rotation of the galaxies (the characteristic time is $T_{rot} \sim 10^8$ years $\ll T_{Mg}$) and also the existence of the relative motion velocities $u \sim 3 \times 10^7$ cm/sec (in a time $T_{Mg} \sim 10^{10}$ years a galaxy moving at this velocity will travel a distance of about 10^{25} cm). The characteristic length l over which the field is changed is probably no greater than the mean distance between galaxies of about 10^{25} cm or within the Local Supergalaxy of about 3×10^{24} cm. The lower limit of the field's inhomogeneity scale is the length of the free path of the particles in the gas $1/\sigma n$. In an ionised gas[192] $\sigma \simeq (e^2/kT)^2 \times \ln(kT/e^2 n_e^{1/3}) \simeq 3 \times 10^{-6} T^{-2} \ln(600T/n_e^{1/3})$. Hence for $n_e \sim 10^{-5}$ cm^{-3} and a temperature $T \sim 10^6$ °K the length of the mean free path is

$\sim 10^{21}$ cm.† The same value is obtained for neutral hydrogen if $\sigma \sim 10^{-16}$ cm^2 and $n \sim 10^{-5}$ cm^{-3}. Below (particularly bearing in mind the region of the Local Supergalaxy) we shall take the scale as $l \sim 10^{24}$ to 10^{25} cm.

Motion within a quasi-homogeneous field can be considered to occur along a helix if the radius of curvature is $r_H = E \sin \theta / 300H \ll l$. Even in a field $H \sim 10^{-8}$ oe with $Z = 1$, $\sin \theta \sim 1/3$ and $E \sim 10^{18}$ eV the radius is $r_H \sim 10^5 E \sim 10^{23} \ll l$ and the above-mentioned condition is fulfilled.

Bearing in mind the presence of "mixing" we shall use the diffusion approximation just as in the case of the halo to describe the motion of the cosmic rays in the intergalactic medium over a sufficiently long period (see section 10; in the present case we can use a time $T \gtrsim 10^9$ years). Then the maximum distance travelled by cosmic rays in a certain direction is of the order of the diffusion path travelled in the time T_{Mg}:

$$R_{max} \sim \sqrt{2DT_{Mg}} = \sqrt{\tfrac{2}{3}lvT_{Mg}} \sim 5 \times 10^{13}\sqrt{l} \text{ cm} \sim 5 \text{ to } 15 \times 10^{25} \text{ cm}$$

$$\simeq 2 \text{ to } 5 \times 10^7 \text{ pc,} \qquad (13.20)$$

where the velocity of motion along the field is $v \sim 10^{10}$ cm/sec.

It follows from this that in the characteristic time of the Metagalaxy's evolution $T_{Mg} \sim 10^{10}$ years cosmic rays can reach the Galaxy only from a region with a radius R_{max}. Allowing for the recession of the galaxies leads to the same result.[6, 399] This conclusion is connected with the fact that as a particle source recedes at a velocity greater than the velocity of diffusion the particle flux drops sharply. In order to make an estimate we shall ignore the change in the effective length of the mean free path with time, i.e., we shall put $R \simeq \sqrt{2Dt} = \sqrt{\tfrac{2}{3}lvt}$, so the "velocity" of diffusion is $(dR/dt)_D \simeq lv/3R$. At the same time the distance to the galaxies is varying due to recession as $(dR/dt)_{Mg} = hR$, where h is Hubble's constant. From the condition $(dR/dt)_D \sim (dR/dt)_{Mg}$ with $h = 1/T_{Mg}$ we come to the

---

† Assuming $T \sim 10^6$ °K we select the greatest value met when estimating the temperature of the gas in the halo or within the Local Group[377] (as T is reduced the length of the path in an ionised gas decreases). In the steady-state cosmology the values $n \sim 10^{-5}$ cm^{-3} and $T \sim 10^9$ degrees are taken in intergalactic space.[398] In this case the field clearly cannot alter at distances less than $\sim 10^{26}$ cm unless they are local fields connected with individual galaxies or clusters. We think it is very hard to accept this picture in which the length of the mean free path and the scale of the field are considerably greater than the mean distance between galaxies.

estimate of the maximum radius $R_{max} = \sqrt{(lv/3)T_{Mg}}$; this estimate agrees with (13.20) since the small difference in the numerical factor lies outside the calculation's limits of accuracy.

Cosmic rays can thus reach the Galaxy, it would appear, only from distances less than about 2 to 5×10^7 pc, which is two orders less than the radius of the part of the Metagalaxy that can be observed in the most powerful telescope.

Let us now turn to estimating the energy losses to which cosmic rays are subjected during motion in the metagalactic medium.

With respect to the proton and nuclear components the losses differ from those occurring in the Galaxy only because of the different value of the gas density. In the Galaxy we have assumed that on the average $n \sim 10^{-2}$ cm^{-3}. Therefore in the Metagalaxy with $n \sim 10^{-5}$ cm^{-3} we obtain (see Table 10)

$$T_p \simeq 3 \cdot 6 \times 10^{12} \text{ yrs}, \qquad T_{Fe} \simeq 1 \cdot 4 \times 10^{11} \text{ yr} \gg T_{Mg} \sim 10^{10} \text{ yr.} \quad (13.21)$$

Since $T_p \gg T_{Fe} \gg T_{Mg}$ we can use the values of (13.21) in the framework of the evolutionary cosmology only if we calculate the number of different secondary particles (nuclei, electrons, γ-rays) being generated at present as the result of nuclear collisions. If we wish to estimate the change in the concentration or energy of the cosmic rays in a time $t \sim T_{Mg}$ we must allow for the change in distances and the density of the gas in that time. The change in the cosmic ray concentration in an expanding world is defined by the equation

$$\frac{dN}{d\tau} = -3h(\tau)N - \frac{N}{T_{nucl}(\tau)}. \quad (13.22)$$

Here $h(\tau) = (dR/d\tau)/R$ is Hubble's constant and τ is the time. In the Einstein–de Sitter model $h(\tau) = \frac{2}{3}\tau = 1/t$ and in accordance with (13.22)

$$N(t) = N(T_{Mg})\left(\frac{T_{Mg}}{t}\right)^2 \exp\left\{\frac{2T_{Mg}}{3T_{nucl, Mg}}\left(\frac{T_{Mg}}{t} - 1\right)\right\}, \quad (13.23)$$

since $T_{nucl}(\tau) = 1/\sigma cn(\tau) = T_{nucl, Mg}(t/T_{Mg})^2$, where $T_{nucl, Mg} = 1/\sigma cn(T_{Mg})$ is the nuclear life for the present gas concentration $n(T_{Mg})$.

As for the particle energy, this changes in accordance with the equation

$$\frac{dE}{d\tau} = -h(\tau)E + \alpha E, \quad (13.24)$$

where the first term on the right-hand side allows for the change in energy due to expansion, whilst the second term appears when there is statistical acceleration (the energy losses in (13.24) are not taken into consideration). If $h(\tau) = \frac{2}{3}\tau$ and $\alpha = 0$

$$E(t) = E(T_{Mg})\left(\frac{2T_{Mg}}{3\tau}\right)^{\frac{2}{3}} \equiv E(T_{Mg})\left(\frac{T_{Mg}}{t}\right)^{\frac{2}{3}}. \qquad (13.25)$$

The cosmic ray energy density is proportional to $N \cdot E$ so

$$w(t) = w(T_{Mg})\left(\frac{T_{Mg}}{t}\right)^{\frac{8}{3}} \exp\left\{\frac{2T_{Mg}}{3T_{nucl,\,Mg}}\left(\frac{T_{Mg}}{t} - 1\right)\right\}. \qquad (13.26)$$

Here, of course, just as in (13.22) and (13.23) we are using the idea of catastrophic collisions in which a particle practically loses all its energy. This assumption is fully justified when the corresponding effective value is selected as the nuclear life T_{nucl}. It is clear from (13.26) that cosmic rays can "survive" until now without being subjected to large nuclear losses only if the time of their generation $t = T_0 \ll T_{Mg}$ satisfies the condition

$$\frac{T_{Mg}^2}{T_{nucl,\,Mg}T_0} \lesssim 1. \qquad (13.27)$$

Hence, by putting $T_{nucl,\,Mg} \sim 3 \times 10^{12}$ years (see (13.21)) and $T_{Mg} \sim 10^{10}$ years, we obtain $T_0 > 3 \times 10^7$ years but for iron nuclei (and VH-nuclei in general)

$$T_0 \gtrsim T_{Mg}\left(\frac{T_{Mg}}{T_{Fe,\,Mg}}\right)^2 \sim 5 \times 10^8 \text{ yr.} \qquad (13.28)$$

Even for M-nuclei $T_{nucl,\,Mg} \sim 4 \times 10^{11}$ years (see Table 10; we must put $n \sim 10^{-5}$ cm^{-3}) and $T_0 \gtrsim 2 \times 10^8$ years.

Thus from the point of view of determining the energy of the cosmic ray nuclear component the behaviour of the Metagalaxy for $t < T_0 \sim 10^8$ years is of no interest. This estimate of the time T_0 agrees approximately with that derived above from other considerations. Bearing in mind the absence of information on the behaviour of the Metagalaxy in the period $t < T_0$ we can proceed as follows in the evolutionary cosmology (on the assumption that the time corresponding to maximum compression T_{min} is less than $\sim 10^8$ years).†

In the period $T_0 < t < T_{Mg}$ the nuclear losses can be ignored and at $t = T_0$ be given by a certain flux and energy density of the "remnant" cosmic rays. The energy density of these remnant cosmic rays at $t > T_0$ varies as (see above)

$$w_p(t) = w_p(T_0)\left(\frac{T_0}{t}\right)^{8/3}. \tag{13.26a}$$

In the case of electrons (and positrons) their energy varies when there is no acceleration as (see (8.11), (8.12) and (13.24))

$$\frac{dE}{d\tau} = -h(\tau)E - \{0{\cdot}98 \times 10^{-3}H_\perp^2(\tau) + 2\times 10^{-14}w_{ph}(\tau)\}\left(\frac{E}{mc^2}\right)^2 \tag{13.29}$$

where E is measured in electron-volts and the time in seconds.

In (13.29) the radiation (bremsstrahlung) losses are ignored since for $n \sim 10^{-5}$ cm^{-3} they correspond to a characteristic time $T_r \gg T_{Mg}$ (with compression allowed for over the range $T_0 < t < T_{Mg}$ the radiation losses can also be ignored). If we drop the first term in (13.29) the electron energy varies as

$$E(t) = \frac{E_0}{1 + \left\{3{\cdot}8 \times 10^{-15}\displaystyle\int_{T_0}^{t} H_\perp^2\, dt + 7{\cdot}7 \times 10^{-26}\displaystyle\int_{T_0}^{t} w_{ph}\, dt\right\}E_0} \tag{13.30}$$

(E is in electron-volts, w_{ph} in eV/cm^3, $H_\perp$ in oersteds and t in seconds). The energy density of the emission of all the galaxies in metagalactic space varies in accordance with law (13.11): $w_{ph}(t) = w_{ph}(T_{Mg})(T_{Mg}/t)$. There is nothing obviously known about the function $H_\perp(t)$. It is most natural to assume that the energy density $H^2/8\pi$ varies in the same way as the gas energy density $\rho u^2/2$. The density of the gas is $\rho(t) = \rho(T_{Mg})(T_{Mg}/t)^2$; with respect to the velocity u we shall make two different assumptions: $u = $ const or $u \sim t^{2/9}$ (under turbulent conditions $u \sim l^{1/3}$ and for the expanding model under discussion $l \sim t^{2/3}$, where l is the characteristic scale of the pulsations). As a result $H^2(t) = H^2(T_{Mg})(T_{Mg}/t)^\delta$, where $\delta = 2$ or $\delta = 14/9$. Another

† We can try to estimate the time T_{min} in the oscillating model by examining the neutrino reabsorption processes.[400]

possibility is connected with the idea of a constant magnetic flux $Hl^2 = \text{const}$ whence $\delta = 8/3$. In all probability we can also assume that $H_\perp^2 \infty H^2$.

Therefore

$$w_{ph}(t) = w_{ph}(T_{Mg})\left(\frac{T_{Mg}}{t}\right), \quad H_\perp^2(t) = H_\perp^2(T_{Mg})\left(\frac{T_{Mg}}{t}\right)^\delta, \quad (13.31)$$

$$\delta = \frac{14}{9} \text{ to } \frac{8}{3}$$

Let us finally estimate the possible part played by statistical acceleration in the intergalactic medium and clusters of galaxies. In the first case the coefficient α in equation (13.24) (for $l \sim 10^{24}$ cm, $u \sim 3 \times 10^7$ cm/sec, $v \sim 10^{10}$ cm/sec) will be of the order

$$\alpha = \frac{u^2 v}{c^2 l} \sim 10^{-20} \sec^{-1}. \quad (13.32)$$

Moreover, even at the present time the first term in equation (13.24) is of the order $-2E/3\tau = -E/T_{Mg} \sim -3 \times 10^{-18}E$, i.e., the slowing down due to the system's expansion is far more efficient than statistical acceleration.

In the case of clusters the term $-h(\tau)E$ must be ignored (in the case of stable clusters this is obviously right; in addition, when the term $-h(\tau)E$ is taken into account the acceleration becomes only less or is even replaced by deceleration). Further, for the Local Group of galaxies, which includes our own Galaxy, we obtain $\alpha \lesssim 10^{-20}$ to 10^{-21} sec^{-1} (with $u \sim 1$ to 3×10^7 cm/sec and $l \sim 10^{24}$ cm). For the cluster of galaxies in Coma ref. 401 takes the values $u \sim 2 \times 10^8$ cm/sec, $l \sim 3 \times 10^{22}$ cm and thus $\alpha \sim 4 \times 10^{-17}$ sec^{-1}. This means that in the time T_{Mg} the particle energy rises $e^{\alpha T_{Mg}} \sim 10^5$ times. In actual fact, however, the value taken for l is too low and it would be better to put $l \sim 10^{23}$ cm, $v \sim 10^{10}$ cm/sec and $\alpha \sim 4 \times 10^{-18}$ sec^{-1}, $e^{\alpha T_{Mg}} \sim 1$. The main thing is that the cluster in Coma is at a distance of about 7×10^7 pc $\gtrsim R_{max} \sim 2$ to 5×10^7 pc and is exceptional in its characteristics (in any case at a shorter distance there are no clusters comparable in the sense of possible efficiency of acceleration).[315, 401] We may thus conclude that clusters of galaxies located at a distance $R \gtrsim R_{max}$ probably cannot accelerate cosmic rays noticeably.

Estimates of the cosmic ray energy density in the Metagalaxy

Cosmic rays may enter metagalactic space in two ways:

(1) as the result of acceleration at the time the galaxies were formed, i.e., at $t < T_0 \sim 1$ to 3×10^8 years (we call these remnant cosmic rays; their energy density was denoted by $w_r(t)$ and varies in accordance with law (13.26a));

(2) as the result of the departure of cosmic rays from the galaxies (energy density $w_{\text{Mg}, g}(t)$, total cosmic ray energy density $w_{\text{Mg}} = w_{\text{Mg}, g} + w_r$).

It is hardly possible at present to estimate the density $w_r(T_0)$ in any reliable way and we would make only one remark in this connexion. The kinetic energy density of random motion in intergalactic space was estimated at $t = T_{\text{Mg}}$ to be $\rho u^2/2 \sim 10^{-14}$ erg/cm^3 (see (13.8)). In accordance with the estimate given in the preceding section $\rho u^2/2$ varies as $(\rho u^2/2)_{T_{\text{Mg}}} \times (T_{\text{Mg}}/t)^\delta$ with $\delta = 14/9$ to 2, whilst $w_r(t) = w_r(T_{\text{Mg}})(T_{\text{Mg}}/t)^{8/3}$. It follows from this that in the past the ratio $\rho u^2/2w_r$ was less than it is now. On the other hand, it is rather hard to imagine that $w_r(T_0) > (\rho u^2/2)_{T_0}$. In fact if cosmic rays are accelerated by a statistical mechanism at the time of the galaxies' formation their energy density cannot in all probability exceed $\rho u^2/2$. No method other than statistical acceleration of the particles can be seen. As a result of these arguments we come to the estimate

$$w_r(T_{\text{Mg}}) < \left(\frac{\rho u^2}{2}\right)_{T_{\text{Mg}}} \sim 10^{-14} \text{ erg/cm}^3. \qquad (13.33)$$

Unfortunately this estimate is not convincing enough.

Some important information on remnant metagalactic cosmic rays can be obtained by examining the question of their chemical composition. The point is that the characteristic time T_0 corresponding to the ending of the acceleration or remnant (pre-galactic) rays can hardly be made more than 10^8 years (this is clear also from the estimate given below for L-nuclei). But in accordance with formula (13.26) for $t = T_0 = 10^8$ years, $T_{\text{Mg}} = 10^{10}$ years and $T_{\text{nucl, Mg}} = T_{\text{Fe, Mg}} = 1\cdot 4 \times 10^{11}$ years the iron nucleus flux in remnant cosmic rays, even without allowing for the factor $(T_{\text{Mg}}/T_0)^{8/3}$ caused by the expansion, will decrease by a factor of $\exp(2T_{\text{Mg}}^2/3T_{\text{nucl, Mg}}T_0) \sim 100$. Further, for the generation of the number of L-nuclei observed on Earth the cosmic rays should pass through a ~ 7 g/cm^2 layer of the interstellar medium (see section 15). This means that the original cosmic rays should have been generated in the time $t = T_L$ determined from the relationship

$$\int_{T_L}^{T_{Mg}} \rho(T_{Mg}) c \left(\frac{T_{Mg}}{t}\right)^2 dt \simeq \rho(T_{Mg}) c \frac{T_{Mg}^2}{T_L} \sim 7 \text{ g/cm}^2;$$

hence $T_L \simeq 10^8$ years for $\rho(T_{Mg}) = 10^{-29}$ g/cm^3. The fact that the time T_L agrees with the value $T_0 \sim 10^8$ years used above shows that there is no reason to change the latter time in any way. We thus come to the conclusion that remnant cosmic rays, in order to have the composition now observed on Earth, should contain a very large number of VH-nuclei at $t = T_0$. To be more precise, this conclusion is true if the present density of the intergalactic gas is $\rho(T_{Mg}) \simeq 10^{-29}$ g/cm^3. If the density is $\rho(T_{Mg}) \ll 10^{-29}$ g/cm^3 the chemical composition of the remnant rays should be considered as having hardly altered in composition for $t > T_0 \sim 10^8$ years. The behaviour of the Metagalaxy for $t < T_0$ is so uncertain that convincing statements can hardly be made about this stage. It is most probable, however, that $\rho(T_{Mg}) \sim 10^{-29}$ g/cm^3 and the conclusion drawn is valid. Moreover, according to modern ideas[402] synthesis of the elements takes place in stars, so at the stage of the galaxies' formation we should expect a particularly small percentage content of heavy elements. Hence it follows that remnant rays, if their flux is large, could scarcely contain many heavy nuclei.

The situation with respect to remnant cosmic rays can be recapitulated as follows. The existence of remnant rays is possible, but it is very hard to expect that their energy density is high, i.e., of the order $w_G \simeq 10^{-12}$ erg/cm^3. Estimate (13.33) is thus more natural as satisfying the condition

$$w_r \ll w_G \simeq 10^{-12} \text{ erg/cm}^3. \tag{13.34}$$

In addition, it is very hard to expect the chemical composition of the remnant rays to be close to the composition of the cosmic rays near the Earth. It can be taken that remnant rays will be poor in heavy nuclei and, for example, contain largely protons and α-particles. It follows also from this, and independently at that, that $w_r \ll w_G$. In actual fact if there were many remnant rays ($w_r \sim w_G$) they would penetrate the Galaxy and the cosmic rays reaching the Earth would be largely of metagalactic (and thus remnant) origin. This assumption is in direct contradiction to the data on the chemical composition of the cosmic rays on the Earth.

The energy density of remnant metagalactic cosmic rays should therefore evidently satisfy inequality (13.34). Here, of course, we are basing ourselves on the evolutionary cosmological model (it is only in this case that we can speak of remnant metagalactic rays) and we also consider valid relationships like (13.26) and the estimate of the gas density $\rho(T_{Mg}) \sim 10^{-29}$ g/cm^3.

Let us now determine the energy density of the metagalactic cosmic rays $w_{Mg.\,g}$ which have come from the galaxies. Here we shall be interested only in that region of the Metagalaxy with a radius $R \lesssim R_{max} \sim 10^{26}$ cm and a volume $V_{max} \sim 3 \times 10^{78}$ cm^3 from which cosmic rays may reach the Galaxy. If in this region the concentration of galaxies is equal to the mean value for the Metagalaxy $\sim 5 \times 10^{-75}$ cm^{-3} (see (13.3)), then the total number of galaxies in the region will be of the order of 10^4. This estimate does not change significantly even when allowing for the fact that the region with $R \sim R_{max}$ includes the Local Supergalaxy with a volume $V \sim 10^{77}$ cm^3, mean concentration of galaxies $\sim 10^{-73}$ cm^{-3} and a total number of galaxies $\sim 10^4$ (the existence of the Local Supergalaxy, as is clear from these figures, can alter the total number of galaxies in the region with $R \sim R_{max}$ only by a factor of the order of unity, i.e., let us say by a factor of two). In this connexion the existence of the Local Supergalaxy may prove to be important when estimating the density $w_{Mg,\,g}$ only in the case that this supergalaxy slowly exchanges cosmic rays with the surrounding space by virtue of the presence of a certain quasi-ordered magnetic field in the supergalaxy. Let us examine two variants appropriate to this.

The first variant corresponds to the case when the cosmic rays are not localised in the supergalaxy and more or less evenly fill the whole Metagalaxy or in any case the region with $R \sim R_{max} \sim 10^{26}$ cm. In this region, as we have said, there are $\sim 10^4$ galaxies. The number of radio galaxies with a radio star magnitude $M_r = -22$ should be 1000 times less, i.e., of the order of 10. The more powerful radio galaxies should have already been allowed for and it is known that there are (for $R \lesssim R_{max}$) evidently only three of them (Virgo A, Centaurus A and Fornax A). We shall take it that the cosmic ray energy in a galaxy is proportional to the power of its radio emission (i.e., radio brightness).† With this assumption we can see that the

---

† The power of the radio emission is $P^{\infty} W_e H^{3/2}$, where W_e is total energy of the electrons and H is the field strength iⁿ the source (see (6.16) and (6.24)). Therefore for a given field and total cosmic ray energy $W_{cr} = \kappa\, W_e \sim 10^2\, W_e$

contribution of all the radio galaxies as cosmic ray sources is less or no greater than the contribution of the normal galaxies. In reality a normal galaxy emits ~ 1 to 3×10^{38} erg/sec in the radio band on the average, whilst the total cosmic ray energy in such galaxies is ~ 1 to 3×10^{56} erg (see Table 8). The weak radio galaxies with $M_r = -22$ emit an order more but there are three orders less of them than of normal galaxies. The three powerful galaxies Virgo A, Centaurus A and Fornax A taken together emit $\sim 5 \times 10^{41}$ erg/sec and contain cosmic rays with an energy $\sim 3 \times 10^{59}$ erg (see Table 9). Therefore the 10^4 normal galaxies emit slightly more than the three above-mentioned rather powerful radio galaxies.

Our Galaxy is normal, emits $\sim 3 \times 10^{38}$ erg/sec in the radio band and cosmic rays with a power $U \sim 10^{40}$ to 10^{41} erg/sec leave it for intergalactic space. In the time $T_{\text{Mg}} \sim 3 \times 10^{17}$ sec this corresponds to an energy of $\sim 3 \times 10^{57}$ to 3×10^{58} erg.† If we multiply this energy by the galaxy concentration 5×10^{-75} cm^{-3} we obtain the cosmic ray energy density

$$w_{\text{Mg}, g}(T_{\text{Mg}}) \sim 10^{-16} \text{ to } 10^{-17} \text{ erg/sec} \simeq (10^{-4} \text{ to } 10^{-5}) w_G. \quad (13.35)$$

Even assuming that all the radio galaxies in the region $R \lesssim R_{\text{max}}$ provide as many cosmic rays as the normal galaxies we cannot change estimate (13.35).

In view of the importance of the question let us estimate the part played by radio galaxies in yet another way. We shall consider that

(see (6.19)) the power P is proportional to W_{cr}. If we assume that the energy W_{cr} is equal to the magnetic field energy in the source $W_H = (H^2/8\pi) V$, then $W_{\text{cr}} \sim P^{4/7}$. Thus by considering the cosmic ray energy in the source W_{cr} to be proportional to the radio emission power P we are more likely to make the value of W_{cr} too high, which only strengthens the conclusion given in the text that the part played by weak radio galaxies is small.

† A more exact calculation must be made with the formula

$$W = \int_{T_0}^{T_{\text{Mg}}} U(t) \left(\frac{t}{T_{\text{Mg}}}\right)^{2/3} dt = \frac{3 T_{\text{Mg}} U}{5} \text{ (with } U = \text{const} \quad \text{and} \quad T_0 \ll T_{\text{Mg}}),$$

where the factor $(t/T_{\text{Mg}})^{2/3}$ allows for the reduction in the cosmic ray energy due to the expansion of the Metagalaxy. Introducing the corrective factor $3/5$ would, however, exceed the accuracy of the estimate itself. Let us now assume that in the past the radio galaxies clearly exploded far more often than they do now.[439] For the sake of an estimate let us assume that all the galaxies passed through the radio-emitting phase in a period $t \lesssim T_0 \lesssim 10^9$ years, cosmic rays with an energy of 2×10^{60} ergs being generated in each galaxy. Allowing for a ten-fold decrease in energy and with the galaxy density (13.3) we come then to the value $w_{\text{Mg}} \sim 10^{-15}$ erg/cm^3.

in all the radio galaxies in the region of interest to us cosmic rays with an energy of 10^{60} erg have been generated. Let us further assume that all the cosmic rays from the radio galaxy depart into intergalactic space on the average in a time $T_{rg} \sim 3 \times 10^6$ years $\simeq 10^{14}$ sec (it is sufficient to say that the diameter of the halo of the Galaxy and many other galaxies in order of magnitude is 10^5 light years). Estimates of the duration of the radio-emitting phase from other considerations is also generally reduced to values not less than 1 to 3×10^6 years. Hence we obtain the cosmic ray injection power $\sim 10^{46}$ erg/sec. Let us assume lastly that this injection power is provided by the radio galaxies for the whole of the time $T_{Mg} \sim 3 \times 10^{17}$ sec. Hence the total cosmic ray energy is of the order of 3×10^{63} erg in the region with a volume 3×10^{78} cm^3, which corresponds to a density $w_{Mg,g} \sim 10^{-15}$ erg/cm$^3 \sim 10^{-3} w_G$. This value by the very nature of the estimate can be considered a maximum one provided there is no significant alteration in the total cosmic ray energy in the radio galaxies or the cosmic rays are not considered to be concentrated in a smaller volume.

This latter assumption is made by Burbidge[387] in connexion with the already mentioned assumption that the cosmic rays are kept within the Local Supergalaxy.† This leads to a 20 to 30-fold increase in the mean density of the galaxies and thus to the same increase in the values of (13.35). As a result $w_{Mg,g} \lesssim 3 \times 10^{-3} w_G$. If we also multiply the maximum estimate given for the radio galaxy contribution by 30 (without altering their number), then

$$w_{Mg,g} \lesssim 3 \times 10^{-2} w_G \sim 3 \times 10^{-14} \text{ erg/sec.} \qquad (13.36)$$

Burbidge[387] obtains a value for the density $w_{Mg,g}$ which is another

---

† In a later article[476] by the same author the suggestion of the high cosmic ray concentration in the Local Supergalaxy is not repeated. Instead he then discusses a volume with a radius of ~ 300 Mpc in which there are now $\sim 10^3$ radio galaxies. Considering the duration of the active (radiogalactic) phase for each radio galaxy to be on the average $\sim 10^6$ years we can conclude that 10^7 radio galaxies have existed in this region in 10^{10} years. If each radio galaxy injects cosmic rays with an energy of 10^{60} to 10^{62} erg the density of the metagalactic cosmic rays is now 10^{-14} to 10^{-12} erg/cm^3. A mean energy generated of 10^{62} erg seems to us, however, to be far too high. In addition, the calculation made in the text relating to a region with a radius of $R \sim R_{max} \sim 30$ Mpc is more consistent and more reliable. Therefore we, at present at least, see no possibility of raising the value of w_{Mg} to more than $\sim 10^{-14}$ erg/cm^3 (see also the estimate below based on measurements of the γ-ray intensity).

order of magnitude greater because of using a metagalactic time $T_{Mg} \sim 3 \times 10^{10}$ years and a radio galaxy life of $T_{rg} \sim 10^6$ years (instead of $T_{Mg} \sim 10^{10}$ years and $T_{rg} \sim 3 \times 10^6$ years).† This change does not seem justified to us (in the case of the estimate of the time T_{Mg} it is clearly quite unsound) unless the power of the radio galaxies in the past was no greater than it is now. On the other hand the presence of the three very powerful radio galaxies in the Local Supergalaxy probably answers for a certain fluctuation so a smaller concentration of powerful radio galaxies should be expected on the average over a time of the order of $T_{Mg} \sim 10^{10}$ years.

To recapitulate, the conclusion may be drawn that because of departure from the normal galaxies the cosmic ray energy density in the Metagalaxy should be considerably (a minimum of three orders) less than in the Galaxy. Unless the cosmic rays are localised (trapped) within the Local Supergalaxy the radio galaxies cannot create a cosmic ray density comparable with that from the galaxy. Only if cosmic rays do not leave the supergalaxy and for a maximum radio galaxy power can we reach the value $w_{Mg,g} \sim 10^{-13}$ erg/sec $\sim 0.1 w_G$. In this last case, of course, the "reserve" is small and satisfaction of the inequality $w_{Mg} \ll w_G$ cannot be considered to be ensured beforehand. We should repeat, however, that disturbance of this inequality corresponds to assumptions that cannot be considered to have any foundation or even be probable. It is enough to say that even the separation of the Local Supergalaxy as a certain real grouping of galaxies is under doubt. As for the existence of some limitations for the departure of cosmic rays from the supergalaxy nothing definite is known. On the basis of the available data and considerations of cosmic rays being retained in the galaxies and in cosmic conditions in general there is no reason to expect any sort of good magnetic "trap" around the supergalaxy. When there is no trap the cosmic rays will leave the supergalaxy rather rapidly since it is very much flattened (the ratio of the axes is about 1/5); this eases the departure of particles if it occurs by diffusion.‡ In addition,

† In addition, the same cosmic ray energy in the radio galaxies $\sim 10^{60}$ erg was obtained by Burbidge[387] by proceeding from slightly different considerations than those given above.

‡ A distance equal to the half-thickness of the supergalactic disk $L \sim 3$ Mpc $\sim 10^{25}$ cm is travelled by cosmic rays as the result of diffusion in the time $T \sim L^2/2D \sim 10^{40}/l \sim 3 \times 10^7$ to 3×10^8 years if $l \sim 10^{24}$ to 10^{25} cm (see (13.20)).

estimating the volume of the supergalaxy and the region occupied by cosmic rays at $V \sim 10^{77}$ cm^3 we took the minor axis of the system as about 6 Mpc. This means that the "trap" should be of the same size. If the "trap" is quasi-spherical, and this is far more natural (if we introduce a trap), then the volume occupied by the cosmic rays must be increased and the density w_{Mg} decreased by a factor of about five. Lastly we cannot consider that the cosmic ray density drops significantly towards the periphery either since in quasi-stationary conditions (as in the case when particles do not leave the system) the possibility of this drop, generally speaking, is unrealistic because of the requirements imposed on the particles' motion by Liouville's theorem. Yet another argument against Burbidge's[387] model follows from recent radio astronomy data[487]. Since, however, the model with localisation of the cosmic rays in the Local Supergalaxy has apparently been dropped by its own author[476] we shall not repeat here the arguments in our paper[487] although we think that these arguments are very convincing. In addition to what we have already said we would add that it is generally assumed, and this is reasonable, that in radio galaxies the equality $H^2/8\pi \sim w_g$ is satisfied, where H is the magnetic field and w_g is the cosmic ray energy density. It is natural to consider that this condition will occur even in metagalactic space filled with cosmic rays ejected from the radio galaxies (when cosmic rays are ejected and the interstellar gas carries with it magnetic fields as undoubtedly follows from the radio astronomy data, and in the case of Virgo A also from the optical observations of the luminous "jet"). But even if $w_{Mg, g} \sim 10^{-2} w_g \sim 10^{-14}$ erg/cm^3 the field is $H \sim \sqrt{8\pi w_{Mg}} \sim 5 \times 10^{-7}$ oersteds which is hardly acceptable for the whole Metagalaxy (see (13.18)). This field is acceptable for the supergalaxy, but if it is still stronger the condition $\rho u^2/2 \gtrsim H^2/8\pi$ is not fulfilled (see (13.8)).

We shall give one more estimate of w_{Mg}. As has already been mentioned (for further detail see section 19) the intensity of the electron component in metagalactic space is at least 30–100 times less than in the Galaxy. Therefore if the rôle of the electron component of the cosmic rays is not higher than in the Galaxy (the opposite is more likely) we come to the inequality $w_{Mg} < 1$ to 3×10^{-14} erg/cm^3.

Thus even the maximum value of $w_{Mg, g}$ is more likely to be one and a half to two orders of magnitude less than w_g. In combination with what has been said previously about remnant cosmic rays we come to the conclusion that in the evolutionary cosmology, in all probability, the metagalactic cosmic ray density is

$$w_{\text{Mg}} = w_{\text{Mg},g} + w_r \ll w_g \sim 10^{-12} \text{ erg/cm}^3. \qquad (13.37)$$

In the steady-state cosmology it is assumed[283, 398] that $w_{\text{Mg}} \sim w_g$. It is true that this conclusion may not be an obligatory consequence of the steady-state model but it is the least unfavourable from the point of view of the Galactic theory of the origin of cosmic rays. Therefore in the steady-state cosmology the first variant we should discuss is the one with $w_{\text{Mg}} \sim w_g$. As has already been mentioned, the astrophysical data are rather against the steady-state model and at the same time there are no arguments which support this model in any definite way. Here we shall not therefore discuss in detail the question of cosmic rays in the steady-state cosmology or criticise[6, 404, 405] the papers by Hoyle and Gold.[283, 398] We would indicate only the basic objection raised by Razin.[404]

Putting $w_{\text{Mg}} \sim w_g \sim 10^{-12}$ erg/cm^3 it must be considered that $H^2/8\pi \ll w_{\text{Mg}}$, otherwise we come to a direct contradiction of the radio astronomy data (see above). To give an actual example Hoyle[283] for the metagalactic magnetic field takes the inequality $H_{\text{Mg}} < 10^{-7}$ oe (this agrees with estimate (13.18)). At the same time $\sqrt{8\pi w_g} \sim 5 \times 10^{-6}$ oe $\gg H_{\text{Mg}}$. Moreover, Razin[404] shows that the latter inequality with probable assumptions cannot be maintained long enough because of the increase in the magnetic field in a turbulent medium which is conductive. Although this discussion has been applied to the conditions accepted by Gold and Hoyle[398] it has an even more general importance. It is, in accordance with the considerations we have already indicated more than once, that calculations[404] show how hard it is to ensure that the inequality $w \gg H^2/8\pi$ is maintained. It can thus be said that in steady-state cosmology the use of the value $w_{\text{Mg}} \sim w_g$ meets with great difficulties if it is at all permissible.

In conclusion one further remark must be made touching soft cosmic rays. In the conditions of the Galaxy we are generally interested only in particles with an energy $E \gtrsim 1$ GeV. For these particles $w_g \sim 1$ eV/cm^3. Allowing for softer particles with respect to the cosmic rays on Earth does not introduce great changes (see section 1). In the conditions of metagalactic space the ionisation losses are three orders of magnitude less than in the Galaxy. In this case, if we think of the various energy estimates, the density

w_{Mg}, which must be taken to mean the total energy density of the cosmic rays, differs from $w_{Mg}(E \gtrsim 1 \text{ GeV})$ because for the above-mentioned and other reasons the contribution made by soft particles may prove to be considerably greater than in the Galaxy. For comparison with the Galaxy, particularly from the point of view of theories of the metagalactic origin of cosmic rays, the value $w_{Mg}(E \gtrsim 1 \text{ GeV})$ is important. Since this value is less than the total energy density w_{Mg} the inequality $w_{Mg}(E \gtrsim 1 \text{ GeV})$ $\ll w_g(E \gtrsim 1 \text{ GeV})$ can be satisfied even if $w_{Mg} \sim w_g(E \gtrsim 1 \text{ GeV})$. These arguments strengthen us still further in the conviction that the inequality of interest to us

$$w_{Mg}(E \gtrsim 1 \text{ GeV}) \ll w_g(E \gtrsim 1 \text{ GeV})' \sim 10^{-12} \text{ erg/sec} \qquad (13.38)$$

is really valid.

The electron component

In galaxies (both normal and radio galaxies) the energy density of the electron component $w_{e,g}$ is generally taken to be 1/100 in order of magnitude of the density of the energy of all the cosmic rays. The same ratio can therefore be expected in the cosmic rays ejected into metagalactic space from the galaxies. The electrons, it is true, may lose more energy than the protons and nuclei because of magnetic bremsstrahlung and Compton losses. These two types of losses, however, drop sharply after ejection of the particles from the Galaxy. In this connexion it is hardly without far-reaching special assumptions to consider that $w_{e,Mg,g} \ll 10^{-2}w_{Mg,g}$ (here $w_{e,Mg,g}$ is the energy density of the electrons ejected from the galaxies and $w_{Mg,g}$ is the energy density of all the ejected cosmic rays).

If $w_{e,Mg,g} \sim 10^{-2}w_{Mg,g}$ and $w_{Mg,g} \sim w_g \simeq 10^{-12} \text{ erg/cm}^3$, then the field in the Metagalaxy should be less than 3×10^{-9} oersteds (see (13.17)). But this is extremely improbable and by virtue of this very fact we obtain yet another weighty argument in favour of the inequality $w_{Mg,g} \ll w_G$.

Let us now estimate the lower limit of the density $w_{e,Mg}$ which can be obtained on the assumption of the secondary nature of the whole electron component in intergalactic space. We shall take it that the number of electrons (and positrons) generated in intergalactic space as the result of $\pi^{\pm} \to \mu^{\pm} \to e^{\pm}$ decay differs from the corresponding number for the Galaxy only by virtue of the difference in the gas densities (this means that the composition and spectrum of the cosmic rays is considered to be identical in the two cases). Then in accordance with (7.24)

$$q_e(E, t) \, dE = 2 \cdot 8 \times 10^{-29} E^{-2 \cdot 64} \frac{\rho(t)}{2 \times 10^{-26}} \frac{w_{Mg}(t)}{w_G} \, dE$$
$$\text{electrons/cm}^3 \cdot \text{sec}, \qquad (13.39)$$

($\rho(t)$ is the density of the gas at a time t and the energy E is measured in GeV) is the number of electrons generated.

The energy reduction for the electrons due to magnetic bremsstrahlung and Compton losses can be determined by expression (13.30). Taking also relationship (13.31) with $\delta = 2$ we have

$$E(T_{Mg}) =$$
$$\frac{E_0}{1 + \left[3 \cdot 8 \times 10^{-15} H_\perp^2(T_{Mg}) \left(\frac{T_{Mg}}{T_0} \right) + 7 \cdot 7 \times 10^{-26} w_{ph}(T_{Mg}) \ln \frac{T_{Mg}}{T_0} \right] T_{Mg} E_0}$$
$$(13.40)$$

Here E_0 is the energy expressed in eV at the time $t = T_0$ (the "singular point" of the cosmological model corresponds to the time $t = 0$), we have assumed that $T_{Mg} \gg T_0$, the time is measured in sec and w_{ph} is measured in eV/cm^3. As was indicated in section 8, $w_{ph}(T_{Mg}) \sim 10^{-3}$ eV/cm^3. Then if $H_\perp(T_{Mg}) < 3 \times 10^{-8}$ oe and $T_0 \gtrsim T_{Mg}/100 \sim 10^8$ years the Compton losses are the main ones in (13.40); if $T_0 \simeq (T_{Mg})/30 \simeq 3 \times 10^8$ years, for example, $E(T_{Mg}) \sim E_0/3$ for the energy $E_0 \sim 3 \times 10^{10}$ eV. At the same time because of the system's expansion the energy of the relativistic particles is reduced $(T_{Mg}/T_0)^{2/3}$ times, i.e., about 10 times in the present case. For $E_0 > 10^{11}$ eV it is the Compton losses and not the expansion that become decisive. We note that in a field $H_\perp \sim 5 \times 10^{-8}$ oe the radio emission in the metric band is determined by the electrons with $E \gtrsim 10^{10}$ eV. Therefore the remnant electron component of the cosmic rays is of no interest for radio astronomy.†

The form of the function $w_{Mg}(t)$ in expression (13.39) depends on the origin of the metagalactic cosmic rays. For the remnant cosmic rays we must put $w_{Mg}(t) = w_{Mg}(T_{Mg}/t)^{8/3}$. Proceeding in this way we

---

† Putting $T_0 = 10^8$ years, $H_\perp = 5 \times 10^{-8}$ oe and $w_{ph}(T_{Mg}) = 10^{-3}$ eV/cm^3 in (13.40) we have $E \lesssim 2 \times 10^9$ eV for any E_0. If we also allow for the energy loss due to expansion it becomes clear that remnant electrons cannot play any part as sources of metagalactic radio emission.

have by virtue of (13.39)

$$w_{e,\,Mg}(E > E_0, T_{Mg}) = \int_{T_0}^{T_{Mg}} dt \int_{E_0\left(\frac{T_{Mg}}{t}\right)^{2/3}}^{\infty} E q_e(E, t)\left(\frac{t}{T_{Mg}}\right)^2 dE$$

$$= 1{\cdot}75 \times 10^{-32} \times 1{\cdot}6 \times 10^{-3} \times \frac{w_{Mg}(T_{Mg})}{w_G E_0^{0{\cdot}64}}$$

$$\times T_{Mg}\left[\left(\frac{T_{Mg}}{T_0}\right)^{1{\cdot}24} - 1\right]$$

$$\simeq 10^{-5}\left[\left(\frac{T_{Mg}}{T_0}\right)^{1{\cdot}24} - 1\right] w_{Mg}(T_{Mg}) \text{ erg/cm}^3.$$

$$(13.41)$$

Here when using equation (13.39) we put $\rho(t) = 10^{-29}(T_{Mg}/t)^2$ g/cm^3, the multiplication of q_e by the factor $(t/T_{Mg})^2$ allows for the change in volume, and integration from the energy $E_0(T_{Mg}/t)^{2/3}$ allows for the change in energy during expansion (the factor $1{\cdot}6 \times 10^{-3}$ corresponds to the change to erg from GeV). In the change to the last expression (13.41) we put $T_{Mg} = 3 \times 10^{17}$ sec $\gg T_0$, $E_0 = 1$ GeV and $w_G = 10^{-12}$ erg/cm^2. If $T_0 = T_{Mg}/100 \sim 10^8$ years $w_{e,\,Mg} \simeq 3 \times 10^{-3}$ eV/cm^{-3}. Allowing for the magnetic bremsstrahlung and Compton losses in this case does not alter the estimate of $w_{e,\,Mg}$.

If the cosmic rays enter metagalactic space from some source (radio galaxy) or other we are more likely to have $w_{Mg}(t) = w_{Mg}(T_{Mg}) (T_{Mg}/t)$. In this case for the same values as above $w_{e,\,Mg}/w_{Mg} \simeq 10^{-5}$. Since a certain number of secondary electrons generated in regions with a greater density should also arrive from the sources this latter estimate is clearly the lower limit.

In order to compare these results with those from the Galaxy we shall use the same expression (13.39) with $\rho(t) = \rho_G = 2 \times 10^{-26}$ g/cm^3 and $w_{Mg}(t) = w_G$, i.e., we use the original formula (7.25). Then

$$w_{e,\,G} = \left(\int_{E_0}^{\infty} E q_e(E)\, dE\right) \times T \simeq 10^{-15} \text{ erg/cm}^3 \sim 10^{-3}\, w_G,$$

where T is the accumulation time for the electrons in the Galaxy and when numerical values are put in $T = 3 \times 10^8$ years, $E_0 = 1$ GeV and $w_G = 10^{-12}$ erg/cm^3 (for more detail on secondary electrons in the Galaxy see sections 7 and 17).

From these estimates, and also bearing in mind what has been said previously the following conclusion can be drawn: in the conditions of the Metagalaxy there is no reason to expect a significant relative attentuation of the electron component when compared with the case of the Galaxy. At first glance this attenuation, when it is a question of secondary electrons, could occur in connexion with a reduction in the density ($\rho_{Mg} \sim 10^{-3}\rho_G \sim 10^{-29}$ g/cm^3). But, on the other hand, in the Galaxy the electron "accumulation time" is $T_e \sim 3$ to 10×10^8 years, whilst in the Metagalaxy it is greater. In addition, the gas density ρ and the cosmic ray energy density w_{Mg} in the Metagalaxy were higher previously and for example

$$\rho(T_0 = \tfrac{1}{10}T_{Mg}) = \rho(T_{Mg})\left(\frac{T_{Mg}}{T_0}\right)^2 = 10^2\rho(T_{Mg}).$$

In 3×10^8 years with a density of $\rho_g \sim 10^{-26}$ g/cm^3 the cosmic rays pass through a thickness of gas of $\rho_g cT \sim 3$ g/cm^3 in the Galaxy. For the Metagalaxy the thickness of gas is

$$\int_{T_0}^{T_{Mg}} \rho(T_{Mg})\left(\frac{T_{Mg}}{t}\right)^2 cdt \sim 3\text{g/cm}^3 \text{ for } \rho_{Mg}(T_{Mg}) \sim 10^{-29} \text{ g/cm}^3$$

$T_{Mg} \sim 10^{10}$ years and $T_0 \sim 3 \times 10^8$ years.

Thus in the metagalactic cosmic rays we cannot expect a very low content of electrons as compared with Galaxy cosmic rays. This fact is very significant in estimates of the energy density w_{Mg} from radio astronomy data. For example we have seen above that if $w_{e, Mg}/w_{e, G} = 1$ for the field in the Metagalaxy we obtain the very rigid inequality $H < 3 \times 10^{-9}$ oersteds (see (13.17)). Moreover, probably $H \gtrsim 5 \times 10^{-8}$ oe so $w_{e, Mg}/w_{e, G} < 10^{-2}$ (we put $K_e H^{1\cdot8} < 3 \times 10^{-32}$; hence $K_e < 5 \times 10^{-19}$, whilst in the Galaxy $K_e \sim 10^{-16}$). Combined with the estimate $w_{e, Mg}/w_{Mg} \sim w_{e, G}/w_G$ this leads to the inequality $w_{Mg}/w_G \sim 10^{-2}$ or, to be more precise, $w_{Mg} \ll w_G$.

We note that in the light of what has been said the previously mentioned difficulties arising in steady-state cosmology increase still more. The point is that in Razin's criticism[404] of Gold and Hoyle's paper[398] the electron concentration was considered to be 10^3 times less than in the Galaxy (it was assumed that $w_{Mg} \sim w_G$ and $w_{e, Mg} = (\rho_{Mg}/\rho_G)w_{e, G} \sim 10^{-3}w_{e, G}$). Moreover, in the Galaxy the life (accumulation time) of electrons is $\sim 3 \times 10^8$ years, whilst in the steady-state model this time is of the order of 10^{10} years or at least $T_{Mg}/3$ $\sim 3 \times 10^9$ years. Therefore in the steady-state cosmology if $w_{Mg} \simeq w_G$ we shall have† $w_{e, Mg} > 10^{-3} w_{e, G}$ and the metagalactic magnetic field should be even far less than 10^{-7} oersteds, whilst $\sqrt{8\pi w_G} \sim 5 \times 10^{-6}$ oersteds.

We would stress once again that radio emission from metagalactic space has not yet been found (this relates in particular to radio emission of the Local Supergalaxy;[261, 262, 403] see also section 5) and it is possible that it is considerably weaker than the accepted upper limit (for example at $v = 400$ Mc/s the metagalactic radio emission temperature $T < 10\,^\circ$K was used above). If we were successful in measuring the effective temperature of the radio emission of metagalactic space it would provide very valuable information.

The nature of radio galaxies

In the discussion of the problem of the origin of cosmic rays in the present book we are chiefly thinking of cosmic rays in the Galaxy. This limitation (or, rather, delimitation) is justified. In the first place the fact that in the case of the Galaxy we can adduce and use information on the primary cosmic rays on Earth is of importance. If it is a question of the other galaxies only radio astronomy data are available on the cosmic rays (an exception is Virgo A with its optical magnetic bremsstrahlung emission from the "jet") together with some indirect information.

But, of course, in the broad view the question of the origin of cosmic rays relates to all galaxies and can be considered particularly acute for the radio galaxies. In fact, for "normal" galaxies we may rely on the fact that cosmic rays are generated and behave in the same way approximately as in the Galaxy. The radio galaxies, however, indubitably need a special investigation. We have already given some data on the radio galaxies and there is a detailed discussion of their properties by Shklovskii.[198] We should like to pause for a short time only now on this question of the nature of radio galaxies, i.e., the mechanism and causes of their "explosion". We

---

† It is considered here, just as by Razin,[404] that the galactic and metagalactic electrons are secondary. In actual fact the major rôle is played by primary electrons (see section 17), which only strengthens the arguments. Moreover, the actual ("hot") steady-state cosmological model discussed by Gold and Hoyle[398] should be rejected[490] because of the data on the cosmic X-radiation.

should point out right from the start that the nature of radio galaxies cannot yet be considered to be explained and in the meantime it is a question of a number of hypotheses.

Certain powerful radio galaxies are twin sources (see, e.g., Fig. 14 which shows diagrammatically the configuration of Cygnus A). This fact has served as a basis for the hypothesis that the most powerful radio galaxies were formed as the result of collisions of galaxies (for more detail on this hypothesis see a paper by Shklovskii[161]). However, these collisions cannot occur often enough and optical observations do not support the assumption of the collision of galaxies even in the case of Cygnus A. As for the twinning of radio sources this need not point also to the presence of two adjacent galaxies.

On the basis of these and certain other arguments the assumption of the connexion between radio galaxies and collisions of galaxies has now been dropped[198, 273, 406-409] and the appearance (explosion) of a radio galaxy is considered to be an explosion-type process similar to that occurring in supernovae. The general picture of an explosion is apparently as follows. For some reason or other cosmic rays start to be generated rapidly in a galaxy. After a certain time these rays can no longer be constrained by the galactic magnetic fields and explode outwards taking with them the galactic gas with the magnetic fields frozen into it (however, if the ejected gas consists largely of fast particles, in particular the actual cosmic rays, then it should also take magnetic fields along with it). It is quite natural to assume that in many cases the cosmic rays will be ejected in both directions along the axis of rotation of the galaxy or, to be more precise, at right angles to the plane of its disk. This is how a twin source is formed.

The main question is what is the cause of the "explosion". There is probably in most cases no reason for considering that it is a question of the formation of new galaxies from the intergalactic medium. The "explosion" is more likely to be connected with the appearance of some instability or other in an already existing galaxy, its transition through a critical state, ... For example, the star formation process depends strongly on the density of the gas and probably on its initial temperature, magnetic field strength, ... Let us assume therefore that at some period or other energetic star formation started in the galaxy. Then, according to Shklovskii[273] and Hoyle[367] there should be a sharp rise in the number of supernova explosions which leads to a rapid accumulation of cosmic rays. Burbidge[410,438] supplemented this point of view by the assumption of the possibility of a chain reaction of supernova explosions in the dense core of the galaxy. This latter hypothesis, however, has not been supported by calculations and seems to us to be rather unlikely. Another possibility, indicated by Ginzburg[411] consists of acceleration of the cosmic rays in the actual star formation process. Estimates show that the gravitational energy evolved during the compression of a cloud into stars is sufficient to accelerate cosmic rays even in Cygnus A. The rate of statistical and systematic acceleration during the formation of stars may also be high enough. However the answer is still missing here as to why the rapid star formation started.

There are also other hypotheses in existence on the nature of the radio galaxies. For example, Ambartsumyan[406] suggested that galaxies may divide, this process being accompanied by the generation of cosmic rays. The hypothesis of the division and flying apart of galaxies is obviously connected with a departure from existing physical ideas. For this reason, just as in the case of the steady-state cosmology, the ideas of galaxy division should be adduced only in an extreme case or under pressure of appropriate convincing observations (as far as we know there are none such). We should also mention the magnetic hypothesis which links the "explosions" of radio galaxies with a mechanism like that of solar flares (but with an increase in the energy of the explosion by a factor of 10^{16}!).[412] This means that over a long period magnetic energy is accumulated in the galaxy and then "evolves" very rapidly. This appears possible if there is a thin "partition" between regions with opposite magnetic fields. Right from the start this point of view is very artificial. In addition, it comes up against serious concrete objections.[198] We should lastly mention the assumption which links the formation of radio galaxies with interstellar gas hitting the core of the galaxy.[198]

The very fact that there are many hypotheses indicates that the nature of radio galaxy explosions is still unexplained. This should not cause surprise if we bear in mind the newness of the actual problem and the absence of enough observational material relating to details of the spectrum and spatial structure of radio galaxies. It is hard to doubt but that there will be a great advance in this field in the near future. Taking this fact and the great uncertainty in the question of the nature of radio galaxies obtaining at present into consideration we have considered it best not to deal in detail with the various hypotheses and information dealing with radio galaxies in the present book.†

General discussion and conclusions

As a result of all these arguments and estimates, which have also been given elsewhere,[434] it is possible to reach the following conclusion: the energy density of the cosmic rays in intergalactic space w_{Mg} is considerably less than the energy density of the cosmic rays in the Galaxy $w_G \simeq 10^{-12}$ erg/sec.

This conclusion is based both upon energy considerations and on radio astronomy data combined with the assumption that there are magnetic fields that are not too weak. It may be taken that the

† No changes have been made in this section of the book when compared with the Russian edition. We still think that we have correctly expounded the state of the question as it was at the beginning of 1963. But now (less than a year later) the position has already changed. The idea of the collapse of large gaseous masses has now become popular since the discovery of "super-stars" (see the end of section 5 and the sub-section on explosions of galactic cores in section 11). In other words, it is a question of gravitational compression of large masses of gas ($M \sim 10^5$ to $10^8 M_\odot \sim 10^{38}$ to 10^{41} g) in the central part (cores) of radio galaxies. In the gravitational collapse of such a mass, allowing for deviations from spherical symmetry, an energy of as much as $0.1 Mc^2 \sim 10^{58}$ to 10^{61} erg can clearly be generated. The maximum energy figuring in the problem is obviously Mc^2, i.e., as much as 10^{62} erg. At some stage of the compression lasting for 10^3 to 10^4 years the generation in question behaves always or sometimes—this is still not known—like a "super-star". At a later stage the optical effect is absent or insignificant and the energy released leaves the core in the form of clouds "filled" with cosmic rays and gas with magnetic fields frozen in. The duration of this radio-galactic phase is 10^6 to 10^8 years. In the case of weak radio galaxies, and possibly also in all or some "normal" galaxies, according to these ideas there may also be explosions in the core but on a smaller scale. For example for the Galaxy, as mentioned in section 11, an energy greater than 10^{56} erg can scarcely be generated in the suggested explosion. Such comparatively small explosions in many respects recall powerful type 2 supernovae and can evidently be called super-supernovae with some justification.

Thus in the first place the source of energy in an explosion of a radio galaxy and galactic cores is in all probability not nuclear but gravitational energy.[411, 438, 474, 476] In the second place, in astrophysics we must examine not only ordinary stars ($M \lesssim 10^2 M_\odot$) but considerably larger starlike masses ($M \sim 10^3$ to $10^8 M_\odot$). In the third place, equilibrium is impossible for such masses and gravitational collapse occurs which should be investigated in the light of the general theory of relativity. At present the theory of such a collapse under actual conditions (allowing for lack of sphericity, rotation, nuclear reactions, ...) has not been developed yet. The problems arising here are as interesting as they are difficult to analyse rigorously. Only the first steps have been taken in this field.[471–475, 484, 492] Nevertheless it is hard to doubt but that the discovery of "super-stars" and the discussion of the problems arising in this connexion signal the entry of astrophysics into a fresh period of development.

metagalactic field is not weaker than 5×10^{-8} to 10^{-7} oersteds since the kinetic energy density of the gas is $\rho u^2/2 \sim 10^{-15}$ to 10^{-14} erg/cm^3. But with a field $H \sim 5 \times 10^{-8}$ oe it must be taken that $w_{Mg} \lesssim 10^{-2} w_G$, otherwise the metagalactic radio emission would be stronger than follows from observations of the upper limit. The following is an independent argument: if $w_{Mg} \sim w_G$ we should expect the appearance of a field $H \sim \sqrt{8\pi w_G} \sim 5 \times 10^{-6}$ oe, which obviously contradicts the radio astronomy data.

It is most probable that in metagalactic space

$$\frac{\rho u^2}{2} \sim \frac{H^2}{8\pi} \sim w_{Mg} \sim (10^{-4} \text{ to } 10^{-3}) \times w_G \sim 10^{-15} \text{ to } 10^{-16} \text{ erg/cm}^3,$$

$$H \sim \sqrt{8\pi w_{Mg}} \sim 3 \times 10^{-8} \text{ to } 10^{-7} \text{ oersteds.} \qquad (13.42)$$

This estimate agrees now with everything that is known or may be assumed with respect to metagalactic space. Of course, changes of an order of magnitude in one direction or the other cannot yet be barred. With this remark in mind the values of (13.42) agree with all the estimates made above and, what is most important, allow us to depend on the inequality $w_{Mg} \ll w_G$ (see (13.13)). But at the same time (and this cannot be stressed too often) in the present state of cosmology, extragalactic astronomy and magnetohydrodynamics there is still no complete and unconditional certainty in the validity of condition (13.13). For example if the metagalactic magnetic field can be incomparably weaker than the field $\sqrt{8\pi w_{Mg}}$ and if it can be considerably weaker than the field $\sqrt{4\pi \rho u^2}$ (or if $\rho_{Mg} \ll 10^{-29}$ g/cm^3), then the radio astronomy data can no longer lead to inequality (13.13). Then with far-reaching additional assumptions on the power of the radio galaxies and the retention of cosmic rays inside the Local Supergalaxy the condition $w_{Mg} \sim w_G$ could be satisfied near our Galaxy. For the reason that this requires too many unfounded assumptions we consider it possible to accept inequality (13.13). The reservations are made to stress the necessity of taking care and continuing investigations.

The study of γ-rays and radio waves of metagalactic origin is particularly promising here.

The γ-ray flux corresponding to a density $\rho \simeq 10^{-29}$ g/cm^3 and an energy $w_{Mg} \simeq w_G$ has already been indicated (see (13.14)). In conditions (13.42) the effective temperature of the metagalactic radio emission, for example at a wavelength of 75 cm, should lie between 0·1 and 5 °K (formula (13.15) is used, i.e., the total emission of the galaxies is not taken into account; the smaller value corresponds to a field $H = 5 \times 10^{-8}$ oe and an electron energy density $w_{e,\,Mg} = 10^{-4} w_{e,\,g}$ or, to be |more precise, the coefficient $K_{e,\,Mg} = 10^{-20}$; in the second case $H = 10^{-7}$ oe and $K_{e,\,Mg} = 10^{-19}$). It is probably impossible to pick out the metagalactic component with a temperature of $\lesssim 1\,°K$ from the background galactic radio emission with $T_{eff} \sim 25\,°K$ (in the 75 cm wavelength) but it is not hopeless at the temperature of $\sim 5\,°K$. The main thing is that any further precision in the upper limit of the metagalactic radio emission intensity would be very useful.

If $w_{Mg} \ll w_G$ the majority of cosmic rays in the Galaxy cannot be of metagalactic origin (the assumption that the cosmic ray flux in the Metagalaxy is highly anisotropic seems to us completely improbable; in the case of isotropy the energy density of the metagalactic cosmic rays in the Galaxy should be equal to the density of their energy outside the Galaxy). Because of this it can only be a question of the Galactic theory of the origin of cosmic rays in the Galaxy.

This is the basic conclusion, but a few more additional remarks must be made.

In the Metagalactic theory of the origin of cosmic rays it must be considered that not only in our Galaxy but also in all other normal galaxies the cosmic rays chiefly come from metagalactic space. But in this case the radio spectra of all the normal galaxies should be expected to be identical. The data in Table 8 indicate that the opposite is more likely.† Furthermore, in the metagalactic theory of the origin of cosmic rays in the Galaxy the cosmic rays in the radio galaxies can in no way be considered Metagalactic. But the radio galaxies have the most widely differing powers and their spectral indices α (intensity $I_\alpha \sim \nu^{-\alpha}$) are generally close to the spectral indices for normal galaxies. Thus in certain cases (radio galaxies) cosmic rays have a definite internal origin. The estimates show that the same is quite possible for the Galaxy (see section 11) and, obviously,

---

† It need not, moreover, be thought that the common origin must lead to identical spectra of the electrons and the magnetic bremsstrahlung radio emission in different galaxies. From the calculations given in section 17 it is clear that the radio emission spectrum depends on many factors (the magnetic field strength, the diffusion coefficient, ...) which may vary noticeably from galaxy to galaxy. Therefore we are by no means inclined to overestimate the value of the argument given which often figures in published works (this argument is given for this very reason).

other normal galaxies. Under these conditions the Metagalactic theory of the origin of cosmic rays seems extremely artificial even if all the other factors are ignored.

The fact that the closeness of the spectral indices of the various galaxies even if it occurs cannot serve as an argument in favour of the common origin of cosmic rays in these galaxies clearly follows from the fact of the closeness of the indices for completely different objects: normal galaxies, radio galaxies and lastly galactic sources—supernova shells (for example in the basic part of the spectrum for Cygnus A $\alpha \simeq 0.75$, for Virgo A $\alpha \simeq 0.8$, for the Galaxy $\alpha \simeq 0.8$ and for Cassiopeia A $\alpha \simeq 0.8$). This closeness of the indices undoubtedly reflects not a common origin or common conditions but most probably approximate observance of the equality of energies $\rho u^2/2 \sim H^2/8\pi \sim w$ (see section 16).

Our next remark relates to remnant cosmic rays.

In the world of the stars the most powerful effect is the explosion forming the shells of supernovae (a release of energy up to 10^{51} erg and a power up to 10^{44} erg/sec on the assumption that the process lasts 10^7 sec). The explosion of galaxies leading to their conversion into radio galaxies is the most powerful phenomenon in the world of the galaxies (energy released up to 10^{61} erg, power up to 10^{47} erg/sec on the assumption that the process lasts 10^{14} sec $= 3 \times 10^6$ years). In both these cases a very large number of cosmic rays is generated—their energy and power are clearly of the same order as the total energy and power of the explosion.

Hence, even though the analogy is simple, the thought arises of the possibility of the efficient generation of cosmic rays in the "explosion" of the whole Metagalaxy as well, i.e., at a comparatively early stage of its expansion. It is these cosmic rays which we discussed previously, calling them remnants. It is important to stress that we by no means consider the existence of remnant rays improbable but have only adduced arguments in favour of the fact that the density of their energy $w_r(T_{Mg})$ is now less than $\sim 10^{-14}$ erg/cm^3 $\sim 10^{-2}w_G$ (see (13.33)). Even if $w_r(T_{Mg}) \sim 10^{-15}$ erg/cm^3 the energy of these cosmic rays in a volume with the radius $R \sim 5 \times 10^{27}$ cm is $W \sim 10^{69}$ erg. Moreover, the kinetic energy of random motion (i.e., without allowing for the velocity of the general expansion of the Metagalaxy) of the $\sim 10^9$ galaxies in this volume with a mass $\sim 5 \times 10^{43}$ g and a velocity $\sim 3 \times 10^7$ cm/sec is $W_k \sim 2 \times 10^{67}$ erg. Thus the density $w_r \sim 10^{-15}$ erg/cm^3 although it is three orders of magnitude less than the Galactic density w_G by no means is small on the metagalactic scale. In this connexion satisfaction of the inequality $w_{Mg} \ll w_G$ (see (13.13)) should not be looked upon as any indication of inefficiency of the cosmic ray acceleration at early stages of the Metagalaxy's evolution.

Rejection of the Metagalactic theory of the origin of cosmic rays need not be connected, as has already been stressed more than once, with the question of the nature of particles of the very high energy $\mathscr{E} \gtrsim 10^{17}$ eV/nucleon ($E = A\mathscr{E} \gtrsim 10^{18}$ to 10^{19} eV for the very heavy nuclei) which are really very hard to accelerate in the Galaxy. We note that particles with ultra-high energy make only a negligible contribution to the total cosmic ray energy density. Therefore considerations connected with allowing for the energy balance give no reason to deny the possibility of particle acceleration to super-high energies even in sources that generate comparatively little energy. This acceleration is, however, essentially limited, for example because of the necessity for retaining the particles in the accelerating region. In this connexion even when the metagalactic component and the most powerful sources are allowed for it is quite possible in practice that there is a break in the cosmic ray spectrum at $E \sim 10^{20}$ to 10^{23} eV. In fact, even in a field $H \sim 10^{-3}$ oe, which may yet be met with in radio galaxies, for protons with an energy of 10^{22} eV the radius of curvature is $r_H \sim 3 \times 10^{22}$ cm and such particles will not be retained for any lengthy period in the Galaxy. Therefore, unless we discuss the possibility of particle acceleration in conditions still unknown to us (in super-stars, ...) particles cannot be accelerated even in a radio galaxy to energies greater than that indicated.

The question of the nature of the cosmic ray spectrum at super-high energies, allowing for the metagalactic component is discussed in section 16.

Finally, the last remark relates to the discussion of the problem of metagalactic cosmic rays in preceding articles by the authors[4-6] and in the present monograph. The present stage in the development of cosmic ray astrophysics started in 1950–53 when a connexion was established between cosmic rays and cosmic radio emission. It then immediately became possible to propose the Galactic theory of the origin of cosmic rays with an indication of the probable sources (supernovae and novae), the energy requirements, ... being satisfied.[4,161] This success shielded to a certain extent the question of metagalactic cosmic rays, which is quite understandable because of the absence at that time of the large amount of information now possessed about the radio galaxies.

The possibility of explaining all the data about cosmic rays in the Galaxy on the basis of the Galactic theory when there were no arguments in favour of the Metagalactic theory caused the latter to be in disfavour and even lightly dismissed in a detailed article[5] published in 1957. But it gradually became clear that Metagalactic cosmic rays deserve greater attention. On the one hand the problem of radio galaxies has acquired tremendous importance, being connected with ideas on cosmic rays inside and outside the various galaxies. On the other hand the convincing rejection of the Metagalactic theory of the origin of cosmic rays in the Galaxy accepted in several works[387, 398] is by no means an easy matter. An analysis of this problem therefore becomes particularly interesting both for the theory of the origin of cosmic rays and on a broader scale for extragalactic astronomy and cosmology. All this has induced the authors to pay more attention to metagalactic cosmic rays in their earlier work[6, 434] and in the present book. Here we have tried not to halt at prepared positions and it is to be hoped that the conclusion drawn above against the Metagalactic theory is sufficiently objective. Despite the conclusion of the galactic origin of most of the cosmic rays in the Galaxy the problem of metagalactic cosmic rays not only cannot be considered to be eliminated but, on the contrary, acquires yet greater interest. The energy density of the metagalactic cosmic rays may be relatively low and they may play only a small part in the Galaxy but what is their influence on the formation and evolution of galaxies? How are cosmic rays connected with motions in the intergalactic medium and with the metagalactic magnetic fields? All these and some other questions should and undoubtedly will attract closer and closer attention.

CHAPTER V

QUANTITATIVE GALACTIC THEORY
OF THE ORIGIN OF COSMIC RAYS

As was shown in Chapter IV the whole complex of data available at present speaks in favour of the Galactic model of the origin of cosmic rays (we are thinking of cosmic rays in the Galaxy). There is therefore every reason to develop a quantitative Galactic theory of the origin of cosmic rays. For this purpose we must discuss the questions of the chemical composition, the energy spectrum and the spatial distribution of the cosmic rays in the Galaxy. This is done below (in sections 15 and 16) for the proton and nuclear components on the basis of the general equations for the transfer of cosmic rays in the interstellar medium (these equations are formulated and discussed in section 14). In addition, section 17 discusses the question of the energy spectrum and the spatial distribution of the secondary electron component as well as the frequency spectrum of the general galactic radio emission which is generated by the electrons as they move in the interstellar magnetic fields. Sections 18 and 19 are devoted mainly to γ-ray astronomy.

14. EQUATIONS DESCRIBING THE BEHAVIOUR OF COSMIC RAYS IN THE INTERSTELLAR MEDIUM

When cosmic rays move in interstellar space their intensity, chemical composition and, generally speaking, energy spectrum vary when compared with the corresponding characteristics in the sources. These variations are caused by the interaction, discussed in Chapter III, with the interstellar gas, the emission field and the interstellar magnetic fields. In order to establish a connexion between the observed properties of the cosmic rays and their properties in the sources we need a quantitative analysis which allows for the influence of the processes indicated in Chapter III. This problem taking one factor or another into account has been discussed in many works.[5, 6, 173, 305, 359, 413–416] In the present section we shall deal with the mathematical formulation and discuss the corresponding equations which will be used later.

General transfer equations for cosmic rays

As above we shall use $N_i(E, r, t)$ to denote the concentration of particles of a kind i at a point r at a time t with respect to a unit energy range E. The concentration N_i is connected with the intensity I_i of the corresponding particles by the relationship

$$N_i(E, r, t) = \frac{1}{v} \int I_i(E, r, t, k)\, d\Omega_k = \frac{4\pi \bar{I}_i}{v}. \tag{14.1}$$

Here v is the velocity of the particles, $I_i(E, r, t, k)$ their intensity in a direction k and $d\Omega_k$ is an element of the solid angle in k-space.

As has already been indicated in section 3 the degree of anisotropy of the cosmic rays is very small so with the exception perhaps of the highest energies it can be assumed with great accuracy that the intensity I_i does not depend on k and is equal to $\bar{I}_i$. The cosmic rays can thus be characterised with equal success both by the concentration N_i and the intensity I_i. In the present chapter we shall largely use the concentration N_i. Only when analysing the question of the cosmic ray anisotropy (section 16), when it is not enough to fix only the concentration, shall we change to the intensity I_i.

The general equation for the concentration $N_i(E, r, t)$, which allows for the spatial diffusion, the energy losses, the acceleration and the transformation of the chemical composition in the interstellar medium, can be written in the form

$$\frac{\partial N_i}{\partial t} - \operatorname{div}(D_i \nabla N_i) + \frac{\partial}{\partial E}(b_i N_i) - \frac{1}{2}\frac{\partial^2}{\partial E^2}(d_i N_i)$$

$$= Q_i(E, r, t) - p_i N_i + \sum_k \int P_i^k(E', E) N_k(E', r, t)\, dE. \tag{14.2}$$

We shall call equation (14.2) the general transfer equation for particles of a kind i; it is the continuity equation in phase space allowing for collisions.

Let us examine in greater detail the meaning of the individual terms in equation (14.2).

The second term on the left-hand side of equation (14.2) describes the spatial diffusion of particles with a diffusion coefficient $D_i = D_i(E, \boldsymbol{r}, t)$ which in the general case depends both on the kind of particle and on all the other variables.† The question of the possibility of using the diffusion approximation for the motion of cosmic rays in the Galaxy has already been discussed in detail in section 10. Here we shall remark only that equation (14.2) with $D_i = 0$ is also valid for describing the regular motion of particles along the lines of force of the magnetic field (see below).

For the majority of cosmic rays with energies $E \lesssim 10^{15}$ eV the dependence of the coefficient of diffusion on the energy is apparently unimportant. We shall therefore ignore this dependence below with the exception of section 16 which discusses the energy spectrum in the high-energy region. In addition, in the actual problems discussed below we shall not take into consideration the possible difference in the values of the diffusion coefficient in different parts of the Galaxy, i.e., the dependence of the diffusion coefficient on the coordinates (at present there are no data which will allow us to take this dependence into consideration with any degree of certainty).

The time-dependence of the diffusion coefficient, and the other coefficients in (14.2), may be caused by a change in the structure and scales of the magnetic field inhomogeneities and also by a change in the concentration and composition of the interstellar gas in the process of the Galaxy's evolution. However, because the life of the cosmic rays in the Galaxy is far less than its age (see section 11 and below) this dependence can be ignored in what follows (we are not dealing now with the non-stationary model of the halo mentioned in section 11).

Lastly, the coefficient of diffusion of particles in interstellar space, generally speaking, depends on the kind of particle i. This is due to the fact that the motion of a particle in the interstellar magnetic fields depends significantly on the particle's radius of curvature (10.2) which depends in its turn for a given energy on the particle's charge eZ. In the case of heavy nuclei it is convenient to use not the energy E but the energy $\mathscr{E}$ per nucleon of a nucleus as the independent variable in equations (14.2). In this case for all nuclei

---

† In (14.2) it is assumed that there is no systematic motion of the medium, e.g., expansion or compression. If there is such a motion the term div $N_i\boldsymbol{u}$, where $\boldsymbol{u}$ is the velocity of the systematic (large-scale) motion, must be added to the left-hand side of equation (14.2).

with $Z \geqslant 2$ the radius of curvature (10.2) and therefore the diffusion coefficient at a fixed energy per nucleon will be identical since for nuclei with $Z > 1$ the ratio A/Z is always close to 2.

For single-charge particles (protons and electrons) the diffusion coefficient at the same energy can in principle be different from that for nuclei with $Z > 1$. However, this difference may only occur in the range of energies where the diffusion coefficient depends in general on the energy (i.e., on the particle's radius of curvature in the interstellar magnetic field). As has already been pointed out, there is no reason to allow for the dependence of the coefficient D on E (and thus on the kind of particle i) in the $E \lesssim 10^{15}$ eV energy range.

Let us now take a look at the third and fourth terms on the left-hand side of equation (14.2). These terms allow for the continuous change of the particles' energy resulting from the action of the acceleration mechanisms and the processes leading to energy losses in collisions. It is assumed here that the energy changes in small amounts (continuously), i.e., in each event the energy increment is small when compared with the particle's initial energy. These conditions are satisfied with sufficient accuracy by the statistical acceleration mechanisms which are discussed in section 9 and also by the ionisation and magnetic bremsstrahlung losses (sections 7 and 8).

The third term on the left-hand side of equation (14.2) describes the systematic energy variation due to these causes. In this case the coefficient $b_i = b_i(E)$ is equal to the mean energy increment of the particle in unit time

$$\frac{dE}{dt} = b_i(E) \tag{14.3}$$

and was determined for the various processes in sections 7, 8 and 9.

The fourth and last term on the left-hand side of equation (14.2) allows for fluctuations in the continuous variation in energy in question. The question of fluctuations in collision and ionisation losses is discussed in detail in published works[71] and we shall not stop to deal with it here. We would only remark that the fluctuations during ionisation and magnetic bremsstrahlung losses are small and need not be allowed for.

We have already mentioned the part played by fluctuations in the statistical acceleration of particles in section 9. The effect of the corresponding term on the cosmic ray energy spectrum will be discussed in section 16. The coefficient $d_i = d_i(E)$ in equation (14.2) in the general case is equal to the mean square of the energy increment per unit time:

$$d_i(E) = \frac{d}{dt} \overline{(\Delta E)^2}. \tag{14.4}$$

On the right-hand side of equation (14.2) the term $Q_i(E, \mathbf{r}\ t)$ is equal to the intensity of the cosmic ray sources. $Q_i(E, \mathbf{r}, t)\ dE\ d^3\mathbf{r}\ dt$ is the number of particles of kind i supplied by the sources in the time dt in an element of volume $d^3\mathbf{r} = dx\ dy\ dz$ in the energy range $(E, E + dE)$.

The second and third terms on the right-hand side of the equation (14.2) allow for "catastrophic" energy losses and also the appearance of new particles when the particles in question interact with the interstellar medium. "Catastrophic" is the name we give to losses in which the particle as such disappears or the energy it loses is so great that the particle is knocked out of the energy range in question. Spallation of heavy nuclei during collisions with interstellar protons and electron radiation losses with the emission of high-energy bremsstrahlung quanta is an example of such processes. In this case p_i is the probability per unit time of such a process for particles of kind i and $p_i N_i$ is the number of particles knocked out per unit time. If T_i is the mean life with respect to the corresponding "catastrophic" collision and σ_i is the effective cross section of the process in question, obviously

$$p_i = \frac{1}{T_i} = nv\sigma_i, \tag{14.5}$$

where n is the medium's particle concentration.

The last term on the right-hand side of equation (14.2) describes the influx of particles as the result of catastrophic collisions. $P_i^k(E',E)$ is the probability per unit time and unit energy range E of the appearance of a particle of kind i with an energy E in a catastrophic collision of a particle of kind k having an energy E'.

In the case of radiation or Compton losses of electrons the value $P_e^e(E', E)$ will be the probability of the process in which an electron with an energy E' gives off an energy $E' - E$ to a photon in one second. The corresponding processes have been studied fully enough and there are analytical expressions for the probabilities $P_e^e(E', E)$[70–73]. We do not need them here, however, since it is enough to use the "mean" losses or characteristic life-times with respect to the processes in question to estimate the effect of these losses on the spectrum and intensity of the electrons, as was done in section 8. Here, of course, it must be borne in mind that, unlike the case of continuous losses, the fluctuations during catastrophic losses are by no means small and should, generally speaking, be allowed for in a stricter solution of the problem.

In the case of nuclei the last term on the right-hand side of equation (14.2) describes the fragmentation process—the formation of nuclear fragments of kind i upon spallation of a nucleus of kind k in the interstellar medium. In this case $P_i^k(E', E)$ is the probability of fragmentation per unit time and unit energy range, allowing for the difference in the energies of the original nucleus and those formed.

Actual forms of equation (14.2) and possible simplifications when solving various particular problems will be discussed below. Here we would remark that the coefficients b_i, d_i, p_i and P_i^k in the general case, just like the diffusion coefficient D_i, are functions of the co-ordinates and time if the concentration of the interstellar gas, its chemical composition and the nature of the macroscopic motions are inhomogenous in the volume of the Galaxy and change during its evolution. However, bearing in mind the remarks made above when discussing the analogous dependence for the diffusion co-efficient we shall generally ignore the dependence of the other coefficients on r and t as well.

Equation (14.2) is applicable, of course, for the description of the behaviour of cosmic rays not only in the Galaxy but also in supernova shells, radio galaxies, intergalactic space, and so on.

Transfer (fragmentation) equations for nuclei

When analysing the question of the chemical composition and fragmentation of heavy nuclei we can use the fact that the energy of the fragments being formed is small (in the rest system of the original nucleus). Therefore in the "laboratory" system of coordinates connected with the Galaxy the fragments move in fact at the same velocity as the original relativistic nucleus. In other words, the energy per nucleon $\mathscr{E}$ is identical for the original nucleus and the fragment nuclei formed. This is clearly true for heavy fragments and may not be true only for individual protons and neutrons appearing in the fragmentation† if upon their formation a noticeable share of the energy is transferred to π-mesons and the nucleus collided with. Due to this a certain "blurring" of the proton energy spectrum may appear but for the question of the chemical composition under discussion this fact has hardly any significance.

Bearing in mind the conservation during the fragmentation process of the energy per nucleon it is convenient to take just this variable $\mathscr{E} = E/A$ as independent in equation (14.2) instead of the total nucleus energy E. Then, by virtue of what has been said above

$$P_k^i(\mathscr{E}', \mathscr{E}) = p_k^i \delta(\mathscr{E}' - \mathscr{E}), \tag{14.6}$$

where

$$p_k^i = p_i p_{ik} = \frac{1}{T_i} p_{ik} \tag{14.7}$$

and p_{ik} are the fragmentation probabilities discussed in section 7 when a nucleus of the kind i is absorbed and T_i is the life with respect to the absorption. Equation (14.2) then takes the form

$$\frac{\partial N_i}{\partial t} - \text{div}(D_i \nabla N_i) + \frac{\partial}{\partial \mathscr{E}}(b_i N_i) - \frac{1}{2}\frac{\partial^2}{\partial \mathscr{E}^2}(d_i N_i)$$
$$= Q_i(\mathscr{E}, r, t) - p_i N_i + \sum_{k < i} p_i^k N_k. \tag{14.8}$$

It is borne in mind here that nuclei of a given kind i can be formed only‡ from heavier nuclei of kind k. In addition, the nuclei (or groups of nuclei) are numbered in decreasing order of the atomic numbers ($k < i$). Thus the index $i = 1$ corresponds to the heaviest of the nuclei under discussion (i.e., the group of nuclei with the highest atomic numbers).

With certain assumptions about the coefficients D_i, b_i, d_i, p_i and p_i^k we can write the general solution of the system of equations (14.8). We assume that:

(1) the coefficients D_i, b_i and d_i do not depend on the kind of nucleus under discussion, whilst p_i and p_i^k do not depend on the coordinates and time;

† Because of the rapid decay neutrons should be included in the proton component of cosmic rays.

‡ We should mention that in (14.8) the probabilities p_i^k are defined as the probabilities of the appearance of the various fragments when a nucleus k is absorbed so $p_k^k = 0$.

(2) on the left-hand side of (14.8) there are no terms containing energy derivatives, or

(2′) the coefficients p_i and p_i^k do not depend on the energy; in addition we shall consider that

(3) the energy spectra and distribution of the cosmic ray sources in space and in time are identical for nuclei of all kinds, i.e.,

$$Q_i(\mathscr{E}, \boldsymbol{r}, t) = q_i \chi(\mathscr{E}, \boldsymbol{r}, t). \qquad (14.9)$$

Before formulating the general solution we shall discuss the above assumptions as applied to the nuclear component of the cosmic rays in the Galaxy.

As for the dependence of the coefficients on the coordinates and time, there is, as has already been mentioned, no reason at present to allow for the dependence. Further, the dependence of D_i, b_i and d_i on the kind of particle i may be connected with the fact that the nature of the particles' motion in the interstellar magnetic field is determined by the radius of curvature of a particle, i.e., for a given energy per nucleon $\mathscr{E}$ depends on the ratio A/Z. In addition, the energy losses of the particle depend on its charge Z.

For all nuclei with $Z > 1$ the ratio $A/Z \simeq 2$ so, as has already been mentioned, their diffusion coefficients and the parameters b_i and d_i defining the acceleration in interstellar magnetic fields should be identical (at one and the same energy per nucleon). There may be a difference only for very high energy protons if the nature of their motion in the Galaxy starts to depend upon the radius of curvature. Further, unless we are speaking of nuclear collisions, which we shall discuss separately, the energy losses of the nuclear component in the Galaxy are small and they may be ignored (section 7). Only non-relativistic nuclei for which ionisation losses start to play a part may be an exception. However, the fullest of the available data on composition and fragmentation probabilities relate to the region of energies of the order of a few GeV/nucleon. For particles with these energies the ionisation losses during the life of the Galaxy are insignificant (see section 7) and it is these particles which will be discussed below.

Condition (1) is therefore satisfied for a wide range of the problems under discussion.

If not only the ionisation losses but also the acceleration of particles in interstellar space are insignificant (there is reason to consider that this is the case; see section 11), then the terms containing energy derivatives in equation (14.8) can be omitted and condition (2) is satisfied. In this case the energy $\mathscr{E}$, on which, generally speaking, the diffusion coefficient D_i, the life times T_i and the fragmentation probabilities p_{ik} depend comes into equation (14.8) only as a parameter. In other words, the transformation of the chemical composition of cosmic rays can in this case be examined separately for each section of the energy spectrum if the latter is related to the energy per nucleon $\mathscr{E}$.

Lastly, the available data indicate that in the $\mathscr{E}_k > 1$ GeV/nucleon energy range the fragmentation probabilities p_{ik} and the lifetimes with respect to absorption T_i depend weakly, or in practice not at all, on the energy, so for the majority of cosmic rays it may be considered that condition (2') is also fulfilled. The dependence of $p_{ik}(\mathscr{E})$ becomes significant for $\mathscr{E}_k = \mathscr{E} - Mc^2 < 1$ GeV/nucleon and should be allowed for when analysing the composition in this energy range.

As for assumption (3), this is clearly satisfied in the simplest case when all the sources supply cosmic rays with one and the same spectrum and composition. However, this requirement may be made less rigid if we assume that there is a large number of sources and condition (14.9) is satisfied only on the average over sufficiently small spatial and time intervals.

To recapitulate what has been said, it can be taken that for the majority of cosmic rays with energies of 1 GeV/nucleon $\lesssim \mathscr{E}_k \lesssim 10^{15}$ eV/nucleon conditions (1), (2) and (2') are satisfied simultaneously. In the energy range $\mathscr{E} > 10^{15}$ to 10^{16} eV condition (1) may be broken (for protons) and for energies of $\mathscr{E}_k < 1$ GeV/nucleon conditions (1), (2) or (2') may be broken.

Upon the above assumptions the general solution of the systems of equations (14.8) can be put in the form

$$N_i(\mathscr{E}, \boldsymbol{r}, t) = \int_0^\infty N_i^{(p)}(\tau) G(\mathscr{E}, \boldsymbol{r}, t, \tau)\, d\tau. \tag{14.10}$$

Here $G(\mathscr{E}, \boldsymbol{r}, t, \tau)$ is an identical propagation function for all kinds of particles satisfying the equation

$$\frac{\partial G}{\partial \tau} + L[G] = 0, \tag{14.11}$$

the necessary boundary conditions of the problem with respect to the variables r and t and the condition (see (14.9))

$$G(\mathscr{E}, r, t, 0) = \chi(\mathscr{E}, r, t). \tag{14.12}$$

In equation (14.11) $L[G]$ is a linear differential operator corresponding to the left-hand side of equation (14.8) as applied to the function G instead of the functions N_i.

The functions $N_i^{(p)}(t)$ which come into the integral (14.10) satisfy the equations

$$\frac{dN_i^{(p)}}{dt} + p_i N_i^{(p)} = \sum_{k<i} p_i^k N_k^{(p)} \tag{14.13}$$

and the conditions (see (14.9))

$$N_i^{(p)}(0) = q_i. \tag{14.14}$$

We can check the validity of solution (14.10) by direct substitution of expression (14.10) in (14.8) bearing equations (14.11) to (14.14) in mind.

Let us now determine the functions $N_i^{(p)}(t)$ which come into expressions (14.10).

Regular motion

Equations (14.13) and (14.14) which are satisfied by the functions $N_i^{(p)}(t)$ are special cases of equations (14.8) for $D_i = b_i = d_i = 0$ and $Q_i = Q_i(t) = q_i\delta(t)$, where $\delta(t)$ is a delta function. This case corresponds to the model of cosmic ray motion in the Galaxy which we have called regular and in which all the particles spend the same time in motion from the source to the point of observation. This situation would be realised in particular if all the particles arrived at a given point (in a given direction) along the same trajectory, for example along the magnetic force lines. The regular model described by equations (14.13) and (14.14) obviously corresponds to the adiabatic motion discussed in section 10 of particles along the lines of force of the interstellar magnetic field.

If we use x (in g/cm²) to denote the thickness of matter passed through by the particles and bear in mind that $x = \rho c t$ and the length of the absorption path is $\lambda_i = \rho c T_i = \rho c / p_i$ (ρ is the density of the medium, c is the velocity of the particles' motion and practically equal to the velocity of light), then equations (14.13) can be written in another, equivalent, form

$$\frac{dN_i^{(p)}}{dx} + \frac{N_i^{(p)}}{\lambda_i} = \sum_{k<i} p_{ki} \frac{N_k^{(p)}}{\lambda_k}. \tag{14.15}$$

The solution of equations (14.13) and (14.15) can be easily found first for $i = 1$ and then by the method of induction for any i. It takes the form

$$N_i^{(p)} = \sum_{k=1}^{i} a_{ik} e^{-p_k t} = \sum_{k=1}^{i} a_{ik} e^{-x/\lambda_k}. \tag{14.16}$$

The coefficients a_{ik} in (14.16) are functions of the quantities p_i, p_i^k and q_i and are defined by the recurrence relationships:

$$a_{ik} = \frac{1}{p_i - p_k} \sum_{l=k}^{i-1} p_i^l a_{lk}, \qquad a_{ii} = q_i - \sum_{k=1}^{i-1} a_{ik}. \tag{14.17}$$

By virtue of the linear dependence of the coefficients a_{ik} on q_i these coefficients can also be given in the form

$$a_{ik} = \sum_{l=1}^{l=k} a_{ikl} q_l, \tag{14.18}$$

where the coefficients a_{ikl} which are not dependent on q_l satisfy relationships similar to (14.17):

$$a_{ikl} = \frac{1}{p_i - p_k} \sum_{j=k}^{i-1} p_i^j a_{jkl}, \qquad a_{iil} = - \sum_{k=l}^{i-1} a_{ikl}, \qquad a_{iii} = 1. \tag{14.19}$$

Using the recurrence relationships (14.19) the coefficients a_{ikl} can be written in the explicit form.[341]

$$a_{ikl} = \sum \frac{p_i^\alpha p_\alpha^\beta \cdots p_\xi^\omega p_\omega^l (p_k - p)}{(p_i - p)(p_\alpha - p) \cdots (p_\xi - p)(p_\omega - p)(p_l - p)} \bigg|_{p = p_k},$$
$$a_{iii} = 1. \tag{14.20}$$

Here summation is carried out over all possible sequences of one, two, etc., up to $i - l$ numbers $\alpha, \beta, \ldots, \xi, \omega, l$ (l is fixed) that satisfy the conditions

$$i > \alpha > \beta > \ldots > \xi > \omega > l. \tag{14.21}$$

If one of these numbers is equal to k the factor $p_k - p$ in the numerator of the corresponding term of the sum (14.20) should be cancelled with the same factor in the denominator before substituting $p = p_k$. The terms of the sum (14.20) for which not one of the numbers (14.21) is equal to k disappear after substituting $p = p_k$. It is assumed all the time that for $i \neq k$ we have $p_i \neq p_k$.

We give here the expression for some of the coefficients a_{ikl} which will be used in future expressed by the fragmentation probabilities $p_{ik} = p_k^i/p_i = T_i p_k^i$ and the absorption paths λ_i introduced in section 7:

$$
\left.
\begin{aligned}
&a_{221} = -a_{211} = \gamma_{21}p_{12} \qquad a_{332} = -a_{322} = \gamma_{32}p_{23} \\
&a_{331} = \gamma_{31}(p_{13} + \gamma_{32}p_{12}p_{23}) \\
&a_{311} = -\gamma_{31}(p_{13} + \gamma_{12}p_{12}p_{23}) \\
&a_{443} = -a_{433} = \gamma_{43}p_{34} \\
&a_{442} = \gamma_{42}(p_{24} + \gamma_{43}p_{23}p_{34}) \\
&a_{441} = \gamma_{41}(p_{14} + \gamma_{42}p_{12}p_{24} + \gamma_{43}p_{13}p_{34} + \gamma_{42}\gamma_{43}p_{12}p_{23}p_{34}) \\
&a_{422} = -\gamma_{42}(p_{24} + \gamma_{23}p_{23}p_{34}) \\
&a_{411} = -\gamma_{41}(p_{14} + \gamma_{12}p_{12}p_{24} + \gamma_{13}p_{13}p_{34} \\
&\qquad\qquad\qquad\qquad\qquad + \gamma_{12}\gamma_{13}p_{12}p_{23}p_{34}).
\end{aligned}
\right\} \quad (14.22)
$$

In these equations we have used for brevity of notation

$$
\gamma_{ik} = \frac{\lambda_i}{\lambda_i - \lambda_k}. \qquad (14.23)
$$

General solution of the fragmentation equations for nuclei

Using expressions (14.16) for the functions $N_i^{(p)}$ the general solution (14.10) of the fragmentation equations (14.8) can be put in the form

$$
N_i(\mathscr{E}, r, t) = \sum_{k=1}^{i} a_{ik} F_k(\mathscr{E}, r, t), \qquad (14.24)
$$

where

$$
F_k(\mathscr{E}, r, t) = \int_0^\infty G(\mathscr{E}, r, t, \tau)e^{-p_k\tau}\, d\tau. \qquad (14.25)
$$

As can be seen from a comparison of solutions (14.16) and (14.24) and (14.25) the propagation function G characterises the distribution of the particles during the time they move in the interstellar medium before reaching the point in question. In other words, $G(\mathscr{E}, r, t, \tau)$

is proportional to the probability that the time elapsed since the acceleration of a particle observed at a time t at the point r is equal to τ (thus the thickness of matter passed through by the particle is $x = \rho c\tau$). By virtue of the assumptions made above the nature of the motion and the distribution of the sources are identical for all kinds of nuclei, so their propagation functions are also identical. This makes it possible to give the general solution in the form (14.24).[6, 331, 341]

In order to determine the functions $F_k(\mathscr{E}, r, t)$ there is no need to use relationship (14.25) and the solution of the corresponding problem for the propagation function G. In fact if we know one of the functions F_k, for example F_1, then, as can be seen from (14.25) any other one of these functions can be obtained simply by replacing p_1 by the appropriate p_k. Therefore in each actual problem it is sufficient to determine just one of the functions F_i. This is most simply done by solving (14.8) for the group of the heaviest nuclei ($i = 1$) since in this case the last term on the right-hand side of equation (14.8) disappears (for $i = 1$ the coefficient $a_{11} = q_1$ and in (14.8) $N_1 = q_1 F_1$).

The actual expressions for the functions F_i corresponding to the various models of the propagation of cosmic rays in the Galaxy will be discussed in section 15 together with a general analysis of the problem of the chemical composition of cosmic rays. Here we shall give only the expressions that allow us to determine the cosmic ray composition in the sources (q_i) for a known composition on Earth (N_i) and a given cosmic ray propagation model, i.e., for given functions F_i.

Using definition (14.18) of the coefficients a_{ik} the functions $N_i = N_i(\mathscr{E}, r, t)$ (see (14.24)) can be represented in the form

$$N_i = \sum_{k=1}^{i} \sum_{l=1}^{k} a_{ikl} F_k q_l = \sum_{l=1}^{i} q_l \sum_{k=l}^{i} a_{ikl} F_k. \tag{14.26}$$

By solving the system of linear equations (14.26) with respect to q_i and using the properties of the coefficients a_{ikl} we can obtain the following general expression:[480]

$$q_i = \sum_{k=1}^{i} \frac{a_{ikk}}{F_k} \sum_{l=1}^{l=k} a_{kkl} N_l = \sum_{k=1}^{i} \frac{1}{F_k} \sum_{l=1}^{l=k} a_{ikl} N_l. \tag{14.27}$$

In particular for $i = 1, 2, 3$ we have

$$q_1 = \frac{N_1}{F_1},$$

$$q_2 = [N_2 + a_{221}N_1]\frac{1}{F_2} + a_{211}N_1\frac{1}{F_1}, \qquad (14.28)$$

$$q_3 = [N_3 + a_{332}N_2 + a_{331}N_1]\frac{1}{F_3}$$

$$+ a_{322}[N_2 + a_{221}N_1]\frac{1}{F_2} + a_{311}N_1\frac{1}{F_1}$$

General solution of the transfer equation for particles of one kind

Let us now discuss the solution of equation (14.8) for particles of one kind when the last term on its right-hand side can be omitted. In this form equation (14.8) may be used for determining the concentration and spectrum of the electrons or for finding the functions F_i in the problem of the composition. We shall consider that the coefficients of the equation do not depend on the spatial coordinates and time and the term describing the fluctuation change of energy can be omitted. As has already been mentioned above, the fluctuations in the energy losses for nuclei are really small and need not be taken into account.

As for the electrons we cannot, generally speaking, ignore the fluctuations in the radiation and Compton losses. Moreover, these losses should, strictly speaking, be taken into consideration in the integral form[415] (see the last term of equation (14.2) and the remark following it). However, in the limits of accuracy of the data with which the results of the calculations must be compared at present the precise radiation or Compton losses can clearly fully justifiably be replaced by their mean value or the corresponding effective life. The rôle of fluctuations during statistical acceleration will be discussed separately in section 16.

Upon these assumptions equation (14.8) takes the form

$$\frac{\partial N}{\partial t} - D\Delta N + \frac{\partial}{\partial E}(bN) + \frac{N}{T} = Q(E, \boldsymbol{r}, t). \qquad (14.29)$$

Here the coefficients $D = D(E)$ and $b = b(E)$ are considered in the general case to depend on the energy.

Let us determine the Green function of equation (14.29), i.e., the function $G(E, r, t; E_0, r_0, t_0)$ satisfying the equation

$$\frac{\partial G}{\partial t} - D\Delta G + \frac{\partial}{\partial E}(bG) + \frac{G}{T} = \delta(E - E_0)\delta(r - r_0)\delta(t - t_0). \quad (14.30)$$

The solution of equation (14.30) is easily found[173] if we change to new variables $t' = t - \tau$ and λ, where

$$\tau \equiv \tau(E, E_0) = \int_{E_0}^{E} \frac{dE}{b(E)} \quad (14.31)$$

and

$$\lambda \equiv \lambda(E, E_0) = \int_{E_0}^{E} \frac{D(E)}{b(E)} \, dE. \quad (14.32)$$

Equation (14.30) now reduces to an equation of the thermal conductivity type. For infinite space the solution takes the form

$G(E, r, t; E_0, r_0, t_0)$

$$= \frac{1}{|b(E)|(4\pi\lambda)^{3/2}} \exp\left\{-\frac{\tau}{T} - \frac{(r - r_0)^2}{4\lambda}\right\}\delta(t - t_0 - \tau), \quad (14.33)$$

where τ and λ are defined by expressions (14.31) and (14.32). The presence of a δ-function in solution (14.33) reflects the regular nature of the change in the energy of the particles $dE/dt = b(E)$ by virtue of which the energy at each point in time is unambiguously connected with the initial energy E_0 at $t = t_0$.

By using the source function (Green function) G (see (14.33)) we can obtain the general solution of equation (14.29) for an arbitrary source distribution

$N(E, r, t)$

$$= \iiint_{-\infty}^{+\infty} d^3r_0 \int dE_0 \int_{-\infty}^{t} dt_0 Q(E_0, r_0, t_0)G(E, r, t; E_0, r_0, t_0), \quad (14.34)$$

where $d^3r_0 = dx_0 \, dy_0 \, dz_0$ is an element of the volume in coordinate space.

In future we shall be largely interested in stationary problems in which the intensity of the sources does not depend upon time. The Green function for the stationary process by virtue of (14.33) and (14.34) is

$G(E, r; E_0, r_0)$

$$= \int_{-\infty}^{t} dt_0 G(E, r, t; E_0, r_0, t_0)$$

$$= \begin{cases} \dfrac{1}{(4\pi\lambda)^{3/2}|b(E)|} \exp\left\{ -\dfrac{\tau}{T} - \dfrac{(r - r_0)^2}{4\lambda} \right\}, & \text{if } \tau > 0, \\ \\ \qquad\qquad 0, & \text{if } \tau < 0. \end{cases} \qquad (14.35)$$

In the case of a process that is non-stationary but is homogeneous in space, when the intensity of the sources does not depend on the coordinates, the Green function is

$$G(E, t; E_0, t_0) = \frac{1}{|b(E)|} e^{-\tau/T} \delta(t - t_0 - \tau). \qquad (14.36)$$

Expressions (14.35) and (14.36) will be used in sections 16 and 17 when discussing the question of the electron distribution and the cosmic ray spectrum in the Galaxy.

15. CHEMICAL COMPOSITION OF COSMIC RAYS AND ITS TRANSFORMATION IN THE INTERSTELLAR MEDIUM

One of the basic problems of the theory of the origin of cosmic rays is the interpretation of the data on their chemical composition on Earth. This composition obviously depends upon the following three factors: the original composition of the elements in the source, the conditions for accelerating the various elements in the source to relativistic energies (these two factors together determine the cosmic ray composition in the source) and lastly the transformation of nuclei in collisions in the interstellar gas on their way from the sources to the Earth. The data that we have at present are insufficient for a definite estimate of the relative parts played by these factors in the formation of the observed composition. Nevertheless, taking the ideas developed above as a basis it is useful to make a more detailed analysis of this problem.

Models of cosmic ray propagation in the Galaxy

Let us start with the question of the transformation of the chemical composition of the cosmic rays in the interstellar medium. For this, of course, we must make a definite model of the propagation of cosmic rays in the Galaxy. Below, in accordance with the arguments given in section 10, most of the attention will be paid to the diffusion approximation. In this approximation the sources are assumed to be concentrated in a certain region (for example in the galactic disk or in the centre of the Galaxy) and the cosmic ray motion is considered to be a random process with a certain isotropic diffusion coefficient D. In the calculations that follow we shall ignore the dependence of the diffusion coefficient on the coordinates and the possible change of the nucleus energy during the diffusion process (see section 14).

At the same time as the diffusion models we shall discuss other models as well for the sake of comparison, in particular the regular model described by equations (14.13) and (14.15).

In the regular model, which corresponds to adiabatic motion along the lines of force of the magnetic field, all the particles arriving at a given point in a fixed direction move along one and the same trajectory. In this case, strictly speaking, we should discuss not the total concentration of particles $N_i(r)$ at a given point but their intensity at a given point in a given direction   To preserve the unity of notation, however, and for comparison with the diffusion model we shall also in the case of the regular model use the particle concentration. In this case, bearing in mind the remark we have made, the concentration $N_i^{(p)}(x)$ in the case of the regular model is taken to mean the number of particles per unit volume with a given velocity direction within unit solid angle. In this case x (g/cm^2) is the same distance for all such particles travelled on their way from the source in the interstellar gas. If the concentration of these particles in the source was $N_i^{(p)}(0) = q_i$ their concentration at a distance x along the trajectory would be defined by equations (14.15).

The regular model equations (14.13) also describe the change with time of the original composition of the cosmic rays which evenly and isotropically fill a closed region and can be used when discussing the question of the composition of the "remnant" cosmic rays in the Galaxy.[363]

Unlike the diffusion model the regular model does not agree with the picture of the motion of cosmic rays in the Galaxy discussed in section 10. This model is often used, however, in published works so it is as well to discuss this possibility also for the sake of comparison.

We shall now give the expressions for the functions F_i which come into the general solution (14.24) of the fragmentation equations. As has already been pointed out earlier, the life of the cosmic rays in the Galaxy is considerably less than its age so we shall limit ourselves to discussing the stationary problems. In addition, for the cosmic ray nuclear component the acceleration and energy losses in interstellar space are small; therefore in equations (14.8) we may omit the terms containing energy derivatives. In this case the energy $\mathscr{E}$ comes into equation (14.8) and the corresponding solutions only as a parameter and we shall not write it down explicitly. The functions $F_i(r)$ should thus satisfy the equations (see (14.25), (14.11) and (14.8); ∇^2 is a Laplace operator)

$$DV^2F_i - \frac{F_i}{T_i} = -Q_i(r). \tag{15.1}$$

In addition, of course, we must use the appropriate boundary conditions for the functions F_i

Let us write out the solutions of equations (15.1) for a point source located at the centre of a spherical region of radius R. These solutions which satisfy the general boundary condition on the surface of a sphere

$$-\frac{dF_i}{dr} = \frac{\beta}{R}F_i \qquad \text{(for } r = R) \tag{15.2}$$

are the functions

$$F_i(r) = \frac{1}{4\pi Dr} \frac{(\kappa_i - 1 + \beta)e^{\kappa_i(1-r/R)} + (\kappa_i + 1 - \beta)e^{-\kappa_i(1-r/R)}}{(\kappa_i - 1 + \beta)e^{\kappa_i} + (\kappa_i + 1 - \beta)e^{-\kappa_i}}. \tag{15.3}$$

Here

$$\kappa_i = \frac{R}{\sqrt{DT_i}}, \tag{15.4}$$

and β is a non-dimensional parameter characterising the conditions for the leakage of particles from the volume in question. In the case of weak leakage of particles ($\beta \ll 1$) the parameter β can be expressed in terms of the time for leakage of particles T_d from the Galaxy, i e.,

$$\beta = \frac{R^2}{3DT_d}. \tag{15.5}$$

This expression can be derived if we use boundary condition (15.2) and take into consideration the fact that the flux of particles through a unit boundary surface $-D(dN_i/dr)|_{r=R}$ is equal to $(4/3)\pi R^3 N_i/4\pi R^2 T_d = RN_i/3T_d$.

The case $\beta = 0$ corresponds to total reflection of the particles at the boundary since it follows from boundary condition (15.2) in this case that the particle flux $-D(dN_i/dr)$ through the volume's surface is zero.

For $\beta = \infty$ expression (15.3) is the solution for an absorbing boundary. Indeed, for $\beta = \infty$ condition (15.2) can be satisfied only if the concentration N_i is kept equal to zero at the boundary the whole time. For the cosmic rays in the Galaxy this situation will be approximately realised if the cosmic rays depart freely from the Galaxy into intergalactic space where their concentration is negligibly small and the diffusion coefficient is large when compared with its value for the Galaxy. This possibility was discussed in sections 10 and 11; it is the most probable one. In this case solution (15.3) takes the form

(I)
$$F_i(r) = \frac{1}{4\pi Dr}\frac{e^{\kappa_i(1-r/R)} - e^{-\kappa_i(1-r/R)}}{e^{\kappa_i} - e^{-\kappa_i}}.$$
(15.6)

If the boundary is far enough away, i e, the conditions $R \gg r$ and $R \gg \sqrt{DT_i}$ are satisfied, then the solution of (15.3) and (15.6) is reduced to the solution for a point source in infinite space:

(II)
$$F_i(r) = \frac{1}{4\pi Dr} e^{-r/\sqrt{DT_i}}.$$
(15.7)

In the opposite case when $R \ll \sqrt{DT_i}$ (to be more precise $R^2/DT_i \ll r/R$) and the particle leakage is small ($\beta \ll 1$) we obtain from (15.3)

(III)
$$F_i = \left[\tfrac{4}{3}\pi R^3\left(\frac{1}{T_i} + \frac{1}{T_d}\right)\right]^{-1} = \frac{T_i'}{\tfrac{4}{3}\pi R^3},$$
(15.8)

where $T_i' = (1/T_i + 1/T_d)^{-1}$ is the total life of nuclei of kind i in the Galaxy (in section 11 and other sections the time T_i' is denoted simply by T since it was assumed that $T_i' \simeq T_d \ll T_i$)

In the case of the regular model (see (14.16) and (14.24)) the functions F_i obviously are

(IV)
$$F_i = e^{-x/\lambda_i}.$$
(15.9)

We shall also give the solution for the case when there are no sources in the spherical volume in question and a constant concentration $N_i(R) = q_i$ is maintained on the boundary. This model corresponds to the assumption that all the cosmic rays reach the Galaxy from intergalactic space (see section 13). By solving equation (15.1) it is easy to confirm that the corresponding functions F_i in (14.24) are

(V)
$$F_i = \frac{R}{r} \frac{e^{r/\sqrt{DT_i}} - e^{-r/\sqrt{DT_i}}}{e^{R/\sqrt{DT_i}} - e^{R/\sqrt{DT_i}}}. \tag{15.10}$$

Below we shall also discuss models corresponding to strong reflexion at the boundaries of the Galaxy. One of these—the diffusion model with a point source at the centre of the Galaxy—is described by equation (15.3) for $\beta \ll |\kappa_i - 1|$. In this case

(VI)
$$F_i(r) = \frac{1}{4\pi Dr} \frac{(\kappa_i - 1)e^{\kappa_i(1-r/R)} + (\kappa_i + 1)e^{-\kappa_i(1-r/R)}}{(\kappa_i - 1)e^{\kappa_i} + (\kappa_i + 1)e^{-\kappa_i}}. \tag{15.11}$$

The second of the models discussed with strong reflexion corresponds to the so-called equilibrium composition: it is assumed that stationary sources fill the whole volume evenly or the life of the particles is so long that their concentration has the time to even out over the whole volume. The corresponding functions F_i can be obtained from (15.8) with $T_d \to \infty$ or from (15.11) with $\kappa_i^2 \ll r/R < 1$. If then we select the intensity of the sources per unit volume as q_i (in the coefficients a_{ik} from (14.24)) we obtain

(VII)
$$F_i = T_i. \tag{15.12}$$

The basic characteristics of the models of cosmic ray propagation in the Galaxy used later are given in Table 14.

In future the characteristic parameter of the model (the argument of the function F_i) will be the mean thickness of matter x (in g/cm^2) passed through by the cosmic rays before reaching the Earth. For the regular model (15.9) the mean thickness is obviously the same as the true thickness, i.e., is

$$x = \rho ct = \rho L, \tag{15.13}$$

where L is the total distance travelled by a particle in the interstellar gas whose density is ρ.

In the case of slow departure from the Galaxy (model III defined by formulae (15.8))

$$x = \rho c T_d \tag{15.14}$$

is the mean thickness of matter passed through by cosmic rays in the Galaxy before leaving it. Lastly, in the diffusion models I, II, V and VI the mean thickness of matter passed through is the quantity

$$x = \rho c t_D = \frac{\rho c r^2}{2D}, \qquad (15.15)$$

where $t_D = r^2/2D$ is the characteristic time of motion of a particle from a source to a point at a distance r from it (in diffusion the mean square of the displacement in a given direction in a time t is $r^2 = 2Dt$). Below when calculating x, the distance from the Sun to the galactic centre $r = 2.5 \times 10^{22}$ cm is taken as r.

TABLE 14

MODELS OF COSMIC RAY PROPAGATION IN THE GALAXY

Model	Approximation	Source	Boundary condition	Formula
I	Diffusion	Point source at centre	Free departure ($N_i = 0$ at $r = R$)	(15.6)
II	Diffusion	Point source at centre	Diffusion in infinite space	(15.7)
III	Diffusion	Point source at centre	Weak leakage ($\beta \ll 1,\ R \ll \sqrt{DT_i}$)	(15.8)
	Homogeneity in space	Sources fill whole region evenly with cosmic rays	Weak leakage	(15.8)
IV	Regular motion	Point source at distance x (g/cm²)	Motion along magnetic line of force without reflexion	(15.9)
	Homogeneity in space	Cosmic rays generated at time $t = x/\rho c = 0$	No leakage	(15.9)
V	Diffusion	Sources located outside Galaxy	Concentration N_i at boundary (at $r = R$) given	(15.10)
VI	Diffusion	Point source at centre	Total reflexion at boundary	(15.11)
VII	Homogeneity in space	Stationary sources fill volume in question evenly	No leakage	(15.12)

The selection as the argument of the functions F_i of quantities that have the same physical meaning of the thickness of the matter passed through makes the comparison of the various models easier.

Cosmic ray composition in the sources

We should use equations (14.27) or (14.28) to determine the chemical composition of the cosmic rays in the sources. In these equations the coefficients a_{ikl} and the concentration N_i are assumed to be known since they can be expressed in terms of directly measurable quantities: the absorption paths, the fragmentation probabilities and the chemical composition of the cosmic rays in Earth. Further, when selecting a definite model of the propagation of cosmic rays in the Galaxy the form of the functions $F(x_i)$ is known. These conditions are, however, still insufficient for determining the quantities q_i characterising the composition of cosmic rays in the sources. The point is that we still do not know the value of the argument of the functions $F_i(x)$, i.e., the thickness x of matter passed through. The latter depends on the density of the interstellar medium and also on the value of the diffusion coefficient D or the age of the cosmic rays observed, i.e., on the quantities whose values can in the best case be estimated only in order of magnitude.

In this connexion a very significant fact is that the value of the parameter x can be determined simply in the problem of the chemical composition of cosmic rays. In actual fact it is sufficient for this purpose to know just one of the values of q_i in questions (14.17) or (14.28). Then the corresponding equation from (14.27) or (14.28) becomes simply an equation† for determining x.

The possibility of drawing a conclusion about certain of the values of q_i in the cosmic ray sources is connected with the fact that the natural frequency of occurrence of a number of elements in the Universe (and clearly also in the cosmic ray sources) is negligibly small when compared with their frequency of occurrence in the cosmic rays. This is particularly true of the L-group of nuclei (Li, Be, B; see section 1) which are present in the cosmic rays in a quantity which is comparable, for example, with the number of C, N and O nuclei; at the same time in stellar atmospheres and

---

† The transcendental equation obtained in this way does not, generally speaking, define x unambiguously. The unique value of x is defined by the following additional conditions: all the values of q_i corresponding to a given x are not negative and, in addition, for the q_i found in this way the concentrations are $N_i(x') \geqslant 0$ for all $x' \leqslant x$.

in the Universe on the average the concentration of L-nuclei when compared with C, N and O nuclei is negligibly small.† This allows us to consider that nuclei of the L-group are not formed directly in the cosmic rays' sources but are entirely fragmentation products of the heavier M- and H-nuclei.‡ By virtue of what has been said we shall in future, as is generally the case in all calculations of the chemical composition, assume that

$$q_L = 0. \tag{15.16}$$

We should remark here that a study of the chemical composition of cosmic rays allows us in principle to obtain far more information than simply determining the composition of the sources and the thickness of matter passed through. In actual fact, and we shall see this again below, not all the possible models of the propagation of cosmic rays (i.e., functions $F_i(x)$) lead to physically permissible solutions of the system of equations (14.27) or (14.28).[5, 6, 341, 416] Indeed, we must require for all i the satisfaction of the additional conditions

$$q_i \geqslant 0. \tag{15.17}$$

Further addition of precision to the data on the chemical composition and the fragmentation probabilities will make it possible to reduce the class of possible models of propagation still more. The point is that the condition of the absence of several kinds of nuclei in the cosmic rays sources (for example nuclei of Li, Be and B looked at separately), i.e., equality to zero of several of the q_i in (14.27) and (14.28), imposes very rigid limitations on the possible form of the functions $F_i(x)$ which make equations (14.27) or (14.28) consistent.

At the present time, however, the data on the cosmic ray composition on Earth and the fragmentation probabilities are still not accurate enough to be able to select a model, basing oneself on this condition. At the same time condition (15.17) can be used even now and allows us to reject, for example, model VI corresponding to strong reflexion

---

† The small number of L-nuclei is due to their rapid "burn-up" in nuclear reactions. In the framework of the existing ideas on the formation of the elements[402] the assumption that there is a large number of L-nuclei in the sources is unacceptable.

‡ We should point out that the assumption of the formation of all or some of the L-nuclei by collisions in the source itself does not qualitatively alter the further conclusions since this assumption is equivalent simply to adding a certain thickness to the matter passed through by the cosmic rays in the source itself. All that is significant is that the L-nuclei appear only as the result of spallation of heavier nuclei.

of the cosmic rays at the boundaries of the Galaxy. The equilibrium model VII is also unacceptable (see (15.12)) since it does not contain a free parameter and the system of equations (15.27) with $q_L = 0$ could be consistent only by chance.

TABLE 15

CHEMICAL COMPOSITION OF COSMIC RAYS IN SOURCES

Propagation model	Variant	Thickness of matter	Ratio of intensities (concentrations)				
		x, g/cm^2	VH/H	M/H	L/H	α/H	p/H
I	a	14·4	0·41	2·0	0	14·6	220
	b	17	0·37	1·8	0	11·3	151
	c	10	0·40	2·3	0	20·6	318
	d	13	0·44	2·2	0	17·2	269
II	a	9·1	0·38	2·0	0	10·8	167
	b	13·4	0·36	1·8	0	8·9	99
	c	5·7	0·38	2·3	0	17·5	254
	d	7·3	0·41	2·2	0	15·1	232
III	a	21	0·37	2·1	0	12	158
	b	54·3	0·34	1·9	0	7·3	63
	c	11·4	0·38	2·6	0	18	274
	d	15·5	0·39	2·3	0	15	243
IV	a	6·6	0·42	1·9	0	7·5	266
	b	7·8	0·40	1·6	0	4·5	185
	c	5·2	0·42	2·2	0	12·5	360
	d	6·4	0·48	2·1	0	17·8	285
V	a	36	0·38	2·0	0	13·5	197
	b	55	0·36	1·8	0	20·2	63
	c	24	0·38	2·3	0	7·6	335
	d	31	0·41	2·2	0	16	256

Calculations have been made for all the models I–VII (see (15.6) to (15.12)) by means of equations (14.28) and a similar equation (see (14.27)) for $q_4 = q_\alpha$. The nuclei were subdivided into the groups H, M, L and α with the corresponding indices $i = 1, 2, 3$ and 4. The results of the calculations† are given in Table 15. The calcula-

† Fuller calculations for models II and IV allowing for the experimental scatter in the values of N_i and the fragmentation parameters p_{ik} from papers by Badhwar et al.[302] and Friedlander et al.[479] are made by Syrovatskii.[480] It turns out that the possible values for the thickness of matter traversed by cosmic rays still lie in very broad limits.

tions used four sets of fragmentation probabilities and absorption paths (denoted respectively by a, b, c and d) from Table 12 on p. 134 and the data on the composition of the cosmic rays on Earth from Table 1.

After the value of the parameter x had been determined for each case the intensity of the VH-nuclei in the source was determined from the relation

$$q_{VH} = N_{VH}/F_{VH}(x), \qquad (15.18)$$

where $F_{VH}(x)$ is a function obtained from $F_i(x)$ by replacing λ_i by the absorption path λ_{VH} of the VH-group of nuclei; the latter is taken to be $\lambda_{VH} = 4\cdot4$ g/cm^2 (see Table 10). The possibility of using relation (15.18) is obviously connected with the fact that the variation in the intensity of the VH-group of nuclei, which includes all nuclei with $Z \geqslant 20$, is caused only by their absorption in the interstellar medium (just like the H-group as a whole).

In Table 15 the intensities (concentrations) of the various groups of nuclei in the source are given in relative units   The intensity of the H-nuclei is to be taken to be 1.

The intensity of the sources q_p with respect to protons was estimated from the total flux on Earth of nucleons which are part of all the cosmic ray nuclei, allowing for absorption on the way from the source and the share of nucleons which belong to nuclei with $Z \geqslant 2$ in the source. The absorption path for nucleons (see Table 10) is taken to be $\lambda_{\text{nucleon}} = \lambda_p = 72$ g/cm^2. Therefore

$$\frac{N_{\text{nucleon}}}{N_H} = \frac{q_{\text{nucleon}}F_{\text{nucleon}}(x)}{q_H F_H(x)},$$

$$q_p = q_{\text{nucleon}} - \sum_{i=H, M, L, \alpha} \bar{A}_i q_i. \qquad (15.19)$$

Here $F_{\text{nucleon}}(x)$ are the functions $F_i(x)$ for $\lambda = \lambda_{\text{nucleon}}$, q_{nucleon} is the intensity of the sources with respect to all the nucleons and $\bar{A}_i$ are the mean atomic weights for the groups in Table 10. In accordance with the data given in Table 1 it is taken in the calculations that $N_{\text{nucleon}}/N_H \simeq 1810/1\cdot9 \simeq 950$.

The values of the mean thickness of matter x passed through by the cosmic rays for each model and each set of fragmentation probabilites are also given in Table 15.

Discussion and conclusions

Before discussing the results given in Table 15 let us examine a very important circumstance which has already been mentioned. For stationary sources when there is strong reflexion from the boundaries (i.e., with weak leakage of particles from the Galaxy) the particle composition observed on Earth cannot be obtained for any source composition unless the boundary is so far away that its influence becomes insignificant.

For example in the diffusion model VI with strong reflexion at the boundaries ($\beta \ll 1$) the condition $q_L \geqslant 0$ is not satisfied for any value of the thickness x of matter passed through. Calculations were made for two values of the radius of the region occupied by cosmic rays in the Galaxy: $R = 12$ kpc and $R = 16$ kpc (the distance of the solar system from the centre of the Galaxy is always taken as $r = 8$ kpc). The negative result obtained in both cases (the absence of a solution with $q_L = 0$) means that in the diffusion model with strong reflexion there should be considerably more nuclei of group L ($N_L > N_H$, $N_L > 0.5 N_M$) than are observed on Earth. It would be possible of course to assume that the boundary is far enough away ($R^2 > DT_i$ for all i). In this case the nuclei would be largely absorbed before they reached the boundary and the problem would be analogous to diffusion in infinite space (model II) for which the difficulty indicated with the composition does not arise. With a sufficiently remote boundary the question of the nature of the reflexion is not, in general, essential. At the same time it should be considered that the volume occupied by the cosmic rays in the Galaxy considerably exceeds the generally accepted value of $V \lesssim 1$ to 5×10^{68} cm^3. There is, however, not only no basis for this assumption but it also contradicts the radio astronomy data on the halo.

Therefore if we exclude the possibility of a significant change in the accepted parameters p_{ik} and λ_i and if at the Earth $N_L \lesssim N_H < 0.5 N_M$ it must be assumed that either the reflexion at the boundaries is small or that the diffusion model taken for the propagation of cosmic rays in the Galaxy is invalid.†

† The difficulties arising in the question of the chemical composition of cosmic rays when allowing for reflexion were first indicated by Davis.[341] It was pointed out by him that when there is reflexion too many protons and α-particles appear. This complication can be avoided by assuming that protons and α-particles are hardly accelerated at all in the sources. We come, however, to the even more radical conclusion of the impossibility of matching even the data only on nuclei of the L, M and H groups.

A similar difficulty arises, of course, in the case of an "equilibrium" composition (model VII) also. This, as we have seen is the limiting case of diffusion with total reflexion at $R \ll \sqrt{DT_i}$.

As for an equilibrium composition allowing for slow leakage (model III), the observed composition here can be explained only by considerable leakage of particles from the Galaxy. It follows from Table 15 that in this model we must take $x = \rho c T_d \simeq 11$ to 54 g/cm^2, whilst the path of protons with respect to absorption is $\lambda_p = \rho c T_p = 72$ g/cm^2. Thus in this model also the leakage of particles is more significant than the absorption in the Galaxy. We note that strict satisfaction of the conditions for applicability of the diffusion approximation is not necessary in order to use model III. All that is important is that the cosmic rays fill the Galaxy evenly and mix rapidly enough (when compared with the departure time) throughout its volume. At the same time because of the rapid departure of particles from the Galaxy these conditions cannot be considered to be satisfied so model III is valid for rough estimates only. The actual situation is clearly best described by diffusion models which allow for inhomogeneity in the spatial distribution of the cosmic rays linked with their leakage from the Galaxy.

Recapitulating the results obtained for the three models examined which allow for reflexion at the boundaries of the Galaxy we come to the conclusion that this reflexion should not play a significant part and that cosmic rays clearly leave the Galaxy fairly freely through its boundaries.

We should stress that this conclusion is based on assumptions of the stationary nature of the process and efficient mixing of the cosmic rays in the Galaxy. If we do not accept the stationary nature of the cosmic ray generation process in the Galaxy and assume, for example, that the cosmic rays appeared at an early stage in the Galaxy's evolution and are kept in it[358] (there is no leakage) the difficulty with the composition does not arise.

In such a model, however, during the Galaxy's life of about 10^{10} years the cosmic rays should have passed through matter $x = 5$ to 8 g/cm^2 thick (see model IV in Table 15), which corresponds to a mean gas concentration in the Galaxy of $n \simeq 2$ to 4×10^{-4} cm^{-3}. It has already been pointed out in section 10 that this value is too low.

On the other hand we could reject the assumption that the cosmic rays are mixed in the Galaxy in favour of strictly regular motion of particles along the lines of force of the Galactic magnetic field. As can be seen from Table 15, the regular model (model IV) does not lead to any contradiction in the question of the cosmic ray composition in the source. If the number of lines of force extending beyond the Galaxy are also small, then in the regular model only a small number of cosmic rays will leave the Galaxy, which to a certain extent is equivalent to the presence of a reflecting boundary.

The regular model thus allows us in principle to match the observed composition with weak leakage of particles from the Galaxy. In this model, however, difficulties arise in explaining isotropy since in regular motion the particles are propagated from the source along each line of force only in one direction. Even if we assume that the cosmic ray fluxes in both directions along a given line of force are identical (which requires special arguments) anisotropy should be observed in the chemical composition of the cosmic rays since the thickness of matter passed through depends essentially on the pitch angle.† In other words, measurement of the chemical composition at one and the same point in space but for cosmic rays arriving from different directions should lead to essentially different results. The important thing is that the remarks made in section 10 are convincingly in favour of efficient mixing of the cosmic rays because of the pressure of the cosmic rays themselves and because of the motion of the gas and rotation of the Galaxy. The regular model is clearly incompatible with these ideas.

Therefore despite the fact that there is still a possibility of altering the model and varying the values of the parameters (the fragmentation probabilities in particular) we think that the least contradictory and most natural model is that of diffusion without reflexion at the boundaries of the Galaxy. In this case the assumption of free departure of cosmic rays from the Galaxy cannot contradict even the model of the galactic magnetic field as "tangled lines of force" if we have in mind departure as the result of instability and the ejection of cosmic rays from the Galaxy connected with it[266] (see also section 10).

By virtue of what has been said most attention will be paid in the future to diffusion models I and II without reflexion at the galactic boundaries. These two models are very close in their characteristics

† If the source is located at a distance L along a line of force and the motion is strictly adiabatic a particle's time of motion in interstellar space is $t = L/v_{\parallel} = L/v \cos \theta$ and the thickness of the matter passed through by the particle is $x = \rho v t = \rho L / \cos \theta$.

and in the present state of the question are actually indistinguishable as far as results go. The formal difference between model I and model II is that in the first of them free departure of cosmic rays is assumed to take place into intergalactic space that is not filled with cosmic rays, whilst in the second the departure proceeds more slowly— it is considered that the diffusion conditions do not change essentially when crossing the Galaxy's boundary.

The "Metagalactic" model V, which corresponds to an influx of cosmic rays into the Galaxy from outside, does not meet with any difficulties in the question of the composition, as can be seen from Table 15. However, the effective thickness of matter† $x \simeq 30$ to 50 g/cm^2 found for this model is too large if we consider that in intergalactic space the cosmic rays contain no nuclei of group L. This is because the solar system is comparatively close to the boundary of the Galaxy so, for the generation of the necessary number of L-nuclei, the density of the interstellar gas should be several times greater than in the case that cosmic rays move towards the Earth from the central regions of the Galaxy. Since the assumption of a high gas density, particularly in the outer regions of the Galaxy, is unacceptable it should be considered in the conditions of model V that there is already a considerable number of L-nuclei in the metagalactic cosmic rays. The problem of metagalactic cosmic rays as a whole has already been examined in section 13 and we shall not dwell on it here.

The next important conclusion that can be drawn upon examination of the results given in Table 15 is that the cosmic rays in the sources should contain a very considerable number of heavy nuclei. Table 16 compares the data on the composition of cosmic rays in sources and on Earth with Suess and Urey's[49] and Cameron's[50] data on the natural abundance of elements in the Universe (see Tables 1 and 15).

As can be seen from Table 16, in the cosmic ray sources the very heavy nuclei (subgroup VH, $Z \geqslant 20$) make up about half of all the nuclei of the H-group, whilst in the natural distribution there would

---

† We should remember that x defines the mean thickness of matter passed through by a particle moving towards the Earth from the centre of the Galaxy (see (15.15)). For the model in question, therefore, x is not the actual thickness of matter passed through but only characterises the conditions of motion—the diffusion coefficient and the density of the medium.

In the calculations the distance from the centre of the Galaxy to its boundary was taken as 12 kpc.

be about an order less of them. The position with protons and α-particles is the opposite. For the same number of H-nuclei in the cosmic ray sources there are 12 to 230 times fewer α-particles and 9 to 110 times fewer protons than in the natural abundances. The cosmic rays in the sources are thus characterised by a considerable excess of heavy nuclei and a small number of protons and α-particles when compared with the natural abundances of elements in the Universe. This difference is particularly significant if we look at the number of very heavy nuclei (group VH, $Z \geqslant 20$) for one and the same number of α-particles and protons: there are two or three orders more VH-nuclei in the cosmic ray sources than in the natural abundances.

TABLE 16

ABUNDANCES OF ELEMENTS IN COSMIC RAYS AND ON AVERAGE IN UNIVERSE

	Abundances (compared with H-group nuclei)				
	VH/H	M/H	L/H	α/H	p/H
Cosmic rays in sources	0·34 to 0·48	1·6 to 2·6	0	4·5 to 21	63 to 360
Cosmic rays on Earth	0·28	3·0	1·0	46	680
On average in the Universe:					
Suess and Urey[49]	0·06	2·6	10^{-5}	258	3360
Cameron[50]	0·05	10	10^{-5}	1040	6830

The conclusion of the considerable excess of heavy nuclei in the cosmic ray sources can be seen from Table 15 to relate to all the models discussed and all the sets of fragmentation probabilities used. In a qualitative respect this conclusion is clear even without solving the problem of the cosmic ray composition in a source if we bear in mind that there is an excess of heavy nuclei in the cosmic rays on Earth and that it should be even greater in the sources since the heavy nuclei are absorbed en route from the source more rapidly than the protons and α-particles are.

At the same time, the quantitative results relating to the content of the different charge groups in the sources are strongly dependent on the choice of model and the values of the fragmentation probabilities. This is particularly true of protons and α-particles and of the VH sub-group for which the fragmentation probability value of $P_{VH, VH} = 0.31$

used (see section 7) should be taken only as a guide. Because of this we still cannot definitely reject the possibility that the H group consists in the sources practically entirely of VH-nuclei and there are practically no protons or α-particles.[†] This limiting case corresponds to acceleration in the cosmic ray sources of very heavy nuclei only and will be discussed later.

The excess of heavy nuclei in the composition of the relativistic particles in the source can scarcely be explained simply by an anomalous content of elements in the source without introducing mechanisms for preferential acceleration of heavy elements. In actual fact the observational data are not in favour of such a high content of very heavy nuclei (relative to the medium nuclei and α-particles) in the stellar atmospheres and in the gas nebulae. In the theory of the origin of the elements a considerable excess of heavy elements can be obtained in the interiors of stars but the question of its preservation as the gas goes out to the surface of a star is still open. It is true that it is often suggested with respect to supernovae[8, 417] that they are anomalously rich in heavy elements but it is still not a question of several orders. Lastly, even if we assume that the cosmic ray sources are considerably richer in heavy elements than known astronomical objects it would still be necessary from the point of view under discussion to show that the particle composition remains unchanged during injection and acceleration from thermal to relativistic energies, which is far from being self-evident.

On the other hand, the possibility indicated in section 9 of preferential acceleration of heavy nuclei does not require a specific source composition and provides a natural explanation for the excess of heavy nuclei in the accelerated particles. It is not assumed, of course, that only very heavy nuclei are accelerated in the sources. As has already been indicated in section 9, the acceleration conditions are most favourable for heavy nuclei but this does not exclude the possibility of acceleration of a certain number of lighter elements too.

Moreover a cosmic ray composition that is fairly close to that observed on Earth can be obtained on the assumption that only very heavy nuclei are accelerated in the sources. This possibility has been discussed by several authors.[12, 331, 418] Table 17 shows as an example the results of calculating the expected composition of cosmic rays on Earth on the assumption that only VH-nuclei are accelerated in the source ($q_H = q_{VH}$, $q_M = q_L = q_\alpha = q_p = 0$). The calculations

† See, however, Refs. 45 and 479, and also the first footnote on p. 315.

are made for diffusion model II without allowing for the effect of the boundaries. Because of the absence of reliable data on the fragmentation probabilities of the *VH*-group in hydrogen the number of *VH*-nuclei on Earth is estimated from the relation

$$\frac{N_{VH}}{N_H} = \frac{F_{VH}}{F_H}. \tag{15.20}$$

It is assumed here that in the source the *H*-group consists entirely of *VH*-nuclei so $q_H = q_{VH}$. The expected number of protons is determined by the relations

$$N_p = N_{\text{nucleon}} - \sum_{i=H, L, M, \alpha} \bar{A}_i N_i, \tag{15.21}$$

$$N_{\text{nucleon}} = q_{\text{nucleon}} F_{\text{nucleon}}, \qquad q_{\text{nucleon}} = \bar{A}_{VH} q_{VH}.$$

Here $\bar{A}_i$ are the mean atomic weights of the groups from Table 10. For the diffusion model II in question the functions $F_i(x)$ are defined as $F_i(x) = (1/4\pi Dr) \exp\{-\sqrt{2x/\lambda_i}\}$, where the values $\lambda_{VH} = 4 \cdot 4$ g/cm^2 and $\lambda_{\text{nucleon}} \simeq \lambda_p = 72$ g/cm^2 are used and the other values of λ_i are taken from Table 12. The calculations are made under the condition that the concentration ratio of nuclei of groups *L* and *H* should agree with the ratio $N_L/N_H = 1$ observed on Earth.

TABLE 17

COMPOSITION OF PRIMARY COSMIC RAYS WITH ONLY
VH-NUCLEI ACCELERATED

Variant	Thickness of matter x, g/cm^2	Expected ratio of concentrations				
		VH/H	*M/H*	*L/H*	α/H	*p/H*
a	35	0·55	1·15	1	22	418
b	55	0·59	1·31	1	33	1100
c	20	0·56	0·95	1	14	165
d	40	0·41	1·37	1	31	338
Observed composition		0·28	3	1	46	680

The results given in Table 17 show that the assumption of the acceleration of *VH*-nuclei only in the sources can explain qualitatively the basic feature in the relative frequency of the groups of nuclei in the cosmic rays on Earth, but nevertheless does not agree satisfactorily in a quantitative respect with the available data. Above all the concentration of M-group nuclei is too low.

This discrepancy can be eliminated if we assume that the cosmic rays pass through a greater thickness of matter than is accepted in Table 17. However, this leads to an extremely high concentration of L-group nuclei as compared to the observed one. In addition, the values given in Table 17 for the thickness of matter x passed through are quite obviously too high. For example, if we take the best value $D \simeq 10^{29}$ cm²/sec for the diffusion coefficient (see below and section 16) the thickness of matter $x \simeq 20$ to 50 g/cm² should correspond to a mean interstellar gas concentration $n \simeq 0.1$ to 0.3 cm⁻³. This is more than an order greater than the previously accepted value of $n \simeq 10^{-2}$ cm⁻³.

These difficulties which are met with by the assumption of acceleration of only heavy nuclei in the sources must not be considered insuperable, particularly if we bear in mind the present uncertainty in the choice of a model of the propagation of cosmic rays in the Galaxy, the values of the fragmentation probabilities† and the magnitude of the diffusion coefficient.‡ At the same time, we should bear in mind the objections[25, 45] connected with the necessity of explaining such finer features of the composition as, e.g., the presence of gaps in the charge spectrum, the relative frequency of the various elements, etc. (see section 1). The answering of these questions as well as the general increasing of the precision in the data on the cosmic ray composition and the values of the fragmentation probabilities will be of decisive importance not only for the assumption of the acceleration of VH-nuclei only but also for the problem of chemical composition as a whole.

It is important, moreover, to bear in mind that the assumption of the exclusive acceleration of only very heavy nuclei is an idealisation

† If the new values for the fragmentation probabilities[479] for hydrogen ($p_{HL} > p_{HM}$; see footnote on page 133) are confirmed, then the possibility of acceleration in the sources of only heavy (H) or very heavy (VH) nuclei can be considered entirely excluded. Indeed, there would in this case be more group L nuclei than group M nuclei for any model of the propagation of cosmic rays.

‡ We shall stress once again here that as applied to cosmic rays in the Galaxy the diffusion coefficient $D = lv/3$ has the meaning of a certain effective quantity characterising the mixing of cosmic rays in space (see section 10). Its value should first be determined from the condition of an uncontradictory interpretation of the whole combination of data on the spatial distribution, chemical composition and anisotropy of cosmic rays in the Galaxy and not simply by identifying the effective length of the free path l with the purely geometrical distance between inhomogeneities observed at a given time in the Galaxy.

and there is no reason to limit ourselves to this extreme case. In actual fact when the conditions discussed in section 9 for preferential acceleration of heavy elements are realised there will be a certain finite, although relatively small, flux of other nuclei from the thermal to the relativistic range of energies. It is important here that the injection conditions are most favourable for heavy nuclei so the number of them in the accelerated particles rises considerably when compared with the original composition of the elements in the source. This situation agrees fully with the results of calculating the chemical composition of the cosmic rays in the sources given in Tables 15, 16.

Let us now discuss the estimates of the value of the diffusion co-efficient and the power of cosmic ray sources in the Galaxy which proceed from the calculations of the chemical composition. Here, in accordance with the remarks made earlier, we shall limit ourselves to discussing the diffusion models without reflexion at the boundaries of the Galaxy (models I and II).

The values given in Table 15 of the value of the mean thickness x of matter passed through allow us to determine (see (15.15)) the value of the diffusion coefficient if the concentration of the interstellar gas n is known. We have

$$D = \frac{\rho c r^2}{2x} \simeq 2 \times 10^{31} \frac{n}{x} \tag{15.22}$$

(the distance of the solar system from the centre of the Galaxy is taken to be $r = 8$ kpc $\simeq 2 \cdot 5 \times 10^{22}$ cm). It can be seen from Table 15 that for diffusion models I and II and the various possible choices of values for the fragmentation probabilities the mean thickness of matter passed through is $x \sim 10$ g/cm^2. With the value we used earlier (see (7.1)) for the mean concentration of gas in the Galaxy $n \simeq 10^{-2}$ cm^{-3} this leads to the value $D \simeq 2 \times 10^{28}$ cm^2/sec. It should, however, be borne in mind that the cosmic ray composition observed on Earth is largely formed in the interior of the Galaxy where the gas concentration is several times greater than the mean concentration over the whole Galaxy. Therefore the most acceptable value for the diffusion coefficient in the Galaxy is

$$D = \frac{lv}{3} \simeq 0 \cdot 5 \text{ to } 1 \times 10^{29} \text{ cm}^2/\text{sec}. \tag{15.23}$$

As we shall see in section 16, this value also agrees with the data on the anisotropy of cosmic rays and the available information on the characteristic sizes l of the galactic magnetic field inhomogeneities.

Let us now move on to an estimate of the power of the cosmic ray sources in the Galaxy. It has been indicated earlier (see section 1) that the total proton intensity on Earth at a period of minimum solar activity, when the effect of high-latitude cut-off can clearly be ignored, is $I_p \simeq 0.2$ protons/cm^2·sterad·sec. Allowing, in accordance with Table 1, for the contribution of nuclei with the same energy per nucleon we obtain for the total intensity of the nucleons in the cosmic ray nuclei on Earth the value $I_{nucleon} \simeq 0.4$ nucleons/cm^2·sterad·sec. Hence the total concentration of relativistic nucleons on Earth is (see (1.5))

$$N_{nucleon} = \frac{4\pi}{\bar{v}} I_{nucleon} \simeq 2 \times 10^{-10} \text{ cm}^{-3}$$

(here it is assumed that $\bar{v} \simeq c$). Further, putting in (15.6) and (15.7) $r = 8$ kpc $= 2.5 \times 10^{22}$ cm, $R = 12$ kpc $= 3.7 \times 10^{22}$ cm, $D = 0.2$ to 1×10^{29} cm^2/sec, $\lambda_{nucleon} \simeq \lambda_p = 72$ g/cm^2 and $x \simeq 10$ g/cm^2 and allowing for the fact that $N_{nucleon} = q_{nucleon} F_{nucleon}(x)$ we find for diffusion models I and II:

(I) $q_{nucleon} \simeq 0.4$ to 2×10^{43} nucleons/sec,

(II) $q_{nucleon} \simeq 0.2$ to 1×10^{43} nucleons/sec. $\qquad$ (15.24)

For a mean energy $\bar{\mathscr{E}}_k \simeq 4$ GeV/nucleon (see (1.5–(1.6)) this corresponds to a source energy power:

(I) $U = \bar{\mathscr{E}}_k q_{nucleon} \simeq 1.6$ to 8×10^{52} eV/sec
$$= 3 \text{ to } 13 \times 10^{40} \text{ erg/sec,}$$

(II) $U \simeq 0.8$ to 4×10^{22} eV/sec $= 1.5$ to 6×10^{40} erg/sec. $\qquad$ (15.25)

In model I the volume of the halo is $V \simeq 2 \times 10^{68}$ cm^3 and the cosmic ray energy is $W \simeq 3 \times 10^{56}$ ergs. Hence at $U \simeq 13$ to 3×10^{40} ergs/sec the life of cosmic rays in the Galaxy is $T_d = W/U \simeq 1$ to 3×10^8 years.

When compared with the "closed" model (see section 11) the open model of the Galaxy, i.e., the assumption of the free leakage of cosmic rays through the galactic boundaries, corresponds to an increase of about an order of magnitude in the energy power of the sources. From the point of view of the energy balance this is still quite compatible with the assumption of the generation of the majority of cosmic rays in supernovae.

All the results obtained above relate to the chemical composition of the majority of cosmic rays with energies of several GeV/nucleon. There are some experimental data (recording of α-particles with an energy of $\simeq 10^{14}$ eV and the absence of any peculiar features in the energy spectrum) which indicate that the composition remains unchanged in the transition to higher energies as well right up to energies of $E \sim 10^{15}$ to 10^{16} eV. The question of the chemical composition of cosmic rays with very high energies $E > 10^{16}$ eV is still unclear (see section 3). We shall return again to this energy range in section 16. Here we shall discuss briefly the question of the chemical composition of cosmic rays in the region of low (non-relativistic) energies $\mathscr{E}_k < 1$ GeV/nucleon.

As has already been pointed out in section 1, a tendency was clearly found[31, 37, 44] for a rise in the number of group L nuclei in the composition of the cosmic rays with energies of $0.2 < \mathscr{E}_k < 0.7$ GeV/nucleon when compared with the number of them at energies of $\mathscr{E}_k > 1$ GeV/nucleon. This rise may be connected either with the dependence of the fragmentation probabilities p_{ik} on the energy that appears in the non-relativistic range or with the fact that the non-relativistic particles pass through a great thickness of matter. Ionisation losses clearly have no part to play since the rise in the number of L-nuclei (when compared with M-nuclei) is not accompanied by a corresponding reduction in the number of H-nuclei.

The available data on the function $p_{ik}(\mathscr{E})$ are not full enough yet but the conclusion can nevertheless clearly be drawn[17] that this dependence is not a cause of the indicated rise in the number of L-nuclei at low energies. In this case it should be assumed that before reaching the Earth the non-relativistic particles pass through a greater thickness of matter than relativistic ones. If this effect is confirmed by further measurements it will be an important argument against the regular model. In actual fact with regular (adiabatic) motion along the lines of force all the particles arriving in a given direction move along one and the same path and independently of their velocity pass from the source to the point of observation through one and the same thickness of matter (see footnote on page 310).

In diffusion propagation of cosmic rays the direct dependence of the diffusion coefficient $D = lv/3$ on the velocity of the particle v cannot be the cause of the change indicated in the composition in the low-energy region either. The point is that the observed chemical composition, as we have already seen, is fully defined by the value of the ratios

$$\frac{x}{\lambda_i} = \frac{r^2}{2DT_i} = \frac{r^2}{ll_{\text{nucl},i}}, \tag{15.26}$$

where l is the diffusion length and $l_{\text{nucl},i}$ the mean free path of a nucleus of kind i before it is absorbed; r is the distance from the source. For nuclei the absorption cross sections (and the mean free paths l_{nucl} respectively) are weakly dependent on the particle energy in the range under discussion. The diffusion length l, generally speaking, depends on the particle's radius of curvature in the magnetic field, i.e., on the particle's momentum. This dependence can, however, be important only at very high energies (see sections 10 and 16) when the radius of curvature is comparable with the size of the interstellar magnetic field inhomogeneities.

Therefore if we consider that the diffusion of particles takes place in a given stationary magnetic field we can see no possibility of explaining the observed change of composition in the non-relativistic energy range. It is otherwise if the diffusion (mixing) of the cosmic rays is caused to a considerable extent by interconnected motions of the cosmic rays and the interstellar gas (see section 10). It is then natural to take it that the nature of the mixing depends essentially on the magnitude of the ratio v/u, where u is the medium's characteristic velocity of motion.† In this case the velocity of the ultra-relativistic particles ($v \simeq c$) is practically constant and the nature of their diffusion will not depend on the energy, whilst for non-relativistic (or weakly relativistic) particles this dependence may be significant particularly if one bears in mind that the chemical composition (number of L-nuclei) is strongly dependent upon the thickness of matter passed through.

The experimental and theoretical elucidation of this question can provide valuable information on the nature of cosmic ray diffusion in the interstellar magnetic fields.

To conclude this section let us formulate the basic conclusions which proceed from the above analysis of the data on the chemical composition of cosmic rays.

1. When compared with the composition of the elements in the atmospheres of stars, nebulae and on the average in the

† This dependence appears, for example, if the rate of mixing depends on the time $t \sim l/v$ spent by a particle in magnetic field inhomogeneities with a scale l moving randomly at a mean velocity u.

Universe, cosmic rays, particularly in their sources, are far richer in heavy nuclei. This fact apparently cannot be explained without assuming preferential acceleration of heavy elements in the cosmic ray sources.

2. The composition observed on Earth is not compatible with the "closed" model of the Galaxy in which it is assumed that the sources are stationary and the life of cosmic rays in the Galaxy is determined chiefly by nuclear interactions in the interstellar gas. Under these conditions the composition would be close to equilibrium and there would be too many L-nuclei, α-particles and protons.

3. The cosmic ray propagation models in which reflexion at the galactic boundaries is inessential lead to similar results with respect to the composition in the sources. In this sense the regular model is indistinguishable from the diffusion model. However, a number of qualitative considerations about the nature of cosmic ray motion in the Galaxy (section 10) together with the available radio astronomy information (section 5) speak in favour of efficient mixing of the cosmic rays in the Galaxy, i.e., in favour of the diffusion model. In addition, we can see a number of consequences of the regular model (anisotropy, difference in the properties of relativistic particles in nearby regions of space and certain others) which can in principle be checked experimentally.

4. The most consistent description of the properties of cosmic rays in the Galaxy at present is provided by the diffusion model without significant reflexion of particles on the galactic boundaries. In this case the life time of cosmic rays in the Galaxy ($T \sim 3 \times 10^8$ years) is approximately an order less and the power required of the sources ($U \sim 3 \times 10^{40}$ erg/sec) is correspondingly an order greater than in the case of the "closed" model. This source power can be ensured with cosmic ray generation by supernovae (see section 11). As will be shown in section 16, the diffusion model without reflexion also agrees with the available data on cosmic ray isotropy.

16. ENERGY SPECTRUM AND SPATIAL DISTRIBUTION (ANISOTROPY) OF COSMIC RAYS

It follows from the experimental data (see section 3) that the cosmic ray energy spectrum on Earth over a very wide range of energies is characterised by a power-law dependence of the intensity on the energy with an identical power index $\gamma \simeq 2 \cdot 5$ for all nuclei.

There is, of course, no direct information on the spectrum far from the solar system and in the cosmic ray sources. However, basing ourselves on the radio astronomy data and their interpretation in the light of the magnetic bremsstrahlung theory of cosmic radio emission we can conclude that as a whole in the Galaxy the energy spectrum of relativistic electrons (at least with energies more than several GeV) is of the form $N(E) = K_e E^{-\gamma}$ with $\gamma \simeq 2$ to 3.

Moreover, radio astronomy data indicate that in other galaxies the electron energy spectrum is close to a power-law one with an index γ within the limits $1 < \gamma < 4$. It may be assumed, therefore, that the process of formation of the energy spectrum of relativistic particles in different regions of the Universe is of a universal nature and depends comparatively little on the actual conditions in one or the other cosmic ray source.

In this section we shall discuss the various mechanisms leading to the formation of a power-law spectrum in the process of cosmic ray acceleration and propagation in the Galaxy. In addition, we shall discuss the possible causes for the change in the cosmic ray energy spectrum in the very high energy region (the spectrum becomes steeper in this region according to observations). Since one of the reasons for this change may be the rapid departure of cosmic rays with high energies from the Galaxy we shall at the same time make estimates of the expected degree of cosmic ray anisotropy in the light of the Galactic theory of their origin.

Energy spectrum formation in the process of particle acceleration

The possibility of explaining the appearance in the acceleration process of cosmic rays with a power-law energy spectrum was first indicated by Fermi.[318] Here the following assumptions were made.

1. The particle acceleration follows law (9.7) which ensures an exponential rise in particle energy with time

$$\frac{dE}{dt} = \alpha E, \qquad E = E_0 e^{\alpha t}, \tag{16.1}$$

where E_0 is the initial energy of the particle.

2. The probability that the acceleration of a particle lasts for a time t and in the interval $t, t + dt$ the particle is knocked out of play is

$$w(t)dt = \frac{1}{T} e^{-t/T} dt. \tag{16.2}$$

Here T is obviously the mean life of a particle in the region where the acceleration mechanism is active.

3. The particle injection and acceleration conditions stay constant for the time necessary for the particle to acquire the maximum observed energy. In other words the parameters α and T are constant and the particle injection is uniform over a time

$$t \gtrsim \frac{1}{\alpha} \ln \frac{E_m}{E_0}, \tag{16.3}$$

where E_m is the maximum particle energy in the spectrum.

Upon these assumptions we obtain from relations (16.1) and (16.2) for the energy range $E > E_0$ the following energy distribution of the particles (see also section 11):

$$N(E)\, dE = KE^{-\gamma}\, dE, \qquad \gamma = 1 + \frac{1}{\alpha T}, \tag{16.4}$$

where K is a normalising coefficient. Spectrum (16.4) can, of course, also be obtained as a solution of the general equation (14.2) if we keep in the latter only the terms defining the systematic acceleration and catastrophic losses with a mean life $T_i = 1/p_i$ (see also formula (16.9) below at $\delta \to 0$).

With a definite choice of parameters α and T we can obtain the required value of the index γ in the power-law particle spectrum (16.4). Fermi[318] considered the acceleration to occur throughout the Galaxy and the mean life of cosmic rays with respect to nuclear collisions (the "closed" model) was taken as T. These assumptions had later to be rejected, however.

Above all when the similarity of the energy spectra of the various nuclei had been established it became clear that the power index cannot depend on the nuclear life $T_{\text{nucl},i}$. Otherwise with $\gamma = 2 \cdot 5$ in the proton spectrum we should have $\gamma \simeq 19$ in the H-nuclei spectrum for example (see (16.4) and T_i from Table 10), which definitely contradicts experiment.

It was therefore later assumed[359] that the acceleration occurs as before in interstellar space (chiefly in the region of the spiral) but the life T is defined as the mean time for diffusion departure from the acceleration region which is identical for all particles. The appropriate strict solution of the problem can be obtained by solving equation (14.2) allowing for the diffusion term but it is clear that the result will be qualitatively the same if we put $1/T = 1/T_d + 1/T_{\text{nucl},i}$ and

$T_d \simeq L^2/D$, where L is the characteristic size of the acceleration region (thickness of the spiral arm), in (16.4). Since the spectrum index γ should not depend on the kind i of the nuclei in question we should consider that $T \simeq T_d \ll T_{\text{nucl},i}$ for all i. In accordance with this we must assume that the acceleration efficiency α is considerably higher than was assumed in the original case[318] in order to obtain $\gamma \simeq 2 \cdot 5$.

The latter assumption only increases the difficulties analysed in section 11 and which are connected with a low efficiency of interstellar acceleration. In actual fact, as was shown in section 11, the acceleration of a particle in interstellar space during the whole of the Galaxy's existence could hardly increase the energy of a particle by more than an order. This means that spectrum (16.4) in the best case would occur in a narrow (tenfold) range of energies. In reality the power-law cosmic ray spectrum covers at least five or six orders with respect to the energy.

Therefore the mechanism suggested by Fermi[318] and by Morrison et al.[359] for the formation of the cosmic ray spectrum cannot occur when applied to the Galaxy as a whole (see also section 11). The situation is still not clear enough as regards the possibility of applying this mechanism to individual cosmic ray sources (e.g., nebulae and supernova shells). Nevertheless the fairly rigid assumptions made when deriving spectrum (16.4) (particularly those about the stationary nature of the process) and the strong dependence of the spectral index γ on the actual values of α and T force us to assume that the spectrum formation mechanism in question clearly cannot relate to cosmic ray sources either. In actual fact the circumstance that the spectral index γ has a value close to $\gamma = 2 \cdot 5$ proves to be pure chance in this scheme, particularly if one bears in mind that the parameters α and T are not interconnected and vary over a very wide range for the various objects in space.

Apart from the mechanism just examined, which is the one most often discussed in published works for the formation of the cosmic ray energy spectrum, other attempts have also been made to obtain a power-law spectrum by proceeding from actual acceleration mechanisms and specific conditions for the motion of particles in accelerating fields.[325, 413, 415, 419, 421] It would, however, be more natural to assume that the form of the cosmic ray energy spectrum, and their generation in general, is a fundamental property of the dynamics of a turbulent magnetised plasma under cosmic conditions. The basis for this is the similarity of the relativistic particle spectra in different regions of the Universe: on Earth, in the Galaxy as a whole, in other galaxies (including radio galaxies) and in many galactic sources of non-thermal cosmic radio emission.

Unfortunately the dynamics of a magnetised plasma, particularly under conditions of considerable turbulence, have as yet been very little studied. There nevertheless exists the possibility[423, 424] of obtaining with certain fairly natural assumptions a power-law cosmic ray spectrum with an index $\gamma \simeq 2 \cdot 5$ that hardly depends at all on the nature of the acceleration or the conditions for particle motion in the cosmic magnetic fields. We shall discuss this possibility a little later. For the present we shall discuss briefly the allowance for fluctuations in the acceleration of cosmic rays.

The part played by fluctuating accelerations

It has already been pointed out that fast particles can appear even if on the average there is no acceleration (i.e., $b(E) = dE/dt = 0$ in equation (14.2)). This will occur, for example, if the particles pass successively through regions with increasing and decreasing magnetic fields, the magnetic field not increasing on the average over the whole region. Under these conditions the appearance of fast particles is connected with a deviation of their behaviour from the mean because of fluctuations (for example, fluctuations in the length of stay of a particle in regions with a rising and falling magnetic field). Of course, if the energy does not rise on the average there will be particles that lose energy as well as ones that are accelerated. The "acceleration process" in this case is described by the fluctuation term $-\frac{1}{2}(\partial^2/\partial E^2)[d(E)N]$ in equation (14.2) and may lead to a change in the form of the cosmic ray energy spectrum.

Let us establish the form of the coefficient $d(E)$ in the case of statistical acceleration due to collisions of particles with moving magnetic field inhomogeneities. For the sake of simplicity, just as in section 9, we shall limit ourselves to only head-on and tail-on collisions with the magnetic clouds. Using expression (9.3) it is then easy to determine the mean square change of the energy in one collision

$$(\Delta E)^2 = \frac{4E^2 u^2 v^2}{c^4} (p_+ + p_-) = \frac{4E^2}{c^4} u^2 v^2, \qquad (16.5)$$

where p_+ and p_- are the probabilities of head-on and tail-on collisions ($p_+ + p_- = 1$). Hence at a collision frequency of $1/\tau = v/l$, where τ is the mean time between collisions and l is the corresponding length of the free path, we obtain

$$d(E) \equiv \frac{d}{dt}(\Delta E)^2 = \frac{4u^2v^2E^2}{\tau c^4}. \qquad (16.6)$$

In the general case

$$d(E) = 2\delta\left(\frac{v}{c}\right)^3 E^2, \quad \text{where} \quad \delta = \xi\frac{u^2}{cl} = \xi\alpha. \qquad (16.7)$$

Here α is the acceleration parameter from (9.7) and ξ is a numerical factor of $\xi = 2$ for head-on collisions and $\xi = \frac{1}{4}$ for collisions with elastic spheres (the length of the path l is here defined as in (9.7)).

Let us now determine the nature of the changes in the energy spectrum (16.4) caused by fluctuations in the acceleration process. Let us assume, as we did when obtaining spectrum (16.4), that stationary sources fill the region of space in question evenly and inject particles with energies $E < E_0$. Then the energy spectrum of the particles in the energy range $E > E_0$ will be defined by the expression (see (14.2))

$$\frac{\partial}{\partial E}(\alpha EN) - \frac{\partial^2}{\partial E^2}(\delta E^2 N) + \frac{N}{T} = 0. \qquad (16.8)$$

Here T is the mean life of the particles in the volume in question and $v = c$ is put in the coefficients (9.7) and (16.7), i.e., the range of relativistic particle energies is the one in question. It can be easily confirmed that the solution of equation (16.8) is of the form

$$N(E) = KE^{-\gamma}, \quad \gamma = \frac{1}{2}\left[3 - \frac{\alpha}{\delta} \pm \sqrt{\left(1 - \frac{\alpha}{\delta}\right)^2 + \frac{4}{\delta T}}\right]. \qquad (16.9)$$

The appearance of two independent solutions (two values of γ) is due to the presence of a second energy derivative in (16.8). In this case the stationary spectrum is determined not only by the particle concentration at a certain energy but also by the particle flux in the energy space.

If $\delta T \gg 1$, the solution does not depend upon T and the corresponding two roots are $\gamma = 2 - \alpha/\delta$ and $\gamma = 1$. In both cases $\gamma < 2$, which does not let us explain the value $\gamma > 2$ in the observed spectrum in this way. A value $\gamma \gtrsim 2$ could be obtained by choosing the appropriate value $\alpha T \sim 1$ in (16.9). In this case, however, the spectral index γ will essentially depend upon the actual values of the parameters α, δ and T and the same difficulties arise as when deriving equation (16.4) without allowing for fluctuations. Allowing for fluctuations, therefore, does not lead to any qualitatively new results with respect to the cosmic ray energy spectrum.

We notice that, as should be the case, when we put $\delta \to 0$ in (16.9) we return to spectrum (16.4) when the plus sign is chosen. It is simpler to obtain this last result, however, directly from (16.8) with $\delta = 0$.

The cosmic ray spectrum when the energies W_{cr}, W_H and W_{turb} in the sources are equal

An important result of observations is the conclusion that under cosmic conditions (both in individual nebulae that are cosmic ray sources and in the Galaxy as a whole) there is an approximate equipartition of energy between the cosmic rays, the magnetic field and the random (turbulent) motions of the gas.

The equality of the magnetic and kinetic energies during the turbulent motion of a magnetised conducting medium is apparently a general consequence of the behaviour of magnetohydrodynamic systems.[425] The point is that random motion of a conducting medium leads to a rise in the initial "frozen in" magnetic field, no matter how weak, and this equality of the magnetic and kinetic energies is the natural limit for this increase.

As for the quasi-stationary relation between the cosmic ray energy W_{cr} and the magnetic field energy

$$W_{magn} = \int \frac{H^2}{8\pi} \, dV,$$

there are at present only a few, qualitative ideas.[426,427] Since the generation and acceleration of cosmic rays is apparently a universal property of a magnetised turbulent plasma the question is reduced to finding the limit to which the cosmic ray energy may rise. If the plasma with a magnetic field in question occupies a limited volume it is natural to consider that this limit is the maximum cosmic ray energy (or pressure) at which they are still held by the magnetic field frozen into this plasma. At a greater energy density (and thus a greater pressure) the cosmic rays "break through" the restraining magnetic field. There will thus be a sort of valve that releases the surplus cosmic rays from the limited volume in question.

It is natural to assume that after this limit is reached a state of quasi-stationary equilibrium is established, which is maintained by leakage of the excess cosmic rays. It may be assumed that in this state the energy is approximately evenly distributed between the three above-mentioned components, i.e., $W_{cr} \sim W_{magn} \sim W_{turb}$. We shall discuss later a fairly general case; at present we shall make a more definite assumption by putting

$$W_{cr} = W_{turb} = W_{magn} = \tfrac{1}{3} W_{tot}. \tag{16.10}$$

Here W_{tot} is the total energy in the volume in question made up of the kinetic energy of the gas' turbulent motion W_{turb}, the magnetic field energy W_{magn} and the cosmic ray energy W_{cr}. As the volume of the cosmic ray source in which equality (16.10) is assumed to be satisfied we must select the shell of a supernova or for a radio galaxy, perhaps, the volume of its central region. Below we shall speak simply of the volume of a nebula.

We shall assume that the quasi-stationary energy distribution (16.10) is reached rapidly when compared with the characteristic time of energy loss to dissipation inside the nebula. We shall, in addition, consider that the injection of fast particles in the nebula has ceased and the decrease of energy proceeds chiefly by cosmic ray leakage. The latter may be caused by diffusion of the cosmic rays through the boundaries of the nebula and by ejection of "clumps" of particles as a result of local magnetic field "breaches" on the nebula's periphery.

Then to maintain the equilibrium of (16.10) the decrease in cosmic ray energy in the nebula as a result of their leakage should be compensated by a rise in the energy of the relativistic particles due to the action of some acceleration mechanism or other. In other words, for equilibrium of (16.10) to be maintained there should be continuous pumping of turbulent and magnetic energy into the cosmic ray energy.

Let us write the energy balance equation for the process in question:

$$dW_{tot} \equiv d(3N_0 E_k) = \bar{E}_k \, dN_0. \tag{16.11}$$

Here N_0 is the number of relativistic particles in the nebula, $\bar{E}_k$ is their mean kinetic energy and use is made of the equality $W_{tot} = 3N_0 \bar{E}_k$ which follows from (16.10). In future we shall discuss only the region of ultra-relativistic energies, when $E_k \simeq E$.

Equation (16.11) gives the following connexion between the number of relativistic particles remaining in the nebula and their mean energy

$$N_0 = \text{const } (\bar{E})^{-1.5}. \tag{16.12}$$

Hence it follows that the differential energy spectrum of the particles leaving the nebula is of the form

$$N(E) \, dE = -dN_0 = \text{const } E^{-2.5} \, dE. \tag{16.13}$$

Here we have replaced the mean energy of the particles in the cloud for a given point in time $\bar{E}$ by the true energy of the particles E. This replacement is obviously valid if all the particles in the nebula have more or less identical energy, which corresponds to the fairly natural assumption of the injection of the accelerated particles during a short period of time (for example at the comparatively short stage of acceleration without injection; see section 9).

This assumption is not obligatory, however, It can be shown[424] that spectrum (16.13) for particles leaving the source nebula will occur with practically any particle spectrum inside the source and for all known acceleration mechanisms. All that is important is that the initial energy spectrum in the source should decrease sufficiently rapidly in the high energy region (more rapidly than spectrum (16.13)) and that the acceleration mechanisms should ensure a rise in energy proportional to the energy of the particle. The first of these conditions is obviously satisfied since the initial spectrum generally does not contain very fast particles. The second condition is satisfied for all the acceleration mechanisms discussed in section 9.

We notice that in the general case if the cosmic ray energy in the state of quasi-stationary equilibrium discussed is a fraction δ of the remaining forms of energy, i.e.,

$$W_{cr} = \delta(W_{tot} - W_{cr}), \tag{16.14}$$

then the differential energy spectrum of the relativistic particles leaving the source will be of the form[423]

$$N(E) \, dE = \text{const } E^{-(2+\delta)} \, dE. \tag{16.15}$$

In the case of equipartition of the energy between the three components, discussed above, we obviously have $\delta = \frac{1}{2}$.

Therefore with general enough assumptions about the nature of the particle generation and acceleration in the sources for particles leaving a source we obtain spectrum (16.13) which is in close agreement with that observed for galactic cosmic rays.†

We notice that in the framework of the scheme discussed the relativistic particle spectrum in the source is in no way connected with their spectrum outside the source and in principle is quite arbitrary. At the same time it follows from the radio astronomy data that the spectrum of the relativistic electrons in supernova shell nebulae is generally close to the galactic cosmic ray spectrum.

It must, however, be pointed out, that the spectra of the radio-emitting electrons in the galactic nebulae sometimes differ significantly from the galactic cosmic ray spectrum. For example for the Crab Nebula the differential energy spectrum of the relativistic electrons is characterised by an index $\gamma = 1{\cdot}7$, whilst from sufficiently general considerations based on an examination of the energy losses it follows that the spectrum of the relativistic electrons (if they and the cosmic rays have a common origin or if they are secondary in nature) can be only softer than the cosmic ray spectrum‡ (this means that γ for electrons is higher than γ for protons and nuclei). In addition, the very question of the nature of the radio-emitting electrons in the shells of supernovae (particularly type 1 supernovae) is still far from clear. There are therefore not yet any serious reasons for requiring that the mechanisms for forming the cosmic ray spectrum must lead to an identical spectrum both inside and outside the sources.

Result (16.15), as we have seen, is very general and therein lies its value. It must not be forgotten, however, that this result was obtained under certain idealised conditions which should by no means always be satisfied. In particular, formula (16.15) will not, generally speaking, be valid under conditions where there is a great

† Above we assumed energetic isolation of the system including the cosmic rays, the gas and the random magnetic field connected with it. In the case of solar cosmic rays which arise in the chromosphere in the region of sunspots this is invalid. In actual fact, in this case the behaviour of the fast particles and the gas in the region of the chromospheric flares is determined by the strong magnetic field of the spots that is caused by external factors. Even in this case, however, we can apply the simple thermodynamic considerations that lead to a power-law spectrum for the solar cosmic rays but with a stronger dependence on the energy (in the differential energy spectrum the spectral index is $\gamma \simeq 3{\cdot}5$ in the non-relativistic energy region and $\gamma \simeq 5$ for the ultra-relativistic particles; for more detail see a paper by Syrovatskii[424]).

‡ If the electrons are secondary the only exception can be the region of low energies corresponding to the energy threshold for the generation of decaying $\pi^{\pm}$-mesons (see section 17).

expenditure of energy of the cosmic rays in shell expansion,† and so on.

Cosmic ray anisotropy

In the diffusion model of cosmic ray propagation in the Galaxy we have taken, there is a constant flux of cosmic rays from the central regions of the Galaxy to its periphery. There should be a definite degree of cosmic ray anisotropy connected with this flux. We shall estimate the magnitude of this anisotropy, basing ourselves on the value of the diffusion coefficient $D \simeq 10^{29}$ cm^2/sec obtained in section 15.

The degree of anisotropy of cosmic rays is usually defined as

$$\delta = \frac{I_{max} - I_{min}}{I_{max} + I_{min}}, \qquad (16.16)$$

where I_{max} and I_{min} are the maximum and minimum values of the intensity at a given point as a function of the direction.

Let us now find the corresponding expression for the degree of anisotropy in the diffusion model. We take the intensity of the cosmic rays as a function of the direction in the form‡

$$I(\theta) = \bar{I} + \delta\bar{I} \cos\theta, \qquad \bar{I} = \tfrac{1}{2}(I_{max} + I_{min}), \qquad (16.17)$$

where $\theta = 0$ corresponds to the direction in which the intensity is maximum ($I = I_{max}$) and $\theta = \pi$ is the direction of minimum intensity ($I = I_{min}$). Then the resultant flux of particles through an area at right angles to the direction $\theta = 0$ is

$$F_D = 2\pi \int_0^\pi I(\theta) \cos\theta \sin\theta \, d\theta = \frac{4\pi}{3} \delta\bar{I}. \qquad (16.18)$$

On the other hand, in the diffusion model the flux of particles through a unit area is defined as

$$F_D = -D\nabla N = -D \frac{dN}{dr}. \qquad (16.19)$$

† A generalisation of formula (16.13) to allow for a change in the volume of the source (i.e. expansion of the shell) is given by Sato.[491] His paper also analyses the form of the spectrum of the secondary electrons generated in the source in nuclear collisions of the cosmic rays during the acceleration process.

‡ Expression (16.17) is not, of course, the most general one possible but in practice we can limit ourselves to it.

Here, when we change to the second equality it is considered that the propagation models we have discussed possess spherical symmetry. In this case we calculate the particle flux through a unit area at right angles to the direction of the source.

Putting expressions (16.18) and (16.19) equal to each other we find $\delta = (3D/4\pi\bar{I})|dN/dr|$ or, if we use connexion (14.1) between the mean intensity $\bar{I}$ and the particle concentration N and in (14.1) make the velocity v for the cosmic rays equal to the velocity of light c

$$\delta = \frac{3D}{c} \frac{1}{N} \left| \frac{dN}{dr} \right|. \tag{16.20}$$

For the diffusion model that takes no account of boundaries (model II; formula (15.7)) and the diffusion model with free departure from the Galaxy (model I; formula (15.6)) it follows from expression (16.20) that

$$\delta_i^{II} = \frac{3D}{cr} \left(1 + \sqrt{\frac{2x}{\lambda_i}} \right),$$

$$\delta_i^{I} = \delta_i^{II} \left\{ 1 + \frac{2\sqrt{2x/\lambda_i}}{1 + \sqrt{2x/\lambda_i}} \frac{1}{\exp\left\{2\left(\frac{R}{r} - 1\right)\sqrt{\frac{2x}{\lambda_i}}\right\} - 1} \right\}. \tag{16.21}$$

Here δ_i is the expected degree of anisotropy for nuclei of kind i†. From expressions (16.21) with $D = 10^{29}$ cm^2/sec, $r = 8$ kpc, $R = 12$ kpc, $x = 10$ g/cm^2 and the value of λ_i from Table 10 we find that the degree of anisotropy of the total cosmic ray flux (consisting largely of protons, $\lambda_p = 72$ g/cm^2) is

$$\delta_p^{I} \simeq 1.7 \times 10^{-3}, \qquad \delta_p^{II} \simeq 6.4 \times 10^{-4}. \tag{16.22}$$

For group H nuclei ($\lambda_H = 6.1$)

$$\delta_H^{I} \simeq 1.2 \times 10^{-3} \qquad \delta_H^{II} \simeq 1.2 \times 10^{-3}. \tag{16.23}$$

These values do not contradict the available data (see section 3). Moreover they are close to the experimentally established upper limit of the possible degree of galactic cosmic ray anisotropy (of

† Strictly speaking expressions (16.21) relate only to the group of the heaviest nuclei and also to the total nucleon flux if in the latter case λ_i is understood to be the mean absorption path of the cosmic ray nucleon component. For the other groups all the terms in expression (14.24) must be taken into consideration.

the order of a few tenths of a per cent) so an increase of an order in the accuracy of the experiment would make it possible to compare the consequences of the diffusion model with the actual situation in the Galaxy. In this connexion the results of Dorman and Inozemtseva[142] are of great interest; here apparently a preferential flux of particles from the centre of the Galaxy was found. Indications were obtained of anisotropy in the moderate energy range by Delvaille et al.[143] and Nikol'skii[145] (see section 3).

From the point of view of selecting a model for the propagation of cosmic rays in the Galaxy it would also be very important to measure the anisotropy for each of the cosmic ray charge groups individually. This, however, requires considerable improvement of the methods of measurement since the actual fluxes of heavy nuclei are small. At the same time an increase of an order in the accuracy of anisotropy measurements of the total cosmic ray flux is evidently a problem which is quite soluble now.[43]

It is curious to note that in the case of the metagalactic origin of cosmic rays the degree of anisotropy would have the "opposite sign", i.e., the intensity would be minimum in the direction of the centre of the Galaxy (see model V; formula (15.10)). It must, however, be borne in mind, of course, that the local conditions in the solar system and near it may introduce considerable distortions into the "mean" degree of anisotropy discussed above, particularly in the low and medium energy range.[2]

In general the inaccuracy of the diffusion approximation, as has already been indicated in section 10, could be reflected in the first place in the value of δ and the direction (on Earth) in which the intensity I is maximum.

It follows from expressions (16.21) that the degree of anisotropy in the diffusion model depends strongly on the value of the diffusion coefficient D. Above, in accordance with the data on the chemical composition of cosmic rays (see section 15), we took the value $D \simeq 10^{29}$ cm^2/sec. In this case the mean concentration of the gas must be taken to be $n \simeq 0.03$ to 0.05 cm^{-3}. Since this concentration relates to the "interior" of the Galaxy (with a radius of the order of the distance from the Sun to the centre of the Galaxy) in which the composition observed on Earth is largely formed it still does not contradict the previously accepted estimate of $n \simeq 10^{-2}$ cm^{-3} for the mean concentration in the Galaxy as a whole.

With $D = 10^{29}$ cm^2/sec the mean time of departure of cosmic rays from the halo with a radius of $R \simeq 12$ kpc $\simeq 3.7 \times 10^{22}$ cm is $T_d \simeq R^2/2D \simeq 7 \times 10^{15}$ sec $\simeq 2 \times 10^8$ years, which is in close agreement with the estimate of the departure time obtained in section 15.

It is hardly possible to increase the value of the diffusion coefficient significantly. In actual fact, this would in the first place force us to consider that the interstellar gas concentration was accordingly greater in order to keep unchanged the mean thickness of matter passed through, $x \simeq 10$ g/cm^2, which follows from an analysis of the chemical composition of cosmic rays. For example for $D \simeq 10^{30}$ cm^2/sec it would be necessary to have $n \simeq 0.3$ to 0.5 cm^{-3}. In the second place the degree of anisotropy of the cosmic rays would also rise in proportion to the diffusion coefficient.† For example with $D \simeq 10^{30}$ cm^2/sec we should have $\delta \gtrsim 1$ per cent which clearly contradicts the available data.

On the other hand, it is clearly impermissible to assume far lower values of the diffusion coefficient than the value $D \simeq 10^{29}$ cm^2/sec that we have taken. It would be necessary in fact to consider in this case that the transport mean free path l in the definition of the diffusion coefficient $D = \frac{1}{3}lv$ is small when compared with the characteristic size of the magnetic field inhomogeneities in the Galaxy. For example, with $D \simeq 10^{28}$ cm/^{2}sec and $v \simeq 10^{10}$ cm/sec the mean free path will be $l \simeq 3 \times 10^{18}$ cm $\simeq 1$ pc, whilst the available data indicate that the sizes of the inhomogeneities in the interstellar gas distribution (and, clearly, the magnetic field) are at least several parsecs and generally even considerably more.

Therefore the order of magnitude of the diffusion coefficient for the majority of the cosmic rays $D \sim 10^{29}$ cm^2/sec is fixed fairly strictly. The position may change for cosmic rays with very high energies. We shall now move on to discuss this region of the energy spectrum.

Energy spectrum, chemical composition and anisotropy in the very high energy region

In the very high energy region $E > 10^{15}$ to 10^{16} eV there are practically no data on the chemical composition of the cosmic rays‡

† This difficulty also arises if we assume that the cosmic rays pass through a considerable thickness of matter in the source itself where the observed composition is practically entirely formed. In this case the thickness of matter passed through in interstellar space would have to be taken as small and the diffusion coefficient as correspondingly large.

‡ According to Hasegawa et al.[144, 147] in the 10^{16} to 10^{18} eV range at least several per cent of the total number of extensive atmospheric showers are caused

and the measurements of the possible degree of anisotropy permit values of $\delta \lesssim 0\cdot1$ for $E \simeq 10^{18}$ eV and $\delta \lesssim 0\cdot3$ for $E \simeq 10^{19}$ eV[458] (see also section 3). There are indications that the slope (index γ) of the energy spectrum in the high-energy range changes in the energy interval $E \sim 10^{15}$ to 10^{16} eV.

Because the picture in the very high energy particle range is still far from clear in the experimental respect we shall discuss below the various possibilities and effects.

Above all there should be an upper energy limit for the cosmic rays supplied by galactic sources. It is natural to consider that this limit is determined by the maximum rigidity of the particles at which they can still be retained and accelerated in the magnetic fields of the sources. If heavy nuclei are present in the composition of cosmic rays right up to the maximum rigidity in question the particles with the maximum energy will be the heaviest of the nuclei in the cosmic rays in this rigidity range. In actual fact if the maximum proton energy is $E_{p, \text{max}}$, then for the same maximum rigidity the maximum energy of nuclei with a charge Z will be $E_{\text{nucl, max}} = Z E_{p, \text{max}}$. This difference in the maximum energies of nuclei with different atomic numbers will lead to considerable "blurring" of the upper limit of the galactic cosmic ray energy spectrum.[131] We recall that in the very high energy region it is the particle energy spectrum that is directly determined (in the study of the extensive atmospheric showers) and not the spectrum with respect to rigidity or energies per nucleon.

There is no doubt that this upper limit exists; the question is at what energies is it located. If the maximum energy for protons is 10^{18} eV and heavy nuclei are present in the cosmic ray composition right up to the rigidity threshold in question, then it may be considered that all the cosmic rays right up to the maximum observed energies of $E \sim 10^{20}$ eV are of galactic origin. In this case the cosmic rays in the $\sim 10^{19}$ eV region should be represented exclusively by heavy nuclei.

Otherwise, if the maximum galactic cosmic ray energy lies, as is sometimes assumed elsewhere,[100, 102, 131] in the $E \sim 10^{-16}$ eV range, then the particles with the highest energies should be of extragalactic origin no matter what their charge. In this case the change in the

by heavy nuclei. At the same time the conclusion is drawn by Linsley et al.[101, 102] that particles with an energy of $E \gtrsim 10^{17}$ eV are homogeneous in their chemical composition and are most likely to be protons (see section 3).

energy spectrum from galactic and metagalactic cosmic rays by virtue of the blurring with respect to Z indicated above could be sufficiently smooth, without any sharply defined breaks (see also sections 3 and 13).

A second effect (apart from the existence of a maximum rigidity for particles of galactic origin) may be a dependence of the diffusion coefficient in the Galaxy on the particle energy. In actual fact, if the effective size of the magnetic field inhomogeneities, in accordance with the choice of $D \simeq 10^{29}$ cm/^{2}sec, is $l \simeq 3 \times 10^{19}$ cm $= 10$ pc, then for particles with energies $E > 300ZHl \simeq 3 \times 10^{16}Z$ eV the radius of curvature in the magnetic field $H \sim 3 \times 10^{-6}$ oe will be greater than the size of the inhomogeneities l. We may then expect noticeable changes in the nature of the motion of the particles in interstellar space due to the increase in the diffusion coefficient D.

The increase in the diffusion coefficient will be accompanied by a change in the energy spectrum, the chemical composition and the anisotropy of the cosmic rays in this energy range.

Let us assume for example that the change in the energy spectrum at $E \sim 10^{16}$ eV indicated by several authors[100, 131, 155] is just caused by the dependence appearing for this energy of the diffusion coefficient on the particle energy (according to Nikol'skii[97] and Vernov et al.[155] the index changes from a value of $\gamma \simeq 2\cdot5$ at $E < 3 \times 10^{15}$ eV to $\gamma \simeq 3$ at $E > 10^{16}$ eV). If we take it that at lower energies the diffusion coefficient does not depend on the energy and is $D \simeq 10^{29}$ cm^2/sec and take into consideration that in the $E \sim 10^{18}$ eV range the possible degree of anisotropy does not exceed 10 per cent (i.e., $\delta \lesssim 0\cdot1$) then in the range $E \simeq 10^{16}$ to 10^{18} eV the diffusion coefficient should not rise more rapidly than $D(E) \infty E$ (in this case, for $E \simeq 10^{18}$ eV it will be $D \simeq 10^{31}$ cm^2/sec and in accordance with (16.21) $\delta_p^{II} \simeq 0\cdot05$ and $\delta_p^{I} \simeq 0\cdot12$). This energy dependence does not correspond to the picture discussed in section 10 (see formula (10.5)) of the motion of particles with $r_H \gg l$. It should, however, be borne in mind that expression (10.5) is obtained with certain simplifying assumptions (the presence is assumed of isolated magnetic clouds with identical characteristic sizes).

If we bear in mind the possible scatter in the sizes of the magnetic field inhomogeneities (clouds)[459] and the more complex nature of the diffusion connected with the motion of the gas and the pressure of the cosmic rays themselves, then the slower function $D(E)$ obtained above cannot yet be considered unacceptable. In this connexion there is great interest in estimating the values of the diffusion coefficient for solar cosmic rays in the interplanetary magnetic fields. Charakhch'yan *et al.*[104, 428] found that for protons with a momentum $p \simeq 0.5$ GeV/c the diffusion coefficient is $D \simeq 5.5 \times 10^{21}$ cm^2/sec and is quintupled for protons with a momentum $p \simeq 5$ GeV/c. It is natural to consider that the diffusion coefficient depends not directly on the particle energy but on its radius of curvature $r_H = cp_\perp/eH$, i.e., on the momentum p. Then the dependence found for solar cosmic rays of the diffusion coefficient on energy changes as $D = lv/3 \infty p^{0.7}$ or $l \infty p^{0.4 \text{ to } 0.5}$.

We note that for solar cosmic rays with the energies in question the characteristic ratio r_H/l is $r_H/l = 0.1$ to 0.3 if the interplanetary field strength is taken as 10^{-5} oersteds and the characteristic size of the inhomogeneities (the diffusion length l) is determined from the experimentally found values $D \simeq 5.5$ to 28×10^{21} cm^2/sec (in this case $l \simeq 1$ to 3×10^{12} cm, which is about one tenth of the distance from the Earth to the Sun). Considering the similarity condition to be satisfied with respect to r_H/l we obtain the same dependence $l \infty p^{0.4 \text{ to } 0.5}$ for the galactic cosmic rays in the range $E \simeq 3 \times 10^{15}$ to 10^{16} eV if $H \simeq 3 \times 10^{-6}$ oe and the characteristic size of the inhomogeneities is $l \simeq 10$ pc $\simeq 3 \times 10^{19}$ cm.

There is therefore some reason for considering that in the $\sim 10^{16}$ eV energy range the diffusion coefficient depends upon the energy as

$$D(E) \infty l(E) \infty E^{0.4 \text{ to } 0.5}. \qquad (16.24)$$

Here it is considered that for ultra-relativistic particles $v \simeq c$ and $E \simeq cp$.

If we take it that the above-mentioned dependence of the diffusion coefficient on the energy is true, then in the $E > 10^{16}$ eV range the nature of the cosmic ray energy spectrum in the Galaxy should change. A strict analysis requires the solution of transfer equation (14.2). A qualitative result may be obtained,[140] however, by leaving in this equation only the terms that describe the energy spectrum of the sources and the particle losses with a characteristic time T; we should choose the mean time T_D of diffusion departure of particles from the Galaxy for this value ($T_D \simeq R^2/2D$, where R is the radius of the volume occupied by cosmic rays). Then from equation (14.2) it follows that

$$N_i(E) = T_D(E)Q_i(E) \infty \frac{Q_i(E)}{D_i(E)}. \qquad (16.25)$$

It is at once clear from (16.25) that if the source energy spectrum $Q(E) \sim E^{-\gamma_0}$ is characterised by an index $\gamma_0 \simeq 2\cdot5$ which is constant over the whole energy range, then the galactic cosmic ray spectrum will also be a power law with an index $\gamma = \gamma_0 \simeq 2\cdot5$ at $E \ll 10^{16}$ eV (when $D(E) = D = \text{const}$) and with an index $\gamma \simeq \gamma_0 + 0\cdot5 \simeq 3\cdot0$ at $E > 10^{16}$ eV when we have the dependence (16.24).

As for the magnitude of the energy range in which the transition from $\gamma = 2\cdot5$ to $\gamma = 3\cdot0$ takes place, it is difficult to estimate this range with any certainty at present since the behaviour of the diffusion coefficient in the transition region is unknown. Moreover, the following factors can be indicated that affect the width of the transition region.

Above all the change in the diffusion coefficient should begin at one and the same rigidity for the various particles. Therefore with the ordinary chemical composition we shall have the "chemical blurring" of the transition region in the energy spectrum discussed above. Since we find nuclei with $Z = 1$ to 30 in cosmic rays in the energy spectrum (we are speaking of the total energy of a nucleus E) with the ordinary composition for cosmic rays the corresponding transition region will be stretched over an energy range 30 times as large.

On the other hand, as the diffusion coefficient increases there is a decrease in the thickness of matter $x = \rho c r^2 / D$ passed through by the cosmic rays (see (15.15)). The chemical composition depends essentially on the thickness of matter they pass through; thus, when the diffusion coefficient changes by a factor of three (i.e., the energy increases by an order of magnitude; see (16.24)) the cosmic ray composition in the Galaxy will hardly differ from their composition in the source. This fairly sharp change in the composition may lead to a noticeable break in the total cosmic ray energy spectrum. For example there will be a sharp break in the proton and α-particle spectrum if the majority of them are spallation products of heavy nuclei (see section 15).

A calculation of the chemical composition and the form of the energy spectrum in the transition region $10^{16} \lesssim E \lesssim 10^{18}$ eV based on these assumptions has been made by Syrovatskii et al.[460]

If the change in the slope of the energy spectrum in the $E \gtrsim 10^{18}$ eV that has been discovered[458] is confirmed it will most probably indicate the essential part played by metagalactic cosmic rays at these energies. In this case it is natural to expect high isotropy of the flux of cosmic rays with $E > 10^{18}$ eV and also a considerable number of protons in their composition. This last conclusion is valid if in the sources, for example radio galaxies, super-high energy particles are generated with the same charge spectrum as at lower energies.

As is clear from what has just been said, such characteristics of very high energy cosmic rays as the energy spectrum, the chemical composition and the degree of anisotropy are closely interconnected. It is only by determining these characteristics with greater precision that a choice is possible between the above-mentioned possibilities and a solution is possible of the most important problem of the nature of very high energy cosmic rays, in particular the part played by cosmic rays of metagalactic origin in this range of energies (see section 13).

17. THE SECONDARY ELECTRON COMPONENT OF COSMIC RAYS AND THE GENERAL GALACTIC RADIO EMISSION SPECTRUM†

In this section we calculate the energy spectrum and the spatial distribution of the secondary electrons generated in nuclear collisions of cosmic rays in the interstellar gas. The motion of the electrons in interstellar space is treated as isotropic diffusion. The magnetic bremsstrahlung, Compton and ionisation energy losses are taken into consideration.

The spectral intensity of the magnetic bremsstrahlung of secondary electrons is calculated. This intensity proves to be considerably less (at least two orders for wavelengths $\lambda \lesssim 1$ m) than that observed. It follows from this that the general galactic radio emission is generated by primary electrons which arrive in interstellar space from the sources (from the shells of supernovae in the stationary model). Some requirements are discussed for such sources as well as questions connected with the non-stationary galactic model (the model in which explosions of the galactic core occur).

As soon as it was found out that the non-thermal radio emission of the Galaxy is the magnetic bremsstrahlung of relativistic electrons in the interstellar magnetic fields the question arose of the origin of these electrons.[5,6] This question is largely that of choosing between two possibilities: are the relativistic electrons primary, i.e., accelerated

† Sections 17, 18 and 19 were added to the English edition and are essentially the same as Refs. 509, 479, and 499; section 17 replaces a different section in the Russian edition and sections 18 and 19 are new.

together with the heavy particles (protons and nuclei) in the cosmic ray sources, or are they generated in secondary processes—in nuclear interactions of the cosmic rays in the interstellar gas?

The calculation of the intensity and the form of the energy spectrum of the primary electrons is made difficult by the lack of information on the sources and their evolution in time. For example radio astronomy data allow us only to judge the number and energy spectrum of the electrons contained in supernova shells at present. At the same time the number and spectrum of the electrons ejected into interstellar space during the whole existence of a shell remain unknown. In the theoretical respect a number of questions connected with the generation mechanism and the ejection of relativistic particles from the sources are not clear either. Therefore in the primary electron model we can at present formulate more or less strictly only the opposite problem—the determination of the spectral power of the electron sources proceeding from data on the non-thermal emission of the Galaxy and its magnetic bremsstrahlung origin. Of course, the solution of this problem only slightly simplifies the solution of the problem of the origin of the electron component by reducing it to the problem of the sources.

In this connexion the secondary electron model attracts particular attention. This model can be calculated with sufficient completeness since the cosmic ray energy spectrum and the basic characteristics of the nuclear interactions and $\pi \rightarrow \mu \rightarrow e$ decays are known. The corresponding estimates and calculations allowing for the various factors have been made.[†][5, 6, 283, 433] The conclusion was drawn in this case that within the limits of accuracy of the available data the secondary electron model is in principle sufficient to explain the Galaxy's non-thermal emission.

The present section discusses more fully the secondary electron model, taking into consideration the form of the electron spectrum from the $\pi \rightarrow \mu \rightarrow e$ decay of the mesons generated in the nuclear interactions of the cosmic rays, the distribution of the interstellar gas in the Galaxy, the diffusion of the electrons in interstellar space and their magnetic bremsstrahlung and ionisation losses. The energy spectrum and spatial distribution of the secondary electrons in the Galaxy found in this way are used to calculate the intensity of the magnetic bremsstrahlung of these electrons for the direction of the galactic pole. This intensity, particularly in the high-frequency

† See also sections 7, 11 and 13 of the present book.

region, is considerably less than that observed.† This result obtained
for secondary electrons in the stationary model of the Galaxy forces
us to consider that in the steady-state model the radio-emitting electrons should be generated in the cosmic ray sources (largely in the
shells of supernovae). Below we shall determine the spectral power
of the electrons' sources in the Galaxy. It turns out that the power
given to radio-emitting electrons is approximately only an order less
than the power received by the cosmic rays. In addition, a non-
stationary model of the galactic halo is discussed[438] and it turns
out that in this case the part played by secondary electrons is
also small.

Secondary electron generation spectrum

Let us examine in turn the chain of processes leading to the
generation of secondary electrons (and positrons) in the nuclear
interactions of cosmic rays with the interstellar gas.

The first of these processes is the generation of charged π-mesons.
The $\pi^{\pm}$-meson generation spectrum can be calculated by taking as a
basis the data on the primary cosmic ray spectrum and the nature of
nuclear interactions at accelerator energies. These data are incom-
plete, however, and the corresponding calculations are rather labor-
ious. It is best therefore to make direct use of the known spectrum
for the generation of π-mesons in the atmosphere, considering that
the difference between the nuclear composition of the air and the
composition of the interstellar gas is of little significance if it is a question of the generation spectrum over the absorption path. It is this
spectrum which is known for the atmosphere. It is shown in
Fig. 19 where $f_{\pi}(\mathscr{E}_{\pi})$ is the $\pi^{\pm}$-meson intensity per unit interval of
non-dimensional energy $\mathscr{E}_{\pi} = E_{\pi}/m_{\pi}c^2$ (E_{π} is the total energy and
m_{π} the rest mass of a π-meson).

In the $E_{\pi} > 500$ MeV energy range this spectrum is based on
the data on the μ-meson component and an analysis of its generation and absorption in the atmosphere.[493,494] For energies of
$2 < E_{\pi} < 100$ GeV the spectrum is a power law with an index

† The results of the preliminary calculations given in section 17 of the Russian
edition of this book contain an error (an essential numerical factor was omitted
from the emission intensity). This led to the incorrect conclusion that it is
possible to explain the general galactic emission by secondary electrons. In the
present English edition section 17 of the Russian edition has been replaced by
the present section.

$\gamma_\pi = 2 \cdot 64 \pm 0 \cdot 05$[67,495] but for energies $E_\pi < 2$ GeV the index decreases to a value of $\gamma_\pi \simeq 2$.

In the very high energy range $(E_\pi \gtrsim 10^{12}$ eV) the spectrum apparently steepens but this energy range is not essential for our calculations.

For energies $E_\pi < 500$ MeV the π-meson generation spectrum obtained from the μ-meson data is less reliable and probably under-estimates the number of π-mesons flying out at large angles to the vertical.[493] In the low-energy region, therefore, starting at an energy of $E_\pi = 1$ GeV the generation spectrum given in Fig. 19 is continued by means of data on the generation of π-mesons in photographic emulsions exposed at great altitudes.[308,496] Here, of course, we must bear in mind the possibility of error because of the specific nuclear composition of the emulsions and the probable difference of the cosmic ray spectrum (the residual thickness of the atmosphere is about 50 g/cm^2) from their primary spectrum.

Bearing in mind the above remarks the spectrum shown in Fig. 19

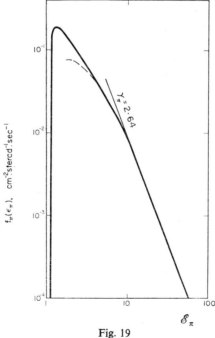

Fig. 19

will be looked upon below as the generation spectrum of charged
π-mesons on the cosmic ray absorption path.

Let us now examine the kinematics of $\pi^\pm \to \mu^\pm + v$ and
$\mu^\pm \to e^\pm + v + \bar{v}$ decays.

In the laboratory system of coordinates a decay μ-meson has
practically the same velocity as the original high-energy π-meson.
Therefore their non-dimensional energies and corresponding energy
spectra are identical:

$$\mathscr{E}_\mu = \mathscr{E}_\pi, \qquad f_\mu(\mathscr{E}_\mu) = f_\pi(\mathscr{E}_\pi). \tag{17.1}$$

Here $\mathscr{E}_\mu = E_\mu/m_\mu c^2$ is the total energy of a μ-meson in units of its
rest energy.

The energy spectrum of the decay electrons in the rest system of
the decaying μ-mesons is of the form:

$$W(\mathscr{E}_0) = \frac{12\mathscr{E}_0\sqrt{\mathscr{E}_0^2 - 1}}{\mathscr{E}_m^4} \{\mathscr{E}_m - \mathscr{E}_0 + \tfrac{2}{9}\rho(4\mathscr{E}_0 - 3\mathscr{E}_m)\}. \tag{17.2}$$

Here $\mathscr{E}_0 = E_0/mc^2$ is the non-dimensional energy of an electron
in this system of coordinates, m is the mass of an electron,
$\mathscr{E}_m \simeq m_\mu/2m \simeq 105$ is the maximum energy of the decay electrons and
ρ is Michel's parameter[431] which at present is taken[432] to be 3/4.
Spectrum (17.2) is normalised to unity so that $W(\mathscr{E}_0)\, d\mathscr{E}_0$ is the probability of the appearance of an electron with an energy in the range $\mathscr{E}_0$,
$\mathscr{E}_0 + d\mathscr{E}_0$.

In the laboratory system the energy of a decay electron $\mathscr{E} = E/mc^2$
is equal to

$$\mathscr{E} = \mathscr{E}_\mu\mathscr{E}_0 + \sqrt{\mathscr{E}_\mu^2 - 1}\sqrt{\mathscr{E}_0^2 - 1}\cos\theta_0, \tag{17.3}$$

where θ_0 is the angle of departure of an electron in the rest system of
a μ-meson. Therefore when the decay electrons are distributed
isotropically with respect to the angles θ_0 the probability of appearance in the laboratory system of an electron with an energy in the
range $\mathscr{E}, \mathscr{E} + d\mathscr{E}$ at given $\mathscr{E}_0$ and $\mathscr{E}_\mu$ is

$$w(\mathscr{E}, \mathscr{E}_0, \mathscr{E}_\mu)\, d\mathscr{E} = \tfrac{1}{2}|d\cos\theta_0| = \frac{d\mathscr{E}}{2\sqrt{\mathscr{E}_\mu^2 - 1}\sqrt{\mathscr{E}_0^2 - 1}}. \tag{17.4}$$

Here $\mathscr{E}$ obviously varies within the limits

$$\mathscr{E}_\mu\mathscr{E}_0 - \sqrt{\mathscr{E}_\mu^2 - 1}\sqrt{\mathscr{E}_0^2 - 1} \leqslant \mathscr{E} \leqslant \mathscr{E}_\mu\mathscr{E}_0 + \sqrt{\mathscr{E}_0^2 - 1}\sqrt{\mathscr{E}_\mu^2 - 1}. \tag{17.5}$$

Therefore the intensity of the secondary electrons appearing on the absorption path of the primary cosmic rays is defined by the expression

$$f_e(\mathscr{E}) = \int_1^{\mathscr{E}_m} d\mathscr{E}_0 W(\mathscr{E}_0) \int d\mathscr{E}_\pi w(\mathscr{E}, \mathscr{E}_0, \mathscr{E}_\pi) f_\pi(\mathscr{E}_\pi). \qquad (17.6)$$

The electron spectrum calculated from this formula is shown in Fig. 20. The spectrum has a maximum at $\mathscr{E} \simeq 60$ ($E \simeq 30$ MeV). As the energy increases the slope of the spectrum increases and in the $E > 1$ GeV energy range becomes constant, corresponding to a power-law spectrum with the index $\gamma = \gamma_\pi = 2\cdot64$.

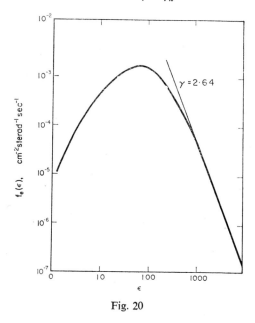

Fig. 20

This result is a consequence of the power-law nature of the π-meson spectrum in the high-energy region. Expressions (17.2) and (17.4) can be used to confirm that the power-law meson spectrum $f_\pi(\mathscr{E}_\pi) = K_\pi \mathscr{E}_\pi^{-\gamma}$ in the $\mathscr{E} \gg \mathscr{E}_m$ energy range corresponds to the power-law spectrum of the decay electrons $f_e(\mathscr{E}) = K_e \mathscr{E}^{-\gamma}$, the coefficients K_e and K_π being connected by the relation

$$K_e = 12 \left(\frac{m_\mu}{m}\right)^{\gamma-1} \frac{1 + \frac{2}{9}\rho(\gamma - 1)}{\gamma(\gamma + 2)(\gamma + 3)} K_\pi. \qquad (17.7)$$

In our case $\rho = 3/4$, $\gamma = 2 \cdot 64$ so $K_e = 1 \cdot 42 \times 10^3 K_\pi$. The charged meson generation spectrum (Fig. 19) in the energy range $\mathscr{E}_\pi > 10$ can be represented in the form $f_\pi(\mathscr{E}_\pi) = 3 \cdot 9 \mathscr{E}_\pi^{-2 \cdot 64}$, so the decay electron spectrum approaches the form $f_e(\mathscr{E}) = 5 \cdot 5 \times 10^3 \mathscr{E}^{-2 \cdot 64}$. It can be seen from Fig. 20 that this asymptotic form of the spectrum is reached at $\mathscr{E} \simeq 2 \times 10^3$ ($E \simeq 1$ GeV).

Let us compare this spectrum with the primary cosmic ray spectrum which in the $E_{cr} > 10$ GeV energy region is of the form[97, 498]

$$I_{cr}(E_{cr}) = 1 \cdot 5 E_{cr}^{-2 \cdot 6} (\text{cm}^2 \cdot \text{sec} \cdot \text{sterad} \cdot \text{GeV})^{-1} \qquad (17.8)$$

and allow for the fact that in nuclear collisions with an energy of several tens of GeV about 5 charged mesons are generated on the average. Hence using the relations $f_e(\mathscr{E}) d\mathscr{E} \simeq 5 I_{cr}(E_{cr}) dE_{cr}$ and $\mathscr{E} = \kappa E_{cr}/5mc^2$ it can be found that on the absorption path a primary nucleon transfers $\kappa \sim 15$ per cent of its energy to secondary electrons. For example a primary nucleon with an energy of ~ 30 GeV generates on the average 5 electrons with energies of ~ 1 GeV.†

Let us now determine the spectral density of the secondary electron sources in interstellar space $Q(\mathscr{E}, r)$ which expresses the number of electrons generated per unit time in a unit volume and a unit energy interval. We shall consider that the cosmic rays fill the volume of the Galaxy evenly with an intensity equal to their intensity on Earth (in actual fact it is sufficient to assume that the intensity is constant only in that part of the Galaxy where the majority of the interstellar matter is concentrated, i.e., within the limits of the plane sub-system). Then obviously

$$Q(\mathscr{E}, r) = \frac{4\pi}{\lambda} \rho(r) f_e(\mathscr{E}), \qquad (17.9)$$

where $\rho(r)$ is the density of the interstellar gas as a function of the coordinates and λ is the cosmic ray absorption path which should be defined as the path over which the nucleon energy decreases by a factor of $e = 2 \cdot 72$. Since the inelastic interaction path in the interstellar medium and the coefficient of inelasticity are $\lambda_{int} \simeq 72$ g/cm^2 and $K \simeq 1/3$, respectively, we find

$$\lambda = -\lambda_{int}/\ln(1 - K) \simeq 180 \text{ g/cm}^2. \qquad (17.10)$$

We should bear in mind the certain amount of conventionality in the

---

† If only one π-meson takes away the majority of the energy, then similar arguments lead to the value $\kappa = \mathscr{E}mc^2/E_{cr} \sim 7 \cdot 5$ per cent.

definition of this quantity which may lead to a reduction in the intensity of the secondary electron sources, but clearly by not more than a factor of two.

The generation spectrum shown in Fig. 20 allows us to calculate the total number N_e and the energy U_e of the secondary electrons generated per unit time in the Galaxy. If the mass of the interstellar gas

$$M = \int \rho(r) \, d^3r$$

is $2 \cdot 8 \times 10^{42}$ g, which corresponds to the gaseous component of the galactic disk, then

$$N_e = \int Q(\mathscr{E}, r) \, d\mathscr{E} \, d^3r = \frac{4\pi M}{\lambda} \int f_e(\mathscr{E}) \, d\mathscr{E} = 8 \cdot 7 \times 10^{40} \text{ sec}^{-1}, \quad (17.11)$$

$$U_e = \frac{4\pi M}{\lambda} \int f_e(\mathscr{E}) \mathscr{E} \, d\mathscr{E} = 1 \cdot 9 \times 10^{49} \text{ eV/sec} \simeq 3 \times 10^{37} \text{ erg/sec}.$$
$$(17.12)$$

In this case a power of

$$U_e(E > 1 \text{ GeV}) = 1 \cdot 0 \times 10^{37} \text{ erg/sec} \quad (17.13)$$

is transferred to the electrons with an energy of $E > 1$ GeV which make the basic contribution to the observed range of radio frequencies.

We should note that the power of the Galaxy's general radio emission is 3 to 5×10^{38} erg/sec. The conclusion could be drawn from this that this emission cannot be explained by secondary electrons. However, if we bear in mind the possible contribution of the halo to the total mass of gas in the Galaxy and also the uncertainty in the choice of the value of λ, then this discrepancy can be reduced by several factors. As we shall see below, fuller information can be obtained from a comparison of the secondary electron magnetic bremsstrahlung spectrum with the observed spectrum of the general galactic radio emission.

Secondary electron distribution in the Galaxy and the magnetic bremsstrahlung intensity

The motion of relativistic electrons in the interstellar magnetic fields averaged over long periods of time can in the first approximation be regarded as a random process with a certain effective diffusion coefficient D (see sections 10 and 14). In this case the electron concentration $N(\mathscr{E}, r)$ is defined by the equation

$$-D\nabla^2 N + \frac{\partial}{\partial \mathscr{E}}[b(\mathscr{E})N] = Q(\mathscr{E}, r). \tag{17.14}$$

We assume here that during the life of the relativistic electrons in the Galaxy the cosmic ray intensity and the interstellar gas density, and thus also $Q(\mathscr{E}, r)$ do not change significantly so the stationary model can be used. The second term in the left-hand side of equation (17.14) allows for a systematic change in the particle energy (the acceleration of the electrons in interstellar space is inessential in the stationary model so $b(\mathscr{E}) = d\mathscr{E}/dt$ expresses the mean energy losses of the electrons).

Below we shall take the following forms of energy loss into consideration: the ionisation losses in a non-ionised gas (90% H + 10% He by number of atoms) with a concentration n

$$-\left(\frac{d\mathscr{E}}{dt}\right)_i = 1{\cdot}64 \times 10^{-14}\{3 \ln \mathscr{E} + 18{\cdot}8\}n, \tag{17.15}$$

the Compton losses in the emission field with an energy density w_{ph} (in eV/cm^3)†

$$-\left(\frac{d\mathscr{E}}{dt}\right)_C = 3{\cdot}92 \times 10^{-20}w_{ph}\mathscr{E}^2 \tag{17.16}$$

and lastly the magnetic bremsstrahlung losses in a random magnetic field with a strength H (it is assumed that on the average $H_\perp^2 = \frac{2}{3}H^2$)

$$-\left(\frac{d\mathscr{E}}{dt}\right)_M = 1{\cdot}28 \times 10^{-9}H^2\mathscr{E}^2. \tag{17.17}$$

The radiation losses (in the case of total screening they are $-(d\mathscr{E}/dt)_r = 9{\cdot}6 \times 10^{-16}n\mathscr{E}$) in the conditions of the interstellar medium are small when compared with those indicated over practically the whole energy range so need not be allowed for in the first approximation.

Replacing $\ln \mathscr{E}$ in the expression for the ionisation losses (17.15)

---

† Here we are using the expression for the losses used in section 8 of the present book. A more accurate calculation for the thermal emission losses leads to having to multiply the right-hand side of formula (17.16) by 1·33 (see section 19). This fact is unimportant in what follows because of the inaccuracy of the given value of w_{ph}.

by its value at $\mathscr{E} = 10^2$ (at high energies these losses are small when compared with the magnetic bremsstrahlung and Compton losses) we obtain the following expression for the total energy losses

$$b(\mathscr{E}) = -\beta(\mathscr{E}_{eq}^2 + \mathscr{E}^2). \qquad (17.18)$$

Here

$$\beta = 1\cdot3 \times 10^{-9}(H^2 + 3 \times 10^{-11}w_{ph}), \qquad \mathscr{E}_{eq}^2 = \frac{4\cdot1 \times 10^{-4}n}{H^2 + 3 \times 10^{-11}w_{ph}}, \qquad (17.19)$$

where $\mathscr{E}_{eq}$ is some dimensionless effective energy for which ionisation losses equal magnetic and Compton losses. For the values of n, H and w_{ph} in the expressions for the losses we shall in future take their mean values in the volume of the Galaxy occupied by relativistic electrons, i.e., $n = 10^{-2}$ cm^{-3}, $H = 3$ to 7×10^{-6} oersteds and $w_{ph} = 1$ eV/cm^3. At the same time, when analysing the spatial distribution of the relativistic electrons and their emission we must allow for the dependence of $Q(\mathscr{E}, r)$, i.e., the density of the interstellar gas $\rho(r)$, on the coordinates. This dependence is unimportant only in the closed model of the Galaxy when there is a sufficiently rapid exchange of particles between the various parts of Galactic space. In this homogeneous model the source distribution plays no part and we may formally put

$$Q(\mathscr{E}, r) \equiv Q(\mathscr{E}) = \frac{4\pi M}{\lambda V} f_e(\mathscr{E}), \qquad (17.20)$$

where V is the volume of the Galaxy.

As the model which is closest to reality we shall take it that the distribution of the interstellar gas has the symmetry of an ellipsoid of rotation and is characterised by the normal law

$$\rho(r) = \frac{M}{\pi^{3/2}p^{1/2}} \exp\left\{-x^2 - y^2 - \frac{z^2}{p}\right\}, \qquad (17.21)$$

where p is the ratio of the squares of the lengths of short and long semi-axes, the direction of the short semi-axis (the axis of rotation) coinciding with the direction of the galactic pole and being chosen as the z axis of a Cartesian system of coordinates with the origin in the centre of the Galaxy. Here and later the unit of length used is the length a of the semi-major-axis.

The majority of the interstellar gas with a mass of $M = 2\cdot8 \times 10^{42}$ g is concentrated within a plane disk sub-system with a radius of 12 to

15 kpc and a thickness of ~ 300 pc. The amount of gas in the quasi-spherical halo ($p \simeq 0.5$ to 1) is not yet known with certainty but in any case it does not exceed the mass of the gas in the disk. Therefore we shall allow below for the gas in the disk ($p = 10^{-4}$, $M = 2.8 \times 10^{42}$ g) and the gas in the halo ($p = 1$) by taking as the upper limit for the ratio α of the mass of the gas in the halo to the mass of the gas in the disk the value $\alpha = 1$.

The solution of equation (17.14) with the right-hand side of (17.9) and (17.21) for infinite space is of the form[173]

$$N(\mathscr{E}, r) = \frac{2M}{\lambda |b(\mathscr{E})|} \int_{\tau > 0} d\mathscr{E}' f_e(\mathscr{E}') \phi(\tau\{\mathscr{E}, \mathscr{E}'\}, r), \qquad (17.22)$$

where

$$\phi(\tau, r) = \frac{2}{\sqrt{\pi}} \frac{\exp\left\{ -\dfrac{x^2 + y^2}{1 + \tau} - \dfrac{z^2}{p + \tau} \right\}}{(1 + \tau)\sqrt{p + \tau}} \qquad (17.23)$$

and

$$\tau = \frac{4D}{a^2} \int_{\mathscr{E}'}^{\mathscr{E}} \frac{d\xi}{b(\xi)} = \eta \left(\arctan \frac{\mathscr{E}'}{\mathscr{E}_{eq}} - \arctan \frac{\mathscr{E}}{\mathscr{E}_{eq}} \right); \qquad (17.24)$$

the non-dimensional parameter

$$\eta = 4D/a^2 \beta \mathscr{E}_{eq} \qquad (17.25)$$

has the meaning of twice the ratio of the characteristic magnetic bremsstrahlung loss time $T_m = 1/\beta\mathscr{E}$ for particles with an energy $\mathscr{E}_{eq}$ to the mean time of diffusion departure of particles from the Galaxy $T_d = a^2/2D$.

In the homogeneous model (see formula (17.20)) the secondary electron spectrum is defined by the expression

$$N(\mathscr{E}) = \frac{4\pi M_{tot}}{\lambda \beta V} \frac{1}{\mathscr{E}_{eq}^2 + \mathscr{E}^2} \int_{\mathscr{E}}^{\infty} f_e(\mathscr{E}') \, d\mathscr{E}', \qquad (17.26)$$

where M_{tot} is the total mass of gas in the disk and in the halo.

The secondary electron intensity on Earth, $I(E) = N(\mathscr{E})c/4\pi mc^2$, calculated by formulae (17.22) and (17.26) is shown in Fig. 21. Here and in the later calculations the following values are used: distance of the solar system from the centre of the Galaxy† 8 kpc, characteristic size of the Galactic halo $a = 12$ kpc $= 3.7 \times 10^{22}$ cm

† If in accordance with new data we make this distance 10 kpc, then with $a = 12$ kpc remaining the same the radio emission intensity is reduced by not more than 25 to 30 per cent.

(hence in formula (17.23) the position of the solar system $x = r_s = 2/3, y = z = 0$), volume of the halo $V = 4\pi a^3/3 \simeq 2 \times 10^{68}$ cm^3, $\lambda = 180$ g/cm^2, $n = 0\cdot01$ cm^{-3}, $w_{ph} = 1$ eV/cm^3, $H = 3 \times 10^{-6}$ oe and the diffusion coefficient is $D = 1\cdot4 \times 10^{29}$ cm^2/sec, corresponding to a departure time of $T_d = a^2/2D = 1\cdot5 \times 10^8$ years.

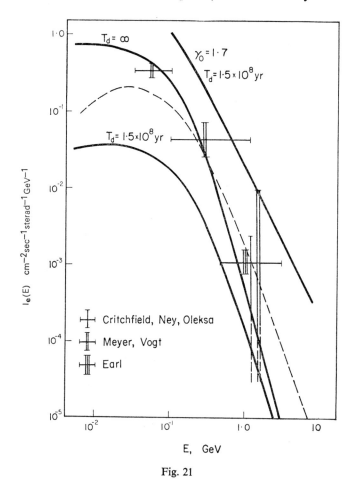

Fig. 21

The mass of the gas in the halo is taken to be equal to the mass of the gas in the disk so in formula (17.22) we have taken the sum of functions (17.23) with $p = 10^{-4}$ and $p = 1$, and in formula (17.26) $M_{tot} = 2M = 5\cdot5 \times 10^{42}$ g.

It can be seen from Fig. 21 that in the open model ($T_d = 1.5 \times 10^8$ years, the lower full-drawn curve) the intensity is 2 to 3 times lower than in the closed one ($T_d = \infty$). In the closed model $I_e(E > 1 \text{ GeV})$ $= 2.3 \times 10^{-4}$ $(\text{cm}^2 \cdot \text{sec} \cdot \text{sterad})^{-1}$. It is hardly possible to increase the secondary electron intensity in the model under discussion (in reality the mass of the halo is evidently $< 2.8 \times 10^{42}$ g and the volume is $V > 2 \times 10^{68}$ cm^3).

According to Earl[57] experimentally $I_e(E > 1 \text{ GeV}) \simeq 1.5 \times 10^{-3}$ $(\text{cm}^2 \cdot \text{sec} \cdot \text{sterad})^{-1}$. Therefore if all these electrons come from the Galaxy it is impossible to consider that they are secondary.

For comparison with our calculations Fig. 21 shows (dashed curve) the spectrum calculated by Hayakawa and Okuda[433] for the homogeneous model allowing for finite life of the electrons in the Galaxy ($T_d = 10^8$ years). In this paper the electron generation spectrum is obtained in a different way by using the primary cosmic ray spectrum in the form $I_{cr}(> E_{cr}) = 0.4 E_{cr}^{-1.15}$ with certain assumptions about the nature of the nuclear interactions at high energies. In the most significant energy range $E_{cr} > 10$ GeV this spectrum gives too high a value for the intensity,[97, 498] which together with the accepted strong anisotropy of the mesons in the centre of mass system possibly just leads to too great a meson (and, consequently, electron) generation spectrum. Figure 21 also shows (according to Hayakawa and Okuda[433]) the experimental values from several authors.[56, 57, 58] It must, however, be borne in mind that the question of the possibility of connecting the observed electron intensity[56, 57, 58] with the

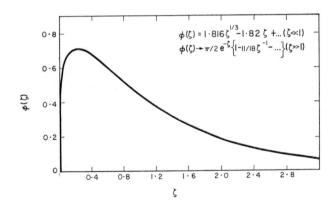

Fig. 22

galactic electron component is still not clear. Because of this it would be premature to discuss the part played by secondary electrons of galactic origin in the low-energy range ($E < 1$ GeV).†

Let us now calculate the intensity of the magnetic bremsstrahlung of the secondary electrons in the Galaxy. This intensity in the case of isotropic electron distribution and a random magnetic field is defined by the formula

$$I_l(v) = \frac{\sqrt{3}e^3}{4\pi mc^2 a^2} \int_1^\infty d\mathscr{E} \int_0^R dlN(\mathscr{E}, r)H(r)\Phi(\zeta\{v, \mathscr{E}, r\}). \quad (17.27)$$

Here integration with respect to dl is carried out in the direction of observation as far as the boundary of the Galaxy, R is the distance to this boundary, $H(r)$ is the absolute magnitude of the magnetic field strength,

$$\zeta = v/v_0\mathscr{E}^2 \quad \text{and} \quad v_0 = 3eH/4\pi mc = 4{\cdot}2 \times 10^6 H, \quad (17.28)$$

whilst the function

$$\Phi(\zeta) = \zeta^3 \int_\zeta^\infty \frac{d\xi}{\xi^2\sqrt{\xi^2 - \zeta^2}} \int_\xi^\infty K_{5/3}(\eta)\, d\eta \quad (17.29)$$

characterises the spectral distribution of the electron emission in the random ("isotropic") magnetic field; its graph is shown in Fig. 22.

We shall limit ourselves to calculating the intensity for the direction of the galactic pole and ignore the dependence of the galactic magnetic field on the coordinates (in the case where $H(r) \neq$ const but there is no systematic dependence on the coordinates, averaging with respect to H can be carried out in the final results). Upon this assumption the integration with respect to dl in formula (17.27) is reduced to calculating the total electron energy spectrum on the line of sight

$$N_l(\mathscr{E}) = \int_0^R dlN(\mathscr{E}, r) = \frac{2M}{\lambda|b(\mathscr{E})|} \int_{\tau > 0} d\mathscr{E}' f_e(\mathscr{E}')\psi_e\{\tau(\mathscr{E}, \mathscr{E}')\}, \quad (17.30)$$

the function $\psi_e(\tau)$ for the direction of the galactic pole being

† See, however, the footnote on p. 355. Here, we note that the calculation of the energy of the secondary electrons generated in metagalactic space using the data given above confirms the estimate given in section 13.

$$\psi_l(\tau) = \int_0^R \phi(\tau, r)\, dl$$

$$= \frac{\exp\left\{-\dfrac{r_s^2}{1+\tau}\right\}}{1+\tau}\, \frac{2}{\sqrt{\pi}} \left\{ \int_0^{R/\sqrt{p+\tau}} e^{-\eta^2}\, d\eta + \alpha \int_0^{R/\sqrt{1+\tau}} e^{-\eta^2}\, d\eta \right\}.$$

$$\text{(17.31)}$$

The factor α allows for the amount of gas in the halo related to the galactic disk (in the calculations we take $\alpha = 1$).

As a result the magnetic bremsstrahlung intensity of the secondary electrons can be expressed as

$$I_l(\nu) = \frac{\sqrt{3}e^3 H}{4\pi mc^2 a^2} \int_1^\infty d\mathscr{E}\, N_l(\mathscr{E}) \Phi(\nu/\nu_0 \mathscr{E}^2). \qquad \text{(17.32)}$$

In the case of a homogeneous model we must put $N_l(\mathscr{E}) = N(\mathscr{E})R$ in this expression (see (17.26)).

We shall take the distance R to the boundary of the Galaxy in the direction of the galactic pole to be $R = \sqrt{1 - r_s^2} \simeq 0\cdot75$ (in units $a = 3\cdot7 \times 10^{22}$ cm) which corresponds to the spherical model of the halo. Strictly speaking, the fact of the presence of the galactic boundary should be allowed for in the solution of equation (17.14) by setting the appropriate boundary conditions. However, it is not possible to formulate these conditions at present without ambiguity. Therefore R, in fact, plays only the part of a certain "effective" distance that allows for the effect of the boundary in the diffusion approximation in question. We note that the nature of the reflexion at the boundaries of the Galaxy is significant only when there is sufficiently rapid diffusion since otherwise the electrons lose energy before reaching the boundary. If there is total reflexion (the closed model of the Galaxy) the homogeneous model corresponds to the extreme case of rapid diffusion.

Results of Calculations and Discussion of Problem of Origin of Relativistic Electrons in the Galaxy

Figures 23 and 24 show the intensity $I_\nu \equiv I_l(\nu)$ calculated for several values of H, T_d and n by formula (17.32). When allowing for the ionisation losses for the mean concentration of the gas in the Galaxy we looked at two values of $n = 0\cdot01$ cm^{-3} and $n = 0\cdot03$ cm^{-3}. The last of these corresponds to the dashed curves in Figs. 23 and 24.

As can be seen, in the observed frequency range the ionisation energy losses of the electrons do not lead to a significant change in the spectrum. The curves in Fig. 23 are plotted for the mean value of the magnetic field strength in the Galaxy including the halo $H = 3 \times 10^{-6}$ oersteds and in Fig. 24 for $H = 7 \times 10^{-6}$ oersteds.

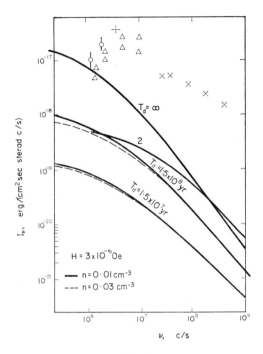

Fig. 23

In addition Fig. 24 also shows curve 1 for the values $H = 2 \times 10^{-5}$ oersteds, $T_d = 1 \cdot 5 \times 10^8$ years and $n = 0 \cdot 1$ cm^{-3} (this value of n is chosen only for simplicity of calculation). Apart from the closed model ($T_d = \infty$) we calculated the diffusion model with two values for the diffusion time of departure of relativistic particles from the Galaxy: $T_d = 1 \cdot 5 \times 10^8$ years and $T_d = 1 \cdot 5 \times 10^7$ years ($D = 1 \cdot 4 \times 10^{29}$ cm^2/sec and $D = 1 \cdot 4 \times 10^{30}$ cm^2/sec).

The experimental values of the general radio emission intensity of the Galaxy given in Figs. 23 and 24 are the mean values with respect to the hemisphere in the direction of the Galaxy's anticentre (see the paper by Walsh et al.[464] which also contains a summary of earlier results[465, 500, 501]). The spectral intensities of the over-all galactic radio emission in the directions of the pole and the anticentre are close to each other† so the experimental values given in Figs. 23 and 24 can be used for comparison with the calculated intensity I_ν in the direction of the galactic pole.

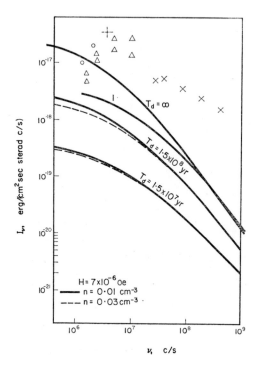

Fig. 24

It can be seen from Figs. 23 and 24 that for the closed model of the Galaxy the secondary electron emission intensity is far lower than that observed.‡ In addition, in this model the spectral emission

---

† We are not here taking into consideration the information[467] (see also below) that the halo is very much flattened (the ratio of the half-axes is $b/a \simeq 1/10$). For this flattened halo with a corresponding reduction of the diffusion coefficient ($D \sim 3 \times 10^{28}$ cm^2/sec and $T_d \sim 10^7$ years) the part played by secondary radio-emitting electrons would be significant.

‡ We are not dealing with the low-frequency range ($\nu \lesssim 3 \times 10^6$ c/s, $\lambda \gtrsim 100$ m) where allowance must be made for absorption of the radio waves in the ionised interstellar gas.

index is $\alpha = 1$ as early as $\nu \gtrsim 20$ Mc/s which contradicts the nature of the observed spectrum ($\alpha < 0.9$ for $\nu < 1000$ Mc/s). This last contradiction is eliminated in the open model if we assume the rapid departure of electrons from the Galaxy ($T_d \sim 10^7$ years, $D \sim 2 \times 10^{30}$ cm^2/sec). In this case, however, the intensity is more than two orders lower than the observed one since only a small fraction of the electron energy is lost in emission within the Galaxy. No way can be seen of eliminating these discrepancies if we continue to assume the secondary nature of the emitting electrons. In actual fact, to do this it would be necessary to increase by two or three orders the product MI_{cr}, where M is the total mass of the gas and I_{cr} is the mean value of the cosmic ray intensity in the Galaxy; otherwise we must take a value considerably greater than 2 to 3×10^{-5} oersteds for the magnetic field strength. In this connexion the suggestion made by Hayakawa and Okuda[433] is also insufficient; this was that with a mean field $H \sim 3 \times 10^{-6}$ oersteds there are regions occupying 5 per cent of the Galaxy's volume in which the field is an order greater. In actual fact the additional intensity caused by these regions for $T_d = 1.5 \times 10^8$ years according to the calculations that were made is shown by curve 2 in Fig. 23.

Therefore the assumption that the radio-emitting electrons in the Galaxy are secondary does not allow us to explain the absolute intensity and form of the spectrum of the observed non-thermal radio emission.† In addition, as is shown in section 18, secondary electrons cannot be responsible either for the X-radiation recently observed.[506]

These conclusions are obtained on the basis of the stationary model which assumes that during the life of electrons in the Galaxy $T_d \sim 10^8$ years there is no noticeable change in the concentration of the interstellar gas or the cosmic ray intensity in the Galaxy. Recently, however, a model of the galactic halo was suggested that is

† The same conclusion is drawn by Lund et al.[502] and also, in a milder form, by Hayakawa[503] after some tightening of the calculations by Hayakawa and Okuda[433]. The experiments of Shong et al.[446], which are briefly discussed in section 2 of this book, are direct experimental proof of the conclusion that primary electrons play the dominant rôle. When using the calculations given above (see Fig. 21) it can be seen that the percentage of positrons with respect to the whole electron-positron component may be as much as 20 to 30 per cent at $E \simeq 10^8$ eV and 2 to 3 per cent at $E \simeq 10^9$ eV. Allowing for the inaccuracy of the calculations and the preliminary nature of the experiments of Shong et al.[446] it can at present be considered that these calculations and measurements do not contradict each other.

a non-stationary one. In this model the halo was formed as the result of the ejection of $\sim 10^7$ solar masses at a velocity of ~ 500 km/sec in an explosion of the galactic core about 10^7 to 10^8 years ago.[438] This hypothesis is discussed in section 11. The conclusion was drawn there that the explosions in the galactic core, if they did occur, were more likely to be comparatively weak. In this variant the Galaxy, from the point of view of the origin of cosmic rays, can as before be considered stationary in the first approximation. In the latter case all the calculations given above relating to secondary electrons remain applicable. Even in the general case, however, when the model is essentially non-stationary because of powerful explosions the part played by secondary electrons remains small. In actual fact, since the thickness of matter x passed through by the cosmic rays from the time they appeared is 5 to 10 g/cm^2 according to the data on the chemical composition of the cosmic rays the total number of secondary electrons in a non-stationary halo cannot be greater than in a stationary one with $T_d = x/\rho c = 5/2 \times 10^{-26} \times 3 \times 10^{10} = 10^{16}$ sec $= 3 \times 10^8$ years. In this case the possible departure of some of the cosmic rays during the expansion of the halo and the reduction in particle energy connected with this expansion play no part since these effects relate equally to secondary electrons as well.

Therefore of the two possibilities discussed at the beginning of this section only one remains—direct generation of relativistic electrons

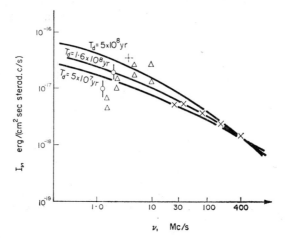

Fig. 25

in the sources (in supernovae, in explosions of the Galactic core, ...).
To estimate the intensity of the primary electron sources on the basis
of the stationary model we can use the formulae given above if
the secondary electron generation spectrum $(4\pi M/\lambda)f_e(\mathscr{E})$ is replaced
by the source spectrum $K\mathscr{E}^{-\gamma_0}$, considering this spectrum in the
first approximation to be a power law and the spatial distribution of
the sources to be gaussian of form (17.21).

TABLE 18

T_d, years	K, sec^{-1}	U, erg/sec
5×10^8	$5\cdot9 \times 10^{43}$	$2\cdot0 \times 10^{39}$
$1\cdot5 \times 10^8$	$8\cdot3 \times 10^{43}$	$2\cdot8 \times 10^{39}$
5×10^7	$1\cdot5 \times 10^{44}$	$5\cdot0 \times 10^{39}$

The results of the corresponding calculations are given in Fig. 25
and Table 18. The source spectrum index chosen (as an example
that does not contradict the observations) is $\gamma_0 = 1\cdot7$, the sources
are considered to be concentrated in the galactic disk ($a = 12$
kpc, $p = 10^{-4}$) and we take the values $H = 3 \times 10^{-6}$ oersteds, $n =$
$0\cdot01$ cm^{-3}, $w_{\text{ph}} = 1$ eV/cm^3. Three values were examined for the
departure time of electrons from the halo: $T_d = 5 \times 10^7$, $1\cdot5 \times 10^8$,
and 5×10^8 years. The coefficient K in the source spectrum was
chosen so that the magnetic bremsstrahlung intensity curves obtained
led to the observed value of the intensity at a frequency of $v =$
400 Mc/s. The corresponding values of the coefficient K and the
source power in the $0\cdot3 < E < 10$ GeV energy range corresponding
to the magnetic bremsstrahlung frequency range† $10^6 < v < 10^9$ c/s
are given in Table 18. The power of the primary electron sources
was calculated as

$$U(E_1, E_2) = mc^2 \int_{E_1/mc^2}^{E_2/mc^2} K\mathscr{E}^{-\gamma_0+1} d\mathscr{E}$$
$$= \frac{K}{2 - \gamma_0} (E_2^{2-\gamma_0} - E_1^{2-\gamma_0})(mc^2)^{\gamma_0-1}. \quad (17.33)$$

Therefore the necessary power for the primary electron sources in
the Galaxy is only an order less than the necessary power for the
sources of all the cosmic rays $U_{\text{cr}} \sim 3$ to 10×10^{40} erg/sec (see sections

† For electrons with an energy E the emission intensity is maximum at a
frequency v, the energy being $E = 5\cdot2 \times 10^2(v/H)^{1/2}$ eV, where H is the strength of
a field that is assumed to be isotropic on the average when $H_\perp{}^2 = \frac{2}{3}H^2$.

11 and 15). At the same time U is an order greater than the power of the Galactic radio emission $U_v \sim 3$ to 5×10^{38} erg/sec; this can be explained by leakage of some of the electrons from the Galaxy and also by the considerable Compton losses of energy which at $w_{ph} = 1$ eV/cm^3 and $H = 3 \times 10^{-6}$ oersteds are three times the magnetic bremsstrahlung losses. Since the power necessary for generating the electrons is nevertheless far less than the total power of the cosmic ray sources no difficulties of an energetic nature apparently arise here. But, of course, the question of the electron acceleration mechanism in the sources which is still unclear now becomes particularly important.

To conclude we shall examine the question of the cosmic ray electron-component on Earth.†

When there is complete mixing electrons should be observed on Earth with an intensity $I_e(E) = (c/4\pi)N_e(E)$, where $N_e(E) = N_e(\mathscr{E})/mc^2$ is defined by formula (17.22) with $r = r_s$. The values of $I_e(E)$ for secondary electrons are shown in Fig. 21 and have been discussed already. For the primary electrons, i.e., directly from radio astronomy data, a value is obtained for $I_e(E)$ which is also shown in Fig. 21 (the curve with $\gamma_0 = 1\cdot7$ and $T_d = 1\cdot5 \times 10^8$ yrs). Here $I_e(E > 1$ GeV$) \simeq 2 \times 10^{-2}$ (cm$^2 \cdot$sec$\cdot$sterad)$^{-1}$ which is an order greater than according to the observations by Earl.[57] This conclusion in a milder form has long been clear[173] (see also section 11) but it can now be drawn with particular certainty. Since Earl's observations[57] were made at a period of high solar activity the galactic value of I_e may be greater; this can be elucidated at a period of minimum solar activity (1964–65). We think it highly improbable, however, that in the change to the minimum $I_e(E > 1$ GeV$)$ will increase by a factor of more than 2 to 3. This, combined with Earl's data,[57] produces the value $I_e(E > 1$ GeV$) \lesssim 5 \times 10^{-3}$ cm^{-2} sec^{-1} sterad^{-1} which is still 4 times less than the value calculated above. The remaining discrepancy can be eliminated by increasing the mean field in the halo by a factor of 2 ($H \simeq 6 \times 10^{-6}$ oersteds) or partly by increasing the size of the halo and varying the other parameters. Another possibility is the suggestion that in the galactic neighbourhood of the Sun the cosmic ray intensity is several times less than the mean intensity on the whole line of sight. If the cosmic rays are generated in the region of the galactic centre and largely enter the halo this hypothesis is not improbable.

† This question is discussed with regard to the cosmic gamma and X-radiation in section 19.

18. GAMMA RAYS AND MAGNETIC BREMSSTRAHLUNG X-RADIATION DUE TO PION DECAY

In this section we calculate the intensity of the γ-rays due to the decay of π°-mesons generated in nuclear collisions of cosmic rays in interstellar and intergalactic space. We find the intensity under the same conditions for the magnetic bremsstrahlung X-radiation of electrons (and positrons) that are $\pi^\pm$-meson decay products. The corresponding values of the γ- and X-ray intensities are several orders lower than the cosmic γ- and X-radiation intensities recorded in some papers.

Experimental data have recently appeared[68, 504–506] which, although they are of a preliminary nature, speak in favour of the suggestion that there is a noticeable flux of γ-rays and X-rays of cosmic origin. The most probable source of γ-rays with an energy $E \gtrsim 50$ MeV is π°-mesons generated in nuclear collisions of cosmic rays in the interstellar or intergalactic medium. In Kraushaar and Clark's experiments[68] all the γ-rays with an energy $E > 50$ MeV were recorded; their expected intensity $I_\gamma(E > 50$ MeV) is proportional to the integral

$$\int nI_{\mathrm{cr}}\, dl$$

along the line of sight (n is the concentration of the gas, I_{cr} is the intensity of the cosmic rays with practically all the energies encountered). There are estimates of the value of $I_\gamma(E > 50$ MeV) for the Galaxy and the Metagalaxy in a number of papers[68, 434] and we shall not repeat them here. In the experiments of Firkowski et al.[504] and Suga et al.[505] it is a question of measurement of the intensity $I_\gamma(E > 10^{15}$ eV) which, according to the data by these authors[504, 505] is of the order of or less than $10^{-3}I_{\mathrm{cr}}(E > 10^{15}$ eV). Giacconi et al.[506] have found X-radiation with a wavelength of $\lambda = 3$ Å and a mean directional energy intensity of $J_X \sim 10^{-8}$ erg/cm$^2 \cdot$ sec·sterad (in the experiment $I_X \sim 2$ photons/cm$^2 \cdot$sec·sterad).

If hard cosmic γ-rays are really observed it is natural to try and connect their appearance with the decay of π°-mesons of the appropriate energies. But then the observed X-radiation could in principle also have the nature of magnetic bremsstrahlung[506, 507] (the generation of a π°-meson is accompanied with the appearance of on the average two $\pi^{\pm}$-mesons leading finally to the appearance of electrons and positrons; the latter produce magnetic bremsstrahlung when they move in the cosmic magnetic fields).

It is hard to overestimate the possible importance of even the first steps in the field of gamma and X-ray astronomy. Of particular importance in this respect are experiments of the kind made by Kraushaar and Clark[68] which permit us to obtain valuable information on metagalactic space.[68, 434] Experiments with hard γ-rays and X-radiation may, of course, also be exceptionally important from the point of view of obtaining fresh information on the cosmos. In this connexion we shall below analyse the question of the intensity of gamma and X-rays generated as the result of nuclear interactions of cosmic rays in the Galaxy and Metagalaxy.

Gamma Ray Intensity

In the range $10 \leqslant E \leqslant 10^6$ to 10^7 GeV we take for the cosmic ray intensity on Earth the value[97]

$$I(E) \, dE = 1 \cdot 5E^{-2 \cdot 6} \, dE = KE^{-\gamma} \, dE \text{ particles/cm}^2 \cdot \text{sec} \cdot \text{sterad}, \quad (18.1)$$

where the particle energy E is measured in GeV (Nikol'skii[97] gives the integral spectrum

$$I(>E) = \int_E^\infty I(E) \, dE = 0 \cdot 93E^{1-\gamma}, \qquad \gamma = 2 \cdot 6 \pm 0 \cdot 03).$$

At the high energies of interest to us ($E > 10^3$ GeV) there is no reliable information on the chemical composition of the cosmic rays. If we extrapolate the composition known for lower energies, then among the particles with an energy greater than the given one the number of protons is about half. On the other hand for nuclei of a given energy each nucleon has less energy, so plays a smaller part from the point of view of calculating the number of π-mesons (see below) of a given energy. Below, however, we shall not take this circumstance into account which could lead to a maximum reduction in the intensity by a factor of two (on the assumption that at a given total energy the number of nuclei does not exceed the number of protons and $\gamma > 2$). In other words, we shall consider all the particles in (18.1) to be protons. There is no reason to make the corresponding adjustment in accuracy (allowance for the chemical composition) if we bear in mind not only the absence of sufficiently complete information on the composition but also the inevitable inaccuracy of all the other data (i.e., the values of the cosmic ray intensity $I \equiv I_{cr}$ and the gas concentration n along the whole line of sight).

Interaction of cosmic rays with nuclei (protons) of the interstellar medium takes place with a cross section of $\sigma \simeq 4 \times 10^{-26}$ cm^2. This results in the generation of π-mesons to a total number $v(E) = v_0 E^\delta$ (with one third each of π°-, π^+- and π^--mesons), their total energy being $v\bar{E}_\pi = kE, k = k_0 E^\alpha$. Below we shall use the values[508]

$$v_0 = 3\cdot3, \qquad \delta = \tfrac{1}{4}, \qquad k_0 = \tfrac{1}{3}, \qquad \alpha = 0. \qquad (18.2)$$

Hence the mean energy of a meson being generated (the energy is always measured in GeV)

$$\bar{E}_\pi = kE/v(E) \simeq 0\cdot1E^{3/4}. \qquad (18.3)$$

In a unit volume $\sigma n(r)I(E)dE$ interactions from cosmic rays with an intensity $I(E)$ take place. The following number of π-mesons is formed (we are dealing with the π-mesons generated by cosmic rays moving within a unit solid angle; the total number of π-mesons can be obtained by multiplying expression (18.4) by 4π since the cosmic rays are isotropic):

$$q_\pi(E_\pi) \, dE_\pi = \sigma n(r)v_0 E^\delta I(E) \, dE = \sigma n(r) K_\pi E_\pi^{-\gamma_\pi} \, dE_\pi,$$

$$E = (E_\pi v_0/k_0)^{1/(1+\alpha-\delta)}, \qquad I(E) = KE^{-\gamma}, \qquad (18.4)$$

$$\gamma_\pi = \frac{\gamma + \alpha - 2\delta}{1 + \alpha - \delta}, \qquad K_\pi = K\frac{v_0}{1+\alpha-\delta}\left(\frac{k_0}{v_0}\right)^{\gamma_\pi - 1}.$$

If we now take the values (18.2) and put $K = 1\cdot5$ and $\gamma = 2\cdot6$ (see (18.1)), then $K_\pi = 0\cdot105$, $\gamma_\pi = 2\cdot8$, $K_{\pi\pm} = \tfrac{2}{3}K_\pi$, $K_{\pi^\circ} = \tfrac{1}{3}K_\pi$ and therefore

$$q_{\pi\pm}(E_\pi) = \sigma n \times 0\cdot07E_\pi^{-2\cdot8}\pi^\pm \text{ mesons/cm}^3 \cdot \text{sec} \cdot \text{sterad} \cdot \text{GeV},$$

$$q_{\pi^\circ}(E_\pi) = \sigma n \times 0\cdot035E_\pi^{-2\cdot8}\pi^\circ\text{-mesons/cm}^3 \cdot \text{sec} \cdot \text{sterad} \cdot \text{GeV}. \qquad (18.5)$$

We note that according to Greisen[66] the $\pi^\pm$-meson generation spectrum in the atmosphere (on the absorption path, i.e., with $n\sigma \simeq 2$) is of the form $q_{\pi\pm}(E_\pi) = 0\cdot156E_\pi^{-2.64} \, dE$. This value for $\sigma n = 1$ and $E_\pi = 1$ GeV practically coincides with (18.5) but for $E_\pi = 10^5$ GeV differs by a factor of about six.

In the decay of a π°-mesons into two γ-quanta the energy of each of the quanta in the rest system of a π°-meson is obviously $E_\gamma^* = m_{\pi^\circ}c^2/2$. In a system in which the total energy of a π°-meson is E_π the energy of a quantum is $E_\gamma = zE_\gamma^* + \sqrt{z^2 - 1} \; E_\gamma^* \cos \theta^*$, where $z = E_\pi/m_\pi c^2$ and θ^* is the angle between the momentum of the quantum and the velocity of the laboratory system measured in the rest system of a π°-meson (in this system decay occurs isotropically). The γ-ray distribution function in the laboratory system is of the form

$$f(E_\gamma, z) \, dE_\gamma = dE_\gamma/E_\gamma^* \sqrt{z^2 - 1}, \qquad z \geqslant (E_\gamma^2 + E_\gamma^{*2})/2E_\gamma E_\gamma^*.$$

Hence

$$q_\gamma(E_\gamma) \, dE_\gamma = dE_\gamma \int_{E_{\pi, \, \text{min}}}^{\infty} \sigma n K_{\pi^\circ} E_\pi^{-\gamma_\pi} f(E_\gamma, z) \, dE_\pi$$

$$= \sigma n K_{\pi^\circ} \frac{2}{\gamma_\pi} \; E_\gamma^{-\gamma_\pi} dE_\gamma$$

(on the assumption that $E_\gamma \gg E_\gamma^* = m_\pi c^2/2$). In our case $\gamma_\pi = 2\cdot8$ and by virtue of (18.5) we have for the number of γ-rays being generated

$$q_\gamma(E_\gamma) = \sigma n \times 0\cdot025E_\gamma^{-2\cdot8} \; (\text{cm}^3 \cdot \text{sec} \cdot \text{sterad} \cdot \text{GeV})^{-1},$$

$$\tag{18.6}$$

$$q_\gamma(>E_\gamma) = \int_{E_\gamma}^{\infty} q_\gamma(E_\gamma) \, dE_\gamma = \sigma n \times 0\cdot014E_\gamma^{-1\cdot8} \; (\text{cm}^3 \cdot \text{sec} \cdot \text{sterad})^{-1}.$$

The γ-ray intensity in a given direction is

$$I_\gamma(>E_\gamma) = \int q_\gamma(>E_\gamma) \, dL$$

$$= 5\cdot6 \times 10^{-28} E_\gamma^{-1\cdot8} N(L) (\text{cm}^2 \cdot \text{sec} \cdot \text{sterad})^{-1}, \tag{18.7}$$

where $N(L) = \int n \, dL$ is the total number of nucleons in the medium on the line of sight.

In accordance with (18.1) and (18.7) the ratio of the intensities of the γ-rays and all the cosmic rays with an energy greater than E will be

$$\xi = I_\gamma(>E)/I(>E) \simeq 6 \times 10^{-28} N(L) E^{-0\cdot2}. \tag{18.8}$$

Since the spectrum (18.1) used in the calculations relates to energies $E \gtrsim 10$ GeV formula (18.8) is valid at $E = E_\gamma \gtrsim 10$ GeV and formula (18.7) at $E_\gamma \gtrsim 1$ to 3 GeV. In addition, if for $E \gtrsim 10^7$ GeV the spectrum (18.1) becomes steeper (which is probable) our calculations provide a value of $I_\gamma(>E_\gamma)$ at $E_\gamma > 10^5$ GeV that is too high. The accuracy of the value -0.2 for the power index in formula (18.8) is, of course, low. It is important, however, that the index is small (even at $E = 10^5$ GeV $= 10^{14}$ eV the factor $E^{-0.2}$ is only 1/10).

For metagalactic space the most probable (but by no means yet established) value is $n \simeq 10^{-5}$ cm^{-3} and $N(L) \simeq 5 \times 10^{22}$ cm^{-2} (the photometric radius of the Universe is $R_{ph} \simeq 5 \times 10^{27}$ cm). Therefore upon the assumption that the cosmic ray spectrum is identical everywhere and is of the form (18.1) we obtain for $E = 10^5$ GeV†

$$\zeta_{Mg} \simeq 3 \times 10^{-5} E^{0.2} = 3 \times 10^{-6}. \tag{18.9}$$

There are weighty reasons for assuming[434] that the cosmic ray intensity in metagalactic space in the comparatively low-energy region ($E \sim 10^9$ to 10^{11} eV) is considerably lower than in the Galaxy. Nothing definite can be said about the high energies. It is most natural to assume that at $E \sim 10^5$ GeV the position still changes but little when compared with that at lower energies and then estimate (18.9) for the ratio of metagalactic γ-rays to galactic cosmic rays is still far too high. Another situation is, however, conceivable in which the metagalactic cosmic-ray spectrum differs essentially from the galactic.

It is simplest to illustrate this with an example. Let us assume that the metagalactic cosmic ray spectrum is of the form $I_{Mg}(E) \simeq 10^{-3} E^{-2}$, i.e., at $E = 1$ GeV the intensity is 10^3 times less than the galactic, but $\gamma = 2$ instead of 2·6. Then with all the other assumptions remaining as above for the Metagalaxy

$$I_\gamma(>E_\gamma) \simeq 5 \times 10^{-30} E_\gamma^{-1} N(L),$$

$$\zeta \simeq 5 \times 10^{-30} N(L) E^{0.6} \sim 3 \times 10^{-7} E^{0.6}$$

(here, of course, the Galactic value is taken for the intensity I in (18.8). For $E = 10^5$ GeV we have $\zeta_{Mg} \simeq 3 \times 10^{-4}$, i.e., two orders higher than estimate (18.9). Thus the value $\zeta \sim 10^{-3}$ for $E \sim 10^6$ GeV

† There is a similar calculation of the γ-ray flux given in Maze and Zawadzki's paper.[65] We are giving the corresponding formulae, however, since we shall need them below when calculating the electron spectrum. The most important discrepancy with the calculations mentioned[65] when changing to numerical estimates is connected with the choice of the value of $N(L)$. Maze and Zawadzki[65] take $n \gtrsim 10^{-3}$ cm^{-3} for metagalactic space, which leads to the estimate $N(L) \gtrsim 5 \times 10^{24}$ cm^{-2}. However, all the available data scarcely permit us to use for the Metagalaxy a value much greater than $n \sim 10^{-5}$ cm^{-3}.

(at this energy there are certain experimental indications[504, 505]) would be compatible with the idea of the metagalactic origin of γ-rays and with a relatively low total cosmic ray energy in the Metagalaxy[434] if their (cosmic ray) spectrum is considerably harder than the galactic one.† In reality, however, it is very hard to make this assumption.

In actual fact, in the example given $I_{Mg}/I_G \sim 10^{-3}E^{0\cdot6}$. But then $I_{Mg}/I_G \gtrsim 1$ for $E \gtrsim 10^5$ GeV which should have a strong effect on the spectrum of the hard cosmic rays in the Galaxy. In other words, when there is sufficiently free exchange of cosmic rays between the Galaxy and the Metagalaxy (and this is most probable) the major rôle on Earth in the case under discussion at energies of $E > 10^5$ GeV would be played by cosmic rays of metagalactic origin. However, for $E > 10^5$ GeV the index γ in the cosmic ray spectrum is not less than but rather more than the value 2·6. Thus the assumption that in the Metagalaxy $\gamma \simeq 2$ is possible only when using far-reaching hypothesis in addition (it could be considered, for example, that a spectrum with $\gamma \simeq 2$ can be observed only beyond the Local Group of galaxies or the Local Supergalaxy, ...). To start on a course of such assumptions would be permissible only under pressure from sufficiently convincing facts. Therefore it is particularly important to check the preliminary data on the existence of hard γ-rays.[504, 505]

Metagalactic gamma and X-rays can be distinguished from galactic ones in the first place by their angular distribution. Metagalactic radiation should be isotropic in the first approximation. At the end of this section we give calculations of the quantity $N(L)$ for the Galaxy since the corresponding expressions may be useful in a number of cases. Here we shall give elementary estimates for $N(L)$ for the three basic directions and for the halo in the direction of the pole. In the latter case $n \sim 10^{-2}$ cm^{-3} and the size is $L \sim 3 \times 10^{22}$ cm (the radius of the halo is $R \sim 4 \times 10^{22}$ cm). In the galactic disk $n \sim 1$ cm^{-3} and in the directions of the centre, the anticentre, and the pole we have $L_c \sim 6 \times 10^{22}$ cm, $L_{ac} \sim 1\cdot2 \times 10^{22}$ cm, $L_p \sim 4 \times 10^{20}$

---

† The estimates show that the total γ-radiation of all the galaxies is in all probability considerably less than the total γ-radiation from the metagalactic medium for $I_{Mg} \sim I_G$, i.e., when the Metagalaxy is filled with cosmic rays of galactic intensity. In addition, there is no indication of the existence of a noticeable flux of hard γ-rays even from the most powerful discrete sources.[69] We should also point out that according to Vernov et al.[155] we have the value $\xi < (1 \text{ to } 4) \times 10^{-4}$ for γ-quanta with $\mathscr{E} \sim 10^{16}$ eV. See also section 19.

cm, respectively. Therefore

$$N_{h,p} \sim 3 \times 10^{20} \text{ cm}^{-2}, \qquad N_c \sim 6 \times 10^{22} \text{ cm}^{-2},$$

$$N_{ac} \sim 1\cdot2 \times 10^{22} \text{ cm}^{-2}, \qquad N_{d,p} \sim 4 \times 10^{20} \text{ cm}^{-2}, \qquad (18.10)$$

$$\xi_c \sim 4 \times 10^{-6}, \qquad \xi_{ac} \sim 7 \times 10^{-7}, \qquad \xi_p \sim 4 \times 10^{-8},$$

where in the estimate of ξ in (18.8) we have put $E = 10^5$ GeV and the value of ξ_p is obtained with allowance made for the contribution of both the disk and the halo (we put $N_p = N_{d,p} + N_{h,p}$). For the Galaxy as a whole (averaged over all angles) $\xi_{av} \sim 10^{-7}$.

All these estimates, allowing for their inevitable approximate nature because of the imprecise knowledge of the concentration n, agree with those given at the end of the present section. It is clear from (18.10) that even in the direction of the centre we cannot expect a value of $\xi \sim 10^{-3}$. This last value is four orders of magnitude larger than the estimate for the whole Galaxy and we can see no way of eliminating this discrepancy by changing one parameter or another. It would therefore be very difficult to explain the discovery of a flux of hard γ-rays with isotropic distribution and $\xi > 10^{-4}$ to 10^{-5}.

Apart from what has already been said, we should point out that the appearance of hard γ-rays in all probability cannot be connected with the process of π°-meson generation as the result of collisions of very hard cosmic rays with thermal photons.[76] In this case it is obvious that $I_\gamma \sim \sigma N_{ph}(L)I$, where σ is the corresponding cross section for the generation of π°-mesons, $N_{ph}(L)$ is the number of photons on the line of sight and I is the cosmic ray intensity (since the energy of thermal photons is $\varepsilon \sim 1$ eV, π°-mesons are generated only by nucleons with an energy of $E \gtrsim 10^{17}$ eV). We shall consider with Hayakawa[76] that $\sigma \sim 5 \times 10^{-28}$ cm^2 (allowing for the generation of several π°-mesons). Further, the photon concentration in the halo is $n_{ph} \sim 1$ cm^{-3} and in the Metagalaxy[434] $n_{ph} \sim 10^{-3}$ cm^{-3}; Hayakawa[76] takes $n_{ph} \sim 0\cdot3$ cm^{-3} for the Metagalaxy but there is no foundation for this. Hence for the halo (in the direction of the pole) $N_{ph} \sim 3 \times 10^{22}$ cm^{-2} and for the Metagalaxy $N_{ph} \sim 5 \times 10^{24}$ cm^{-2} and we have $\zeta_G = I_\gamma/I \sim 10^{-5}$ and $\zeta_{Mg} \sim 2 \times 10^{-3}$ respectively. Here, however, the cosmic ray intensity relates to the particles with an energy $E > 10^{17}$ eV that create γ-rays with an energy of the order of 10^{15} to 10^{16} eV. If we determine the ratio $\zeta = I_\gamma(>E)/I(>E)$ as we have done above then the values of ζ decrease by several orders (in this region of the spectrum $I(>E) \sim E^{-2}$ and therefore the transition from an energy of 10^{17} eV to an energy of 10^{16} eV corresponds to a change in I by a factor of 10^2).

We should point out here that with $n_{ph} \sim 10^{-3}$ cm^{-3} ($w_{ph} = \varepsilon n_{ph} \sim 10^{-3}$ eV/cm^3) the absorption of hard γ-rays in metagalactic space (by the generation of electron-positron pairs on thermal photons)[75] can generally be ignored (the maximum value of the absorption coefficient corresponding to γ-rays with $E \sim 10^{12}$ eV is $\mu_{max} \simeq 7 \times 10^{-26} w_{ph}$, where w_{ph} is measured in eV/cm^3 and μ in cm^{-1}; if $w_{ph} = 10^{-3}$ eV/cm^3, then even on a path $L = 5 \times 10^{27}$ cm we have only $\mu L \sim 0.35$).

Intensity of Secondary Electron Magnetic Bremsstrahlung X-Radiation

Let us now estimate the number of electrons generated as the result of charged π-meson decay and determine the intensity of the magnetic bremsstrahlung of these electrons in the interstellar magnetic fields.

An analysis of the kinematics of $\pi^{\pm} \to \mu^{\pm} + \nu$ and $\mu^{\pm} \to e^{\pm} + \nu + \bar{\nu}$ decays leads to the following expression for the intensity of the sources of these electrons (see the end of this section):

$$q_e(E)\, dE = \sigma n(r)\kappa(\gamma) K_{\pi^{\pm}} E^{-\gamma}\, dE. \qquad (18.11)$$

Here $K_{\pi^{\pm}}$ is the coefficient in the differential energy spectrum for the generation of charged π-mesons, γ is the power-law index of this spectrum and the coefficient $\kappa(\gamma)$ is defined by the relation

$$\kappa(\gamma) = \left(\frac{m_{\mu}}{m_{\pi}}\right)^{\gamma-1} \frac{2(\gamma + 5)}{\gamma(\gamma + 2)(\gamma + 3)}, \qquad \kappa(2.8) \simeq 0.12, \quad (18.12)$$

where m_{μ} and m_{π} are the masses of μ- and π-mesons.

For the charged π-meson generation spectrum obtained above for $\sigma = 4 \times 10^{-26}$ cm^2 we find

$$q_e(E) = n(r) \times 3.6 \times 10^{-28} E^{-2.8} \text{ electrons/cm}^3 \cdot \text{sec} \cdot \text{sterad} \cdot \text{GeV}. \qquad (18.13)$$

The energy of the electrons, whose maximum magnetic bremsstrahlung intensity is at a frequency ν, is defined by the expression

$$E \simeq 4.7 \times 10^2 (\nu/H_{\perp})^{1/2} \text{ eV}. \qquad (18.14)$$

Here $H_{\perp}$ is the component of the magnetic field at right angles to the direction of motion of a particle (measured in oersteds). The frequency ν is measured in cycles per second. For $\nu = 10^{18}$ c/s

($\lambda \simeq 3$ Å) and a mean value of $H_{\perp} \sim 5 \times 10^{-6}$ oersteds the electrons, in accordance with (18.14), should have an energy $E \simeq 2 \times 10^{14}$ eV. The electrons with an energy $E \gtrsim 10^{14}$ eV of interest to us are subject in practice only to magnetic bremsstrahlung losses when they move in the interstellar or intergalactic medium. These losses are (with $E \gg mc^2$)

$$-\left(\frac{dE}{dt}\right)_m = \beta E^2 = \frac{2c}{3}\left(\frac{e^2}{mc^2}\right)^2 H_{\perp}^2\left(\frac{E}{mc^2}\right)^2$$

$$= 0.98 \times 10^{-3} H^2 \left(\frac{E}{mc^2}\right)^2 \text{ eV/sec.} \quad (18.15)$$

If at a time $t = 0$ an electron had an energy E_0, then $E(t) = E_0$ $(1 + 3.8 \times 10^{-15} H_{\perp}^2 E_0 t)^{-1}$, where E is in eV and t in seconds. For $E_0 \sim 10^{14}$ eV the energy of an electron in a field $H_{\perp} \sim 3 \times 10^{-6}$ oersteds is halved in a time $t_{1/2} \sim 2.5 \times 10^{11}$ sec $\sim 10^4$ years. In this time an electron moving along the lines of force at a velocity $v_{\parallel} \sim 10^{10}$ cm/sec travels a distance of $L \sim 3 \times 10^{21}$ cm. In the case of the Galaxy the magnetic field is, in all probability, tangled and distorted, and the characteristic dimension of a region with a quasi-homogeneous field is $l \lesssim 100$ pc $\simeq 3 \times 10^{20}$ cm. Under these conditions the movement of an electron (from the place where it was generated) in the time $t_{1/2}$ is of the order of $L \sim \sqrt{lvt_{1/2}} \lesssim 10^{21}$ cm. This distance is still small when compared with the distance from the Sun to the centre of the Galaxy $L_c \simeq 2.5 \times 20^{22}$ cm or the radius of the halo $R \sim 3$ to 5×10^{22} cm. Therefore in the first approximation it can be taken that in the time $t \sim t_{1/2}$ electrons with an energy $E \sim 10^{14}$ eV remain in the region in which they were generated. In other words, unlike the problem of the magnetic bremsstrahlung galactic radio emission of comparatively soft electrons ($E \sim 10^9$ eV; see Refs. 173, 509, and section 17) the diffusion can be ignored in the case of the hard electrons under discussion here.

The statement made above on the possibility of ignoring the losses which are not of a magnetic bremsstrahlung nature is clear from the following expressions for the Compton and magnetic bremsstrahlung losses:

$$-E^{-1}(dE/dt)_{\text{brems}} = 8 \times 10^{-16} n \text{ sec}^{-1}, \quad (18.16)$$

$$-\left(\frac{dE}{dt}\right)_c \sim c\pi\left(\frac{e^2}{mc^2}\right)^2 n_{\text{ph}} \frac{(mc^2)^2}{\varepsilon} \ln\frac{2\varepsilon E}{(mc^2)^2} \sim$$

$$\sim 10^{-14}\left(\frac{mc^2}{\varepsilon}\right)^2 w_{\text{ph}}\ln\frac{2\varepsilon E}{(mc^2)^2} \text{ eV/sec,} \quad (18.17)$$

where n is the gas concentration (hydrogen in practice) and w_{ph} is the energy density of thermal photons with an energy ε expressed in eV. Formula (18.17) for the Compton losses relates to the case when the electron energy is $E \gg (mc^2)^2/\varepsilon \sim 3 \times 10^{11} \text{eV}$ (with $\varepsilon \sim 1\,\text{eV}$ as is the case under cosmic conditions). We note that the losses due to the generation by fast electrons of electron-positron pairs on thermal photons are still an order less than the losses (18.17). With $E \sim 10^{14}\,\text{eV}, H_\perp \sim 3 \times 10^{-6}$ oersteds, $n \sim 1\,\text{cm}^{-3}$ and $w_{ph} \sim 1\,\text{eV/cm}^3$, according to (18.15) to (18.17), the losses are $-(dE/dt)_m \sim 4 \times 10^2\,\text{eV/}$ sec, $-(dE/dt)_{brems} \sim 0 \cdot 1\,\text{eV/sec}, -(dE/dt)_C \sim 10^{-2}\,\text{eV/sec}$, which confirms what has been said above.

On the assumption that the change in the energy of the electrons is determined only by the magnetic bremsstrahlung losses and the spatial diffusion is insignificant the electron energy spectrum can be obtained from the relations

$$-\frac{\partial}{\partial E}\{\beta E^2 N(E)\} = 4\pi q_e(E), \qquad N(E) = \frac{4\pi}{\beta E^2}\int_E^\infty q_e(E')\,dE'. \quad (18.18)$$

Here $\beta = 3 \cdot 8 \times 10^{-15} H_\perp^2$ $(\text{eV} \cdot \text{sec})^{-1}$ is the coefficient in expression (18.15) for the magnetic bremsstrahlung losses. Using the source spectrum (18.13) and putting $H_\perp \simeq 5 \times 10^{-6}$ oersteds we find

$$N(E) = n(\mathbf{r}) \times 2 \cdot 5 \times 10^{-11} E^{-3 \cdot 8}\,\text{cm}^{-3} \cdot \text{GeV}^{-1}$$
$$= n(\mathbf{r}) \times 3 \cdot 7 \times 10^{-19} E^{-3 \cdot 8}\,\text{cm}^{-3} \cdot \text{erg}^{-1}. \quad (18.19)$$

To determine the spectral intensity of the magnetic bremsstrahlung of these electrons we use the well-known relation (see section 6; we use now J for the energy intensity and I for the photon or particle intensity):

$$J(v) = 1 \cdot 35 \times 10^{-22} a(\gamma_e) K_L H^{(\gamma_e+1)/2} (6 \cdot 26 \times 10^{18}/v)^{(\gamma_e-1)/2}$$
$$\text{erg/cm}^2 \cdot \text{sec} \cdot \text{sterad} \cdot (\text{c/s}), \quad (18.20)$$

where γ_e is the index of the electron differential spectrum (in our case $\gamma_e = 3 \cdot 8$; see (18.19)), $a(3 \cdot 8) = 0 \cdot 073$ and K_L is the coefficient in the electron spectrum on the line of sight. For spectrum (18.19) this coefficient is

$$K_L = 3 \cdot 7 \times 10^{-19}\int n(\mathbf{r})\,dL = 3 \cdot 7 \times 10^{-19} N(L),$$

where integration is carried out along the line of sight in some direction of interest to us.

Substituting the corresponding values in formula (18.20) and putting $H \simeq (3\bar{H}_\perp^2/2)^{1/2} \simeq 6 \times 10^{-6}$ oersteds we obtain

$$J(v) = N(L) \times 2 \cdot 2 \times 10^{-28} v^{-1 \cdot 4} \text{ erg/cm}^2 \cdot \text{sec} \cdot \text{sterad} \cdot (c/s)$$

$$J(>v) = \int_v^\infty I(v)\, dv = N(L) \times 5 \cdot 5 \times 10^{-28} v^{-0 \cdot 4} \text{ erg/cm}^2 \cdot \text{sec} \cdot \text{sterad},$$

$$(18.21)$$

which is equivalent to the X-ray quanta intensity ($E_X = hv$ is measured in keV)

$$I(>E_x) = \int_{E_X/h}^\infty \frac{I(v)\, dv}{hv} \simeq 1 \cdot 1 \times 10^{-26} N(L) E_x^{-1 \cdot 4}$$

$$\text{quanta/cm}^2 \cdot \text{sec} \cdot \text{sterad}. \quad (18.22)$$

Formula (18.20) is valid for power-law electron spectrum without limitations on the frequency range; formulae (18.21), (18.22) are based on the use of the actual spectra (18.13) and (18.19) and relate only to electrons with energies of $E > 1$ to 5 GeV.

Thus the expected intensity of the magnetic bremsstrahlung X-radiation with wavelengths of $\lambda \leqslant 8$ Å ($v \geqslant 4 \times 10^{17}$ sec^{-1}; $E_X \geqslant 1 \cdot 7$ keV) is

$$J(v > 4 \times 10^{17}) \simeq N(L) \times 5 \cdot 0 \times 10^{-35}$$
$$\text{erg/cm}^2 \cdot \text{sec} \cdot \text{sterad},$$

$$I(E_X > 1 \cdot 7 \text{ keV}) \simeq N(L) \times 5 \cdot 2 \times 10^{-27}$$

$$(18.23)$$

$$\text{quanta/cm}^2 \cdot \text{sec} \cdot \text{sterad}.$$

Using the values (18.10) for the amount of gas on the line of sight $N(L)$ in the various galactic directions it is easy to obtain the following estimates for the expected intensity of the X-radiation with a wavelength of $\lambda < 8$ Å (in quanta/cm$^2 \cdot$ sec $\cdot$ sterad):

$$I_c \simeq 3 \times 10^{-4}, \qquad I_{ac} \simeq 6 \times 10^{-5},$$
$$I_p \simeq 4 \times 10^{-6}, \qquad I_G \simeq 10^{-5}. \qquad (18.24)$$

Here for the direction of the galactic pole it is taken into account that the disk and the galactic halo make approximately the same contribution if the masses of gas they contain are the same.†

If the cosmic ray intensity and the magnetic field strength are the same everywhere in the Metagalaxy and are equal to the galactic

† See Ref. 524 for a discussion of magnetic bremsstrahlung X-radiation from discrete sources.

values the expected intensity of the X-ray quanta is

$$I_{Mg} \simeq 2.6 \times 10^{-4} \text{ quanta/cm}^2 \cdot \text{sec} \cdot \text{sterad}. \qquad (18.25)$$

However, the assumption that such conditions exist in the Metagalaxy, particularly with respect to the field, is quite improbable.[434]

We note that the absorption of X-rays with $\lambda < 8$ Å in the interstellar medium is comparatively small.[510] For example at $\lambda \simeq 3$ Å the optical thickness is $\tau \simeq 7 \times 10^{-24} N(L)$, i.e., even for $N(L) = 5 \times 10^{22}$ cm^{-2} the value is $\tau \simeq 0.4$; for $\lambda = 8$ Å the absorption is approximately five times greater and is thus significant for the Metagalaxy or in the direction of the galactic centre. But even in the direction of the anticentre, not to mention the pole, $N(L) \sim 1.2 \times 10^{22}$ cm^{-2} and $\tau(\lambda = 8 \text{ Å}) \simeq 3.3 \times 10^{-23} N(L) \sim 0.4$. Giacconi et al.[506] measured the X-ray flux in the 2–8 Å wavelength range, the mean value used being $\lambda = 3$ Å. In the transition from $\lambda = 8$ Å to $\lambda = 3$ Å the values of (18.24) and (18.25) are divided by 4. Since the X-ray flux observed by Giacconi et al.[506] was $I \sim 2$ quanta/cm$^2 \cdot$ sec·sterad it is quite clear that it is not possible in all probability to explain this flux by a magnetic bremsstrahlung mechanism[507] (if, of course, there are not enough high-energy primary electrons in interstellar space, these electrons could come, for example, from the shells of supernovae).

Calculation of the Function N(L) for a Model of the Galaxy

We shall consider that the gas distribution in the Galaxy has the symmetry of an ellipsoid of rotation, so

$$n(r) \, d^3r = \frac{N_t}{\pi^{3/2} a^2 c} \exp\left\{ -\frac{(x - x_\odot)^2 + y^2}{a^2} - \frac{z^2}{c^2} \right\} dx \, dy \, dz$$

$$= \frac{N_t}{\pi^{3/2} a^2 c} \exp\{-(r^2 \cos^2 b - 2rq \cos b \cos l + q^2$$

$$+ \varepsilon r^2 \sin^2 b)\} \, dV. \qquad (18.26)$$

Here N_t is the total number of nucleons in the system, l and b are the galactic longitude and latitude, $\varepsilon = a^2/c^2$ and $q = x_\odot/a$ is the distance from the Sun to the galactic centre; r and q are measured in units of a (a is the length of the semi-major-axis).

The number of particles along the line of sight is

$$N(l, b) = \int_0^\infty n(r) \, dL$$

$$= \frac{M}{2\pi ac} (\cos^2 b + \varepsilon \sin^2 b)^{-1/2}$$

$$\times \exp\left\{ -q^2 \frac{\cos^2 b \sin^2 l + \varepsilon \sin^2 b}{\cos^2 b + \varepsilon \sin^2 b} \right\} \frac{2}{\sqrt{\pi}} \int_{\xi_0}^\infty e^{-\xi^2} \, d\xi;$$

$$\xi_0 = -q(\cos^2 b + \varepsilon \sin^2 b)^{-1/2} \cos b \cos l. \tag{18.27}$$

For the galactic pole ($b = \pm \pi/2$)

$$N_p = \frac{N_t}{2\pi a^2} \exp\{-q^2\}. \tag{18.28}$$

In the galactic plane ($b = 0$)

$$N(l) = \frac{N_t}{2\pi ac} \exp\{-q^2 \sin^2 l\} \left(1 + \frac{2}{\sqrt{\pi}} \int_0^{q \cos l} e^{-\xi^2} \, d\xi \right). \tag{18.29}$$

For the centre ($l = 0, b = 0$) and the anticentre ($l = \pi, b = 0$)

$$N_c = \frac{N_t}{2\pi ac} \left\{ 1 + \frac{2}{\sqrt{\pi}} \int_0^q e^{-\xi^2} \, d\xi \right\},$$

$$N_{ac} = \frac{N_t}{2\pi ac} \left\{ 1 - \frac{2}{\sqrt{\pi}} \int_0^q e^{-\xi^2} \, d\xi \right\}. \tag{18.30}$$

For the disk we put $N_t = M/1.67 \times 10^{-24} \simeq 1.7 \times 10^{66}$ (the mass of the gas in the disk is $M = 2.8 \times 10^{42}$), $a = 12$ kpc $\simeq 3.7 \times 10^{22}$ cm, $c = 130$ pc $\simeq 4 \times 10^{20}$ cm, $q = 0.67$ (the distance from the Sun to the galactic centre is $x_\odot \simeq 8$ kpc). In the case of the halo we put $N_t = 1.7 \times 10^{66}$, $a = c = 3.7 \times 10^{22}$ cm.

Then we come to the values

$$N_{h, p} = 1.3 \times 10^{20} \text{ cm}^{-2}, \qquad N_c = 3 \times 10^{22} \text{ cm}^{-2},$$

$$N_{ac} = 6.4 \times 10^{21} \text{ cm}^{-2}, \qquad N_{d, p} = 1.3 \times 10^{20} \text{ cm}^{-2}, \tag{18.31}$$

These values are approximately half the values (18.10). The cause of this difference is simply that in (18.10) we put $n \sim 1$ cm^{-3}, whilst the value taken above for the mass M corresponds rather to an average concentration $n \simeq 0.5$ cm^{-3}. Let us also calculate the mean value over all angles:

$$\bar{N} = \frac{1}{4\pi} \int N(l, b) \, d\Omega = \frac{1}{4\pi} \int_0^\pi dl \int_{-\pi/2}^{+\pi/2} N(l, b) \cos b \, db, \quad (18.32)$$

in the case of spherical symmetry (with $a = c$)

$$\bar{N} = \frac{N_t}{2\pi a^2} e^{-q^2}\left\{1 + \frac{q^2}{3} + \frac{q^4}{10} + \cdots\right\}, \quad (18.33)$$

which at the accepted values for the halo gives

$$\bar{N}_h = 1.5 \times 10^{20} \text{ cm}^{-2}. \quad (18.34)$$

If $a \gg c$ and $q < 1$,

$$\bar{N} = \frac{N_t}{2\pi a^2} e^{-q^2}\left\{\ln \frac{2a}{c} + \frac{q^2}{2}\left(1 - \frac{c^2}{a^2} \ln \frac{2a}{c}\right) + \cdots\right\}. \quad (18.35)$$

Hence

$$\bar{N}_d \simeq 6.8 \times 10^{20} \text{ cm}^{-2}. \quad (18.36)$$

Kinematics of $\pi \to \mu \to e$ Decay

The probability of the appearance of an electron with an energy $y = E^*/mc^2$ in the $\mu^\pm \to e^\pm + v + \bar{v}$ decay of a rest μ-meson is defined by the expression

$$W(y) \, dy = 12yy_m^{-4}\sqrt{y^2 - 1}\{(y_m - y) + \tfrac{2}{9}\rho(4y - 3y_m)\}, \quad (18.37)$$

where $y_m \simeq m_\mu/2m \simeq 105$ is the maximum energy of a decay electron and the experimental value of Michel's parameter ρ is close to $\rho = 3/4$.

In the decay of a meson with an energy $z = E_\mu/m_\mu c^2$ the energy of an electron $x = E/mc^2$ flying away in the rest system of a μ-meson at an angle θ^* with an energy y is

$$x = yz + \sqrt{y^2 - 1}\sqrt{z^2 - 1} \cos \theta^*. \quad (18.38)$$

Isotropic distribution with respect to the angles θ^* corresponds to an energy distribution

$$f(x, y, z) \, dx = dx/2\sqrt{z^2 - 1}\sqrt{y^2 - 1} \quad (18.39)$$

in the range

$$|x - yz| \leqslant \sqrt{y^2 - 1}\sqrt{z^2 - 1}. \quad (18.40)$$

Therefore the energy spectrum of μ-mesons $I_\mu(z)$ corresponds to the decay electron energy spectrum

$$I_e(x)\,dx = dx \int\int \frac{W(y)I_\mu(z)\,dy\,dz}{2\sqrt{z^2-1}\,\sqrt{y^2-1}}, \qquad (18.41)$$

where integration is carried out over the region of the variables y and z corresponding to condition (18.40) and the condition $y \leqslant y_m$.

In a $\pi^\pm \to \mu^\pm + \nu$ decay the kinetic energy of a μ-meson in the rest system is small ($E^*_{k,\,\mu} \simeq 4\,\mathrm{MeV}$) and the difference between its velocity and the velocity of a decaying high-energy π-meson can be ignored; hence we put $E_\pi/m_\pi c^2 \simeq E_\mu/m_\mu c^2 = z$ and $I_{\pi^\pm}(z)\,dz = I_\mu(z)\,dz$. In the case of a power-law π-meson spectrum $I_{\pi^\pm}(E) = K_{\pi^\pm}E^{-\gamma}$ (i.e. $I_{\pi^\pm}(z) = (m_\pi c^2)^{-\gamma}K_{\pi^\pm}z^{-\gamma}$) integration in (18.41) with the condition $x \gg y_m$ leads to the following expression for the decay electron spectrum (with an accuracy up to terms of the order of $1/y_m^2$):

$$I_e(E)\,dE = K_e E^{-\gamma}\,dE, \qquad (18.42)$$

$$K_e = \left(\frac{m_\mu}{m_\pi}\right)^{\gamma-1}\frac{12[1 + \tfrac{2}{9}\rho(\gamma-1)]}{\gamma(\gamma+2)(\gamma+3)}K_{\pi^\pm}. \qquad (18.43)$$

With $\rho = 3/4$ we have expression (18.12) given in the text.

19. GAMMA AND X-RADIATION CONNECTED WITH GALACTIC AND METAGALACTIC COSMIC RAYS

In this section we calculate the intensity of γ-rays produced in various interaction processes of cosmic rays (including their electron component) with the gas and thermal emission in interstellar and intergalactic space. The major contribution to the γ-ray intensity is made by the scatter of relativistic electrons on thermal photons, although the γ-rays from π°-meson decay and electron bremsstrahlung may also be important. A comparison of the calculations with the observations allows us to consider that the intensity of the cosmic ray electron component in the Metagalaxy is at least one and a half to two orders less than in the Galaxy. In addition, we discuss the high-energy electron range which could produce magnetic bremsstrahlung X-radiation and cause the atmospheric showers with an anomalously small number of mesons.

The study of cosmic gamma and X-radiation, i.e., the development of gamma and X-ray astronomy, is at present an extremely interesting and at the same time quite real problem (see also Ref. 523).

Cosmic X-radiation may arise in the atmospheres of stars,[511] in the interaction of sub-cosmic rays (particles with an energy of $E \lesssim 1$ to 3×10^8 eV) with the interstellar medium[512, 513] and thermal emission, and lastly by the action of cosmic rays. As for the γ-rays with an energy $E_\gamma \gtrsim 5 \times 10^7$ eV (it is this range we have in mind below), they can in practice be generated only as the result of collisions of cosmic ray particles in interstellar and intergalactic space. Thus a study of cosmic γ-radiation, and under certain conditions of X-radiation, may be an irreplaceable source of information on the cosmic rays and gas in the Universe. The corresponding analysis is promising particularly since we already have a whole series of data on cosmic rays beyond the Earth, whilst there is essentially no information on sub-cosmic particles.

From the point of view of the generation of γ-rays with $E_\gamma \gtrsim 5 \times 10^7$ eV the following processes are of interest:

1. The decay of π°-mesons generated in cosmic ray collisions in the interstellar gas.

2. Bremsstrahlung of the relativistic electrons (and positrons) making up the electron component of cosmic rays. Here we may include the emission during the annihilation of positrons and during the generation of the electron component itself by $\pi^\pm \to \mu^\pm \to e^\pm$ decay.

3. Scatter of the electron component particles on thermal photons (the "inverse" Compton effect).

Processes 2 and 3 also make a contribution to the X-radiation but the major rôle is played by the soft part of the cosmic ray spectrum where these rays meet sub-cosmic particles whose spectrum is not known. Therefore if we are talking about the cosmic rays themselves (to be more precise, their electron component) only the following process is responsible for the X-radiation.

4. Magnetic bremsstrahlung X-radiation.

The question of the gamma and X-radiation connected with cosmic rays has already been discussed in a whole series of papers[68, 506, 514–517] (see also section 18). However, the results are strongly dependent on the values of the parameters being used, and, largely for this reason, disagree by several orders in the various estimates. Meanwhile, processes 1 to 4 are well known and the focal point of the problem is in the field of actual calculations and estimates based on a definite choice of cosmic ray spectrum, thermal emission energy density, etc. The purpose of this section is to carry out and discuss such calculations using the data that at present appear the most reliable and, partially, have been accepted or used by us recently.[434, 509]

Initial Data

In the $10 \lesssim E \lesssim 10^6$ GeV energy range the intensity of all the cosmic rays can be expressed in the form (where the energy E is measured in GeV)

$$I_{cr}(E) = 1 \cdot 5E^{-2 \cdot 6} \text{ particles/cm}^2 \cdot \text{sec} \cdot \text{sterad} \cdot \text{GeV}. \quad (19.1)$$

This spectrum taken in section 18 from Nikol'skii's data[97] agrees with the spectrum given by Brook et al.[498]* For $E < 10$ GeV spectrum (19.1) leads to an intensity that is somewhat too high. We shall therefore also give the approximate value we are using for the total cosmic ray intensity on Earth, which relates in practice to the particles with a total energy $E \gtrsim 2$ GeV.

$$I_{cr}(E > E_{min}) = \int_{E_{min}}^{\infty} I_{cr}(E) \, dE = 0 \cdot 23 \text{ particles/cm}^2 \cdot \text{sterad} \cdot \text{sec}.$$
$$(19.2)$$

In accordance with contemporary ideas we shall consider that the cosmic rays with spectrum (19.1) fill the whole Galaxy evenly including the halo, i.e., a quasi-spherical volume with a radius of 5×10^{22} cm.

The relativistic electron intensity in the Galaxy can be determined from the data on the intensity of the general galactic radio emission. If we take the value of $\gamma = 1 \cdot 7$ for the electron source spectral index, then in the diffusion model with a particle departure time from the galactic volume of $T_d = 1 \cdot 5 \times 10^8$ years and a magnetic field strength of $H = 3 \times 10^{-6}$ oersteds the power necessary for the electron sources in the Galaxy is (see section 18, Table 18)

$$Q_e(E) \, dE = 8 \cdot 3 \times 10^{43} \left(\frac{E}{mc^2} \right)^{-1 \cdot 7} \frac{dE}{mc^2}$$

$$= 4 \cdot 1 \times 10^{41} E^{-1 \cdot 7} \, dE \text{ electrons/sec}, \quad (19.3)$$

---

* Within the limits of accuracy of the available data and calculations we may take the value of 2·7 for the power-law index in (19.1) instead of the 2·6 indicated.[518, 519]

where E in the last expression is measured in GeV. The electron intensity in the vicinity of the solar system caused by these sources is shown by the solid line in Fig. 26. In calculating this intensity it was assumed that the sources are concentrated in the galactic disk (for further details we refer to section 17).

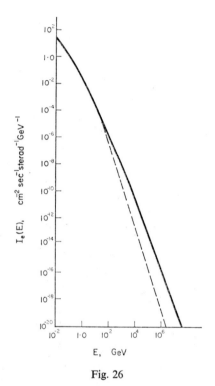

Fig. 26

In the 0·5 to 10 GeV energy range the spectrum shown in Fig. 26 can be approximated by the expression

$$I_e(E) = 2 \times 10^{-2}E^{-2} \text{ electrons/cm}^2 \cdot \text{sec} \cdot \text{sterad} \cdot \text{GeV}. \qquad (19.4)$$

For the $0·05 < E < 0·5$ GeV energy range this formula gives a value for the intensity that is not more than one and a half to two times too high.

It must be stressed that spectra (19.3) and (19.4) lead on Earth to the intensity $I_e(E > 1 \text{ GeV}) = 2 \times 10^{-2}$ electrons/cm$^2 \cdot$sec$\cdot$sterad, which is too high. Therefore the values of (19.3) and (19.4) must

probably be reduced by a factor of 3 to 4, which is quite possible
with a sensible choice of parameters (we are thinking in the first place
of increasing the field strength by a factor of 1·5 to 2). Nevertheless
we give and use spectrum (19.3) and (19.4) since it was for this that
we made our calculations in section 17.

At higher energies ($E > 10$ GeV) the electron intensity on Earth
obtained by the method indicated (on the assumption that the source
spectrum (19.3) is valid for the whole energy range) is

$$I_e(E)\, dE = 8{\cdot}9 \times 10^5 \frac{dE}{mc^2} \left(\frac{E}{mc^2}\right)^{-2} \int_{E/mc^2}^{\infty} d\mathscr{E}$$

$$\times \mathscr{E}^{-1{\cdot}7} \left[1 + 8{\cdot}3 \times 10^7 \left(\frac{mc^2}{E} - \frac{1}{\mathscr{E}}\right)\right]^{-1}. \quad (19.5)$$

At $E > 10^5$ GeV with sufficient accuracy

$$I_e(E)\, dE = 1{\cdot}3 \times 10^6 \left(\frac{E}{mc^2}\right)^{-2{\cdot}7} \frac{dE}{mc^2} = 3{\cdot}2E^{-2{\cdot}7}\, dE, \quad (19.6)$$

where in the last expression the energy E must be taken in GeV.
Because of the rapid loss of energy in magnetic bremsstrahlung the
electrons with $E > 10^5$ GeV should obviously be concentrated in the
region of the sources, i.e., within the galactic disk (see section 18).
It must be remembered, however, that there is no direct reason for
continuing spectrum (19.3) into the $E > 10$ GeV energy range since
the radio astronomy data relate to electrons with $E \lesssim 10$ GeV.
The spectrum (19.5)–(19.6) is therefore given here only because it will
be used for the preliminary estimates later on.

In accordance with the available data (see section 18) we shall below
take the values given in Table 19 for L, $N(L)$, $M(L)$, where L is the
distance along the line of sight in the Galaxy, $N(L)$ is the number of gas
atoms on the line of sight and $M(L) = 2 \times 10^{-24}N(L)$ is the mass of this
gas in g/cm^2 (for the interstellar medium which contains about 90% H
and about 10% He the mean mass of the atoms is 2×10^{-24}g).
It should be borne in mind that the table gives rounded-off values
and even for the disk $N(L)$ may be twice as much. The concentration
$n = 10^{-2}$cm^{-3} taken for the halo is probably almost an order too high.
This fact, however, is of little significance from the point
of view of calculating $N(L)$ even in the direction of the pole. In
addition, Table 19 gives values for the thermal emission energy

density w_{ph} and data for the Metagalaxy which are also by way of a guide (see section 8 and below).

TABLE 19

	L, cm	$N(L)$, cm^{-2}	$M(L)$, g/cm^2	w_{ph}, eV/cm^3
Galaxy				
in direction of centre	7×10^{22}	3×10^{22}	6×10^{-2}	⎫
in direction of anti-centre	$1\cdot5 \times 10^{22}$	6×10^{21}	$1\cdot2 \times 10^{-2}$	⎬ 0·2
in direction of pole (including contribution from the halo)	—	3×10^{20}	6×10^{-4}	⎫
averaged directionally (including contribution from the halo)	—	8×10^{20}	$1\cdot6 \times 10^{-3}$	⎬ 0·8
halo (in direction of pole)	$3\cdot5 \times 10^{22}$	$1\cdot5 \times 10^{20}$	3×10^{-4}	⎭
Metagalaxy	$R_{ph} = 5 \times 10^{27}$	5×10^{22}	0·1	2×10^{-3}

Galactic Gamma Radiation

The intensity of the γ-rays arising as the result of the interaction of cosmic rays with the interstellar medium is

$$I_\gamma(E) = N(L) \int_{E_\gamma}^\infty \sigma(E_\gamma, E)I(E)\,dE, \tag{19.7}$$

where $\sigma(E_\gamma, E)$ is the differential cross section for the generation of a γ-quantum with an energy E_γ from a particle with an energy E and $I(E)$ is the intensity of the isotropic (according to the assumption) cosmic rays $I_{cr}(E)$ (process 1) or of their electron component $I_e(E)$ (processes 2 and 3; in the case of process 3 we have $N_{ph}(L)$— the number of photons on the line of sight—instead of $N(L)$). For the γ-rays from π°-meson decay (process 1) we have (see section 18)

$$I_{\gamma,\,\pi^\circ}(>E_\gamma) = \int_{E_\gamma}^\infty I(E_\gamma)\,dE_\gamma$$
$$= 5\cdot6 \times 10^{-28}E_\gamma^{-1\cdot8}N(L)\ (\text{cm}^2 \cdot \text{sec} \cdot \text{sterad})^{-1}, \tag{19.8}$$

where E_γ is measured in GeV. This formula is valid for $E_\gamma \gtrsim 1$ to 3 GeV. It is possible that it is more correct to use a value of 1·6 to

1·7 for the power-law index in (19.8) instead of 1·8. This fact, however, does not in essence alter the conclusions of the preceding section. In the low-energy range a power-law spectrum can no longer be used. In accordance with the threshold $E_\gamma = 5 \times 10^7$ eV indicated in the preceding section we give here the numerical value (see page 28);

$$I_{\gamma, \pi^\circ}(E_\gamma > 5 \times 10^7 \text{ eV}) = 8 \times 10^{-27} N(L). \tag{19.9}$$

For the electron bremsstrahlung we can with sufficient accuracy put

$$N(L)\sigma(E_\gamma, E) = \frac{M(L)}{66} E_\gamma^{-1}, \qquad E_\gamma \leqslant E, \tag{19.10}$$

where for the interstellar medium the shower unit is taken[520] as 66 g/cm². In accordance with (19.7) and (19.10)

$$I_{\gamma, \text{brems}}(E_\gamma) = 1·5 \times 10^{-2} M(L) \frac{I_e(>E_\gamma)}{E_\gamma} \tag{19.11}$$

or for the spectrum (19.4)

$$I_{\gamma, \text{brems}}(E_\gamma) = 3 \times 10^{-4} M(L) E_\gamma^{-2},$$
$$I_{\gamma, \text{brems}}(>E_\gamma) = 3 \times 10^{-4} M(L) E_\gamma^{-1}. \tag{19.12}$$

The values of $I_{\gamma, \pi^\circ}(> E_\gamma)$ and $I_{\gamma, \text{brems}}(> E_\gamma)$ are compared in Table 20 for $E_\gamma = 1$ GeV and $E_\gamma = 5 \times 10^7$ eV.

Since the accepted electron intensity (19.4) should, as has been indicated, be reduced by a factor of 3 and in addition for $E_\gamma \gtrsim 5 \times 10^7$ eV the spectrum (19.12) is still 1·5 to 2 times too high it may be considered that the gamma bremsstrahlung is comparable with but nevertheless 2 to 3 times weaker than the γ-rays due to π°-meson decay.

It is easy to show that the γ-radiation arising in the generation of electrons and positrons ($\pi \to \mu \to e$ decay) and the annihilation of positrons is considerably weaker than the bremsstrahlung (at $E_\gamma \gtrsim 5 \times 10^7$ eV). In fact during the generation of a particle with an energy $E = mc^2/\sqrt{1 - v^2/c^2} \gg mc^2$ an energy is emitted ($\alpha = e^2/\hbar c$)

$$a W_\gamma = \frac{\alpha}{\pi} \left(\frac{c}{v} \ln \frac{c + v}{c - v} - 2 \right) dE_\gamma \simeq \frac{2\alpha}{\pi} \left(\ln \frac{2E}{mc^2} - 1 \right) dE_\gamma.$$

TABLE 20

Gamma Radiation Intensity $I_\gamma(>E)$ (in cm^{-2}·sec^{-1}·sterad^{-1})

Process	Galactic radiation				Metagalaxy	E_γ
	towards centre	towards anticentre	towards pole	averaged directionally		
(a) $\pi^\circ \to \gamma + \gamma$	$1 \cdot 7 \times 10^{-5}$	$3 \cdot 4 \times 10^{-6}$	$1 \cdot 7 \times 10^{-7}$	$4 \cdot 5 \times 10^{-7}$	$2 \cdot 8 \times 10^{-5} \xi_{cr}$	
(b) Bremsstrahlung	$1 \cdot 8 \times 10^{-5}$	$3 \cdot 6 \times 10^{-6}$	$1 \cdot 8 \times 10^{-7}$	$4 \cdot 8 \times 10^{-7}$	$3 \times 10^{-5} \xi_e$	1 GeV
(c) Inverse Compton effect	10^{-5}	3×10^{-6}	2×10^{-5}	2×10^{-5}	$10^{-2} \xi_e$	
(a) $\pi^\circ \to \gamma + \gamma$	$2 \cdot 4 \times 10^{-4}$	5×10^{-5}	$2 \cdot 4 \times 10^{-6}$	$6 \cdot 6 \times 10^{-6}$	$4 \times 10^{-4} \xi_{cr}$	
(b) Bremsstrahlung	$3 \cdot 6 \times 10^{-4}$	$7 \cdot 2 \times 10^{-5}$	$3 \cdot 6 \times 10^{-6}$	$9 \cdot 6 \times 10^{-6}$	$6 \times 10^{-4} \xi_e$	5×10^7 eV
(c) Inverse Compton effect	5×10^{-5}	10^{-5}	10^{-4}	10^{-4}	$4 \times 10^{-2} \xi_e$	

This classical expression[165] for the estimate is also valid for $E_\gamma \leqslant E$. The number of photons is dW_γ/E_γ and the γ-ray intensity is

$$I_{\gamma,\,\text{gen}}(E_\gamma) = \frac{L}{4\pi} \int_{E_\gamma}^{\infty} \frac{dW_\gamma}{dE_\gamma} \frac{q_e(E)\,dE}{E_\gamma} \simeq 4 \times 10^{-4} \left(\ln \frac{2\bar{E}_\gamma}{mc^2} - 1 \right) \frac{Q_{e,L}(E > E_\gamma)}{E_\gamma}$$

where $Q_{e,L}(E > E_\gamma)$ is the total number of particles generated per second on the line of sight (the path L). Using the electron generation spectrum of Fig. 20 on p. 343, we can show that on a path of $M(L)$ g/cm^2 the total number of electrons generated is

$$Q(E > 0) = \frac{4\pi M(L)}{180} \times 0{\cdot}44 \simeq 3 \times 10^{-2} M(L).$$

Hence, for example,

$$I_{\gamma,\,\text{gen}}(E_\gamma = 5 \times 10^{-2} \text{ GeV}) \simeq 1 \times 10^{-3} M(L),$$

whilst

$$I_{\gamma,\,\text{brems}}(E_\gamma = 5 \times 10^{-2} \text{ GeV}) \simeq 0{\cdot}12 M(L).$$

The annihilation cross section for a positron of energy E_+ is

$$\sigma_{\text{an}} = \pi r_e^2 \frac{mc^2}{E_+} \left(\ln \frac{2E_+}{mc^2} - 1 \right), \qquad E_+ \gg mc^2,$$

one photon acquiring an energy $E_\gamma \simeq E_+$. Therefore

$$I_{\gamma,\,\text{an}}(E_\gamma) = N(L)\sigma_{\text{an}} I_{e^+}(E_\gamma) \simeq 0{\cdot}1 M(L) \frac{mc^2}{E_\gamma} \left\{ \ln \frac{2E_\gamma}{mc^2} - 1 \right\} I_{e^+}(E_\gamma).$$

Here $N(L)$ is the number of electrons, but for the interstellar medium we can use the value given above for the number of atoms so $N(L)$ is replaced by $M(L)/2 \times 10^{-24}$. For a spectrum (19.4) $I_{e^+}(E) \lesssim \frac{1}{2} I_e(E) = 10^{-2} E^{-2}$ (see (19.4)) we have

$$I_{\gamma,\,\text{an}}(E_\gamma) < 10^{-3} \left\{ \ln \frac{2E_\gamma}{mc^2} - 1 \right\} M(L) \frac{mc^2}{E_\gamma} E_\gamma^{-2}.$$

Even for $E_\gamma = 5 \times 10^{-2}$ GeV this value is 7 times less than $I_{\gamma,\text{brems}}$ (see (19.12)).

Let us now examine process 3 (the inverse Compton effect). The importance of allowing for this when calculating the γ-ray intensity was stressed recently.[515]

Obviously

$$I_\gamma(E_\gamma) = N_{ph} \int_{E_\gamma}^\infty \bar\sigma(E_\gamma, E)I_e(E)\, dE, \qquad (19.13)$$

where

$$N_{ph}\bar\sigma(E_\gamma, E) = L \int n_{ph}(\mathscr{E})\sigma(E_\gamma, \mathscr{E}, E)\, d\mathscr{E},$$

$n_{ph}(\mathscr{E})$ is the concentration of thermal photons in the energy range $\mathscr{E}, \mathscr{E} + d\mathscr{E}$,

$$N_{ph} = L \int n_{ph}(\mathscr{E})\, d\mathscr{E} = Ln_{ph}$$

is the number of photons along the line of sight and $\sigma(E_\gamma, \mathscr{E}, E)$ is the effective cross section for the generation of a γ-photon with an energy E_γ in the scatter of a photon with an energy $\mathscr{E}$ on an electron with a total energy E; here both the thermal and the electron emission are considered to be distributed isotropically.

We shall first calculate $\sigma(E_\gamma, E)$ by an approximate method similar to that used by Felton and Morrison.[515] The energy loss of an electron with an energy E due to scatter in unit time is (for $E_\gamma \gg \mathscr{E}$ and $E \ll (mc^2/\mathscr{E})mc^2$)

$$-\frac{dE}{dt} \equiv cn_{ph} \int E_\gamma\sigma(E_\gamma, E)\, dE_\gamma = \tfrac{4}{3}cw_{ph}\sigma_T\left(\frac{E}{mc^2}\right)^2$$

$$= 2\cdot67 \times 10^{-14}w_{ph}\left(\frac{E}{mc^2}\right)^2 \text{ eV/sec.} \qquad (19.14)$$

Here

$$w_{ph} = \int \mathscr{E}n_{ph}(\mathscr{E})\, d\mathscr{E} = n_{ph}\bar{\mathscr{E}}, \qquad \bar{\mathscr{E}} = 2\cdot7kT,$$

$$\sigma_T = \frac{8\pi}{3}\left(\frac{e^2}{mc^2}\right)^2 = 6\cdot65 \times 10^{-25} \text{ cm}^2$$

and in the last expression of (19.14) the energy density w_{ph} is measured in eV/cm^3; formula (19.14) follows from Feenberg and Primakoff's paper[313] and is also derived at the end of this section (an approximate expression was obtained earlier in the book which is three quarters the value of (19.14)). To obtain formula (19.14) we may put†

$$\sigma(E_\gamma, E) = \sigma_T \delta\left[E_\gamma - \tfrac{4}{3}\bar{\mathscr{E}}\left(\frac{E}{mc^2}\right)^2\right]. \tag{19.15}$$

If we substitute (19.15) in (19.13) we obtain

$$I_\gamma(E_\gamma) = \frac{\sqrt{3}}{4}\frac{N_{ph}\sigma_T mc^2}{\sqrt{\bar{\mathscr{E}}E_\gamma}}I_e\left(mc^2\sqrt{\frac{3E_\gamma}{4\bar{\mathscr{E}}}}\right)$$

$$= \frac{N_{ph}\sigma_T}{2}(mc^2)^{1-\gamma}(\tfrac{4}{3}\bar{\mathscr{E}})^{(\gamma-1)/2}K_e E_\gamma^{-(\gamma+1)/2}, \tag{19.16}$$

where in the last expression we have $I_e(E) = K_e E^{-\gamma}$ and $N_{ph} = n_{ph}L$. We show at the end of this section that formula (19.16) is obtained in a precise calculation, the factor $f(\gamma)$ appearing in addition. In this case, for example $f(2) \simeq 0.8$ and $f(3) \simeq 1.0$. By putting also $\bar{\mathscr{E}} = 2.7kT \simeq 1.2$ eV ($T = 5000°$) and measuring E_γ in eV, w_{ph} in eV/cm^3 and K_e in $(cm^2 \cdot sec \cdot sterad)^{-1}$ $(GeV)^{\gamma-1}$ we have

$$I_\gamma(E_\gamma) = 2.8 \times 10^{-25}(2.5 \times 10^3)^{\gamma-1}f(\gamma)Lw_{ph}K_e E_\gamma^{-(\gamma+1)/2}$$
$$\text{photons/cm}^2 \cdot \text{sec} \cdot \text{sterad} \cdot \text{eV},$$

$$I_\gamma(>E_\gamma) = 5.6 \times 10^{-25}(2.5 \times 10^3)^{\gamma-1}\frac{f(\gamma)Lw_{ph}}{\gamma-1}K_e E_\gamma^{-(\gamma-1)/2}$$
$$\text{photons/cm}^2 \cdot \text{sec} \cdot \text{sterad}. \tag{19.17}$$

The formula (19.14) for energy losses is valid only if

$$4\bar{\mathscr{E}}\frac{E}{mc^2} < mc^2,$$

i.e., for the energies

$$E < 5 \times 10^{10}\,\text{eV}. \tag{19.18}$$

† In accordance with (19.15) the total cross section is

$$\int \sigma(E_\gamma, E)\,dE_\gamma = \sigma_T,$$

as should be the case at $E < (mc^2/\bar{\mathscr{E}})mc^2$. From this and from (19.14) it is clear that the mean energy of a γ-photon is $\tfrac{4}{3}\bar{\mathscr{E}}(E/mc^2)^2$ and this is also taken into consideration in (19.15).

Obviously formulae (19.16) to (19.17) can be used only in region (19.18). If $E > 5 \times 10^{10}$ eV, formulae (19.16) to (19.17) produce a value for the intensity I_γ that is too high. In the region $E \gg 5 \times 10^{10}$ eV we put approximately

$$\sigma = \pi r_e^2 \frac{(mc^2)^2}{\bar{\mathscr{E}}E} \ln \frac{2\bar{\mathscr{E}}E}{(mc^2)^2}$$

and consider that the energy of the scattered photon is equal to the initial energy of the electron E. Then if we proceed in the approximate way similar to that used for deriving formula (19.16)

$$I_\gamma(E_\gamma) = N_{ph}\pi r_e^2 \frac{(mc^2)^2}{\bar{\mathscr{E}}} \int_{E_\gamma}^\infty E_\gamma^{-1} \ln \frac{2\bar{\mathscr{E}}E}{(mc^2)^2} I_e(E)\delta(E_\gamma - E) \, dE$$

$$= 2 \cdot 5 \times 10^{-25} \frac{(mc^2)^2}{\bar{\mathscr{E}}^2} Lw_{ph}E_\gamma^{-1}I_e(E_\gamma) \ln \frac{2\bar{\mathscr{E}}E}{(mc^2)^2}. \tag{19.19}$$

For the spectrum (19.4) we have from (19.17)

$$I_\gamma(>E_\gamma) = 2 \cdot 2 \times 10^{-23} Lw_{ph}E_\gamma^{-1/2}, \tag{19.20}$$

where E_γ is measured in eV and w_{ph} in eV/cm^3. The mean energy of a γ-quantum from an electron with an energy E is

$$E_\gamma = \tfrac{4}{3}\bar{\mathscr{E}}\left(\frac{E}{mc^2}\right)^2 = 1 \cdot 6\left(\frac{E}{mc^2}\right)^2 \text{ eV}. \tag{19.21}$$

Since the spectrum (19.4) relates to the range $0 \cdot 5 \lesssim E \lesssim 10$ GeV, the spectrum (19.20) is applicable for the range 1 MeV $\lesssim E_\gamma \lesssim 600$ MeV. However, even right up to $E_\gamma \simeq 2$ to 3 GeV the inaccuracy of spectrum (19.20) is not too bad. Table 20 gives the values of $I_\gamma(> E_\gamma)$ in accordance with (19.20) using the data in Table 19. Rounding off is carried out here and in particular the mean value in all directions is considered to be the same as in the direction of the pole (the error here does not exceed a factor of two). The characteristic feature of the γ-radiation from the scatter of electrons on thermal photons is the approximate isotropy of the intensity, whilst the remaining processes (interaction with the gas) lead to sharp anisotropy. This, of course, was clear right from the start (see Table 19). According to Kraushaar and Clark[68] the mean directional value is $I_\gamma(E_\gamma > 5 \times 10^7 \text{ eV}) = (3 \cdot 7 \text{ to } 11) \times 10^{-4}$ photons/cm$^2 \cdot$ sec $\cdot$ sterad or on the average

$$I_\gamma(E_\gamma > 5 \times 10^7 \text{ eV}) = 5 \cdot 5 \times 10^{-4} \text{ photons/cm}^2 \cdot \text{sec} \cdot \text{sterad}. \tag{19.22}$$

It is still not clear whether this value is the upper limit or the actual flux of γ-rays from the cosmos.† In the latter case if the intensity is quasi-isotropic (according to Kraushaar and Clark[68] this is apparently the case) the corresponding γ-rays can be considered galactic only by connecting them with process 3—scatter on thermal photons. Even in this case, however, there is a discrepancy of an order or even more since the electron spectrum (19.4) is, as has already been indicated, too high. It is therefore necessary to estimate the intensity of the γ-radiation from the Metagalaxy.

Metagalactic Emission

The density of the gas in metagalactic space is unknown but the most probable values (for more details see section 13) are

$$n = 10^{-5} \text{ cm}^{-3}, \qquad \rho = 2 \times 10^{-29} \text{ g/cm}^3,$$

$$N(L) = 5 \times 10^{22} \text{ cm}^{-2}, \qquad M(L) = 0 \cdot 1 \text{ g/cm}^2, \qquad (19.23)$$

where the path L is the photometric radius of the Metagalaxy $R_{ph} = 5 \times 10^{27}$ cm. The possibility that the gas concentration in the Metagalaxy is $n \ll 10^{-5}$ cm^{-3} cannot be considered to be excluded but the opposite inequality is impossible for considerations used on relativistic cosmology. The selection of the value for the mean thermal photon energy density is also very important. In published papers wide use is made of the value $w_{ph} = 0 \cdot 25$ eV/cm^3 but we think that this is two orders too high. From observational data and estimates we have the estimate‡

$$w_{ph} \simeq 2 \times 10^{-3} \text{ eV/cm}^3. \qquad (19.24)$$

This corresponds, if we are speaking of energy density, to thermal emission with a temperature $T = 0 \cdot 8 \, °K$. The density (19.24) is a lower limit, but we know no actual reason for increasing w_{ph} although this has not yet been excluded.

We have no direct information on the cosmic rays in metagalactic space. Therefore for the metagalactic gamma and X-radiation, which should be highly isotropic (we are not now thinking of discrete

---

† According to recent data[447]
$$I_\gamma(E_\gamma > 4 \times 10^7 \text{ eV}) \leqslant (3 \cdot 3 \pm 1 \cdot 3) \times 10^{-4}.$$

‡ Here it is assumed that the emission intensity of all the galaxies is equivalent to half the intensity of a galaxy of 10th photographic stellar magnitude per square degree. If we take for the Sun $m_{pq} = -26 \cdot 26$ we obtain $w_{ph} = 1 \cdot 8 \times 10^{-3}$ eV/cm^3 (see also section 8).

sources) it is more correct to set the problem as follows. Let us say that in the whole of metagalactic space in a definite energy range

$$I_{cr}(E) = K_{cr}E^{-\gamma}, \qquad I_e(E) = K_eE^{-\gamma_e} \qquad (19.25)$$

It is then easy to find the intensity of the γ-rays for all the processes 1 to 3 under discussion. The results, if we are dealing with the integral spectrum $I_\gamma(> E_\gamma)$, depend comparatively little on the choice of the indices γ and γ_e in (19.25). In this connexion we shall limit ourselves to two examples. We shall consider that the cosmic ray spectrum in the Metagalaxy $I_{cr,\,Mg}$ differs from the galactic spectrum (see, e.g., (19.1)) only by the factor ξ_{cr}. Then for the γ-rays from the decay of π°-mesons we can use formulae (19.8) and (19.9). The corresponding values are given in Table 20. Obviously the value (19.22) can be obtained only if $\xi_{cr} \sim 1$, which seems to us to be highly improbable (see ref. 434 and section 13). We shall now consider that the metagalactic electrons have galactic spectrum (19.4) multiplied by ξ_e. Then, by using the above data (see Table 19), we come to the intensities given in Table 20.

If $\xi_e \sim 10^{-2}$, the flux $I_\gamma(E_\gamma > 5 \times 10^7$ eV) reaches the value (19.22). We think that this result is very important. Even if we reduce the galactic value (19.4) by a factor of 3 the electron intensity in the Metagalaxy should be 30 times less than in the Galaxy. This, in any case, does not lead to contradictions of an energetic nature and is possible[434] (for further detail see also section 13).

As a check we shall assume that in the Metagalaxy

$$I_e(E) = K_eE^{-2\cdot6}. \qquad (19.26)$$

Then from formula (19.17) and the experimental value (19.22) we find

$$K_e = 8\cdot3 \times 10^{-4} \text{ GeV}^{1\cdot6}\cdot\text{cm}^{-2}\cdot\text{sterad}^{-1}\cdot\text{sec}^{-1}$$

$$= 6\cdot0 \times 10^{-8} \text{ cm}^{-2}\cdot\text{sterad}^{-1}\cdot\text{sec}^{-1}\cdot\text{erg}^{1\cdot6}. \qquad (19.27)$$

This leads to an electron intensity $I_{e,\,Mg}(E > 1$ GeV$) = 5\cdot2 \times 10^{-4}$ (cm$^2\cdot$sec$\cdot$sterad)$^{-1}$, i.e., about 40 times less than the electron intensity in the Galaxy according to (19.4). Let us also estimate the possible γ-ray intensity from the whole combination of galaxies $I_{\gamma,\,gal}$. Our Galaxy emits in the γ-band (as the result of the inverse Compton effect) about as much as in the radio band, i.e., its power is $L_\gamma \sim 3 \times 10^{38}$ erg/sec. The γ-ray flux will be too high only if we consider all the galaxies to be just as powerful γ-emitters (the majority of galaxies emit less than ours and the contribution from radio galaxies, particularly bearing in mind that the thermal emission density in them is not high,† is probably considerably less than the contribution from normal galaxies). Furthermore $J_{\gamma,\,\mathrm{gal}} = N_g L_\gamma R_{\mathrm{ph}}/4\pi$, where $N_g \sim 5 \times 10^{-75}$ cm^{-3} is the concentration of the galaxies and L_γ is their mean power. Hence $J_{\gamma,\,\mathrm{gal}} \lesssim 6 \times 10^{-10}$ erg/cm$^2 \cdot$sec$\cdot$sterad or

$$I_{\gamma,\,\mathrm{gal}}(E_\gamma > 5 \times 10^7 \text{ eV}) \lesssim \frac{J_{\gamma,\,\mathrm{gal}}}{E_\gamma} \lesssim 10^{-5} \text{ photons/cm}^2 \cdot \text{sec} \cdot \text{sterad.}$$

This estimate is not, of course, particularly accurate but it may nevertheless be taken that the contribution of $I_{\gamma,\,\mathrm{gal}}$ is essentially less than value (19.22). We would also mention that the value (19.24) for w_{ph} is a lower limit and it may turn out that it has to be increased several times. In such an increase, of course, the coefficient ξ_e is decreased by the same factor.

Therefore to explain the experiments of Kraushaar and Clark[68] (see (19.22)) it is sufficient to consider that in metagalactic space there are electrons (with $E \gtrsim 1$ GeV) whose concentration is 1·5 to 2 orders less than the galactic concentration. This value, however, as follows from what is said below, is still rather high and should be looked upon as an upper limit (the nature of Kraushaar and Clark's measurements[68] points to the same thing).

The metagalactic electrons with an energy E produce radio emission largely at a frequency $v = 4\cdot6 \times 10^{-6} H_\perp (E \text{ eV})^2$. Even in a field $H \sim 10^{-7}$ oersteds at a frequency $v = 400$ Mc/s it is largely electrons with $E \sim 3 \times 10^{10}$ eV that are emitters. At these and greater energies there is every reason to use a spectrum with $\gamma > 2$. Therefore, just as earlier in this book, we shall take $\gamma = 2\cdot6$ and shall make the effective temperature of the metagalactic radio emission at a frequency of 400 Mc/s less than 10°. Then from the formula (see 13.15), but with the coefficient K_e referring to the intensity I_e rather than to the concentration $N_e(E)$

$$\frac{4\pi}{c} K_e H_{\mathrm{Mg}}^{(\gamma+1)/2} = \frac{8\cdot9 \times 10^{22} T_{\mathrm{eff}}}{a(\gamma)L} \left(\frac{v}{6\cdot26 \times 10^{18}}\right)^{(\gamma+3)/2}, \quad a(2\cdot6) = 0\cdot083$$

---

† We are not thinking now of galaxies of the "super-star" type. If the optical emission of these galaxies (3C273-B etc.) is of the nature of magnetic bremsstrahlung the γ-ray flux (due to the inverse Compton effect for the same electrons) from these galaxies may be very large.[475] In view of the small number of these sources their contribution can be picked out in measurements even with measurements with a comparatively poor angular resolution.

we can obtain for the spectrum (19.26), (19.27)

$$H_{Mg} < \left(\frac{6 \times 10^{-32}}{\frac{4\pi}{c} K_e} \right)^{0 \cdot 555} \simeq 10^{-8} \text{ oersteds.} \qquad (19.28)$$

The field $H_{Mg} \sim 10^{-8}$ oersteds is still less than the equilibrium field $H_{Mg} = \sqrt{4\pi\rho u^2} \gtrsim 10^{-7}$ oersteds (here $\rho u^2/2 \gtrsim 10^{-15}$ erg/cm^3 is the kinetic energy density of the metagalactic gas). The value of K_e, however, can probably be reduced by several factors so there is no need to think of any difficulties here. In addition, we should mention that according to an estimate[187], which is based on as yet unconfirmed measurements of the polarisation of source 3C295, the field is $H_{Mg} < (3 \text{ to } 10) \times 10^{-8}$ oersteds.

High-Energy Electrons and Magnetic Bremsstrahlung X-Radiation

The very important question arises of the nature of the electron spectrum at high energies since the spectrum (19.4) relates only to the region $1 < E < 10$ GeV and the extrapolated spectrum (19.6) is only by way of illustration. If the spectrum (19.6) were valid up to energies of $E \sim 10^{15}$ eV the electron intensity in this region of the spectrum would be about half the intensity of the proton-nuclear component. Moreover, if these electrons do exist they would produce the extensive showers which are anomalously poor in μ-mesons and are generally ascribed to γ-rays.[155, 505, 514] The number of these showers is not more than 10^{-3} to 10^{-4} of the number of all the showers with the same primary particle energy.

Of course, electrons are equivalent to γ-rays as the sources of these showers.† The above-mentioned data[155, 505, 514] may therefore be looked upon as an indication of the upper limit of the electron intensity. A similar result is obtained from the data on X-radiation.[506] If we continue spectrum (19.6) up to an energy $E \sim 10^{15}$ eV we should obtain magnetic bremsstrahlung emission (see (18.20) or (19.31)) with an intensity $I_x(E_x > 1 \cdot 7 \text{ keV}) \simeq 1 \cdot 7 \times 10^3$ quanta/cm$^2 \cdot$sec$\cdot$sterad in the direction of the centre of the Galaxy. At the same time experimentally $I_x \simeq 5$ quanta/cm$^2 \cdot$sec$\cdot$sterad. In addition, the electron injection power would be

$$\int_{E \ll E_{max}}^{E_{max}} Q_e(E)E \, dE \simeq 2 \cdot 8 \times 10^{44} mc^2 \left(\frac{E_{max}}{mc^2} \right)^{0 \cdot 3} = 1 \cdot 4 \times 10^{41} \text{ erg sec.}$$

† The effect of the Earth's magnetic field[521] is significant only at energies $E > 1$ to 5×10^{17} eV.

It is thus clear that the intensity (19.6) can and must be reduced by at least three orders, thus opening up a basic possibility of explaining recent results.[506, 514, 516,] As an example we shall consider that the source spectrum (19·3) is valid only for $E < 10^{10}$ eV, while for $E > 10^{10}$ eV

$$Q_e(E) = 1·6 \times 10^{42} E^{-2·3} \text{ electrons/sec} \cdot \text{GeV}. \qquad (19.29)$$

Then in the $E > 10^5$ GeV energy range

$$I_e(E) = 6·8 E^{-3·3} \text{ electrons/cm}^2 \cdot \text{sec} \cdot \text{sterad}. \qquad (19.30)$$

Spectrum (19.30) is shown by a dotted line in Fig. 26.

In accordance with (19.30) $I_e(E > 10^{15}$ eV$) = 4·8 \times 10^{-14}$ electrons/ cm$^2 \cdot$ sec $\cdot$ sterad whilst $I_{cr}(E > 10^{15}$ eV$) = 2·4 \times 10^{10}$ electrons cm$^2 \cdot$ sec $\cdot$ sterad. At the same time the source power is

$$U_e = \int_{10 \text{ GeV}}^{\infty} E Q_e(E)\, dE = 4·3 \times 10^{39} \text{ erg/sec}$$

which is only 1·5 times higher than the power

$$U_e = \int_{0·3 \text{ GeV}}^{10 \text{ GeV}} E Q_e(E)\, dE = 2·8 \times 10^{39} \text{ erg/sec}$$

obtained in section 17 for the spectrum (19.3). The magnetic bremsstrahlung X-radiation for electrons with the spectrum (19.3) has the intensity (see section 18)

$$I_x(v) = 5·4 \times 10^{19} a(\gamma) L K_e H^{(\gamma+1)/2} \left(\frac{1·6 \times 10^{13}}{v} \right)^{(\gamma+1)/2}$$

$$= 3 \times 10^{-19} L \left(\frac{4·8 \times 10^7}{v} \right)^{2·15} \frac{\text{photons}}{\text{cm}^2 \cdot \text{sec} \cdot \text{sterad c/s}} \qquad (19.31)$$

where in the second expression K_e is the coefficient in the spectrum $I_e(E)\, dE = K_e E^{-\gamma}\, dE$ and E is measured in GeV. In accordance with (19.31) for $L = 7 \times 10^{22}$ cm (the direction of the centre of the Galaxy)

$$I_x (1·6 \text{ keV} < hv < 6·4 \text{ keV}) = 2·6 \text{ photons/cm}^2 \cdot \text{sec} \cdot \text{sterad}. \qquad (19.32)$$

Since the ultra-high energy electrons will be distributed only in the region of the disk (the region of the sources) or near it the intensity of the X-radiation towards the pole is two orders less than the value (19.32). The magnetic bremsstrahlung intensity will also be far greater than the thermal emission intensity in the Galaxy in the far ultraviolet region. For example, with a thermal emission energy density of $w_{ph} = 0.2$ eV/cm^3 (for $T = 5000\,°K$) the intensity is

$$I_\nu\left(10^3 \text{ Å} < \lambda = \frac{c}{\nu} < 1.5 \times 10^3 \text{ Å}\right) \simeq 0.3 \text{ photon/cm}^2 \cdot \text{sec} \cdot \text{sterad,}$$

whilst for the magnetic bremsstrahlung even in the direction of the pole ($L = 100$ pc) in the same range $I_\nu \simeq 4$ photons/cm$^2 \cdot$sec$\cdot$sterad.

Thus if we assume that electrons with a spectrum like (19.29) are generated in the Galaxy it would really be possible to obtain a flux of electrons with an energy $E > 10^{15}$ eV necessary to explain the experiments of Firkowski et al.,[514] Suga et al.,[505] and of Giaconni et al.[506] in relation to the anisotropic component of the X-radiation. This does not, of course, mean that electrons with a spectrum like (19.29) do exist. We wish only to stress that the assumption that these electrons exist does not contradict the available data and energy considerations. A certain difficulty connected with this assumption is that the electrons with $E \sim 10^{14}$ to 10^{15} eV lose half their energy in a time of 10^3 to 10^4 years. Their sources should therefore be operative at present, i.e., a contribution of explosions of the galactic core is excluded. Even if it is a question of supernovae there should be large fluctuations in the spatial distribution of ultra-high energy electrons at a mean supernova explosion frequency of 10^{-2} explosions/year. However, a decisive method of checking the hypothesis under discussion would be direct measurements of the intensity of the cosmic ray electron component at energies of $E > 10^{10}$ eV. In particular even if we reduce the source power (19.29) by a factor of 3 to 4 the electron intensity at an energy $E \sim 10^{11}$ to 10^{12} eV should be of the order of one per cent of the intensity of all cosmic rays. Clearly, there are at present possible experimental ways for finding electrons with this intensity.

Effective Cross Section for "Inverse" Compton Scattering

Let us calculate the effective cross section $\sigma(E_\gamma, \mathscr{E}, E)dE_\gamma$ (see formula (19.13) above and the paragraph following it) for the generation of a γ-quantum with an energy in the range dE_γ during the scatter of a thermal photon with an energy $\mathscr{E}$ on an electron whose total energy is E. We shall consider the photon distribution to be isotropic.

We shall use the Compton cross section taken in the general invariant form:[73]

$\sigma_C(k_1, k_2, v) \, d\Omega_2$

$$= 2r_e^2 \frac{E_\gamma^2}{m^2 c^4 \kappa_1^2} \left\{ 4\left(\frac{1}{\kappa_1} + \frac{1}{\kappa_2}\right)^2 - 4\left(\frac{1}{\kappa_1} + \frac{1}{\kappa_2}\right) - \left(\frac{\kappa_1}{\kappa_2} + \frac{\kappa_2}{\kappa_1}\right) \right\} \, d\Omega_2,$$

(19.33)

where

$$\kappa_1 = -\frac{2}{m^2 c^4} \mathscr{E} E \left(1 - \frac{v}{c} \cos \Theta_1\right),$$

(19.34)

$$\kappa_2 = \frac{2}{m^2 c^4} E_\gamma E \left(1 - \frac{v}{c} \cos \Theta_2\right),$$

$r_e = e^2/mc^2$, m and e are the mass and charge of an electron, k_1 and k_2 are the momenta of the original and scattered photons, Θ_1 and Θ_2 are the angles between these momenta and the velocity of the electron v, $d\Omega_1$ and $d\Omega_2$ being corresponding solid angles.

The energy of the scattered photon is (Θ is the angle between k_1 and k_2)

$$E_\gamma = \frac{\mathscr{E}\left(1 - \frac{v}{c} \cos \Theta_1\right)}{1 - \frac{v}{c} \cos \Theta_2 + \frac{\mathscr{E}}{E}(1 - \cos \Theta)} = \phi(\mathscr{E}, E, \Theta_1, \Theta_2, \Theta).$$

(19.35)

The desired cross section is defined by the expression

$$\sigma(E_\gamma, \mathscr{E}, E) = \frac{1}{4\pi} \int \left(1 - \frac{v}{c} \cos \Theta_1\right) \sigma_C(k_1, k_2, v)$$

$$\times \delta\{E_\gamma - \phi(\mathscr{E}, E, \Theta_1, \Theta_2, \Theta)\} \, d\Omega_1 \, d\Omega_2.$$

(19.36)

To calculate the integrals in (19.36) we shall use a convenient approximate form[313] of relation (19.35) for $\mathscr{E} \ll E_\gamma < E$:

$$E_\gamma = \frac{\mathscr{E}\left(1 - \frac{v}{c} \cos \Theta_1\right)}{1 - \frac{v}{c} \cos \Theta_2 + \frac{\mathscr{E}}{E}\left(1 - \frac{v}{c} \cos \Theta_1\right) \cos \Theta_2}$$

(19.37)

and limit ourselves to the case

$$4\mathscr{E} \frac{E}{mc^2} \ll mc^2.$$

(19.38)

Upon these assumptions the direct calculation of (19.36) leads to the cross section

$$\sigma(E_\gamma, \mathscr{E}, E) = \frac{\pi r_e^2}{4} \frac{(mc^2)^4}{\mathscr{E}^2 E^3}$$

$$\times \left\{ 2\frac{E_\gamma}{E} - \frac{(mc^2)^2 E_\gamma^2}{\mathscr{E} E^3} + 4\frac{E_\gamma}{E} \ln \frac{(mc^2)^2 E_\gamma}{4\mathscr{E} E^2} + \frac{8\mathscr{E} E}{(mc^2)^2} \right\}, \quad (19.39)$$

where E_γ is within the limits

$$\mathscr{E} \leqslant E_\gamma \leqslant 4\mathscr{E} \left(\frac{E}{mc^2} \right)^2. \quad (19.40)$$

By virtue of (19.39) and (19.40) the total scattering cross section is

$$\sigma_t = \int \sigma(E_\gamma, \mathscr{E}, E) \, dE_\gamma = \frac{8\pi}{3} r_e^2 \equiv \sigma_T \quad (19.41)$$

which is equal to the Thomson cross section and corresponds to the approximation (19.38) under discussion. The mean energy losses of an electron are obviously

$$-\frac{dE}{dt} \simeq c \iint \sigma(E_\gamma, \mathscr{E}, E) n_{\text{ph}}(\mathscr{E}) E_\gamma \, dE_\gamma \, d\mathscr{E}$$

$$= c \frac{8\pi}{3} r_e^2 \left(\frac{E}{mc^2} \right)^2 \frac{4}{3} \int \mathscr{E} n_{\text{ph}}(\mathscr{E}) \, d\mathscr{E} = c n_{\text{ph}} \sigma_T \tfrac{4}{3} \bar{\mathscr{E}} \left(\frac{E}{mc^2} \right)^2, \quad (19.42)$$

where the total number of photons per unit volume and their mean energy are

$$n_{\text{ph}} = \int n_{\text{ph}}(\mathscr{E}) \, d\mathscr{E} \quad \text{and} \quad \bar{\mathscr{E}} = \frac{1}{n_{\text{ph}}} \int \mathscr{E} n_{\text{ph}}(\mathscr{E}) \, d\mathscr{E}. \quad (19.43)$$

It follows from expressions (19.41) and (19.42) that the mean energy of a scattered photon is

$$\bar{E}_\gamma = \tfrac{4}{3} \bar{\mathscr{E}} \left(\frac{E}{mc^2} \right)^2. \quad (19.44)$$

Let us now determine the intensity of the scattered γ-quanta if on the path L the electron intensity $I_e(E)$ and photon concentration $n_{\text{ph}}(\mathscr{E})$ are homogeneous and isotropic. Obviously

$$I_\gamma(E_\gamma) = L \int_0^\infty n_{\text{ph}}(\mathscr{E}) \, d\mathscr{E} \int_{E_{\text{min}}}^\infty \sigma(E_\gamma, \mathscr{E}, E) I_e(E) \, dE, \quad (19.45)$$

where the lower limit $E_{min} = mc^2(E_\gamma/4\mathscr{E})^{1/2}$ is determined from (19.40). For a power-law electron spectrum

$$I_e(E) = K_e E^{-\gamma} \tag{19.46}$$

we find

$$\int_{E_{min}}^{\infty} \sigma(E_\gamma, \mathscr{E}, E)I_e(E)\, dE$$

$$= 2^\gamma \frac{\gamma^2 + 4\gamma + 11}{(\gamma + 1)(\gamma + 3)^2(\gamma + 5)}\, 8\pi r_e^2 K_e(mc^2)^{1-\gamma}\mathscr{E}^{(\gamma-1)/2}E_\gamma^{-(\gamma+1)/2}. \tag{19.47}$$

For black radiation

$$n_{ph}(\mathscr{E})\, d\mathscr{E} = \frac{n_{ph}}{2\cdot404(kT)^3}\, \frac{\mathscr{E}^2 d\mathscr{E}}{e^{\mathscr{E}/kT} - 1}, \qquad \bar{\mathscr{E}} = 2\cdot7kT. \tag{19.48}$$

Substituting expressions (19.47) and (19.48) in the expression for the intensity (19.45) and integrating with respect to $d\mathscr{E}$ we obtain

$$I_\gamma(E_\gamma) = f(\gamma)\tfrac{2}{3}\sigma_T L w_{ph}(mc^2)^{1-\gamma}(\tfrac{4}{3}\bar{\mathscr{E}})^{(\gamma-3)/2}K_e E_\gamma^{-(\gamma+1)/2}, \tag{19.49}$$

where

$$f(\gamma) = 4\cdot74(1\cdot05)^\gamma \frac{\gamma^2 + 4\gamma + 11}{(\gamma + 1)(\gamma + 3)^2(\gamma + 5)}\Gamma\left(\frac{\gamma + 5}{2}\right)\zeta\left(\frac{\gamma + 5}{2}\right), \tag{19.50}$$

$\Gamma(x)$ is an Euler gamma-function and

$$\zeta(x) = \sum_{n=1}^{\infty} \frac{1}{n^x}$$

is a Riemann function.[351]
  In particular

$$f(1) = 0\cdot84, \qquad f(2) = 0\cdot86, \qquad f(3) = 0\cdot99, \qquad f(4) = 1\cdot4. \tag{19.51}$$

It is easy to see that expression (19.49) agrees with formula (19.16) given earlier with an accuracy up to the factor $f(\gamma)$.

CONCLUSION

PROGRESS in the field of the theory of the origin of cosmic rays has been achieved by extensive use of astrophysical (in particular radio astronomy) data combined with a study of the primary cosmic rays on Earth and an analysis of certain theoretical questions. Further progress can be expected only as a result of the complex use of various possibilities and the completion of a number of fresh experiments.

Radio astronomy methods must be used to obtain more precise data on the radio emission (intensity, spectrum and in certain cases polarisation) in the halo, the disk, the spiral and the centre of the Galaxy and also data on the emission of galactic nebulae (in the first place of supernova shells). As we have seen in section 5 the spectral index $\alpha = (\gamma - 1)/2$ for the general galactic radio emission, according to certain data, varies from 0·8 at a wavelength of $\lambda = 75$ cm to 0.35 at a wavelength of $\lambda = 8$ m. However, there is not yet the necessary clarity in this very important question. The obtaining of reliable data on the radio emission spectrum over a wide range of frequencies and for various directions in the Galaxy is a very real problem. In particular it is very important to find the spectrum in the decimetric band (the radio emission spectrum of the electrons generated in an explosion of the galactic core should have a break at a wavelength of the order of 30 cm: see section 11).

Questions relating to the radio emission of novae and certain other exploding stars are of interest. A study of different galaxies at several frequencies, particularly of those similar to our own Galaxy (the nebula M31 in Andromeda, ...), with large radio-telescopes will probably make it possible to obtain information on the nature of the galactic boundaries and possibly on the relativistic electrons and magnetic fields between galaxies. The question of the density of the gas in the halo remains a very real one; this problem must be studied by different methods, radio astronomy in particular (on the neutral hydrogen line, the spectrum of the long-wave cosmic radio emission and the residual polarisation of the Galactic magnetic bremsstrahlung). It is no less important to determine the form of the halo more exactly and study its structure (clouds, magnetic fields, ...). The problem of the halo's origin and the elucidation of the part played by hypothetical explosions of the galactic core can be referred to this.

Astrophysical investigations dealing with the structure of the Galaxy and the galactic magnetic fields, the interstellar and intergalactic medium, non-steady-state stars (supernovae in particular), and so on, also bear a direct relation to the problem of the origin of cosmic rays.

It is particularly necessary to mention the theoretical problems connected with elucidating the features of the motion of cosmic rays in the magnetic fields (the accuracy of the diffusion approximation, the part played by instability and magnetohydrodynamic waves, ...) with the mechanism of the explosion and flying apart of supernova shells and with the acceleration of cosmic rays in these shells and with explosions of galactic cores.

A whole number of essential factors should, of course, be explained by a study of the primary cosmic rays on Earth. For example a more precise determination of the primary cosmic ray spectrum with respect to charge will make it possible to establish which nuclei are accelerated in the sources. In the field of studying the chemical composition of cosmic rays we must advance by determining the individual nuclei and isotopes.

Apart from the direct determination of the chemical composition of the cosmic rays on Earth we must know the probability of transformation and fragmentation of various nuclei as they move in the interstellar medium (hydrogen and helium) in order to discover their composition in the sources. It is hard to find these probabilities by using only data obtained from photographic plates and it is clearly necessary to make extensive use of radio-chemical and other methods linked with the use of accelerators or the observation of nuclear fragments formed by cosmic rays passing through a layer of liquid hydrogen taken aloft by balloons.

Another important problem is the determination of the chemical composition of cosmic rays at high energies. As we have seen in sections 11 and 16, the very heavy nuclei with an energy of $\lesssim 10^{19}$ eV may still apparently be of galactic origin, whilst the protons with the same energy should, in all probability, come from the Metagalaxy (this conclusion may be altered if the high-energy particles are generated in explosions of the galactic core which may occur in the Galaxy). This problem is also closely connected with the question of changes in the energy spectrum at high energies and of the possible connexion of these changes with the inconstancy of the chemical composition of the cosmic rays or an increase in the part played by cosmic rays of metagalactic origin. The study of high and ultra-high energy cosmic rays is also essential from the point of view of finding the degree of anisotropy δ (see sections 3 and 16). The determination of δ is possible, moreover, at lower energies as well, particularly at a period of minimum solar activity. The finding of the anisotropy and determination of δ is essential both in a qualitative and a quantitative respect (the existence of some slight anisotropy follows from the diffusion model we have used; in the light of this model we can estimate the diffusion coefficient D if we know δ; see section 16).

The greatest achievement in the field of studying primary cosmic rays on Earth in the last few years is the discovery of electrons. Work has, however, only just begun here—we must next determine the energy spectrum of the electrons and positrons. The very great importance of data of this kind is obvious from what has been said in sections 2 and 11 and in sections 17 and 19.

The value of even the first successful steps in the field of γ-astronomy scarcely needs arguing. The determination of the γ-ray flux from the Metagalaxy is a problem of the present whose solution can be expected very shortly.

The future is less clear in the field of neutrino astronomy but even here there is undoubtedly a certain hope of success.

The study of cosmic rays of solar origin and also of the variations of cosmic ray intensity is becoming, as is well known, a more and more effective method of investigating the interplanetary magnetic fields and processes on the Sun. At the same time the mechanism of cosmic ray acceleration on the Sun is also of interest from the point of view of the theory of the origin of cosmic rays (it is particularly important to discover the spectrum of cosmic rays of solar origin with respect to charge for the various solar flares). The problem of the variations is also connected with the question of the "high-latitude cut-off" of the cosmic ray spectrum. Is this cut-off purely magnetic and does it occur only within the solar system or does it somehow also reflect the nature of cosmic ray acceleration in the sources? This important question is still not finally solved although it is hard to doubt that the cut-off is largely caused by random fields in the interplanetary medium or by the effect of the solar system's ordered magnetic field. In the low-energy range, however, particularly at the time of a solar minimum, a cut-off (change) of the spectrum occurring in the cosmic ray sources or in interstellar space could be noticeable.

It is therefore possible to indicate a whole series of quite definite experiments and methods of observation whose use will make it possible to answer many of the questions that are still open. It is true that the making of these experiments will require great efforts (this is the case, for example, for the study of the highest energy particles). On the other hand, solutions of some individual problems can be expected in the near future (the determination of the flux of γ-rays from the Galaxy, more precise information on the chemical composition of cosmic rays in the low-energy range, ...). There is thus every reason for counting on a further rapid advance in the field of cosmic ray astrophysics. It is hard to escape the conclusion that this field of astrophysics and physics will in the course of time play a more and more important part in astronomy and space physics.

SOME CONSTANTS AND UNITS OF MEASUREMENT

Charge of an electron $e = 4 \cdot 803 \times 10^{-10}$ esu

Mass of an electron $m = 9 \cdot 108 \times 10^{-28}$ g

Mass of a proton $M_p = 1 \cdot 672 \times 10^{-24}$ g; $M_p/m = 1836$

Boltzmann constant $k = 1 \cdot 380 \times 10^{-16}$ erg/°K

Velocity of light in a vacuum $c = 2 \cdot 9979 \times 10^{10}$ cm/sec

Planck's constant $h = 6 \cdot 625 \times 10^{-27}$ erg·sec, $\hbar = h/2\pi = 1 \cdot 054 \times 10^{-27}$ erg/sec.

Gravitational constant $\kappa = 6 \cdot 670 \times 10^{-8}$ dyne·cm²·g⁻².

Frequency of the hydrogen atom radio line $v = 1420 \cdot 4$ Mc/s ($\lambda = c/v = 21 \cdot 1$ cm)

$e/mc = 1 \cdot 7589 \times 10^7$ esu

$mc^2 = 5 \cdot 11 \times 10^5$ eV

$M_p c^2 = 9 \cdot 39 \times 10^8$ eV $\simeq 1 \cdot 5 \times 10^{-3}$ erg

1 eV $= 1 \cdot 602 \times 10^{-12}$ erg $= 1 \cdot 16 \times 10^4$ °K

10^9 eV $= 1$ GeV

$1\gamma = 10^{-5}$ oersted.

ASTROPHYSICAL QUANTITIES

Light year = 9.460×10^{17} cm
Parsec (pc) = 3·26 light years = 3.086×10^{18} cm
kpc = 1000 pc, Mpc = 10^6 pc $\simeq 3 \times 10^{24}$ cm
Number of seconds in a year = 3.156×10^7
Astronomical unit (mean distance from the Earth to the Sun)
1 a.u. = 1.496×10^{13} cm
Radius of the solar system (radius of Pluto's orbit) $\simeq$ 40 a.u. $\simeq$ 6×10^{14} cm
Total energy emitted per second by the Sun = 3.86×10^{33} erg/sec
Radius of the Sun (photosphere) = 6.960×10^{10} cm
Mass of the Sun $M_\odot = 1.99 \times 10^{33}$ g.

THE GALAXY

Mass of the Galaxy $\simeq 1 \times 10^{11} M_\odot \simeq 2 \times 10^{44}$ g
Mass of gas in the Galaxy $\simeq 3 \times 10^{42}$ g (about 5% of all this gas is ionised)
Velocity of galactic rotation in vicinity of Sun = 220 ± 20 km/sec (the value 250 km/sec can also be found in published papers)
Distance from the Sun to the galactic centre = 8.2 ± 0.8 kpc (it has recently been considered more probable that the distance is 10 kpc)
Period of rotation about the galactic centre (for the vicinity of the Sun) = 2.2×10^8 years
Age of the Galaxy $T_G \sim 10^{10}$ years
Radius of the halo $R = 10$ to 15 kpc $\simeq 3$ to 5×10^{22} cm
Volume of the halo $V \sim 4\pi R^3/3 \simeq 1$ to 5×10^{68} cm^3
Power of optical emission (brightness) $L \simeq 4 \times 10^{43}$ erg/sec
Thermal emission energy density $w_{ph} \simeq 0.3$ to 1 eV/cm^3
Characteristic magnetic field strength $H \sim 3$ to 10×10^{-6} oersted.

THE LOCAL GROUP OF GALAXIES

Consists of 15 to 20 galaxies of which the largest are our Galaxy (mass $M \simeq 1 \times 10^{11} M_\odot$) and the galaxy M31 ($M \simeq 4 \times 10^{11} M_\odot$). Distance between the centres of these galaxies $R = 0.6$ Mpc $\simeq 1.8 \times 10^{24}$ cm and their relative velocity is $u \sim 100$ km/sec. The closest members of the Group to the Galaxy are the Large and Small Magellanic Clouds (distance from the centre of the Galaxy $R = 53$ kpc, masses $M \simeq 6.5 \times 10^{11} M_\odot$ and $M = 1 \times 10^{10} M_\odot$). The total mass of all the galaxies in the Group is $M \simeq 6.5 \times 10^{11} M_\odot$, the radius of the Group is $R \lesssim 0.7$ Mpc and the relative velocities are $u \lesssim 200$ km/sec.

THE LOCAL SUPERGALAXY

Major axis ~ 30 Mpc, minor axis ~ 6 Mpc
Volume $\sim 10^{77}$ cm^3, mass of all galaxies $\sim 10^{14} M_\odot$
Total number of galaxies $\sim 10^4$, concentration of galaxies $N_g \sim 10^{-73}$ cm^{-3}
Relative velocity of galaxies (without allowing for general expansion) ~ 300 km/sec.

THE METAGALAXY
(ALL VALUES RELATE TO THE PRESENT STATE OF THE SYSTEM)

Density of gas $\rho \lesssim 10^{-29}$ g/cm^3
Concentration of galaxies $N_g \simeq 5 \times 10^{-75}$ cm^{-3}
Mean mass of galaxies $\overline{M} \sim 3 \times 10^{10} M_\odot \sim 5 \times 10^{43}$ g
Mean number of galaxies in the cluster about 200
Mean diameter of cluster $\sim 10^{25}$ cm
Thermal emission energy density in metagalactic space $w_{\mathrm{ph}} \simeq 2 \times 10^{-3}$ eV/cm^3
Characteristic time of evolution of Metagalaxy $T_{\mathrm{Mg}} \sim 10^{10}$ years $\simeq 3 \times 10^{17}$ sec (the time T_{Mg} can be defined as the inverse of Hubble's constant $h = u/R$, where u is the recessional velocity of a distant galaxy and R is the distance to it; in recent years it has generally been taken that $T_{\mathrm{Mg}} = 1/h \simeq 1 \times 10^{10}$ years, $h = 100$ km/sec·Mpc, but the accuracy of this value is low).
Characteristic distance $R = cT_{\mathrm{Mg}} \simeq 10^{28}$ cm
Photometric radius of the Metagalaxy $R_{\mathrm{ph}} \simeq 5 \times 10^{27}$ cm.

COSMIC RAYS (ROUGH VALUES)

Intensity of all cosmic rays (on Earth) $I \simeq 0\cdot2$ particle/cm^2·sterad· sec $\simeq 0\cdot4$ nucleon/cm^2·sterad·sec (this value is close to the maximum corresponding to a period of minimum solar activity)

Concentration $N \simeq (4\pi/c)I \sim 10^{-10}$ particle/sec

Electron concentration $N_e \sim 10^{-2}N$

Energy density of cosmic rays in the Galaxy $w_G \sim 0\cdot3$ to 1 eV/cm^3 $\sim 10^{-12}$ erg/cm^3

Total energy of cosmic rays in the Galaxy $W \sim w_G V \sim 1$ to 5×10^{56} ergs

Life in Galaxy (determined by the departure of particles from the system) $T \sim 3 \times 10^8$ years $\simeq 10^{16}$ sec

Nuclear life in the Galaxy (at a mean gas density of $\rho = 2 \times 10^{-26}$ g/cm^3):

for protons $T_p \simeq 4 \times 10^9$ years

for iron nuclei $T_{Fe} \simeq 1\cdot4 \times 10^8$ years

Power (energy losses per unit time and power of sources) of cosmic rays in the Galaxy $U \sim U_{source} \sim W/T \sim 10^{40}$ to 10^{41} erg/sec.

Total power of galactic radio emission $P \sim 3 \times 10^{38}$ erg/sec

Energy density of cosmic rays in intergalactic space (probable value) $w_{Mg} \sim 10^{-3}$ to $10^{-4}w_G \sim 10^{-15}$ to 10^{-16} erg/cm^3

Field $H_{Mg} = \sqrt{8\pi w_{Mg}} \sim 3$ to 10×10^{-8} oersteds.

VALUES OF THE FUNCTIONS $F(x) = x \int_x^\infty K_{5/3}(\eta)\, d\eta$
AND $F_p(x) = xK_{2/3}(x)$

x	$F(x)$	$F_p(x)$	x	$F(x)$	$F_p(x)$
0·001	0·213	0·107	1·0	0·655	0·494
0·005	0·358	0·184	1·2	0·566	0·439
0·01	0·445	0·231	1·4	0·486	0·386
0·025	0·583	0·312	1·6	0·414	0·336
0·050	0·702	0·388	1·8	0·354	0·290
0·075	0·722	0·438	2·0	0·301	0·250
0·10	0·818	0·475	2·5	0·200	0·168
0·15	0·874	0·527	3·0	0·130	0·111
0·20	0·904	0·560	3·5	0·0845	0·0726
0·25	0·917	0·582	4·0	0·0541	0·0470
0·30	0·919	0·596	4·5	0·0339	0·0298
0·40	0·901	0·607	5·0	0·0214	0·0192
0·50	0·872	0·603	6·0	0·0085	0·0077
0·60	0·832	0·590	7·0	0·0033	0·0031
0·70	0·788	0·570	8·0	0·0013	0·0012
0·80	0·742	0·547	9·0	0·00050	0·00047
0·90	0·694	0·521	10·0	0·00019	0·00018

Approximate expressions:

if $x \gg 1$

$$F(x) \simeq \sqrt{\frac{\pi}{2}}\, e^{-x} x^{1/2} \left\{ 1 + \frac{55}{72} x^{-1} - \frac{10151}{10368} x^{-2} - \ldots \right\}$$

$$F_p(x) \simeq \sqrt{\frac{\pi}{2}}\, e^{-x} x^{1/2} \left\{ 1 + \frac{7}{72} x^{-1} - \frac{455}{10368} x^{-2} - \ldots \right\}$$

if $x \ll 1$

$$F(x) = \frac{4\pi}{\sqrt{3}\,\Gamma(\frac{1}{3})} \left(\frac{x}{2}\right)^{1/3} \left\{ 1 - \frac{\Gamma(\frac{1}{3})}{2} \left(\frac{x}{2}\right)^{2/3} + \frac{3}{4}\left(\frac{x}{2}\right)^2 - \ldots \right\}$$

$$F_p(x) = \frac{2\pi}{\sqrt{3}\,\Gamma(\frac{1}{3})} \left(\frac{x}{2}\right)^{1/3} \left\{ 1 - \frac{3\Gamma(\frac{1}{3})}{2\Gamma(\frac{2}{3})} \left(\frac{x}{2}\right)^{4/3} + 3\left(\frac{x}{2}\right)^2 - \ldots \right\}.$$

REFERENCES†

1. N. A. DOBROTIN and YE. L. FEINBERG. *Cosmic Rays* (in Russian). Akad. Nauk SSSR (in course of publication).
2. L. I. DORMAN. *Cosmic Ray Variations and Space Research* (in Russian). Akad. Nauk SSSR (1963).
3. B. J. O'BRIEN, *Space Sci. Rev.* 1, 415 (1963).
4. V. L. GINZBURG. *Usp. fiz. nauk*, 51, 343 (1953); *Fortsch. d. Phys.*, 1, 659 (1954); see also *Nuovo Cimento*, Suppl., 3, 38 (1956).
5. V. L. GINZBURG. *Usp. fiz. nauk*, 62, 37 (1957); *Progress in Elementary Particle and Cosmic Ray Physics*, vol. 4, ch. 5. Amsterdam (1958).
6. V. L. GINZBURG and S. I. SYROVATSKII. *Usp. fiz. nauk*, 71, 411 (1960), *Soviet Phys.-Uspekhi*, 3, 504 (1961); alternative revised version: *Progr. Theor. Phys.*, Suppl., No. 20, 1 (1961).
7. V. L. GINZBURG. *Usp. fiz. nauk*, 74, 521 (1961), *Soviet Phys.-Uspekhi*, 4, 553 (1962) (popular discussion).
8. S. HAYAKAWA, K. ITO and Y. TERASHIMA. *Progr. Theor. Phys.*, Suppl., 6, 1 (1958).
9. P. MORRISON. The Origin of Cosmic Rays. *Handbuch d. Phys.*, 46/1, 1 (1961).
10. J. G. WILSON (Ed.) *Progress in Elementary Particle and Cosmic Ray Physics*. North-Holland, 1952–58, Vols. I–IV.
11. Cosmic Rays. *Handbuch d. Phys.*, 46 (1961).
12. S. F. SINGER. *Progress in Elementary Particle and Cosmic Ray Physics*, Chap. IV. North-Holland, 1958.
13. L. I. DORMAN. *Variations in Cosmic Rays* (in Russian). Gostekhizdat (1957); *Cosmic Rays*, 3, 5 (1961).
14. V. SARABHAI. *PICCR*, A II, 500 (1962).
15. H. V. NEHER. *PICCR*, A II, 492 (1962)
16. H. KOMORI. *J. Phys. Soc. Japan*, 17, 620 (1962)
17. P. S. FREIER, E. P. NEY and C. J. WADDINGTON. *Phys. Rev.*, 113, 921 (1959).
18. P. S. FREIER, E. P. NEY and C. J. WADDINGTON. *Phys. Rev.*, 114, 365 (1959).
19. A. N. CHARAKHCH'YAN and T. N. CHARAKHCH'YAN. *Zh. exp. i teoret. fiz.*, 35, 1088 (1958), *Soviet Phys.—JETP*, 8, 761 (1959); *Proc. Internat. Conf. Cosmic Rays*, vol. III (in Russian). Akad. Nauk SSSR, p. 144 (1960).

† References to Proc. Internat. Conf. Cosmic Rays and the Earth Storm, *J. Phys. Soc. Japan*, 17, Suppl., AI, AII, AIII (1962) are given in the form *PICCR*, A I–III, 1962.

References to material from the International Conference on Cosmic Rays in India (Jaipur, India, December 1963) are given in the form *ICCR*, India, 1963.

20. R. R. DANIEL, P. J. LAVAKARE and P. K. ADITYA. *Nuovo Cimento*, **17**, 837 (1958).
21. A. ENGLER, M. F. KAPLON and J. KLARMAN. *Phys. Rev.*, **112**, 597 (1958).
22. F. B. MACDONALD. *Nuovo Cimento*, Suppl., **8**, 500 (1958).
23. P. H. FOWLER, P. S. FREIER and E. P. NEY. *Nuovo Cimento*, Suppl., **8**, 492 (1958).
24. C. J. WADDINGTON. *Progress in Nuclear Physics.* Pergamon Press, N.Y., **8**, p. 3–45 (1960).
25. C. J. WADDINGTON. *PICCR*, A III, 63 (1962).
26. M. V. K. APPA RAO. *Phys. Rev.*, **123**, 295 (1961); *J. Geophys. Res.*, **67**, 1289 (1962); M. V. K. APPA RAO and M. F. KAPLON. *PICCR*, A III, 48 (1962).
27. E. M. BURBIDGE and G. R. BURBIDGE. *PICCR*, A III, 161 (1962).
28. O. A. SCHAEFFER. *Physics Today*, **13**, No. 2, 18 (1960).
29. L. V. KURNOSOVA, V. I. LOGACHEV, L. A. RAZORENOV and M. I. FRADKIN. *Isk. Sput. Zemli*, No. 5, p. 30 (1960).
30. L. V. KURNOSOVA, L. A. RAZORENOV and M. I. FRADKIN. *Isk. Sput. Zemli*, No. 8, p. 87 (1961).
31. K. I. ALEKSEYEVA, L. L. GABUNIYA, G. B. ZHDANOV, YE. A. ZAMCHALOVA, M. I. TRET'YAKOVA and M. N. SHCHERBAKOVA. *PICCR*, A III, 30 (1962).
32. J. H. NOON, A. J. HERZ and B. J. O'BRIEN. *Nuovo Cimento*, **5**, 854 (1957).
33. R. CESTER, A. DEBENEDETTI, C. M. GARELLI, A. QUASSIATI, L. TALLONE and M. VIGONE. *Nuovo Cimento*, **7**, 371 (1958).
34. V. BISI, R. CESTER, C. M. GARELLI and L. TALLONE. *Nuovo Cimento*, **10**, 881 (1958).
35. C. J. WADDINGTON. *Nuovo Cimento*, Suppl., **8**, 513, 518 (1958).
36. M. KOSHIBA, G. SCHULTZ and M. SCHEIN. *Nuovo Cimento*, **9**, 1 (1958).
37. M. KOSHIBA, E. LOHRMANN, H. AIZU and E. TAMAI. *PICCR*, A III, 34 (1962); *Phys. Rev.*, **131**, 2962 (1963).
38. R. R. DANIEL and N. DURGAPRASAD. *Nuovo Cimento*, Suppl., **23**, 82 (1962); *PICCR*, A III, 15 (1962).
39. J. VAN HEERDEN and B. JUDEK. *Canad. J. Phys.*, **38**, 964 (1960).
40. C. M. GARELLI, B. QUASSIATI and M. VIGONE. *Nuovo Cimento*, **15**, 121 (1960).
41. M. V. K. APPA RAO, S. BISWAS, R. R. DANIEL, K. A. NEELAKANTAN and B. PETERS. *Phys. Rev.*, **110**, 751 (1958).
42. F. W. O'DELL, M. M. SHAPIRO and B. STILLER. *Proc. of the Moscow Cosmic Ray Conf.* (Moscow, 1960), vol. III, p. 118; *Proc. Internat. Cosmic Ray Conf.* Akad. Nauk SSSR **3**, 133 (1960); *PICCR*, A III, 23 (1960).
43. V. L. GINZBURG, L. V. KURNOSOVA, L. A. RAZORENOV and M. I. FRADKIN. *Geomagnet. i aèron.*, **2**, 193 (1962); *Space Sc. Reviews* **2**, 778 (1964).
44. H. AIZU, Y. FUJIMOTO, S. HASEGAWA, M. KOSHIBA, I. MITO, J. NISHIMURA, K. YOKOI and M. SCHEIN. *Phys. Rev.*, **116**, 436 (1959); **121**, 1206 (1961); *Proc. of the Moscow Cosmic Ray Conf.* (Moscow, 1960), vol. III, p. 96; *Progr. Theoret. Phys.*, Suppl., No. 16, 52–148 (1961).
45. K. KRISTIANSSON, O. MATHIESEN and A. STENMAN. *Arkiv f. Fysik*, **23**, 479 (1963).
46. H. HASEGAWA. *Nuovo Cimento*, **23**, 292 (1962).
47. P. L. JAIN, E. LOHRMAN and M. W. TEUCHER. *Phys. Rev.*, **115**, 636, 654 (1959).
48. G. ALVIAL. *PICCR*, A III, 44, 1962; *Nuovo Cimento* Suppl., **19**, 18 (1961); G. ALVIAL and J. RIQUELME. *ICCP*, Jaipur, India, 1963.

49. H. E. Suess and H. C. Urey. *Rev. Mod. Phys.*, **28**, 53 (1956).
50. A. G. W. Cameron. *Astrophys. Journ.*, **129**, 676 (1959).
51. G. R. Burbidge and A. G. W. Cameron. *Astrophys. Journ.*, **131**, 519, 521 (1960).
52. L. V. Kurnosova, L. A. Razorenov and M. I. Fradkin. *Isk. Sput. Zemli*, No. 2, p. 70 (1958).
53. C. Q. Orsini. *Nuovo Cimento*, **16**, 1040 (1960).
54. N. L. Grigorov, D. A. Zhuravlev, M. A. Kondrat'yeva, N. D. Rapoport and I. A. Savenko. *Isk. Sput. Zemli*, No. 10, p. 96 (1961).
55. M. I. Fradkin. *Zh. exp. i teoret. fiz.*, **29**, 147 (1955); *Soviet Phys.—JETP*, **2**, 87 (1956).
56. C. L. Critchfield, E. P. Ney and S. Oleksa. *Phys. Rev.*, **85**, 461 (1952).
57. J. A. Earl. *Phys. Rev. Letters*, **6**, 125 (1961).
58. P. Meyer and R. Vogt. *Phys. Rev. Letters*, **6**, 193 (1961).
59. V. L. Ginzburg and V. V. Zheleznyakov. *Astr. zh.*, **38**, 3 (1961); *Soviet Astronomy—AJ*, **5**, 1 (1961).
60. P. Meyer and R. Vogt. *J. Geophys. Res.*, **66**, 3950 (1961); *PICCR*, A III, 5 (1962).
61. P. Meyer and R. Vogt. *Phys. Rev. Letters*, **8**, 387 (1962).
62. S. Hayakawa. *Progr. Theor. Phys.*, **8**, 517 (1952); **19**, 219 (1958).
63. P. Morrison. *Nuovo Cimento*, **7**, 858 (1958).
64. M. P. Savedoff. *Nuovo Cimento*, **13**, 12 (1959).
65. R. Maze and A. Zawadzki. *Nuovo Cimento*, **17**, 625 (1960).
66. K. Greisen. *Ann. Rev. Nucl. Sci.*, **10**, 63 (1960).
67. A. Braccesi and M. Ceccareli. *Nuovo Cimento*, **17**, 691 (1960).
68. W. L. Kraushaar and G. W. Clark. *Phys. Rev. Letters*, **8**, 106 (1962); *Sci. American*, **206**, No. 5, 52 (1962); *PICCR*, A III, 1 (1962).
69. A. Ye. Chudakov, V. I. Zatsepin, N. M. Nesterova and V. L. Dadykin. *PICCR*, A III, 106 (1962).
70. S. Z. Belen'kii. *Shower Processes in Cosmic Rays* (in Russian). Gostekhizdat (1948).
71. B. Rossi. *High-Energy Particles*. Prentice-Hall, N.Y., 1952.
72. W. Heitler. *Quantum Theory of Radiation*, Oxford University Press, 1954.
73. A. I. Akhiyezer and V. B. Berestetskii. *Quantum Electrodynamics* (in Russian). Fizmatgiz (1959) (English translation to be published by Interscience).
74. V. L. Ginzburg, G. G. Getmantsev and M. I. Fradkin. *Proc. of Third Conf. on Questions of Cosmogony* (in Russian). *Akad. Nauk SSSR*, p. 149 (1954).
75. A. I. Nikishev. *Zh. exp. i teoret. fiz.*, **41**, 549 (1961); *Soviet Phys.—JETP*, **14**, 393 (1962).
76. S. Hayakawa. *Physics Letters* **1**, 234 (1962).
77. M. A. Markov and I. M. Zheleznykh. *Nuclear Physics*, **27**, 385 (1961).
78. G. T. Zatsepin and V. A. Kuz'min. *Zh. exp. i teoret. fiz.*, **41**, 1818 (1961); *Soviet Phys.—JETP*, **14**, 1294 (1962).
79. V. M. Kharitonov. *Dokl. Akad. Nauk SSSR*, **141**, 66 (1961), *Soviet Phys. —Doklady*, **6**, 985 (1961).
80. B. M. Pontecorvo and Ya. A. Smorodinskii. *Zh. exp. i teoret. fiz.*, **41**, 239 (1961), *Soviet Phys.—JETP*, **14**, 173 (1962).
81. Ya. B. Zel'dovich and Ya. A. Smorodinskii. *Zh. exp. i teoret. fiz.*, **41**, 907 (1961); *Soviet Phys.—JETP*, **14**, 647 (1962).
82. B. M. Pontecorvo and A. Ye. Chudakov. *Zh. exp. i teoret. fiz.*, **43**, 1967 (1962); *Soviet Phys.—JETP*, **16**, 1385 (1963).

83. V. I. RITUS. *Zh. exp. i teoret. fiz.*, **41**, 1285 (1961); *Soviet Phys.—JETP*, **14**, 915 (1962).
84. H. Y. CHIU. *Ann. of Phys.*, **15**, 1; **16**, 321 (1961).
85. B. M. Pontecorvo, *Usp. fiz. nauk*, **79**, 3 (1963); *Soviet Phys.—Uspekhi*, **6**, 1 (1963).
86. F. B. McDONALD. *Phys. Rev.*, **109**, 1367 (1958).
87. W. R. WEBBER. *Nuovo Cimento*, Suppl., **8**, 532 (1958).
88. A. ENGLER and U. HABER-SCHAIM. *Phys. Rev.*, **95**, 1700 (1954).
89. M. F. KAPLON and D. M. RITSON. *Phys. Rev.*, **88**, 386 (1952).
90. C. J. WADDINGTON and P. H. FOWLER. *Phil. Mag.*, **1**, 637 (1956).
91. C. E. FICHTEL. *Nuovo Cimento*, **19**, 1100 (1961).
92. S. BISWAS, P. J. LAVAKARE, K. A. NEELAKANTAN and P. G. SHUKLA. *Nuovo Cimento*, **16**, 644 (1960); *Proc. of the Moscow Cosmic Ray Conf.* (Moscow, 1960), vol. III, p. 102.
93. M. F. KAPLON, B. PETERS, H. L. REYNOLDS and D. M. RITSON. *Phys. Rev.*, **85**, 295 (1952).
94. R. E. DANIELSON. *Phys. Rev.*, **113**, 1311 (1959).
95. L. T. BARADZEI, V. I. RUBTSOV, YU. A. SMORODIN, M. V. SOLOV'YEV and B. V. TOLKACHEV. *PICCR*, A III, 433 (1962).
96. P. H. BARRETT, L. M. BOLLINGER, G. COCCONI, Y. EISENBERG and K. GREISEN. *Rev. Mod. Phys.*, **24**, 133 (1952).
97. S. I. NIKOL'SKII. *Usp. fiz. nauk*, **78**, 365 (1962); *Soviet Phys.—Uspekhi*, **5**, 849 (1963); *Proc. of the First All-Union Conf. on the Space Physics Aspect of Cosmic Ray Research* (in Russian). Yakutsk, 1962 (in course of publication).
98 G. CLARK, I. ESCOBAR and T. HERSIL. *Proc. of the Fifth Inter-American Symposium on Cosmic Rays.* La Paz, Bolivia, 1962, vol. II, 36.
99. B. ROSSI. *Proc. of the Moscow Cosmic Ray Conf.* (Moscow, 1960), vol. II, p. 18; *Sci. American*, **201**, No. 11, 135 (1959); *Phys. Rev.*, **122**, 637 (1961).
100. G. V. KULIKOV and G. B. KHRISTIANSEN. *Zh. exp. i teoret. fiz.*, **35**, 635 (1959); *Soviet Phys.—JETP*, **8**, 441 (1960).
101. J. LINSLEY, L. SCARSI and B. ROSSI. *PICCR*, A III, 91 (1962).
102. J. LINSLEY and J. SCARSI. *Phys. Rev. Letters*, **9**, 123 (1962); J. LINSLEY. *Phys. Rev. Letters*, **9**, 126 (1962).
103. K. A. NEELAKANTAN and P. G. SHUKLA. *PICCR*, A III, 20 (1962).
104. A. N. CHARAKHCH'YAN, V. F. TULINOV and T. N. CHARAKHCH'YAN. *Zh. exp. i teoret. fiz.*, **41**, 735 (1961); *Soviet Phys.—JETP*, **14**, 530 (1962); *Geomagn. i aèronom.*, **1**, 150 (1961).
105. F. B. McDONALD (Ed.) *Solar Proton Manual.* NASA Tech. Report R-169 (1963).
106. C. E. FICHTEL and D. E. GUSS. *Phys. Rev. Letters*, **6**, 495 (1961); see also *PICCR*, A II, 321 (1962).
107. H. JAGODA, R. FILZ and K. FUKUI. *Phys. Rev. Letters*, **6**, 626 (1961); *PICCR*, A II, 320 (1962).
108. L. V. KURNOSOVA, L. A. RAZORENOV and M. I. FRADKIN. *Isk. Sput. Zemli*, No. 6, p. 132 (1960).
109. R. VOGT. *Phys. Rev.*, **125**, 366 (1962); *PICCR*, A II, 436 (1962).
110. H. V. NEHER. *Annual Review of Nuclear Sci.*, **8**, 217 (1958).
111. F. B. McDONALD and W. R. WEBBER. *Phys. Rev.*, **115**, 194 (1959); *J. Geophys. Res.*, **65**, 767 (1960).
112. F. B. McDONALD. *Phys. Rev.*, **116**, 462 (1959).
113. F. B. McDONALD and W. R. WEBBER. *PICCR*, A II, 428 (1962).
114. F. B. McDONALD and W. R. WEBBER. *J. Geophys. Res.*, **67**, 2119 (1962).

115. H. V. NEHER. *Phys. Rev.*, **103**, 228 (1956); **107**, 588 (1957).
116. J. R. WINKLER and K. A. ANDERSON. *Phys. Rev.*, **108**, 148 (1957).
117. P. H. FOWLER, C. J. WADDINGTON, P. S. FREIER, J. NAUGLE and E. P. NEY. *Phil. Mag.*, **2**, 157 (1957).
118. P. J. DUKE. *Proc. of the Moscow Cosmic Ray Conf.* (Moscow, 1960), vol. III, p. 89.
119. E. TAMAI. *Phys. Rev.*, **117**, 1345 (1960).
120. D. EVANS. *Proc. of the Moscow Cosmic Ray Conf.* (Moscow, 1960), vol. III, p. 92.
121. S. HAYAKAWA, M. KOSHIBA and Y. TERASHIMA. *Proc. of the Moscow Cosmic Ray Conf.* (Moscow, 1960), vol. III, p. 181.
122. S. F. SINGER. *Nuovo Cimento*, Suppl., **8**, 342 (1958).
123. H. ELIOT, R. I. HYNDS, I. I. QUENBY and G. J. WENK. *Proc. of the Moscow Cosmic Ray Conf.* (Moscow, 1960), vol. IV, p. 311.
124. E. N. PARKER. *Ap. J.*, **128**, 664 (1958).
125. L. I. DORMAN. *Proc. of the Internat. Conf. on Cosmic Rays* (in Russian), vol. 4. *Akad. Nauk SSSR*, p. 328 (1960).
126. Y. TERASHIMA. *Progr. Theoret. Phys.*, **23**, 1138 (1960).
127. M. V. K. APPA RAO and M. F. KAPLON. *Nuovo Cimento*, **21**, 369 (1961).
128. J. R. ARNOLD, M. HONDA and D. LAL. *J. Geophys. Res.*, **66**, 3519 (1961).
129. J. R. ARNOLD. *Ann. Rev. Nuclear Sci.*, **11**, 349 (1961).
130. H. WÄNKE, E. VILCSEK. *Zs. Naturf.*, **14a**, 929 (1959).
131. B. PETERS. *Proc. of the Moscow Cosmic Ray Conf.* (Moscow, 1960), vol. I, p. 157; *Nuovo Cimento*, **22**, 800 (1961).
132. J. LINSLEY, L. SCARSI, P. J. ECCLES and B. ROSSI. *Phys. Rev. Letters*, **8**, 286 (1962).
133. S. I. NIKOL'SKII, YU. N. VAVILOV and V. V. BATOV. *Dokl. Akad. Nauk SSSR*, **111**, 71 (1956); *Soviet Phys.—Doklady*, **1**, 625 (1956).
134. S. I. NIKOL'SKII and A. A. POMANSKII. *Proc. of Internat. Cosmic Ray Conf.* (in Russian), vol. II, p. 235. *Akad. Nauk SSSR* (1960).
135. O. I. DOVZHENKO, G. T. ZATSEPIN, YE. A. MURZINA, S. I. NIKOL'SKII and V. I. YAKOVLEV. *Proc. of the Internat. Cosmic Ray Conf.* (in Russian), vol. II, p. 144. *Akad. Nauk SSSR* (1960).
136. S. N. VERNOV, G. B. KHRISTIANSEN, V. I. ATRASHKEVICH, V. A. DMITRIYEV, YU. FOMIN, B. A. KHRENOV, G. V. KULIKOV, YU. A. NECHIN and V. I. SOLOV'YEVA. *PICCR*, A III, 118 (1962); see also *Izv. Akad. Nauk SSSR*, **26**, 651 (1962). Translation in *Bulletin Acad. Sc. USSR*, vol. **26**, 650 (1962).
137. G. T. MURTHY, B. PETERS, P. V. RAMAMANURTHY and B. V. SHREKANTAN. *Proc. of the Moscow Cosmic Ray Conf.* (Moscow, 1960), vol. III, p. 150.
138. S. FUKUI, H. HASEGAWA, T. MATANO, I. MIURA, M. ODA, K. SUGA, G. TANAHASHI and Y. TANAKA. *Suppl. Progr. Theoret. Phys.*, **16**, 1 (1960).
139. I. L. ROZENTAL'. *PICCR*, A III, 105 (1962); also in: *Some Questions in the Physics of the Atomic Nucleus and Elementary Particles* (in Russian). Atomizdat (1962).
140. N. N. GORYUNOV, L. G. DEDENKO and G. T. ZATSEPIN. *PICCR*, A III, 103 (1962); *Izv. Akad. Nauk SSSR, ser. fiz.*, **26**, 685 (1962); Translation in *Bulletin Acad. Sc. USSR*, vol. **26**, 684 (1962).
141. J. DELVAILLE, F. KENDZIORSKI and K. GREISEN. *Proc. of the Moscow Cosmic Ray Conf.* (Moscow, 1960), vol. III, p. 143.
142. L. I. DORMAN and O. I. INOZEMTSEVA. Trans. of the XII Symposium of the General Assembly in Helsinki (July, 1960); *Kosm. luchi*, No. 4, 209 (1961).
143. J. DELVAILLE, F. KENDZIORSKI and K. GREISEN. *PICCR*, A III, 76 (1962).
144. H. HASEGAWA, T. MATANO, I. MIURA, M. ODA. *PICCR*, A III, 86 (1962).

145. S. I. Nikol'skii. *Proc. of the First All-Union Conf. on the Space Physics Aspect of Cosmic Ray Research* (in Russian). Yakutsk, 1962 (in course of publication).
146. A. M. Conforto. *PICCR*, A III, 144 (1962).
147. H. Hasegawa, T. Matano, I. Miura, M. Oda, G. Tanahashi, Y. Tanaka, S. Higashi, T. Kitamura, Y. Mishima, S. Miyamoto, K. Shibata and Y. Watase. *Phys. Rev. Letters*, **8**, 284 (1962); see also *PICCR*, A III, 89 (1962); *ICCR*, Jaipur, India (1963).
148. J. L. Pawsey and R. N. Bracewell. *Radio Astronomy*, Oxford (1955).
149. H. Alfvén and N. Herlofson. *Phys. Rev.*, **78**, 616 (1950).
150. K. O. Kiepenheuer. *Phys. Rev.*, **79**, 738 (1950).
151. V. L. Ginzburg. *Dokl. Akad. Nauk SSSR*, **76**, 377 (1951).
152. G. G. Getmantsev. *Dokl. Akad. Nauk SSSR*, **83**, 557 (1952).
153. V. L. Ginzburg and M. I. Fradkin. *Dokl. Akad. Nauk SSSR*, **92**, 531 (1953).
154. V. L. Ginzburg. *Dokl. Akad. Nauk SSSR*, **92**, 1133 (1953).
155. S. N. Vernov, V. I. Solov'yeva, B. A. Khrenov and G. B. Khristiansen. *Paper at First All-Union Conf. on the Space Physics Aspect of Cosmic Ray Research.* Yakutsk, 1960 (in course of publication).
156. I. S. Shklovskii. *Astr. zh.*, **29**, 418 (1952).
157. A. Unsöld. *Zs. Phys.*, **141**, 70 (1955).
158. I. M. Gordon. *Dokl. Akad. Nauk SSSR*, **94**, 813 (1954); *Proc. of the Third Conf. on Questions of Cosmogony* (in Russian). *Akad. Nauk SSSR*, p. 253, 267 (1954); *Byull. KISO Akad. Nauk SSSR*, No. 10, 49 (1954).
159. I. S. Shklovskii. *Dokl. Akad. Nauk SSSR*, **90**, 983 (1953).
160. V. L. Ginzburg. *Proc. of the Third Conf. on Questions of Cosmogony* (in Russian). *Akad. Nauk SSSR*, p. 260 (1954).
161. I. S. Shklovskii. *Cosmic Radio Emission* (in Russian). Moscow, Gostekhizdat (1956); *Cosmic Radio Waves*, Harvard Univ. Press (1960).
162. *Proc. of the Fifth Conf. on Questions of Cosmogony* (in Russian). Akad. Nauk SSSR (1956).
163. *Paris Symposium on Radio Astronomy* (Stanford Univ. Press, 1959).
164. J. L. Pawsey and E. R. Hill. *Reports on Progress in Physics*, **24**, 69 (1961).
165. L. D. Landau and E. M. Lifshitz. *The Classical Theory of Fields*, Pergamon Press, Oxford (1962).
166. K. C. Westfold. *Astrophys. Journ.*, **130**, 241 (1959).
167. S. Chandrasekhar. *Radiative Transfer*, Oxford University Press (1950).
168. G. V. Rozenberg. *Usp. Fiz. Nauk*, **56**, 77 (1955).
169. B. A. Trubnikov. *Dokl. Akad. Nauk*, **118**, 913 (1958), *Soviet Phys.—Doklady*, **3**, 136 (1958).
170. A. A. Korchak and S. I. Syrovatskii. *Astr. zh.*, **38**, 885 (1961); *Soviet Astronomy—AJ*, **5**, 678 (1962).
171. G. M. Garibyan and I. N. Gol'dman. *Izv. Akad. Nauk Arm. SSR*, **7**, 31 (1954).
172. A. A. Korchak. *Astr. zh.*, **34**, 365 (1957); *Soviet Astronomy—AJ*, **1**, 360 (1957).
173. S. I. Syrovatskii. *Astr. zh.*, **36**, 17 (1959); *Soviet Astronomy—AJ*, **3**, 22 (1959).
174. V. A. Razin. *Radiotekhn. i elektron.*, **1**, 846 (1956); Translation in *Radio Engineering and Electronic Physics*; *Astr. zh.*, **35**, 241 (1958); *Soviet Astronomy—AJ*, **2**, 216 (1959).
175. G. Westerhout, Ch. L. Seeger, W. H. Brouw and J. Tinbergen. *Bull. Astron. Inst. Netherlands*, **16**, 187, 213 (1962).

176. R. Wielebinski, J. J. Shakeshaft and I. I. K. Pauliny-Toth. *Observatory*, **82**, 158 (1962).
177. S. B. Pikel'ner. *Astr. zh.*, **33**, 785 (1956).
178. J. H. Oort, Th. Walraven. *Bull. Astr. Inst. Netherlands*, **12**, 285 (1956).
179. C. H. Mayer, T. P. McCullough and R. M. Sloanaker. *Astrophys. J.*, **126**, 468 (1957); *Astron. J.*, **64**, 339 (1959).
180. A. D. Kuz'min and V. A. Udal'tsov. *Astr. zh.*, **38**, 1114 (1961); *Soviet Astronomy—AJ*, **5**, 850 (1962); see also *Astr. zh.*, **39**, 849 (1962); *Soviet Astronomy—AJ*, **6**, 665 (1963).
181. O. Struve. *Sky and Telescope*, **18**, 364 (1959).
182. J. Borat, J. Lequeuz and E. Le Roux. *C. R. Acad. Sci. Paris*, **251**, 2476 (1961).
183. C. H. Mayer, T. P. McCullough and R. M. Sloanaker. *Astrophys. J.*, **135**, 656 (1962).
184. F. F. Gardner and J. B. Whiteoak. *Phys. Rev. Letters*, **9**, 197 (1962).
185. B. F. Cooper and R. M. Price. *Nature*, **195**, 1084 (1962); **196**, 761 (1962).
186. R. N. Bracewell, B. F. Cooper and T. E. Cousins. *Nature*, **195**, 1289 (1962).
187. V. L. Ginzburg and V. V. Pisareva. *Izv. vyssh. ucheb. zav. Radiofiz.*, **6**, 877 (1963).
188. V. L. Ginzburg. *Paris Symposium on Radio Astronomy*. Stanford (1959).
189. F. Hoyle in *Radio Astronomy* (Russian edition), p. 107 (1961).
190. G. G. Getmantsev and V. A. Razin. *Proc. of the Fifth Conf. on Questions of Cosmogony*, p. 495. Akad. Nauk SSSR (1956).
191. V. V. Pisareva. *Izv. vyssh. ucheb. zav. Radiofiz.*, **3**, No. 2, 165 (1960).
192. V. L. Ginzburg. *Propagation of Electromagnetic Waves in a Plasma*, Pergamon Press, Oxford (1964).
193. V. N. Tsytovich. *Vestn. Mosk. gos. un-ta*, **11**, 27 (1951).
194. V. A. Razin. *Radiofizika*, **3**, 584 (1960).
195. Ye. V. Chayevskii and S. Ya. Braude. *Radiofizika*, **5**, 211 (1962).
196. Ye. A. Benediktov, G. G. Getmantsev and V. L. Ginzburg. *Isk. Sput. Zemli*, No. 7, p. 3 (1961); *Planetary and Space Science*, **2**, 109 (1962).
197. R. Q. Twiss. *Phil. Mag.*, **45**, 249 (1954).
198. I. S. Shklovskii. *Usp. fiz. nauk*, **77**, 3 (1962); *Soviet Phys.—Uspekhi*, **5**, 365 (1962); see also *Astr. zh.*, **39**, 591 (1962); *Soviet Astronomy—AJ*, **6**, 465 (1963).
199. P. J. Coleman, L. Davis and C. P. Sonett. *Phys. Rev. Letters*, **5**, 43 (1960).
200. R. D. Richtmyer and E. Teller. *Phys. Rev.*, **75**, 1729 (1949).
201. S. B. Pikel'ner. *Dokl. Akad. Nauk SSSR*, **88**, 229 (1953).
202. J. Baldwin. *Observatory*, **75**, 229 (1955).
203. G. Westerhout. *Bull. Astron. Inst. Netherlands*, **14**, 215 (1958).
204. B. Y. Mills, E. R. Hill and O. B. Slee. *Observatory*, **78**, 116 (1958); *Austral. J. Phys.*, **11**, 530 (1958).
205. R. Hanbury-Brown and C. Hazard. *Monthly Notices Roy. Astron. Soc.*, **119**, 297 (1959).
206. B. Y. Mills. *Paris Symposium on Radio Astronomy*. Stanford (1959), p. 431.
207. B. Y. Mills. *Publ. Astron. Soc. Pacific*, **71**, 267 (1959); *Observatory*, **81**, 75 (1961).
208. R. Adgie and F. S. Smith. *Observatory*, **76**, 181 (1956).
209. C. H. Costain. *Monthly Notices Roy. Astron. Soc.*, **120**, 248 (1960).
210. J. E. Baldwin. *PICCR*, A III, 173 (1962).
211. A. J. Turtle, J. F. Pugh, S. Kenderdine and I. I. K. Pauling-Toth. *Monthly Notices Roy. Astron. Soc.*, **124**, 296 (1962).

212. R. HANBURY-BROWN and C. HAZARD. *Observatory*, **80**, 137 (1960).
213. B. FIELD. *Publ. Astron. Soc. Pacific*, **72**, 303 (1960).
214. R. D. DAVIES and C. HAZARD. *Monthly Notices Roy. Astron. Soc.*, **124**, 147 (1962).
215. M. I. LARGE, D. S. MATHEWSON and C. G. J. HASLAM. *Monthly Notices Roy. Astron. Soc.*, **123**, 112 (1961).
216. M. M. KOMESAROFF. *Austral. J. Physics*, **14**, 515 (1961).
217. C. W. ROUGOOR and J. H. OORT. *Proc. Nat. Acad. Sci. Amer.*, **46**, 1 (1960).
218. S. B. PIKEL'NER. *Physics of the Interstellar Medium* (in Russian). Akad. Nauk SSSR (1959).
219. G. ELWERT. *Erg. exakten Naturwiss.*, **23**, 1 (1959).
220. J. H. OORT, F. J. KERR and G. WESTERHOUT. *Monthly Notices Roy. Astron. Soc.*, **118**, 379 (1958); *Sci. American*, **201**, No. 2, 44 (1959); *Astrophysics, IV, Stellar Systems, Handbuch d. Physik*, **53** (1959).
221. F. J. KEER. *Monthly Notices Roy. Astron. Soc.*, **123**, 327 (1962).
222. L. WOLTJER. *Ap. J.*, **130**, 38 (1959).
223. YU. N. PARIISKII. *Dokl. Akad. Nauk SSSR*, **129**, 1261 (1959); *Soviet Phys.—Doklady*, **4**, 1172 (1959); *Astr. zh.*, **38**, 242 (1961); *Soviet Astronomy—AJ*, **5**, 182 (1961).
224. S. A. KAPLAN and S. B. PIKEL'NER. *The Interstellar Medium* (in Russian). Fizmatgiz (1963).
225. F. D. DRAKE. *Sky and Telescope*, **18**, 428 (1959).
226. M. WALKER, A. LALLEMAND and M. DUCHESNE. *C.R. Acad. Sci. Paris*, **250**, 975 (1960).
227. H. ALFVÈN. *Cosmic Electrodynamics*. Oxford (1950).
228. S. B. PIKEL'NER. *Usp. fiz. nauk*, **58**, 285 (1956).
229. G. A. SHAIN. *Astr. zh.*, **32**, 110, 381 (1955).
230. A. SCHLÜTER and L. BIERMANN. *Zs. Naturf.*, **5a**, 237 (1950).
231. S. B. PIKEL'NER. *Fundamentals of Cosmic Electrodynamics* (in Russian). Fizmatgiz (1961).
232. L. WOLTJER. *Astrophys. J.*, **133**, 352 (1961).
233. R. D. DAVIS, C. H. SLATER, W. L. H. SHUTER and P. A. T. WILD. *Nature*, **187**, 1088 (1960).
234. R. D. DAVIES, G. L. VERSCHUUR and P. A. T. WILD. *Nature*, **196**, 563 (1962).
235. J. P. HEPPNER, N. F. NESS, T. L. SKILLMAN and C. S. SCEARCE. *PICCR*, A II, 546 (1962).
236. F. HOYLE and J. G. IRELAND. *Monthly Notices Roy. Astron. Soc.*, **122**, 35 (1961).
237. J. G. IRELAND. *Monthly Notices Roy. Astron. Soc.*, **122**, 461 (1961).
238. H. TUNMER. *Phil. Mag.*, **3**, 370 (1958).
239. R. HANBURY BROWN, R. D. DAVIES and C. HAZARD. *Observatory*, **80**, 191 (1960).
240. H. M. JOHNSON. *Phil. Mag.*, **4**, 877 (1959).
241. I. PAULINY-TOTH, J. E. BALDWIN and J. R. SHAKESHAFT. *Monthly Notices Roy. Astron. Soc.*, **122**, 279 (1961).
242. J. M. THOMPSON. *Nature*, **180**, 495 (1957).
243. J. L. PAWSEY and E. HARTING. *Austral. J. Phys.*, **13**, 740 (1960).
244. V. A. RAZIN. *Astr. zh.*, **35**, 829 (1958); *Soviet Astronomy—AJ*, **2**, 778 (1959).
245. D. TER HAAR. *Rev. Mod. Phys.*, **22**, 119 (1950).
246. M. ODA and H. HASEGAWA. *PICCR*, A III, 171 (1962).
247. M. I. LARGE, M. J. S. QUIGLEY and C. G. T. HASLAM. *Monthly Notices Roy. Astron. Soc.*, **124**, 405 (1962).

248. R. MINKOWSKY. *Paris Symposium on Radio Astronomy.* Stanford (1959), p. 315.
249. I. S. SHKLOVSKII. *Proc. of the Internat. Cosmic Ray Conf.* (in Russian), vol. III, p. 209. Akad. Nauk SSSR (1960).
250. YU. N. PARIISKII. *Dokl. Akad. Nauk SSSR*, **137**, 307 (1961); *Soviet Phys.— Doklady*, **6**, 187 (1961).
251. V. I. MOROZ. *Astr. zh.*, **37**, 265 (1960), *Soviet Astronomy—AJ*, **4**, 250 (1960).
252. A. A. KORCHAK. *Tr. Fiz. In-ta Akad. Nauk SSSR*, **17**, 149 (1962).
253. D. E. HARRIS. *Thesis, California Inst. Techn.* (1961).
254. J. BALDWIN and C. H. COSTAIN. *Monthly Notices Roy. Astron. Soc.*, **121**, 413 (1960).
255. C. R. LYNDS. *Publ. Nat. Radio. Astr. Observ.*, **1**, 112 (1961).
256. A. D. KUZ'MIN. *Astr. zh.*, **38**, 905 (1961); *Soviet Astronomy—AJ*, **5**, 692 (1962).
257. N. S. KARDASHEV, A. D. KUZ'MIN and S. I. SYROVATSKII. *Astr. zh.*, **39**, 216 (1962); *Soviet Astronomy—AJ*, **6**, 167 (1962).
258. D. C. HEESCHEN. *Astrophys. J.*, **133**, 322 (1961).
259. C. M. WADE. *Austral. J. Phys.*, **12**, 471 (1959).
260. I. S. SHKLOVSKII. *Astr. zh.*, **31**, 533 (1954).
261. E. R. HILL. *Austral. J. Phys.*, **11**, 580 (1958).
262. M. I. LARGE, D. S. MATHEWSON and C. G. T. HASLAM. *Nature*, **183**, 1250, 1663 (1959).
263. G. WESTERHOUT. *Paris Symposium on Radio Astronomy*, ed. Bracewell. Stanford (1959), p. 447.
264. S. N. VERNOV, A. YE. CHUDAKOV, P. V. VAKULOV and YU. A. LOGACHEV. *Dokl. Akad. Nauk SSSR*, **125**, 304 (1959); *Soviet Phys.—Doklady*, **4**, 108 (1959).
265. F. HOYLE and J. G. IRELAND. *Monthly Notices Roy. Astron. Soc.*, **120**, 173 (1960).
266. S. B. PIKEL'NER and I. S. SHKLOVSKII. *Astr. zh.*, **34**, 145 (1957); *Soviet Astronomy—AJ*, **1**, 149 (1958); *Rev. Mod. Phys.*, **30**, 935 (1958); *Ann. Astrophys.*, **22**, 913 (1959).
267. I. S. SHKLOVSKII. *Astr. zh.*, **37**, 256 (1960); *Soviet Astronomy—AJ*, **4**, 243 1960.
268. J. A. HÖGBOM and J. R. SHAKESHAFT. *Nature*, **189**, 561 (1961); **190**, 705 (1961).
269. I. S. SHKLOVSKII. *Astr. zh.*, **37**, 369 (1960); *Soviet Astronomy—AJ*, **4**, 355 (1960).
270. K. I. KELLERMAN, R. I. LONG, L. R. ALLEN and M. MORAN. *Nature*, **195**, 692 (1962).
271. G. R. BURBIDGE. *Astrophys. J.*, **129**, 849 (1959).
272. R. HANBURY BROWN and C. HAZARD. *Monthly Notices*, **122**, 479 (1961); **123**, 279 (1961).
273. I. S. SHKLOVSKII. *Astr. zh.*, **37**, 945 (1960); *Soviet Astronomy—AJ*, **4**, 685 (1961).
274. J. L. STEINBERG and J. LEGUEUX. *Radio-Astronomie.* Dunod. Paris (1960).
275. D. W. DEWHIRST. *Paris Symposium on Radio Astronomy.* Stanford Univ. Press (1959), p. 507.
276. YU. P. PSKOVSKII. *Astr. zh.*, **39**, 222 (1962); *Soviet Astronomy—AJ*, **6**, 172 (1962).
277. L. BIERMANN and L. DAVIS. *Zs. Astrophys.*, **51**, 19 (1960).
278. G. MÜNCH and H. ZIRIN. *Astrophys. J.*, **133**, 11 (1961).

279. V. L. GINZBURG. *Izv. vyssh. ucheb. zav. Radiofiz.*, **1**, No. 5–6, 3 (1958); *Paris Symposium on Radio Astronomy.* Stanford Univ. Press (1959), p. 589.

280. G. R. ELLIS. *J. Geophys. Res.*, **62**, 229 (1957).

281. V. A. RAZIN. *Izv. vyssh. ucheb. zav. Radiofiz.*, **3**, 921 (1960).

282. F. D. KAHN and L. WOLTJER. *Astrophys. J.*, **130**, 705 (1959).

283. F. HOYLE. *Monthly Notices Roy. Astron. Soc.*, **120**, 338 (1960).

284. V. N. TSYTOVICH. *Zh. eksp. teoret. fiz.*, **42**, 803 (1962); *Soviet Phys.—JETP*, **15**, 561 (1962).

285. O. B. FIRSOV. *Zh. eksp. teoret. fiz.*, **36**, 1517 (1959); *Soviet Phys.—JETP*, **9**, 1076 (1959).

286. YA. A. TEPLOVA, V. S. NIKOLAYEV, I. S. DMITRIYEV and L. N. FATEYEVA. *Zh. eksp. teoret. fiz.*, **42**, 44 (1962); **34**, 559 (1958); *Soviet Phys.—JETP*, **15**, 31 (1962); **7**, 387 (1958).

287. R. POST. *High-Temperature Plasma and Controlled Thermonuclear Reactions* (Russian edition), p. 24 (1961); compare *Rev. Mod. Phys.*, **28**, 338 (1956).

288. P. K. WEYL. *Phys. Rev.*, **91**, 289 (1953); see also *Handbuch d. Phys.*, **34**, 193 (1958).

289. N. BOHR. *Proc. Royal Dan. Acad. Sci.*, **18**, No. 8 (1948).

290. V. I. PUSTOVOIT and M. YE. GERTSENSHTEIN. *Zh. eksp. teoret. fiz.*, **42**, 163 (1962); *Soviet Phys.—JETP*, **15**, 116 (1962).

291. V. L. GINZBURG and G. F. ZHARKOV. *Zh. eksp. teoret. fiz.* (in course of publication).

292. G. T. ZATSEPIN. *Dokl. Akad. Nauk SSSR*, **80**, 577 (1951).

293. N. M. GERASIMOVA and G. T. ZATSEPIN. *Zh. eksp. teoret. fiz.*, **38**, 1245 (1960); *Soviet Phys.—JETP*, **11**, 899 (1960).

294. N. M. GERASIMOVA and I. L. ROZENTAL'. *Zh. eksp. teoret. fiz.*, **41**, 488 (1961); *Soviet Phys.—JETP*, **14**, 350 (1962).

295. R. M. KALBACH, J. J. LORD and C. H. TSAO. *Phys. Rev.*, **113**, 330 (1959).

296. A. ASHMORE, G. COCCONI, A. N. DIDDENS and A. WETHERELL. *Phys. Rev. Letters*, **5**, 576 (1960).

297. L. RIDDIFORD, A. W. WILLIAMS. *Proc. Roy. Soc.*, **A275**, 316 (1960).

298. B. PETERS. *Progress in Cosmic Ray Physics.* North-Holland. Amsterdam, 1952, **1**, Ch. IV, 193.

299. B. A. VORONTSOV-VEL'YAMINOV. *Astr. zh.*, **39**, 174 (1962); *Soviet Astronomy —AJ*, **6**, 131 (1962).

300. V. RADJOPADHYE and C. H. WADDINGTON. *Phil. Mag.*, **3**, 19 (1958).

301. E. LOHRMAN and M. W. TEUCHER. *Phys. Rev.*, **115**, 636 (1959).

302. G. D. BADHWAR, R. R. DANIEL, B. VIJAYALAKSHMI. *Progress Theor. Phys.*, **28**, 607 (1962).

303. A. P. ZHDANOV and P. N. FEDOTOV. *Zh. exp. i teoret. fiz.*, **37**, 392 (1959); *Soviet Phys.—JETP*, **10**, 280 (1960).

304. F. S. ROWLAND and R. L. WOLFGANG. *Phys. Rev.*, **110**, 175 (1959).

305. V. L. GINZBURG. *Izv. Akad. Nauk SSSR, seriya fiz.*, **20**, 5 (1956); *Bulletin Acad. Sc. USSR*, **20**, 1 (1956).

306. G. R. BURBIDGE. *Astrophys. J.*, **124**, 416 (1956).

307. G. COCCONI. *Proc. of 1960 Internat. Conf. on High Energy Physics, Rochester*, p. 779.

308. P. H. FOWLER. *Phil. Mag.*, **41**, 163 (1950).

309. J. G. WILSON (Ed.) *Progress in Cosmic Ray Physics*, Amsterdam (1958), vol. III.

310. E. C. RAY. *Handbuch d. Phys.*, **46/1**, 130 (1960).

311. J. G. Wilson (Ed.) *Progress in Cosmic Ray Physics*, Amsterdam (1953), vol. I.
312. V. V. Guseva, N. A. Dobrotin, N. G. Zelevinskaya, K. A. Kotel'nikov, A. M. Lebedev and S. A. Slavatinskii. *PICCR*, A III, 375 (1962).
313. E. Feenberg, H. Primakoff. *Phys. Rev.*, 73, 449 (1948).
314. T. M. Donahue. *Phys. Rev.*, 84, 972 (1951).
315. C. W. Allen. *Astrophysical Quantities*. London (1955).
316. S. A. Colgate and M. H. Johnson. *Phys. Rev. Letters*, 5, 235 (1960).
317. W. F. G. Swann. *Proc. Internat. Conf. on Cosmic Rays* (in Russian), vol. III, p. 183 (1960); see also *Phys. Rev.*, 126, 757 (1962); *PICCR*, A III, 176 (1962).
318. E. Fermi. *Phys. Rev.*, 75, 1169 (1949); *Ap. J.*, 119, 1 (1954).
319. G. Hellwig. *Zs. Naturf.*, 10a, 508 (1955).
320. F. Hertweck and A. Schlüter. *Zs. Naturf.*, 12a, 844 (1957).
321. N. G. Denisov. *Izv. vyssh. ucheb. zav. Radiofiz.*, 2, 374 (1959).
322. L. Spitzer. *Physics of a Fully Ionized Gas* (Interscience) (1956).
323. L. I. Dorman. *Proc. Internat. Conf. on Cosmic Rays* (in Russian), vol. III, p. 245. Akad. Nauk SSSR (1960).
324. A. A. Logunov and Ya. P. Terletskii. *Vestn. Mosk. gos. un-ta*, No. 3, 63 (1956); *Izv. Akad. Nauk SSSR, seriya. fiz.*, 17, 119 (1953); *Zh. exp. i teoret. fiz.*, 26, 129 (1954).
325. H. Alfvén. *Proc. Internat. Conf. on Cosmic Rays* (in Russian), vol. III, p. 196. *Akad. Nauk SSSR* (1960); *Max. Planck-Festschrift*, p. 83 (1958).
326. W. B. Thompson. *Proc. Roy. Soc.*, A233, 402 (1955).
327. V. M. Byakov and R. G. Avalov. *Zh. exp. i teoret. fiz.*, 35, 1181 (1958); *Soviet Phys.—JETP*, 8, 826 (1959).
328. V. N. Tsytovich. *Radiofiz. Izv. Vuzov*, 6, 641 (1963); *Astron. zh.*, 40, 612 (1963); *Soviet Astronomy—AJ*, 7, 471 (1964); see also *Zh. exp. i teoret. fiz.*, 43, 327 (1962); *Soviet Phys.—JETP*, 16, 234 (1963).
329. E. N. Parker. *Phys. Rev.*, 107, 830 (1957).
330. A. A. Korchak, S. I. Syrovatskii. *Dokl. Akad. Nauk SSSR*, 122, 792 (1958); *Soviet Phys.—Doklady*, 3, 983 (1958).
331. A. A. Korchak and S. I. Syrovatskii. *Proc. of Internat. Conf. on Cosmic Rays*, vol. III, p. 216 (in Russian). Akad. Nauk SSSR (1960).
332. V. L. Ginzburg. *Dokl. Akad. Nauk SSSR*, 92, 727 (1953).
333. V. L. Ginzburg, S. B. Pikel'ner and I. S. Shklovskii. *Astr. zh.*, 32, 503 (1955); 33, 447 (1956).
334. E. N. Parker and D. A. Tidman. *Phys. Rev.*, 111, 1206 (1958).
335. A. V. Gurevich. *Zh. exp. i teoret. fiz.*, 38, 1597 (1960); *Soviet Phys.—JETP*, 11, 1150 (1960).
336. H. Alfvén. *Cosmic Electrodynamics*, Oxford University Press (1949).
337. G. G. Getmantsev. *Astr. zh.*, 36, 422 (1959); *Soviet Astronomy—AJ*, 3, 415, (1959); *Izv. vyssh. ucheb. zav. Radiofiz.*, 2, 3 (1959).
338. A. A. Logunov and Ya. P. Terletskii. *Zh. exp. i teoret. fiz.*, 29, 701 (1955); *Soviet Phys.—JETP*, 2, 353 (1956).
339. S. Fukui, S. Hayakawa, H. Nishimura and H. Obayashi. *PICCR*, A III, 169 (1962).
340. G. G. Getmantsev. *Izv. vyssh. ucheb. zav. Radiofiz.*, 5, 172, 459 (1962); *Astr. zh.*, 39, 607 (1962); *Soviet Astronomy—AJ*, 6, 477 (1963).
341. L. Davis. *Proc. Internat. Conf. on Cosmic Rays* (in Russian), vol. III, p. 225. Akad. Nauk SSSR (1960).
342. R. Hanbury Brown. *Monthly Notices Roy. Astron. Soc.*, 124, 35 (1962).
343. J. A. Simpson. *Astrophys. Journ. Suppl.*, 4, 378 (1960).

344. T. Gold. *Astrophys. Journ. Suppl.*, **4**, 406 (1960).
345. N. A. Krall and M. N. Rosenbluth. *Trapping instabilities in a slightly inhomogeneous plasma.* Preprint (1961).
346. V. L. Ginzburg. *Proc. of Internat. Conf. on Cosmic Rays* (in Russian), vol. III, p. 200. Akad. Nauk SSSR (1960).
347. H. Babcock. *Phys. Rev.*, **109**, 2210 (1958).
348. I. M. Gordon. *Tr. Astron. observ. Khar'k. gos. un-ta*, **12**, 15 (1957); *Astr. zh.*, **34**, 739 (1957); **35**, 458 (1958); **37**, 246 (1960); *Soviet Astronomy—AJ*, **1**, 719 (1959); **2**, 420 (1959); **4**, 234 (1960); *Zh. exp. i teoret. fiz.*, **37**, 853 (1958); *Soviet Phys.—JETP*, **10**, 608.
349. P. N. Kholopov. *Astr. zh.*, **36**, 434 (1959); *Soviet Astronomy—AJ*, **3**, 425 (1959).
350. K. A. Anderson, R. Arnoldy, R. Hoffman, L. Peterson and J. R. Winckler. *J. Geophys. Res.*, **64**, 1133, 1959.
351. L. D. Landau and E. M. Lifshitz. *Statistical Physics*, Pergamon Press, Oxford (1958).
352. Yu. P. Pskovskii. *Astr. zh.*, **38**, 656 (1961); *Soviet Astronomy—AJ*, **5**, 498 (1962).
353. W. Baade and F. Zwicky. *Proc. Nat. Acad. Sci. Amer.*, **20**, 259 (1934).
354. I. S. Shklovskii. *Dokl. Akad. Nauk SSSR*, **91**, 475 (1953).
355. G. Cocconi. *Nuovo Cimento*, **3**, 1433 (1956).
356. G. Cocconi. *Astrophys. J. Suppl.*, **4**, 417 (1960).
357. C. Payne-Gaposchkin. *Handbuch d. Phys.*, **51**, 572 (1958).
358. G. R. Burbidge. *Phys. Rev.*, **101**, 906 (1956).
359. P. Morrison, S. Olbert and B. Rossi. *Phys. Rev.*, **94**, 440 (1954).
360. E. N. Parker. *Phys. Rev.*, **99**, 241 (1955).
361. J. H. Piddington. *Austral. J. Phys.*, **10**, 515 (1957).
362. B. N. Gershman. *Astr. zh.*, **36**, 190 (1959); *Soviet Astronomy—AJ*, **3**. 193 (1959).
363. L. Biermann and L. Davis. *Zs. Naturf.*, **13a**, 909 (1958); *Proc. of the Moscow Cosmic Ray Conf.* (Moscow, 1960), vol. III, p. 228.
364. E. Salpeter. *Astrophys. J.*, **129**, 608 (1959).
365. I. S. Shklovskii. *Nuovo Cimento*, Suppl., **8**, 421 (1958).
366. V. L. Ginzburg. *Nuovo Cimento*, Suppl., **8**, 430 (1958).
367. F. Hoyle. *Montly Notices Roy. Astron. Soc.*, **120**, 436 (1960).
368. H. Alfvén. *Phys. Rev.*, **75**, 1732 (1949); **77**, 375 (1950).
369. A. Unsöld. *Phys. Rev.*, **82**, 857 (1951).
370. B. B. Kadomtsev. *Yadern. sintez*, **1**, 286 (1961); A. A. Vedenov, Ye. P. Velikhov, R. Z. Sagdeyev. *Usp. fiz. nauk*, **73**, 701 (1961); *Soviet Phys.—Uspekhi*, **4**, 332 (1961).
371. L. A. Artsimovich. *Controlled Thermonuclear Reactions* (in Russian). Fizmatgiz (1961).
372. R. R. Davies and G. L. Verschuur. *Nature*, **197**, 32 (1963).
373. G. G. Getmantsev. *Astr. zh.*, **35**, 722 (1958); *Soviet Astronomy—AJ*, **2**, 676 (1959).
374. V. L. Ginzburg. *Dokl. Akad. Nauk SSSR*, **99**, 703 (1954).
375. G. G. Getmantsev. *Izv. vyssh. ucheb. zav. Radiofiz.*, **5**, 1051 (1962).
376. V. L. Ginzburg. In collection: *Einstein and the Development of Physical and Mathematical Thought* (in Russian). Akad. Nauk SSSR, p. 117 (1962); *Proc. Internat. Conf. on Relativistic Theories in Gravitation*, Paris and Warsaw, p. 55 (1964).
377. D. Sciama. *Monthly Notices Roy. Astron. Soc.*, **123**, 317 (1962).
378. A. E. Godferson. *Astrophys. J.*, **134**, 257 (1961).

379. YA. B. ZEL'DOVICH. *Uspekhi fiz. nauk*, **78**, 549 (1962); *Soviet Phys.—Uspekhi*, **5**, 931 (1963).
380. *Proceedings of the Conference on Instability of Systems of Galaxies. Astron. J.*, **66**, 533 (1961).
381. S. CHANDRASEKHAR and E. FERMI. *Astrophys. J.*, **118**, 116 (1953).
382. A. EINSTEIN. *The Essence of Relativity Theory.* Appendix I (Russian edition) (1955).
383. E. M. LIFSHITZ and I. M. KHALATNIKOV. *Adv. in Phys.*, **12**, 185 (1963).
384. YA. A. SMORODINSKII. In collection: *Einstein and the Development of Physical and Mathematical Thought* (in Russian), p. 94. Akad. Nauk SSSR (1962).
385. G. MACVITTIE. *General Relativity and Cosmology*, London (1956).
386. H. BONDI. *Cosmology.* Cambridge (1960).
387. G. R. BURBIDGE. *Progress Theoret. Phys.*, **27**, 999 (1962).
388. F. HOYLE. *Proc. Phys. Soc.*, **77**, 1 (1961).
389. F. HOYLE. *Monthly Notices Roy. Astron. Soc.*, **120**, 256 (1960).
390. R. L. AGACY and W. H. MCCREA. *Monthly Notices Roy. Astron. Soc.*, **123**, 383 (1962).
391. M. RYLE and R. W. CLARK. *Monthly Notices Roy. Astron. Soc.*, **122**, 349 (1961).
392. F. HOYLE and J. V. NARLIKAR. *Monthly Notices Roy. Astron. Soc.*, **123**, 133 (1961).
393. W. DAVIDSON. *Monthly Notices Roy. Astron. Soc..*, **123**, 424 (1962); **124**, 79 (1962).
394. W. DAVIDSON. *Nature*, **196**, 155 (1962).
395. G. C. MCVITTIE. *Phys. Rev.*, **128**, 2871 (1962).
396. L. D. LANDAU and E. M. LIFSHITZ. *Electrodynamics of Continuous Media*, Pergamon Press, Oxford (1960).
397. V. A. AMBARTSUMYAN. *Astron. J.*, **66**, 533 (1961).
398. T. GOLD and F. HOYLE. *Paris Symposium on Radio Astronomy* (1959), p. 104.
399. G. COCCONI. *Nuovo Cimento*, Suppl., **8**, 472 (1958).
400. S. WEINBERG. *Nuovo Cimento*, **25**, 15 (1962); Phys. Rev., **128**, 1457 (1962).
401. G. R. BURBIDGE. *Phys. Rev.*, **107**, 269 (1959.
402. E. M. BURBIDGE, G. R. BURBIDGE, W. A. FOWLER and F. HOYLE. *Rev. Mod. Phys.*, **29**, 547 (1957).
403. J. E. BALDWIN and J. R. SHAKESHAFT. *Paris Symposium on Radio Astronomy* (1958).
404. V. A. RAZIN. *Astr. zh.*, **39**, 29 (1962); *Soviet Astronomy—AJ*, **6**, 20 (1962).
405. I. S. SHKLOVSKII and S. B. PIKEL'NER. *Astr. zh.*, **38**, 196 (1961); *Soviet Astronomy—AJ*, **5**, 146 (1961).
406. V. A. AMBARTSUMYAN. *Izv. Akad. Nauk Arm. SSR*, **11**, No. 5, 9 (1958).
407. B. A. VORONTSOV-VEL'YAMINOV. *Astr. zh.*, **35**, 208 (1958); *Soviet Astronomy—AJ*, **2**, 186 (1958).
408. G. R. BURBIDGE. *Paris Symposium on Radio Astronomy.* Stanford Univ. Press, 1959, p. 541; see also *Nature*, **194**, 367 (1962).
409. A. CAMERON. *Nature*, **194**, 963 (1962); see also *Nature*, **196**, 881 (1962).
410. G. R. BURBIDGE. *Nature*, **190**, 1053 (1961).
411. V. L. GINZBURG. *Astr. zh.*, **38**, 380 (1961); *Soviet Astronomy—AJ*, **5**, 282 (1961).
412. F. HOYLE. *Observatory*, **81**, 39 (1961).
413. A. A. LOGUNOV and YA. P. TERLETSKII. *Izv. Akad. Nauk SSSR, ser. fiz.*, **17**, 119 (1953); *Zh. exp. i teoret. fiz.*, **26**, 129 (1954); see also *Zh. exp. i teoret. fiz.*, **23**, 682 (1952).

414. M. F. KAPLON, J. H. NOON and G. W. RACETTE. *Phys. Rev.*, **96**, 1408 (1954).
415. S. A. KAPLAN. *Zh. exp. i teoret. fiz.*, **29**, 406 (1955); *Soviet Phys.—JETP*, **2**, 203 (1956).
416. D. B. CHANG. *Three cosmic ray problems.* Thesis (1960).
417. S. HAYAKAWA, C. HAYASHI, K. ITT, J. JUGAKU, M. NISHIDA and N. OHYAMA. *Proceedings of the Moscow Cosmic Ray Conference* (Moscow, 1960), p. 171.
418. S. F. SINGER. *Nuovo Cimento*, Suppl., **8**, 549 (1958).
419. H. ALFVÉN and E. ASTRÖM. *Nature*, **181**, 330 (1958).
420. D. W. SCIAMA. *Nature*, **196**, 760 (1962).
421. L. DAVIS. *Phys. Rev.*, **101**, 351 (1956); *Nuovo Cimento*, Suppl., **8**, 444 (1958).
422. G. R. A. ELLIS, M. D. WATERWOORTH and M. BESSELL. *Nature*, **196**, 1079 (1962).
423. S. I. SYROVATSKII. In collection: *Questions of Magnetic Hydrodynamics and Plasma Dynamics* (in Russian), pp. 45–48. Akad. Nauk Latv. SSR, Riga (1959).
424. S. I. SYROVATSKII. *Zh. exp. i teoret. fiz.* **40**, 1788 (1961); *Soviet Phys.—JETP* **13**, 1257 (1961).
425. S. I. SYROVATSKII. *Usp. fiz. nauk.*, **62**, 247 (1957).
426. E. N. PARKER. *Phys. Rev.*, **109**, 1328 (1958).
427. S. B. PIKEL'NER. *Astr. zh.*, **38**, 21 (1961), *Soviet Astronomy—AJ*, **5**, 14 (1961).
428. A. N. CHARAKHCH'YAN and T. N. CHARAKHCH'YAN. *Geomagn. i aèron.*, **2**, 233 (1962).
429. N. S. KARDASHEV. *Astr. zh.*, **39**, 393 (1962); *Soviet Astronomy—AJ*, **6**, 317 (1962).
430. R. B. LEIGHTON, C. D. ANDERSON and A. J. SHERIFF. *Phys. Rev.*, **75**, 1432 (1949); C. P. SARGENT, M. RINEHART, L. M. LEDERMAN and K. C. ROGERS. *Phys. Rev.*, **99**, 885 (1955).
431. L. MICHEL. *Nature*, **163**, 959 (1949); *Proc. Phys. Soc.*, **63A**, 514 (1950).
432. A. I. ALIKHANOV. *Ninth Internat. Annual Conf. on High Energy Physics*, Moscow (1960) VI–IX, p. 163.
433. S. HAYAKAWA, H. OKUDA. *Progress Theor. Phys.*, **28**, 517 (1962).
434. V. L. GINZBURG and S. I. SYROVATSKII. *Astr. zh.*, **40**, 466 (1963); *Soviet Astronomy—AJ*, **7**, 356 (1964).
435. IAU Symposium No. 20. *Abstracts* (1963).
436. T. A. MATTHEWS and A. SANDAGE. *Publ. Astron. Soc. Pacific*, **74**, 406 (1962).
437. A. T. MOFFET and P. MALTBY. *Astrophys. Journ. Suppl.*, **7**, No. 67 (1962); *Astrophys. Journ.* **137**, 153 (1963).
438. G. R. BURBIDGE and F. HOYLE. *Astrophys. Journ.*, **138**, 57 (1963).
439. J. H. OORT. *Some considerations concerning the study of the Universe by means of large radio telescopes.* Preprint (1962).
440. S. N. GANGULI, N. KAMESWARA RAO and M. S. SWAMI. *The flux of primary cosmic ray deuterons at a geomagnetic latitude of 7.6° N. ICCR*, India (1963).
441. M. V. K. APPA RAO and P. J. LAVAKARE. *Nuovo Cimento*, **26**, 740 (1962).
442. H. HASEGAWA, S. NAKAGAWA and E. TAMAI. *On the isotopic composition of hydrogen nuclei in low energy primary cosmic radiation. ICCR*, India (1963).
443. M. V. K. APPA RAO, C. DAHANAYAKE, M. F. KAPLON and P. J. LAVAKARE. *The isotopic composition and the energy spectrum of low energy helium nuclei in primary cosmic radiation. ICCR*, India (1963).

444. H. Aizu. *Isotopic abundance of helium nuclei in primary cosmic radiation.* ICCR, India (1963).
445. B. Hildebrand, F. W. O'Dell, M. M. Shapiro, R. Silberberg and B. Stiller. *The helium isotopes in the primary cosmic radiation.* ICCR, India (1963).
446. J. A. De Shong, R. H. Hildebrand and P. Meyer. *The ratio of electrons to positrons in the primary cosmic radiation.* Preprint (1963).
447. W. L. Kraushaar et al. *Cosmic gamma ray results from Explorer XI.* ICCR, India, Abstracts (1963).
448. S. Miyake, V. S. Narasimhan and P. V. Ramana Murtyh. *Cosmic ray intensity measurements deep underground.* ICCR, India, Abstracts (1963).
449. M. G. K. Menon, P. V. Ramana Murthy and B. V. Sreekantan. *Nuovo Cimento*, **30**, 1208 (1963).
450. H. Y. Chiu. *Cosmic neutrino sources.* ICCR, India (1963).
451. A. W. Wolfendale. *High energy muons.* ICCR, India (1963) preprint; see also *Nature*, **198**, 1293 (1963).
452. G. T. Zatsepin, S. I. Nikolsky and G. B. Khristiansen. *Extensive air showers of cosmic radiation.* ICCR, India (1963), preprint.
453. J. Geiss. *Experimental evidence on the history of cosmic radiation.* ICCR, India (1963).
454. P. Meyer and R. Vogt. *Changes in the primary cosmic ray proton spectrum in 1962 and 1963.* ICCR, India (1963).
455. G. D. Badhwar, N. Durgaprasad and B. Vijayalakshmi. *A study of the multiply charged nuclei of the primary cosmic radiation near the geomagnetic equator using nuclear emulsions.* ICCR, India (1963).
456. H. Wanke. *Cosmic ray data derived from isotope studies in meteorites.* ICCR, India (1963).
457. G. Clark, H. Bradt, M. La Pointe, V. Domingo, I. Escobar, K. Murakami, K. Suga, Y. Toyoda and Y. Hersil. *The primary energy spectrum from* 3×10^{14} *to* 3×10^{17} *eV.* ICCR, India (1963).
458. J. Linsley. *Primary cosmic rays of energy* 10^{17} *to* 10^{20} *eV. The energy spectrum and arrival directions.* ICCR, India (1963).
459. Yu. A. Fomin and G. B. Khristiansen. *Zh. exp. i teoret. fiz.*, **44**, 666, (1963); *Soviet Phys.—JETP*, **17**, 451 (1963).
460. S. I. Syrovatskii, Yu. A. Fomin and G. B. Khristiansen. *Zh. exp. teoret. fiz.*, **45**, 1595 (1963); *Soviet Phys.—JETP*, **18**, No. 5 (1964).
461. S. Hayakawa and Y. Yamamoto. *Progr. Theor. Phys.*, **30**, 71 (1963).
462. S. Biswas. *The composition of solar particle radiation.* Preprint ICCR, India (1963).
463. A. D. Bray, D. F. Crawford, D. L. Jauncey, C. B. A. McCusker, P. C. Poole, M. H. Pathgeber, J. Ulrichs, R. H. Wand, M. M. Winn and A. Ueda. *The detailed electromagnetic structure of air shower cores.* ICCR, India (1963).
464. D. Walsh, F. T. Haddock and H. F. Schulte. *Cosmic radio intensities at 1.225 and 2.0 Mc/s up to an altitude of* 1,700 *km.* Cospar 6th Plenary Meeting. Warsaw (June 1963).
465. G. R. A. Ellis, M. D. Waterworth, M. Bessel. *Nature*, **196**, 1079 (1962); F. Hoyle and G. R. A. Ellis. *Austr. J. Phys.*, **16**, 1 (1963).
466. D. S. Mathewson and J. M. Rome. *Observatory*, **83**, 20 (1963); *Austr. J. Phys.*, **16**, 360 (1963).
467. *Observatory*, **83**, 150 (1963).
468. F. J. Kerr. *Mon. Not. Roy. Astron. Soc.*, **123**, 327 (1962).
469. R. X. McGee, J. D. Murray and J. A. Milton. *Austr. J. Phys.*, **16**, 136 (1963).

418 REFERENCES

470. O. B. Slee, L. H. Solomon and G. E. Patston. *Nature*, **199**, 991 (1963).
471. M. Schmidt. *Nature*, **197**, 1040 (1963).
472. J. L. Greenstein and T. A. Matthews. *Nature*, **197**, 1041 (1963).
473. H. J. Smith and D. Hoffleit. *Nature*, **198**, 650 (1963).
474. F. Hoyle, W. A. Fowler, G. R. Burbidge and E. M. Burbidge. *On relativistic astrophysics*. Preprint (1963).
475. V. L. Ginzburg, L. M. Ozernoi and S. I. Syrovatskii. *The emission mechanism of the galaxy 3C 273-B*. *Dokl. Akad. Nauk SSSR* **157**, 557 (1964); *Soviet Phys.—Doklady*, **9**, No. 4 (1964); short note: *Astron. Tsirkulyar Akad. Nauk SSSR*, No. 267 (1963).
476. G. Burbidge. *The production of cosmic rays in violent events in galaxies*. *ICCR*, India (1963).
477. I. S. Shklovskii. *Astr. Zh.*, **40**, 972 (1963); *Soviet Astronomy—AJ*, **7**, No. 6 (1964).
478. P. Maltby, T. Matthews and A. T. Moffet. *Ap. J.*, **137**, 153 (1963).
479. M. W. Friedlander, K. A. Neelakantan, S. Tokunaga, G. R. Stevenson and C. J. Waddington. *Phil. Mag.*, **8**, 1691 (1963).
480. S. I. Syrovatskii. *Problems of nuclear chemistry* (in Russian) Moscow (1964, in course of publication).
481. S. A. Colgate and A. G. W. Cameron. *Nature*, **200**, 870 (1963).
482. S. A. Colgate and R. H. White. *Cosmic rays from large supernovae*. Preprint (1963).
483. D. G. Wentzel. *Ap. J.*, **137**, 135 (1963).
484. C. R. Lynds and A. R. Sandage. *Astrophys. Journ.*, **137**, 1005 (1963).
485. J. B. Pollack and G. G. Fazio. *Phys. Rev.*, **131**, 2684 (1963).
486. N. A. Vlasov. *An optical method of searching for antimatter in the Universe* (in Russian). Preprint (1963).
487. V. L. Ginzburg and S. I. Syrovatskii. *The origin of cosmic rays*. *ICCR*, India (1963).
488. A. G. Pacholczyk. *Nature*, **200**, 765 (1963).
489. R. W. Clarke, P. E. Scott and F. G. Smith. *Mon. Not. Roy. Astron. Soc.*, **125**, 195 (1963).
490. R. G. Gould and G. R. Burbidge. *X-rays from the Galactic centre, external galaxies and the intergalactic medium*. Preprint (1963).
491. H. Sato. *Progr. Theor. Phy.*, **28**, 213 (1962). *Cosmic ray energy spectrum and high-energy particles in supernovae*. Preprint (1963); *ICCR*, India (1963).
492. V. L. Ginzburg. *Dokl. Akad. Nauk SSSR* **156**, 43 (1964); *Soviet Phys.— Doklady*, **9**, No. 3 (1964).
493. J. Puppi. *Progress of Cosmic Ray Physics*, Amsterdam, vol. **3** (1957).
494. H. Komori. *J. Phys. Soc. Japan*, **17**, 620 (1962).
495. G. Brook, P. J. Hayman, F. E. Taylor and A. W. Wolfendale. *J. Phys. Soc. Japan*, **17**, Suppl. AIII, 311 (1962).
496. U. Camerini, W. Lock and D. Perkins, in *Progress of Cosmic Ray Physics*, Amsterdam, vol. **1** (1953).
497. V. L. Ginzburg and S. I. Syrovatskii, *Zh. Exp. i teoret. fiz.*, **45**, 353 (1963); *Soviet Phys.—JETP*, **18** (1964).
498. G. Brook, P. J. Hayman, Y. Kamiya and A. W. Wolfendale. *Nature*, **198**, 1293 (1963).
499. V. L. Ginzburg and S. I. Syrovatskii, *Zh. exp. i teoret. fiz.*, **46**, No. 5 (1964); *Soviet Phys.—JETP*, **19**, No. 5 (1964).
500. J. E. Baldwin, T. T. K. Pauling-Toth, A. J. Turtle and S. Kenderdine. *Monthly Notices Roy. Astr. Soc.*, **115**, 684 (1955); **124**, 61, 297, 459 (1962).
501. A. R. Molozzi, C. A. Franklin and J. P. J. Tyas. *Nature*, **190**, 616 (1961).

502. N. LUND, B. SWANEBERG, Y. TANAKA and A. H. WAPSTRA. *Some problems in connection with Galactic electrons. Abstract. Internat. Conf. on Cosmic Rays.* Jaipur, India (December 1963).

503. S. HAYAKAWA. *Electrons and Photons in Primary Cosmic Rays.* Preprint (1963).

504. R. FIRKOWSKI, J. GAWIN, R. MAZE, A. ZAWADZKI. *J. Phys. Soc. Japan,* 17, Suppl. A–III, 123 (1961); *C.R. Paris,* 255, 2411 (1962).

505. K. SUGA, I. ESCOBAR, G. CLARK, W. HAZEN, A. HENDAL, K. MURAKAMI. *J. Phys. Soc. Japan,* 17, Suppl. A–III, 128 (1961); *Proc. of the Fifth Inter-American Seminar on Cosmic Rays,* La Paz (Bolivia), 2, 43 (1962).

506. R. GIACONNI, H. GURSKY, F. R. PAOLINI, B. ROSSI. *Phys. Rev. Lett.,* 9, 439 (1962). These data have been confirmed (Preprint, 1963).

507. G. W. CLARK. *The relation between cosmic X-rays and gamma rays.* Preprint (1962).

508. *Proc. Intern. Conf. on Cosmic Rays and the Earth Storm, J. Phys. Soc. Japan,* 17, Suppl. A–III, 106 (1962).

509. V. L. GINZBURG and S. I. SYROVATSKII. *Astron. zh.* 41, No. 3 (1964); *Soviet Astronomy—AJ,* 8, No. 3 (1964).

510. S. E. STROM and K. M. STROM. *Publ. Astron. Soc. Pacific,* 73, 43 (1961).

511. G. M. NIKOL'SKII. *Dokl. Akad. Nauk SSSR,* 151, 536 (1963); *Soviet Phys.—Doklady,* 8, 646 (1964).

512. Γ. HOYLE. *Ap. J.,* 137, 993 (1963).

513. S. HAYAKAWA and M. MATSUOKA. *Progr. Theoret. Phys.,* 29, 612 (1963); *Proc. 4th Internat. Space Sc. Sym.* COSPAR, preprint (1963).

514. R. FIRKOWSKI, J. GAVIN, A. ZAWADZKI and R. MAZE. *Nuovo Cim.,* 29, 19 (1963).

515. T. E. FELTON and P. MORRISON. *Phys. Rev. Lett.,* 10, 453 (1963).

516. M. W. FRIEDLANDER. *Nuovo Cimento* (preprint).

517. T. B. POLLACK and G. G. FAZIO. *Phys. Rev.,* 131, 2684 (1963).

518. L. G. DEDENKO and G. T. ZATSEPIN. *Proc. of Internat. Cosmic Ray Conf.,* July 1959 (in Russian), vol. 2, Akad Nauk SSSR, p. 222 (1960); L. G. LEDENKO, *Zh. exp. i teoret. fiz.,* 40, 630 (1961); *Soviet Phys.—JETP,* 13, 439, (1961).

519. L. T. BARADZEI, V. I. RUBTSOV, YU. A. SMORODIN, M. V. SOLOV'YEV and B. V. TOLKACHEV. *Izv. Akad. Nauk SSSR, ser. fiz.,* 26, 575 (1962); Translation in *Bulletin Acad. Sc. USSR,* vol. 26, 573 (1962).

520. O. I. DOVZHENKO and A. A. POMANSKII. *Zh. exp. i teoret fiz.,* 45, 268 (1963); *Soviet Phys.—JETP,* 18, 187 (1964).

521. I. YA. POMERANCHUK, *Zh. exp. i teoret. fiz.* 9, 919 (1939).

522. V. V.VLADIMIRSKII, *Zh. exp. i teoret. fiz.* 18, 392 (1948).

523. V. L. GINZBURG and S. I. SYROVATSKII. *Some problems of γ- and X-ray-astronomy. Space Sci. Rev.* (in course of publication)

524. V. L. GINZBURG and S. I. SYROVATSKII. *On the nature of discrete X-ray sources. Dokl. Akad. Nauk SSSR* (in course of publication).

SUBJECT INDEX

INDEX OF CELESTIAL OBJECTS